# A Textbook for
# Heat Transfer
# Fundamentals

**Yildiz Bayazitoglu**

Rice University

and

**M. Necati Ozisik**

begell
New York • Connecticut

**A TEXBOOK FOR HEAT TRANSFER FUNDAMENTALS**
YILDIZ BAYAZITOGLU
M. NECATI OZISIK

ISBN: 978-1-56700-306-2

PRINTED IN THE UNITED STATES OF AMERICA 1 2 3 4 5 6 7 8 9 0

---

**Library of Congress Cataloging-in-Publication Data**

Bayazitoglu, Yildiz.
A textbook for heat transfer fundamentals / Yildiz Bayazitoglu, Rice University and Necati Ozisik.
    pages cm–Includes bibliographical references and index.
ISBN 978-1-56700-306-2 (hardcover : alk. paper) 1. Heat–Transmission. Ozisik, M. Necati, II. Title.
 QC320.B384 2012
 536'.2–dc23

2012030863

**Direct inquires to Begell House, Inc., 50 Cross Highway, Redding, CT 06896**

# TABLE OF CONTENTS

About the Authors . . . . . . . . . . . . . . . . . . . . . . . . . . . . .   v

Preface . . . . . . . . . . . . . . . . . . . . . . . . . . . . . . . . . .   vi

*Chapter 1:  Mechanisms of Heat Flow* . . . . . . . . . . . . . . . . . . . .   1
    1.1:   Conduction Phenomena . . . . . . . . . . . . . . . . . . . . . . .   2
        1.1.1   Conduction due to Drift of Free Electrons . . . . . . . . . . .   2
        1.1.2   Conduction due to Phonons and Lattice Atoms as Harmonic Oscillators   3
        1.1.3   Conduction due to Kinetic Motion of Molecules . . . . . . . . .   6
        1.1.4   Fourier Law of Conduction . . . . . . . . . . . . . . . . .   7
        1.1.5   Thermal Conductivity of Materials . . . . . . . . . . . . . .   12
        1.1.6   Non-Fourier Heat Conduction . . . . . . . . . . . . . . . .   17
    1.2:   Convection . . . . . . . . . . . . . . . . . . . . . . . . . .   19
        1.2.1   Continuum concept . . . . . . . . . . . . . . . . . . . .   19
        1.2.2   Thermal Properties of Nanofluids . . . . . . . . . . . . . .   19
        1.2.3   Heat transfer coefficient . . . . . . . . . . . . . . . . . .   23
    1.3:   Radiation Phenomena . . . . . . . . . . . . . . . . . . . . .   25
        1.3.1   Emission of Radiation:Stefan-Boltzmann law . . . . . . . . .   27
        1.3.2   Absorption of Radiation . . . . . . . . . . . . . . . . . .   28
        1.3.3   Thermal Radiation Heat Exchange . . . . . . . . . . . . . .   28
        1.3.4   Radiation Heat Transfer Coefficient . . . . . . . . . . . . .   30
    1.4:   Combined Mechanisms of Heat Transfer . . . . . . . . . . . . .   31
        1.4.1   Earth . . . . . . . . . . . . . . . . . . . . . . . . . .   32
        1.4.2   Light Bulb . . . . . . . . . . . . . . . . . . . . . . . .   33
        1.4.3   Building Climate . . . . . . . . . . . . . . . . . . . . .   34
    1.5:   Units, Dimensions, and Conversion Factors . . . . . . . . . . .   35
    Problems . . . . . . . . . . . . . . . . . . . . . . . . . . . . .   36

*Chapter 2:  Transient Lumped Systems* . . . . . . . . . . . . . . . . . .   41
    2.1:   Lumped System Concept . . . . . . . . . . . . . . . . . . . .   41
    2.2:   Examples of Lumped Systems . . . . . . . . . . . . . . . . . .   42
        2.2.1   Convection Over All Boundary Surfaces . . . . . . . . . . . .   43
        2.2.2   Criteria for Lumped Systems . . . . . . . . . . . . . . . .   46
        2.2.3   Convection Over Part of the Boundary Surface . . . . . . . . .   49
        2.2.4   Physical Meaning of the Biot Number . . . . . . . . . . . . .   55
    Problems . . . . . . . . . . . . . . . . . . . . . . . . . . . . .   60

*Chapter 3:  Diffusion of Heat and Mass—Governing Equations* . . . . . . . .   65
    3.1:   Derivation of One-Dimensional Time-dependent Heat Conduction Equation .   65
    3.2:   Compact form of One-Dimensional Time-dependent Heat Conduction Equation   69
    3.3:   One-Dimensional Non-Fourier (Cattaneo's) Heat Conduction Equation . . .   71
    3.4:   Significance of Thermal Diffusivity . . . . . . . . . . . . . .   72
    3.5:   Three-Dimensional Time-dependent Heat Conduction Equation . . . . .   74
    3.6:   Boundary and Initial Condition Concepts . . . . . . . . . . . .   75
        3.6.1   Prescribed Temperature Boundary Condition (B.C. First Kind) . . .   76

|  | 3.6.2 | Prescribed Heat Flux Boundary Condition (B.C. Second Kind) . . . | 77 |
|  | 3.6.3 | Convection Boundary Condition (B.C. Third Kind) . . . . . . . . | 78 |
|  | 3.6.4 | Thermal and Geometric Symmetry . . . . . . . . . . . . . . . | 80 |
| 3.7: | | Governing Equations of Heat Conduction Problems . . . . . . . . . . . . | 82 |
| 3.8: | | One-Dimensional Mass Diffusion Equation . . . . . . . . . . . . . . . | 84 |
|  | 3.8.1 | Definitions of Mass Flux . . . . . . . . . . . . . . . . . . . | 84 |
|  | 3.8.2 | Fick's First Law . . . . . . . . . . . . . . . . . . . . . . | 85 |
|  | 3.8.3 | Mass Diffusivity . . . . . . . . . . . . . . . . . . . . . . | 89 |
| | Problems . . . . . . . . . . . . . . . . . . . . . . . . . . . . . . | 89 |

*Chapter 4: Steady Conduction Without Energy Generation: Thermal Resistance Concept*    95

| 4.1: | | Single Layer . . . . . . . . . . . . . . . . . . . . . . . . . . . | 95 |
|  | 4.1.1 | Plane Wall . . . . . . . . . . . . . . . . . . . . . . . . . | 96 |
|  | 4.1.2 | Plane Wall, Prescribed Temperature at $x = 0$, Convection at $x = L$ . . . . . . . . . . . . . . . . . . . | 98 |
|  | 4.1.3 | Plane Wall, Convection at Both Boundaries . . . . . . . . . . | 100 |
|  | 4.1.4 | Long Hollow Cylinder . . . . . . . . . . . . . . . . . . . . | 101 |
|  | 4.1.5 | Hollow Sphere . . . . . . . . . . . . . . . . . . . . . . . | 107 |
| 4.2: | | Multilayers . . . . . . . . . . . . . . . . . . . . . . . . . . . | 111 |
|  | 4.2.1 | Multilayer Plane Wall . . . . . . . . . . . . . . . . . . . . | 111 |
|  | 4.2.2 | Multilayer Hollow Cylinder . . . . . . . . . . . . . . . . . | 114 |
|  | 4.2.3 | Multilayer Hollow Sphere . . . . . . . . . . . . . . . . . . | 118 |
|  | 4.2.4 | Overall Heat Transfer Coefficient Concept . . . . . . . . . . | 120 |
| 4.3: | | Contact Resistance Concept . . . . . . . . . . . . . . . . . . . . | 122 |
| 4.4: | | Two-Dimensional Steady-State Heat Conduction: Conduction Shape Factors | 125 |
| 4.5: | | Extended Surfaces . . . . . . . . . . . . . . . . . . . . . . . . | 130 |
| | Problems . . . . . . . . . . . . . . . . . . . . . . . . . . . . . . | 136 |

*Chapter 5: Steady Conduction with Energy Generation: Analytic and Numerical Solutions*   147

| 5.1: | | Analytic Solutions . . . . . . . . . . . . . . . . . . . . . . . | 147 |
|  | 5.1.1 | Plane Wall with Energy Generation and Constant Surface Temperatures | 147 |
|  | 5.1.2 | Plane Wall with Energy Generation and Convection . . . . . . . | 150 |
|  | 5.1.3 | Solid Cylinder with Energy Generation and Constant Surface Temperature . . . . . . . . . . . . . . . . . . . . . . . . | 153 |
|  | 5.1.4 | Solid Cylinder with Energy Generation and Convection . . . . . | 155 |
|  | 5.1.5 | Sphere with Energy Generation and Convection . . . . . . . . | 159 |
| 5.2: | | Numerical Analysis . . . . . . . . . . . . . . . . . . . . . . . | 161 |
|  | 5.2.1 | Plane Wall — Finite-Difference Formulation . . . . . . . . . . | 162 |
|  | 5.2.2 | Cylinder—Finite-Difference Formulation . . . . . . . . . . . | 169 |
|  | 5.2.3 | Sphere — Finite-Difference Formulation . . . . . . . . . . . | 177 |
| 5.3: | | Computer Solutions . . . . . . . . . . . . . . . . . . . . . . . | 179 |
| | Problems . . . . . . . . . . . . . . . . . . . . . . . . . . . . . . | 180 |

*Chapter 6: Transient Heat Conduction* . . . . . . . . . . . . . . . . . . . 187

| 6.1: | | Transient Temperature Distribution in a Semi-Infinite Solid . . . . . . . | 187 |
|  | 6.1.1 | Sudden Change in Boundary Temperature . . . . . . . . . . . | 188 |
|  | 6.1.2 | Suddenly Imposed Boundary Surface Heat Flux . . . . . . . . | 190 |
|  | 6.1.3 | Suddenly Imposed Convection on the Boundary Surface . . . . . | 190 |
| 6.2: | | One Dimensional Transient Temperature and Heat Flow: Heisler Charts . . . | 193 |

|          | 6.2.1 | Transient-Temperature Chart for Slab . . . . . . . . . . . . . . . . . | 193 |
|          | 6.2.2 | Transient-Temperature Chart for Long Cylinder . . . . . . . . . | 199 |
|          | 6.2.3 | Transient-Temperature Chart for a Sphere . . . . . . . . . . . | 203 |
| 6.3:     |       | Numerical Analysis and Solutions . . . . . . . . . . . . . . . . . . | 204 |
|          | 6.3.1 | Inclusion of Heat Capacity in Finite-Difference Equations for Boundary Nodes . . . . . . . . . . . . . . . . . . . . . . . . . . | 214 |
| 6.4:     |       | Product Solution for Transient Multidimensional Heat Conduction . . . . . . | 218 |
| 6.5:     |       | Transient Mass Diffusion . . . . . . . . . . . . . . . . . . . . . . . | 224 |
| 6.6:     |       | Transient Bioheat Equation . . . . . . . . . . . . . . . . . . . . . . | 226 |
|          | Problems . . . . . . . . . . . . . . . . . . . . . . . . . . . . . . . . . . | 228 |

**Chapter 7:**  *External Forced Convection Heat Flow* . . . . . . . . . . . . . . . . . . . . . 235

| 7.1:     |       | Basic Concepts . . . . . . . . . . . . . . . . . . . . . . . . . . . . . | 235 |
|          | 7.1.1 | Dimensionless Parameters . . . . . . . . . . . . . . . . . . . . | 236 |
|          | 7.1.2 | Velocity Boundary Layer . . . . . . . . . . . . . . . . . . . . | 237 |
|          | 7.1.3 | Thermal Boundary Layer . . . . . . . . . . . . . . . . . . . . | 240 |
| 7.2:     |       | Laminar Flow over a Flat Plate . . . . . . . . . . . . . . . . . . . | 244 |
|          | 7.2.1 | Velocity Distribution . . . . . . . . . . . . . . . . . . . . . . | 244 |
|          | 7.2.2 | Drag Coefficient . . . . . . . . . . . . . . . . . . . . . . . . . | 246 |
|          | 7.2.3 | Temperature Distribution . . . . . . . . . . . . . . . . . . . . | 248 |
|          | 7.2.4 | Heat Transfer Coefficient . . . . . . . . . . . . . . . . . . . | 251 |
| 7.3:     |       | Turbulent Flow over a Flat Plate . . . . . . . . . . . . . . . . . . | 257 |
|          | 7.3.1 | Drag Coefficient . . . . . . . . . . . . . . . . . . . . . . . . . | 257 |
|          | 7.3.2 | Heat Transfer Coefficient . . . . . . . . . . . . . . . . . . . | 259 |
| 7.4:     |       | Flow Across a Single Circular Cylinder . . . . . . . . . . . . . . | 262 |
|          | 7.4.1 | Average Drag Coefficient . . . . . . . . . . . . . . . . . . . | 262 |
|          | 7.4.2 | Average Heat Transfer Coefficient . . . . . . . . . . . . . . | 263 |
|          | 7.4.3 | Variation of $h(\theta)$ around the Cylinder . . . . . . . . . . . | 264 |
| 7.5:     |       | Flow across a Single Noncircular Cylinder . . . . . . . . . . . | 266 |
| 7.6:     |       | Flow across a Single Sphere . . . . . . . . . . . . . . . . . . . . | 267 |
|          | 7.6.1 | Average Drag Coefficient . . . . . . . . . . . . . . . . . . . | 267 |
|          | 7.6.2 | Average Heat Transfer Coefficients . . . . . . . . . . . . . . | 268 |
| 7.7:     |       | Nanofluid Flows over a Flat Plate . . . . . . . . . . . . . . . . . | 270 |
|          | 7.7.1 | Nanofluid Flows over a Flat Plate . . . . . . . . . . . . . . . | 270 |
| 7.8:     |       | Mass Transfer . . . . . . . . . . . . . . . . . . . . . . . . . . . . | 274 |
|          | 7.8.1 | Mass Transfer in Boundary Layer Flow over a Flat Plate . . . . . | 275 |
| 7.9:     |       | Note . . . . . . . . . . . . . . . . . . . . . . . . . . . . . . . . . . | 278 |
|          | Problems . . . . . . . . . . . . . . . . . . . . . . . . . . . . . . . . . . | 278 |

**Chapter 8:**  *Internal Forced Convection Heat Flow* . . . . . . . . . . . . . . . . . . . . . 285

| 8.1:     |       | Basic Concepts . . . . . . . . . . . . . . . . . . . . . . . . . . . . . | 285 |
|          | 8.1.1 | Hydrodynamic Entry Region . . . . . . . . . . . . . . . . . . | 285 |
|          | 8.1.2 | Thermal Entry Region . . . . . . . . . . . . . . . . . . . . . | 286 |
|          | 8.1.3 | Fully Developed Region . . . . . . . . . . . . . . . . . . . . | 287 |
|          | 8.1.4 | Bulk Mean Fluid Temperature . . . . . . . . . . . . . . . . . | 288 |
|          | 8.1.5 | Heat Transfer Coefficient . . . . . . . . . . . . . . . . . . . | 288 |
|          | 8.1.6 | Logarithmic Mean Temperature Difference . . . . . . . . . . | 290 |
|          | 8.1.7 | Friction Factor . . . . . . . . . . . . . . . . . . . . . . . . . | 290 |
|          | 8.1.8 | Dimensionless Parameters . . . . . . . . . . . . . . . . . . . | 291 |

8.2:    Fully Developed Laminar Flow . . . . . . . . . . . . . . . . . . 293
        8.2.1   Flow Inside a Circular Tube . . . . . . . . . . . . . . 293
        8.2.2   Flow Inside Ducts of Various Cross Sections . . . . . . . . . 296
        8.2.3   Hydrodynamic and Thermal Entry Lengths . . . . . . . . . . 299
8.3:    Developing Laminar Flow . . . . . . . . . . . . . . . . . . 301
        8.3.1   Thermally Developing, Hydrodynamically Developed Laminar Flow   302
        8.3.2   Simultaneously Developing Laminar Flow . . . . . . . . . . 304
        8.3.3   Empirical Correlations . . . . . . . . . . . . . . . 305
8.4:    Fully Developed Turbulent Flow . . . . . . . . . . . . . . . . 309
        8.4.1   Friction Factor . . . . . . . . . . . . . . . . . . 309
        8.4.2   Heat Transfer Coefficient . . . . . . . . . . . . . . 311
        8.4.3   Noncircular Ducts . . . . . . . . . . . . . . . . . 313
        8.4.4   Effects of Surface Roughness and Property Variation . . . . . . 313
8.5:    Liquid Metals Flows . . . . . . . . . . . . . . . . . . . 316
        8.5.1   Uniform Wall Heat Flux . . . . . . . . . . . . . . . 316
        8.5.2   Uniform Wall Temperature . . . . . . . . . . . . . . 317
        8.5.3   Thermal Entry Region . . . . . . . . . . . . . . . 317
8.6:    Nanofluids in Pipe Flow . . . . . . . . . . . . . . . . . . 319
8.7:    Fluid Flow in Microchannels . . . . . . . . . . . . . . . . . 321
8.8:    Fluid Flow through Channels with Micro Structured Walls . . . . . . . 324
8.9:    Mass Transfer in Ducts . . . . . . . . . . . . . . . . . . 326
        8.9.1   Mass Transfer in Laminar Flow with Fully Developed Velocity and
                Concentration Distributions inside Ducts . . . . . . . . . 327
        8.9.2   Mass Transfer in Turbulent Flow inside Pipes . . . . . . . . 327
        Problems . . . . . . . . . . . . . . . . . . . . . . . 328

Chapter 9:  *Convection due to Buoyancy Forces (Free Convection)* . . . . . . . . 335
9.1:    Basic Concepts . . . . . . . . . . . . . . . . . . . . . 335
9.2:    Free Convection on a Flat Plate . . . . . . . . . . . . . . . . 338
        9.2.1   Vertical Plate . . . . . . . . . . . . . . . . . . 338
        9.2.2   Horizontal Plate . . . . . . . . . . . . . . . . . 344
        9.2.3   Inclined Plates . . . . . . . . . . . . . . . . . . 348
9.3:    Free Convection on a Long Cylinder . . . . . . . . . . . . . . . 351
        9.3.1   Vertical Cylinder . . . . . . . . . . . . . . . . . 351
        9.3.2   Horizontal Cylinder . . . . . . . . . . . . . . . . 351
9.4:    Free Convection on a Sphere . . . . . . . . . . . . . . . . . 352
9.5:    Simplified Equations for Air . . . . . . . . . . . . . . . . . 353
9.6:    Free Convection in Enclosed Spaces . . . . . . . . . . . . . . . 356
        9.6.1   Basic Concepts . . . . . . . . . . . . . . . . . . 356
        9.6.2   Vertical Layer, $\phi = 90°$ . . . . . . . . . . . . . . 358
        9.6.3   Inclined Layers, $90° < \phi \leq 60°$ . . . . . . . . . . . 359
        9.6.4   Inclined Layers, $0° \leq \phi \leq 60°$ . . . . . . . . . . . 360
        9.6.5   Horizontal Cylindrical Annulus . . . . . . . . . . . . 363
        9.6.6   Spherical Annulus . . . . . . . . . . . . . . . . 364
9.7:    Plumes generated by Free Convection . . . . . . . . . . . . . . 366
        Problems . . . . . . . . . . . . . . . . . . . . . . . 366

Chapter 10: *Phase Change Heat Transfer: Condensation and Boiling* . . . . . . . 373
10.1:   Laminar Film Condensation . . . . . . . . . . . . . . . . . 374

10.1.1    Condensation on Vertical Surfaces . . . . . . . . . . . . . . . . . 374

10.1.2    Condensation on Inclined Plates . . . . . . . . . . . . . . . 376

10.1.3    Condensation on a Single Horizontal Tube . . . . . . . . . . . 378

10.1.4    Condensation on Horizontal Tube Banks . . . . . . . . . . . 379

10.1.5    Calculation of Reynolds Number . . . . . . . . . . . . . . . 380

10.2:   Turbulent Film Condensation . . . . . . . . . . . . . . . . . 382

10.3:   Dropwise Condensation . . . . . . . . . . . . . . . . . . . . 385

10.4:   Condensation in the Presence of Noncondensible Gas . . . . . . . . 385

10.5:   Pool Boiling . . . . . . . . . . . . . . . . . . . . . . . . . . 386

10.5.1    Free-Convection Regime . . . . . . . . . . . . . . . . . 387

10.5.2    Nucleate Boiling Regime . . . . . . . . . . . . . . . . . 388

10.5.3    Peak Heat Flux . . . . . . . . . . . . . . . . . . . . . . 391

10.5.4    Film Boiling Regime . . . . . . . . . . . . . . . . . . . . 393

Problems . . . . . . . . . . . . . . . . . . . . . . . . . . . . . . . 394

*Chapter 11: Basic Radiation Heat Transfer Concepts* . . . . . . . . . . . . . . . 399

11.1:   Introduction . . . . . . . . . . . . . . . . . . . . . . . . . . 399

11.2:   Blackbody Radiation Laws . . . . . . . . . . . . . . . . . . . . 402

11.2.1    Blackbody Emissive Power . . . . . . . . . . . . . . . . 404

11.2.2    Wien's Displacement Law . . . . . . . . . . . . . . . . . 407

11.2.3    Stefan - Boltzmann Law . . . . . . . . . . . . . . . . . . 408

11.2.4    Blackbody Radiation Function . . . . . . . . . . . . . . . 409

11.3:   Radiation Energy from Real Surfaces . . . . . . . . . . . . . . . 413

11.3.1    Radiation Intensity Independent of Direction . . . . . . . . . 414

11.4:   Radiation Incident on a Surface . . . . . . . . . . . . . . . . . 414

11.4.1    Radiation Intensity Independent of Direction . . . . . . . . . 415

11.5:   Radiation Properties of Surfaces . . . . . . . . . . . . . . . . . 415

11.5.1    Emissivity . . . . . . . . . . . . . . . . . . . . . . . . 416

11.5.2    Absorptivity . . . . . . . . . . . . . . . . . . . . . . . 419

11.5.3    Graybody Approximation . . . . . . . . . . . . . . . . . 420

11.5.4    Kirchhoff's Law . . . . . . . . . . . . . . . . . . . . . 420

11.5.5    Reflectivity . . . . . . . . . . . . . . . . . . . . . . . . 420

11.5.6    Bi-Directional Reflectivity . . . . . . . . . . . . . . . . . 422

11.5.7    Transmissivity . . . . . . . . . . . . . . . . . . . . . . 423

11.6:   Diffuse Surface Radiation Heat Transfer . . . . . . . . . . . . . . 424

11.6.1    View Factor between Two Elementary Surfaces . . . . . . . . 425

11.7:   View Factor between Two Finite Surfaces . . . . . . . . . . . . . 427

11.8:   Properties of View Factors . . . . . . . . . . . . . . . . . . . . 428

11.9:   View-Factor Determination . . . . . . . . . . . . . . . . . . . . 431

11.9.1    Evaluation of View Factors . . . . . . . . . . . . . . . . 431

11.9.2    Area Integration . . . . . . . . . . . . . . . . . . . . . 431

11.9.3    Contour Integration . . . . . . . . . . . . . . . . . . . . 433

11.9.4    Graphical Form of the View Factors . . . . . . . . . . . . . 434

11.9.5    View Factor Algebra . . . . . . . . . . . . . . . . . . . . 434

11.9.6    Crossed-String Method . . . . . . . . . . . . . . . . . . 440

11.9.7    Inside Sphere Method . . . . . . . . . . . . . . . . . . . 441

11.10: Radiation Exchange in an Enclosure . . . . . . . . . . . . . . . . 442

11.10.1 Radiosity Concept . . . . . . . . . . . . . . . . . . . . . 443

11.11: Network Method for Radiation Exchange in an Enclosure . . . . . . . . 444

11.11.1  Radiation Resistance at a Surface . . . . . . . . . . . . . . . . . . . 445
11.11.2  Radiation Resistance across Two Surfaces . . . . . . . . . . . . 446
11.11.3  Radiation Network for Two Surfaces . . . . . . . . . . . . . . . . 447
11.11.4  Radiation Transfer between Two Parallel Plates . . . . . . . . . 448
11.11.5  Radiation Exchange in Three or More Zone Enclosures . . . . . . 448
11.12: Radiation Shields . . . . . . . . . . . . . . . . . . . . . . . . . . . . . 453
Problems . . . . . . . . . . . . . . . . . . . . . . . . . . . . . . . . . . . . 455

*Chapter 12: Thermal Analysis of Heat Exchangers* . . . . . . . . . . . . . . . . 463
12.1:  Types of Heat Exchangers . . . . . . . . . . . . . . . . . . . . . . . 464
12.2:  Fluid Temperature Distributions . . . . . . . . . . . . . . . . . . . . 467
12.3:  Overall Heat Transfer Coefficient and Thermal Resistances . . . . 469
12.4:  Logarithmic Mean Temperature Difference (LMTD) Method . . . . . . . 476
12.5:  Correction for the LMTD . . . . . . . . . . . . . . . . . . . . . . . . 480
12.6:  Effectiveness and Number of Transfer Units ($\epsilon$-NTU) Method . . . . . . . 480
12.7:  A Note on Compact Heat Exchangers . . . . . . . . . . . . . . . . . . 492
Problems . . . . . . . . . . . . . . . . . . . . . . . . . . . . . . . . . . . . 493
Appendix A: CONSTANTS AND CONVERSION FACTORS . . . . . . . . . . . . 501
Appendix B: SELECTED PHYSICAL PROPERTIES . . . . . . . . . . . . . . 504
Appendix C: RADIATION PROPERTIES . . . . . . . . . . . . . . . . . . . . 520
Appendix D: ERROR FUNCTION . . . . . . . . . . . . . . . . . . . . . . . . 523
Appendix E: MATHEMATICAL IDENTITIES . . . . . . . . . . . . . . . . . . 524
References . . . . . . . . . . . . . . . . . . . . . . . . . . . . . . . . . . . 527
Index . . . . . . . . . . . . . . . . . . . . . . . . . . . . . . . . . . . . . 533

I dedicate this book to my husband **Yildirim Bayazitoglu** and I like to take this opportunity to thank him for his unconditional and irreplaceable support and love. I want to express my appreciation to my sons **Ozgur, Matt (Mert), and Kent (Kunt)** for being ideal children. I am sincerely obliged to all my immediate and extended family members providing me the support for the opportunity to be a mother, a grandmother, a university professor and a scholar.

Yildiz Bayazitoglu
*Rice University Houston, Texas*

# ABOUT THE AUTHORS

**Yildiz Bayazitoglu** is Harry S Cameron Chair Professor of mechanical engineering at Rice University. She received her B.S. in mechanical engineering from Middle East Technical University and M.S. and Ph.D. degrees from the University of Michigan, where she was a Rackham and a Barbour Fellow. She published in reputable journals and high caliber proceedings and her inventions received patent rights. Professor Bayazitoglu made significant contributions to thermophysical property determination and containerless processing of materials, radiation and convective heat transfer, phase-change heat transfer, oil reservoir fluid flow heat transfer, cryogenic tank thermal analysis, hydrogen-oxygen fuel cells, solar collector analysis, micro and nano scale heat transfer, and thermal modeling of the human head and optimization of hypothermic therapies. Her honors include Society of Women Engineers (SWE) Distinguished Educator Award, Rice University Brown Superior Teaching Award, Rice University Outstanding College Associate Award, Hershel M. Rich Outstanding Invention Award and Graduate Student Association Teaching/Mentoring Award, Rice University Chance Teaching Prize Rice University Faculty Impact Award and Rice University Presidential Mentoring Award. She received the American Society of Mechanical Engineers (ASME) society wide Heat Transfer Memorial Award. She is a Fellow of the ASME, a Fellow of the American Association of Advancement of Science (AAAS), an associate Fellow of the American Association of Aeronautics and Astronautics (AIAA). She served as the chair of the ASME Heat Transfer Division and served in the executive committee of International Center of Heat and Mass Transfer (ICHMT). During 2012, she is selected to be an Honorary Member of the ASME and she also received the SWE's Achievement Award which is the highest award given by the SWE.

**Necati M. Ozişik** passed away peacefully on October 04, 2008, while sleeping in his home in Turkey. He dedicated his life to education and research in heat transfer. His legacy is left for us and for those yet to come to the rich field of Heat Transfer. He was a good friend, a mentor and a pleasant person to be with. He retired as Professor Emeritus of the Mechanical and Aerospace Engineering Department of North Caroline State University in 1998, where he spent most of his academic career. He was also a Visiting Professor for several occasions in INSA-Lyon, University of Nantes and ETH-Zurich. A graduate of the University of London, Professor Ozişik has been honored here and abroad for his sustained contributions to heat transfer research and education. In London, he received the F. Bernard Hall Price Award from the institution of Mechanical Engineers; in the United States, he received the Western Electric Fund Award of ASEE, Alcoa Foundation Research Award, Alcoa Foundation Distinguished Engineering Research Award, Turkish Science Award, O. Max Gardner Award, R.J.R. Nabisco Award, and the American Society of Mechanical Engineers (ASME) society wide Heat Transfer Memorial Award. He was a fellow of the American Society of Mechanical Engineers. He was the author or coauthor of several books and research papers in the areas of heat transfer, mass diffusion, radiation, and heat exchangers.

Heat transfer background is becoming vital for scientist and engineers in several branches of technological development including *Mechanical, Chemical, Electrical, Materials, Environmental, Civil, Aerospace and Bio Engineering* and further expanding into *Biosciences, Material Science, Chemistry and Physics*. The purpose of this textbook is to teach undergraduate students the fundamentals of heat transfer within one semester without their becoming overwhelmed with the details or with mathematical complications. The intent is to introduce the physical principals and fundamental concepts of heat transfer efficiently and effectively and to develop the skills to identify basic problems in various applications and seek their solutions.

One of the objectives of this book is to engage the students to read and comprehend concepts without hassle in a short time. The book makes an effort to introduce basic concepts of heat transfer using simple language making them easy to understand. Students are exposed to many challenging interruptions during the school years, so rather than having them struggle with difficult and puzzling explanations they are led to focus on important essentials.

The aim was not to produce a thick book with excessive reference information and derivations. Rather, it was to teach almost all material included in the chapters. Today in academic society the students are exposed to large amounts of electronic information and in general they do not have the time to read thick textbooks as the earlier generation did. Several excellent graduate level textbooks, reference books and web sites are available on specific topics. The students, if their schedule permits and if they so desire, can access these resources by simply searching each topic presented in the book to further enhance their knowledge. In other words my emphasis is to *teach how to walk first, then they can run later*.

**CONTENTS OF THE CHAPTERS:** There are over 100 example problems and over 500 problems arranged in the same order as the material presented. Chapter 1 discusses the basic concepts of the mechanisms of heat flow and introduces the SI system of units. The particular laws, and the thermal properties of solids and fluids are discussed. The nanofuids are discussed and approximate thermal properties of the nanofluids are given.

In Chapter 2, the time variation of temperature is demonstrated by introducing the lumped system analysis assumption concept. Chapter 3 emphasizes the physical significance of the heat conduction equation and illustrates the similarities between the diffusion of heat and diffusion of mass. The temperature transients and heat flow concepts are introduced. It develops the background needed to formulate the heat conduction equation with its boundary conditions. In Chapter 4, one-dimensional steady-state heat conduction problems in bodies of single- and multi-layers having simple shapes of a plate, a cylinder, and a sphere are studied. The thermal resistance concept is introduced to solve the temperature distribution of the medium without any heat generation. The conduction shape factors of simple geometries are given in order to study the steady-state two-dimensional heat conduction. The extended surfaces (fins) are analyzed and the basic temperature distributions are obtained. Chapter 5 covers the steady-state heat conduction with heat generation problems. The analytical expressions to the temperature distributions of heat conduction problems with various boundary conditions are given. The fundamentals of finite-difference numerical method for the solution of steady heat conduction problems are presented. In Chapter 6, the solution to one-dimensional transient heat flow problems are introduced. The solution to the temperature distributions and heat flows in the form of charts (called Heisler Charts) are given. The finite difference formulation for transient one dimensional problems with numerical examples are presented.

Chapter 7 gives the background for the physical significance of various concepts and deals with forced convection over bodies. The drag and the heat transfer coefficient expressions are developed. The emphasis is given to understand the concept of velocity and temperature distribution. The forced convection heat transfer of nano fluids over a flat plate and the basics of mass transfer in external boundary layer flows are studied. Chapter 8 deals with forced convection for internal flows inside ducts. The nano fluid flow in pipes, and the fluid flow in microchannels are discussed. Chapter 9 covers the flows due to buoyancy forces (free convection), and Chapters 10 introduces condensation and boiling phase change heat transfer in fluids. The flow regimes of boiling heat transfer are discussed and basic correlation equations are given.

Chapter 11 is devoted to heat transfer by thermal radiation. The basic concepts to study radiative heat transfer are introduced. The radiation heat exchange among surfaces separated with non-participating medium, which is also called the surface radiation heat exchange is covered. In order to provide insight for the physics of the heat flow, the network analogy method is introduced.

Chapter 12 is introducing the basic heat exchanger thermal design concepts. Simplified methods for the design and evaluation of basic flow configurations are given.

For the instructors who adapt the book for their classes, the *Solutions Manual* for the problems at the end of the chapters and the *Slides* for lectures are available. They can be requested from the publisher.

**ACKNOWLEDGEMENTS:** I acknowledge that the roots of this book come from my earlier collaborations with Professor M.N. Ozişik who was my colleague, my mentor and a very dear friend.

I am indebted to the heat transfer community and my colleagues around the world with appreciation for their support not only in writing this book but also for their continual encouragement throughout my professional career as a scientist and a teacher. I acknowledge my former and current graduate and undergraduate students, and the staff members of my department at Rice for their contributions and assisting me during different phases of preparing this book.

Yildiz Bayazitoglu
*Rice University Houston, Texas*

# CHAPTER 1

# *Mechanisms of Heat Flow*

The science of *thermodynamics* deals with the relationship between heat and other forms of energy, but the science of *heat transfer* is concerned with the analysis of the rate of heat transfer taking place in a system. The energy transfer by heat flow cannot be measured directly, but the concept has physical meaning because it is related to the measurable quantity called *temperature*. Heat flows from one body to another as a result of the difference in temperature. That is, if two bodies at different temperatures are brought together, heat flows from the hotter body to the colder body. As a result, in the absence of phase change such as melting or solidification, the temperature of the colder body increases and that of the hotter body decreases. Since heat flow takes place whenever there is a temperature gradient in a system, a knowledge of the temperature distribution in a system is essential.

The *heat flux* is a quantity of practical interest and is defined as the amount of heat transfer per unit area per unit time. At macroscopic scale once the temperature distribution is known, this quantity is readily determined from a particular law (also called constitutive relation) which relates the heat flux to the temperature gradient. At micro and nanoscale, the question inevitably arises as to whether one should entertain the idea of temperature definition at nanoscale space and time. Tackling this question is beyond the scope of this book but its importance should be pointed out when one studies the nanoscale heat transfer by molecular dynamics, Monte Carlo method and by using the Boltzmann equation.

In the design of heat exchangers such as boilers, condensers, radiators, etc., for example, heat transfer analysis is essential for sizing such equipment. In the design of nuclear-reactor cores, a thorough heat transfer analysis of fuel elements is important for proper sizing of fuel elements to prevent burnout. Thus, the temperature distribution and the heat flow are of interest. In aerospace technology, the temperature distribution and heat transfer problems are crucial because of weight limitations and safety considerations. In heating and air conditioning applications for buildings, a proper heat transfer analysis is necessary to estimate the amount of insulation needed to prevent excessive heat loss or gain.

In heat transfer literature, it is customary to consider three distinct mechanisms of heat flow: *conduction, convection,* and *radiation.* Heat is transferred by conduction in a solid or fluid at rest. The word *fluid* refers to liquids and gases. Conduction phenomena needs a medium (either solid, fluid or gas) in which to take place, whereas radiation can take place in a vacuum with no material carrier. Heat is also transferred by convection in fluids in motion. Although conduction and radiation are the two basic modes of heat flow, convection can be regarded as conduction with fluid in motion and depends on mechanical mass transport.

The temperature distribution in a medium is mainly controlled by the combined effects of conduction, convection and radiation mechanisms of heat flow. It is not possible to completely isolate one from the others. However, when one mechanism is dominant, the others can be neglected, and with such a restriction we present below a brief qualitative description of each of these three different mechanisms of heat transfer, including some fundamental micro/nano scale understanding.

## 1.1. CONDUCTION PHENOMENA

Conduction is the mechanism of heat transfer in which energy exchange transported from the region of high temperature to that of low temperature, that is from a more energetic region to the less energetic region. Conduction heat transfer becomes very important in very important applications including electronics. The mechanisms of conduction from a sense of micro/nano scales in *solids* are by

(i) the heat transport due to drift of free electrons due to their *free* movement within the medium and

(ii) the vibration of the atoms that constitute the lattice (phonons). However in *fluids* by

(iii) the kinetic motion or direct impact of molecules.

### 1.1.1 Conduction due to Drift of Free Electrons

One of the mechanisms of heat conduction is due to the motion of free electrons in solids, mostly in metals. In a solid which is a good electric conductor, a large number of free electrons move about in the lattice; hence materials that are good electric conductors are generally good heat conductors (i.e., copper, silver, etc.). For the electrons to be considered as free there are two main assumptions: (a) The interactions between the atoms are ignored and (b) The potential energy of the electrons is assumed to be constant, which may be set to zero with no loss of generality. In other words, the interaction of the electrons with ions in the lattice is not taken into account. The valence electrons of metal atoms, which are the electrons in the outermost energy level of an atom, are thought to be separate from the ions and form an electron gas, also referred to as the free electron gas.

Consider the electrons located on the hot side of a metal bar. The high thermal energy of the hot side excites the electrons in this part of the metal rod, thus the kinetic energies of the electrons increase. Because the electrons interact with each other, the high thermal energy starts to spread through the metal rod in terms of collisions and momentum transfers, each electron affecting the one next to it. This process continues until all the electrons, even in the cold end of the rod, come to a complete equilibrium.

The electron contribution to heat conduction is acoustic only in the solids whose valence electrons are capable to move through the conduction band easily, namely the metals. For insulators, the valence electrons can't wander in the conduction band so this mechanism is not dominant in solids other than the metals.

### 1.1.2 Conduction due to Phonons and Lattice Atoms as Harmonic Oscillators

Another mechanism of heat conduction in solids is due to oscillations of the atoms forming the crystal lattice, or the periodic atomic arrangement, of the material. From a simplified perspective, the atoms of a lattice can be considered as masses attached to each other via springs. It is then obvious that the oscillatory motion of one atom affects the net force on the surrounding atoms and transfers energy from one location to another similar to a traveling wave. In reality, the connections between atoms are not springs but atomic interactions, both bonded and non-bonded, meaning the true interactions are more complex and not limited to nearest-neighbors. In either case, the atomic oscillations can occur at multiple frequencies, and each individual frequency has an energy associated with it given by

$$E = (n + 1/2)\, h\, \omega \tag{1-1}$$

where h is the *Planck constant* ($6.626 \times 10^{-34}\ m^2 \cdot kg/s$), $\omega$ is the vibrational frequency ($1/s$) and n represents the modes of oscillations (0, 1, 2, ...) which are positive integers or zero. Each vibrational mode corresponds to a different propagating wave in the crystal at a discrete (or quantized) energy level. Phonons are packets of *mechanical waves* that define certain quanta of energy. Simply a *phonon* is a *quantum of vibrational energy*. The lower energy phonons are classified as acoustic and the higher energy phonons are classified as optical. Acoustic phonons are called so because they are responsible for transmitting sound waves through a given material. The optical phonons always have a certain minimum frequency no matter the size of wavelengths. Optical phonons are excited easily by light and are common in ionic crystals.

Phonons play a prominent role in predicting the specific heat and thermal conductivity of solids, most notably in semi-conductors as they contain relatively few free electrons when compared to metals. Although, at low temperatures, phonons are also the dominant mode of energy transfer in metals, becoming less dominant as the material warms, though still a contributing factor.

While these properties can be calculated explicitly for a given lattice, doing so requires extensive knowledge of solid state physics and complicated mathematics which is too complicated a discussion to present in this text. Instead, the focus will shift to the models of Debye and Einstein. These models attempt to simplify the complex mathematics into a more manageable, and subsequently useful, formulation by making different approximations regarding the travel of waves through solids. The main difference between the two models is that Debye takes a classical approach to modeling particle dynamics which better predicts the contribution from acoustic modes, while the Einstein model treats the particles in a quantum fashion, leading to a better prediction of the optical modes. The overall results of the two models differ only slightly.

Before going much further, it is necessary to introduce the *Debye temperature*, $\theta_D$, which is a parameter defined for convenience within the Debye model and used to extract thermophysical property information from both the Debye and Einstein models. The

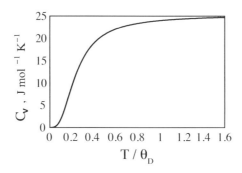

**FIG. 1.1.** Debye model predictions of specific heat as a function of normalized temperature.

Debye temperature is constant for a given material and is a measure of the highest temperature attainable due solely to vibrational energy as well as the temperature at which free electron motion begins to dominate the properties of the material. For most elements, typical values of Debye temperature range between 200 and 600 Kelvin.

This temperature is useful in estimating the phonon contribution to specific heat, $C_v$, through the use of one of the models described above. Fig. 1.1 gives the predictions based on the Debye model for $C_v$ on a molar basis as a function of a dimensionless $T/\theta_D$ ratio.

It is noteworthy to mention this curve and the theory behind it makes no assumption of the type of material aside from state of matter; this theory is only valid for materials in the solid state. Once the Debye temperate is determined, which can often be found tabulated for elements and most common compounds, Fig. 1.1 can be used to approximate the phonon contribution to the specific heat. At low temperatures in metals and much of the spectrum in semi-conductors, this approximation is quite good. The agreement of this theory with measured values depends on temperature because it cannot be forgotten that free electrons are also a component of specific heat.

For metallic elements and compounds, the Debye theory best agrees with measured values at very low temperatures, $T < \theta_D$. It is also possible to approximate the phonon contribution to thermal conductivity, but doing so is even more complicated than the determination of specific heat and is outside the scope of this discussion.

**EXAMPLE 1-1** Estimate the constant volume specific heat of bulk silicon at room temperature, knowing that the Debye temperature for silicon is $\theta_D = 625$ K.

**SOLUTION** Since room temperature is $\approx 300$ K,

$$\frac{T}{\theta_D} = \frac{300}{625}$$

$$= 0.48$$

From Fig. 1.1, we have $C_v = 20.514 \frac{\text{J}}{\text{mol K}}$.

Using its molecular weight, we determine the specific heat of silicon as

$$c_v = \frac{20.514\frac{J}{mol\,K}}{28.086\frac{g}{mol}}$$

$$= 0.73\frac{J}{g\,K}$$

This value, calculated using the Debye model, is very close to the experimentally-determined value of $0.712\frac{J}{g\,K}$ and is certainly within the error bounds of this calculation.

**EXAMPLE 1-2** Calculate the phonon contribution to the constant volume specific heat of $H_2O$ under 1 atm of pressure at 250 K and 300 K and compare to the available standard values. Comment on the agreement or disagreement between the values. The Debye temperature of water is 220 K.

**SOLUTION** At 300 K:

As in the previous example, we first calculate the temperature ratio as

$$\frac{T}{\theta_D} = \frac{300}{220}$$

$$= 1.36$$

From Fig. 1.1, we have $C_v = 24.57\frac{J}{mol\,K}$. Using the molecular weight of water, we determine the specific heat of water as

$$c_v = \frac{24.57\frac{J}{mol\,K}}{18\frac{g}{mol}}$$

$$= 1.349\frac{J}{g\,K}$$

This compares poorly to the tabulated specific heat of water near $4\frac{J}{g\,K}$ because at 1 atm, water is in its liquid state, and the theory developed in this section does not apply.

At 250 K:

$$\frac{T}{\theta_D} = \frac{250}{220}$$

$$= 1.13$$

From Fig. 1.1, we have $C_v = 24.27\frac{J}{mol\,K}$. Using its molecular weight, we determine the specific heat of water as

$$c_v = \frac{24.27 \frac{\text{J}}{\text{mol K}}}{18 \frac{\text{g}}{\text{mol}}}$$

$$= 1.365 \frac{\text{J}}{\text{g K}}$$

This compares well to the tabulated specific heat of ice at 250 K, $1.38 \frac{\text{J}}{\text{g K}}$. In this case, since the substance is a crystalline solid, the Debye theory is applicable for estimating the phonon contribution to specific heat.

When comparing the theoretical results to measured values, it is also important to be mindful of phenomena limiting the specific heat and thermal conductivity not covered by the theories described. Phonon-phonon scattering is one such phenomenon. At very low temperatures, conductivity and specific heat are dominated by the size and shape of the crystal structure and the resulting phonon energy transfer.

As the material increases in temperature, more waves begin oscillating through the material at different wavelengths and amplitudes leading to greater and greater collisions between vibrating lattice atoms. These collisions result in energy transfer between phonons and changes in momentum of the waves, causing less than ideal energy transfer through the material. Because of these phonon-phonon interactions, the vibrational frequencies within the crystal, and therefore the phonon contributions to specific heat and thermal conductivity, are limited.

Electron-phonon interactions are the other phenomenon producing less than ideal results for thermal conductivity and specific heat. This occurs when the temperature is such that free electrons are flowing, and the path of the electrons is disrupted by phonons. Frequently phonon-phonon interaction occurs first, followed by electron-phonon interactions as the temperature continues to increase. Both contribute to the divergence of measured results from theory.

### 1.1.3 Conduction due to Kinetic Motion of Molecules

The conduction phenomena can also be explained by the diffusion of energy due to molecular activity. That is the transfer of energy due to interactions between the molecules in fluids (gases or liquids) from the more energetic to the less energetic molecules while there is no bulk or macroscopic motion. The individual molecules will still have random motions proportional to the temperature of the fluid. In the presence of a temperature gradient, a net energy transfer from the higher energy region to the lower energy region takes place called diffusion of energy. In liquids, the molecules are more closely packed and the molecular interactions are stronger than gases.

The kinetic theory to explains the macroscopic properties of gases, such as pressure, volume, and temperature, by considering the molecular composition and the molecular motion of the gases. The theory explained conduction of heat to and from gases and within other mediums. Prior to the kinetic theory, for modeling heat transfer, the caloric theory was used. This theory stated that heat was a tangible but massless, colorless, and odorless substance called *caloric* that could be physically transferred from one body to another. As caloric would leave a body, that object would become cooler, and as it entered another, that one would become warmer. It was believed that a body could only contain, or lose, a specified amount of caloric, and it was this assumption that led to the breakdown of the theory. The scientists were able to conclusively show that heat could be continuously created through friction, definitively disproving the concept of caloric heat transfer.

### 1.1.4 Fourier Law of Conduction

The macroscopic conduction law is based on experimental observations made by Biot. Later named after Fourier who proposed the constitutive relation in 1822. The *Fourier law* states that the rate of heat flow by conduction in a given direction (say, the $x$ direction) is proportional to:

> The gradient of temperature in that direction, $dT/dx$
> The area normal to the direction of heat flow, $A$

Then for heat flow in the $x$ direction, we have

$$Q_x = -kA \frac{dT}{dx} \quad \text{W} \tag{1-2}$$

where $Q_x$ is the rate of heat flow in the positive $x$ direction, through area $A$ normal to the $x$ direction, and $\dfrac{dT}{dx} = \lim\limits_{\Delta x \to 0} \dfrac{\Delta T}{\Delta x}$ is the gradient of temperature in that direction. The proportionality constant $k$, called the *thermal conductivity*, is a property of the material.

The reason for including the minus sign on Eq. (1-2), as illustrated in Fig. 1.2, is as follows: If temperature decreases in the positive $x$ direction, $dT/dx$ is negative; then $Q_x$ becomes a positive quantity because of the presence of the negative sign, and hence heat flow is in the positive $x$ direction, as illustrated in Fig. 1.2a . Likewise, if temperature increases in the positive $x$ direction, $dT/dx$ is positive, and hence $Q_x$ becomes negative and the heat flow is in the negative $x$ direction, as illustrated in Fig. 1.2b.

Thus the notation used in Eq. (1-2) implies that when $Q_x$ is a *positive* quantity, the *heat flow is in the positive x direction,* and vice versa.

To illustrate the application of this concept, we consider a slab (i.e., a plate) with a linear temperature distribution within the body, as shown in Fig. 1.3. Equation (1-2) becomes

$$
\begin{aligned}
Q_x &= -kA \frac{dT}{dx} \\
&= -kA \frac{T_2 - T_1}{x_2 - x_1} = kA \frac{T_1 - T_2}{x_2 - x_1} \\
&= kA \frac{\Delta T}{L}
\end{aligned}
\tag{1-3}
$$

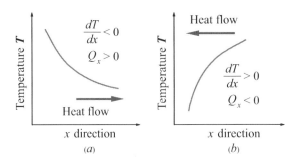

**FIG. 1.2.** Heat flow sign.

where $x_2 - x_1 = L$, the thickness of the slab, is a positive quantity.

For the specific situation shown in Fig. 1.2, we have $T_1 > T_2$, and hence $\Delta T = T_1 - T_2$ is also a positive quantity. Thus the heat flow $Q_x$ is in the positive $x$ direction.

Conversely, if we had $T_2 > T_1$, then $T_1 - T_2$ would be negative and the heat flow would be in the negative $x$ direction.

The heat flow rate per unit area is called the *heat flux*. Therefore, $Q_x$ divided by the area $A$,

$$\boxed{q_x = \frac{Q_x}{A}} \quad \text{W/m}^2 \tag{1-4}$$

is the heat flux in the $x$ direction. Thus $q_x$ represents the *amount of heat flow per unit area, per unit time in the $x$ direction*. When heat flow $Q_x$ is in watts and heat flux $q_x$ in watts per square meter, then the thermal conductivity $k$ has the dimension $\text{W/(m} \cdot {}^\circ\text{C)}$ or $\text{J/(m} \cdot \text{s} \cdot {}^\circ\text{C)}$.

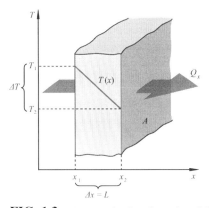

**FIG. 1.3.** Heat conduction through a slab.

The thermal conductivity $k$ in Eqs. (1-2) must have the dimensions $\text{W/(m} \cdot {}^\circ\text{C)}$ or $\text{J/(m} \cdot \text{s} \cdot {}^\circ\text{C)}$ if the equations are dimensionally correct. For English System of units the conversion constant is $1 \text{ W/(m} \cdot {}^\circ\text{C)} = 0.578 \text{ Btu/(hr} \cdot \text{ft} \cdot {}^\circ\text{F)}$.

**EXAMPLE 1-3** A brick wall of thickness 20 cm with a thermal conductivity 0.5 W/(m $\cdot$ ${}^\circ$C) is maintained at 20°C at one surface and 10°C at the other surface. Determine the heat flow rate across a 5-m² surface area of the wall.

**SOLUTION** The origin of the $x$ coordinate is placed on the hot surface at $T_1 = 20°C$. Then the cold surface $T_2 = 10°C$ is located at $x_2 = L = 0.20\,\text{m}$. Knowing the thermal conductivity of the wall $k = 0.5\,\text{W/(m}\cdot°\text{C)}$, Eq. (1-3) is applied to determine the heat flow rate across the surface area of the wall $A = 5\,\text{m}^2$.

$$Q_x = kA\frac{T_1 - T_2}{x_2 - x_1} = kA\frac{\Delta T}{L}$$

$$= 0.5\,\text{W/(m}\cdot°\text{C)} \times 5\,\text{m}^2 \times \frac{(20-10)°\text{C}}{0.20\,\text{m}}$$

$$= 125\,\text{W} = 0.125\,\text{kW}$$

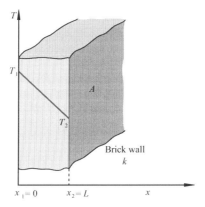

**FIGURE EXAMPLE 1-3**

**EXAMPLE 1-4** The heat flow rate through a wood board between two surfaces of thickness $L = 3\,\text{cm}$, for a temperature difference of $\Delta T = 30°C$ is 200 W/m². How do we calculate the thermal conductivity of the wood?

**SOLUTION** From equation (1-3), we have:

$$q = k\frac{\Delta T}{L}$$

$$200 = k\frac{30}{0.03}$$

$$k = 0.2\,\text{W/(m}\cdot°\,\text{C)}$$

**EXAMPLE 1-5** In rocket science, heat transfer issues must be addressed. One can use the accompanying figure to become familiar with the basic design of a rocket. The heat flow from the inside surface of the throat wall to the outside surface of the throat wall is by conduction.

(a) An experimental rocket's combustion thrust chamber, as illustrated, has an outside (cool) wall temperature of 135 °C at the nozzle throat. The heat flow rate through the throat wall is measured to be $2 \times 10^7 \mathrm{W/m^2}$. The throat wall is made of 0.3 cm thick stainless stell with k=26 W/(m · °C). Calculate the inner wall (that is the hot wall) temperature at the throat using the given information.

(b) The calculated inner or hot wall's temperature at the throat in part (a) is too high and will cause the stainless steel to fail. The inner throat is lined with a protective layer to prevent failure. Assume the protective layer is a ceramic liner of conductivity 5 W/(m · °C). With this protective layer, the inner or hot wall of the stainless steel is kept at 1150 °C, while the cool side remains at 135 °C. Calculate the new heat transfer rate in the wall.

(c) Assume the heat transfer rate is the same in the wall as in the ceramic and the temperature at the inner wall of to be 3595 °C. Calculate the thickness of the ceramic used.

(d) Instead of stainless steel, in problem part (a), a composite with a higher thermal conductivity of 52 W/(m · °C) is used. What would be the inner wall temperature of the throat without the added protective layer?

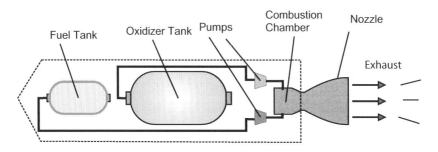

**FIGURE EXAMPLE 1-5**

**SOLUTION (a):**

$T_{wh} \equiv$ wall's temp on hot , inner side $\qquad q_x = 2 \times 10^7 \mathrm{\ W/m^2}$

$T_{wc} \equiv$ wall's temp on cool, outer side $= 135\,^\circ\mathrm{C}$ $\qquad l = 0.3\mathrm{cm} = 0.003\mathrm{\ m}$

$k = 26 \mathrm{\ W/(m \cdot \,^\circ C)}$

Using Fourier's law:

$$q_x = \frac{Q_x}{A}$$
$$= -k \frac{dT}{dx}$$

with

$$dT = \Delta T = T_{wc} - T_{wh}$$
$$dx = \Delta x = L.$$

we have

$$q_x = -k \frac{T_{wc} - T_{wh}}{L} = -26 \text{ W/(m} \cdot {}^\circ\text{C)} \frac{135^\circ\text{C} - T_{wh}}{0.003 \text{ m}}$$
$$= 2 \times 10^7 \text{ W/m}^2.$$

Knowing $q_x$, we can solve for $T_{wh}$:

$$T_{wh} = \frac{2 \times 10^7 \text{ W/m}^2}{26 \text{ W/(m} \cdot {}^\circ\text{C)}} 0.003 \text{ m} + 135 \, {}^\circ\text{C}$$
$$= 2{,}443 \, {}^\circ\text{C}$$

**SOLUTION (b):** The ceramic has the effect of lowering the inner wall temperature to 1150 °C, and the outer wall temperature is still 135 °C. Therefore $\Delta T = 1150^\circ\text{C} - 135^\circ\text{C}$. Using Fourier's law:

$$q_x = -k \frac{\Delta T}{L} = -26 \text{ W/(m} \cdot {}^\circ\text{C)} \frac{1150 \, {}^\circ\text{C} - 135 \, {}^\circ\text{C}}{0.003 \text{ m}}$$
$$= 8.80 \times 10^6 \text{ W/m}^2$$

**SOLUTION (c):** Knowing the numerical values of the heat flux, the thermal conductivity, the temperatures of the inner ceramic layer $T_{icl}$, and the outer ceramic layer $T_{ocl}$ as

$$q_x = 8.8 \times 10^6 \text{ W/m}^2$$
$$k = 5 \text{ W/(m} \cdot {}^\circ\text{C)}$$
$$T_{icl} = 3595 \, {}^\circ\text{C}$$
$$T_{ocl} = 1150 \, {}^\circ\text{C}.$$

Then we can calculate the temperature difference using the Fourier law

$$q_x = -k \frac{\Delta T}{\Delta x}$$
$$\Delta x = -k \frac{\Delta T}{q_x}$$
$$= \frac{(-5 \text{ W/(m} \cdot {}^\circ\text{C)})(1150 \, {}^\circ\text{C} - 3595 \, {}^\circ\text{C})}{8.8 \times 10^6 \text{ W/m}^2}$$
$$= 0.0014 \text{ m} = 0.14 \text{ cm}$$

**SOLUTION (d):**

$$T_{wh} = \frac{qL}{k} + T_{wc} = \frac{(2 \times 10^7 \text{ W/m}^2)(0.003 \text{ m})}{52 \text{ W/(m} \cdot {}^\circ\text{C)}} + 135 \,{}^\circ\text{C}$$
$$= 1288.8 \,{}^\circ\text{C}$$

### 1.1.5 Thermal Conductivity of Materials

As illustrated in Fig. 1.4, the range of thermal conductivity among various engineering materials is quite wide. Between gases (i.e., air) and highly conducting metals (i.e., copper), $k$ varies by a factor of about $10^4$. The thermal conductivity of diamond is not shown in the figure which is very high, 2200 W/(m $\cdot^\circ C$). Recently discovered Single Wall Carbon Nantubes(SWNT), Double Wall Carbon Nantubes(DWCN) and graphene, at room temperatures have thermal conductivities as high as 3500 and 5000 W/(m $\cdot^\circ C$). However these are pure material properties, when they are embedded in other host materials the thermal conductivity of the composites reduce dramatically.

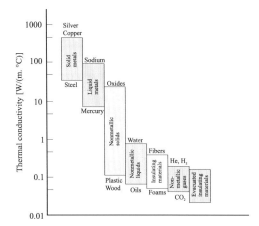

**FIG. 1.4.** Range of thermal conductivity of various materials.

The thermal conductivity also varies with changes in temperature and should be accounted for. For some materials the variation over certain temperature ranges is small enough to be neglected, but in many situations the variation of $k$ with temperatures is significant. At very low temperatures, near absolute zero, $k$ varies very rapidly with temperature. For example, the thermal conductivities of copper, aluminum, or silver reach values 50 to 100 times those that occur at room temperature.

Actual values of thermal conductivity of various materials are given in Appendix B. Figure 1.5 illustrates the variation of thermal conductivity of some engineering materials with temperature.

The use of materials with different thermal conduction properties are very critical to the functionality of systems we create. For example the main body of the Space Shuttle Orbiter is made of aluminum, similar to any large aircraft, which can only withstand

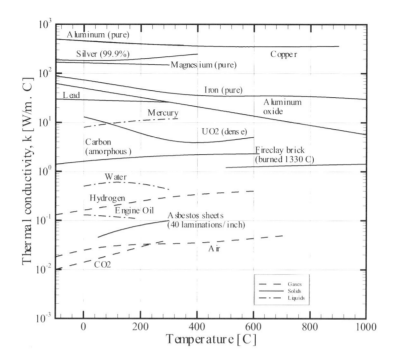

**FIG. 1.5.** Effect of temperature on thermal conductivity of materials.

temperatures not exceeding 350 degrees Fahrenheit. During ascent and entry, aerothermal heating caused by friction with the air creates temperatures above 350 degrees Fahrenheit and sometimes well above the melting temperature of steel (1220 degrees Fahrenheit). To protect spacecraft from the extreme temperatures of ascent and atmospheric re-entry, they are covered with a variety of insulating materials capable of withstanding those very high temperatures and with very low thermal conductivities so heat is not conducted through the insulating material to the sensitive body. One type of such material used for thermal insulation is the Fibrous Refractory Composite Insulation Tiles (FRCI). About 70 percent of the Space Shuttle Orbiter's external surface is covered with more than 24,000 thermal tiles of different types.

## Thermal Conductivity Calculations

In this section we present some of the simplified equations for the thermal conductivity of solids and fluids.

**DUE TO FREE ELECTRONS:**

The basic expression for the thermal conductivity due to free electrons is given by the Wiedemann-Franz Law. The work of Sommerfeld, who proposed the expression for the electrical conductivity of metals having free electrons, followed that of Wiedemann and

Franz. The Wiedemann-Franz law states that the ratio of thermal conductivity to electrical conductivity at a given temperature is constant for all the metals. The expression is

$$\frac{k_{el}}{\sigma_e\, T} = \frac{\pi^2}{3}\left(\frac{k_b}{e}\right)^2 = L_o \qquad (1\text{-}5a)$$

where $\sigma_e$ is electrical conductivity (ohm/meter), $k_{el}$ is the thermal conductivity due to free electrons, $\text{W}/(\text{mK})$ and $T$ is the absolute temperature. In the right hand side of the equation, $k_b$ is the Boltzmann constant $(1.38 \times 10^{-23}\ \text{W.s.}/\text{K} = 8.6 \times 10^{-5}\ \text{eV/K})$ and $e$ is the electron charge $(1.602 \times 10^{-19}$ coulomb$)$. All the constants in the right hand side are collected to give a universal constant, which is called the Lorenz number. Its value is

$$L_o = 2.45 \times 10^{-8}\ \ \text{W} \cdot ohm/\text{K}^2 \qquad (1\text{-}5b)$$

For example, Silver is a good electrical conductor and at $273$ K, it's thermal conductivity is $386$ W/m/K. Following Wiedemann-Fraanz Law, we can estimate its electrical conductance as

$$\sigma_e = \frac{k_{el}}{L_o\, T} = \frac{386\ \text{W/m/K}}{2.45 \times 10^{-8}\ \text{W} \cdot ohm/\text{K}^2 \ \times 273\ \text{K}} = 5.8 \times 10^7\ ohm^{-1} \qquad (1\text{-}5c)$$

Because the treatment involves the motion of free electrons, it is not unlikely that the electrical and thermal conductivities are interrelated. Qualitatively, the thermal conductivity of the metals increases as temperature increases because the electrons which are the carriers for the thermal energy are more energetic and their velocities increase, consequently on the average, forward transport of the thermal energy increases. However, the situation is different for electrical conductivity where the increase in the electron velocities results in greater number of collisions between electrons, diverting them subsequently from the preferred direction, or the current flow. So as the temperature increases, the electrical conductivity decreases.

When the experimental and theoretical values for the Lorenz number are compared, one should keep in mind that the thermal conductivity value given by the Wiedemann-Franz law is only due to the kinetic energies of free electrons. In fact, the mechanism of the vibrations of the lattice atoms in solids, is also effective in the thermal conductivity measurements.

## DUE TO PHONONS:

For nonmetallic solids (e.g. diamonds), the thermal conductivity is mainly due to phonons, and the same factors previously described that limit specific heat capacity also limit thermal conductivity. At temperatures less than the Debye temperature, the conductivity depends on the size and the shape of the crystal and increases with temperature. Increasing temperature results in higher vibrational energies and amplitudes in the crystal atoms where the probability of phonon-phonon scattering increases, limiting the oscillatory frequencies. At low temperatures, phonon-phonon collisions are all normal and do not contribute to thermal resistance. At higher temperatures, however, all collisions are considered, and the number of phonons is not conserved. Therefore as the temperature increases, the number of phonon-phonon interactions increases resulting in lowered thermal conductivity. Electron-phonon scattering whereby the motion of free conducting electrons is disturbed by phonons also takes place with increased frequency as temperature rises, further limiting the thermal conductivity.

To illustrate, the thermal resistance in thin-filmed $SiO_2$ is up to one order of magnitude smaller than bulk $SiO_2$. In this case, the effective thermal conductivity was reduced to between 75-90 percent of the bulk material values. Research has found that interfacial resistances from phonon scattering were just as important as the internal thermal resistance associated with a particular layer. Thin films of Silicon are subject to phonon-phonon interactions and scattering at the boundary of the material, and these interactions lead to a minimum thermal conductivity as the mean free path of the phonon goes towards the lattice constant. The conductivity is also dependent on the ratio of mean free path of the phonon to the layer thickness.

Qualitative statements on the contributions of phonons to thermal conductivity have been made, but the calculation of lattice thermal conductivities due to phonons, $k_{ph}$ involves complex mathematics and a deep understanding of solid state physics which is well beyond the scope of this book. However, there are situations in solids (e.g. alloys) when both electrons and phonons contribute to the transport of energy. Although it should be used with care, in such situations one may combine the effects from each to calculate the resultant numerical value for the thermal conductivity as: $k = k_{el} + k_{ph}$ if the thermal conductivity due to electron ($k_{el}$) and phonon ($k_{ph}$) effects are known.

## KINETIC THEORY FOR CONDUCTION IN SOLIDS:

The conduction phenomena in solids can also be explained basically by kinetic theory and the discussion of the molecular activity normally made for fluids can be extended to non-crystalline solids for electrons, phonons or atoms. This theory is based on the particles (either molecules, electrons, phonons or atoms) which interact with each other with collisions and transfer any property. If the transferred property is momentum, the analysis ends up with the expression for viscosity coefficient and if the transferred property is energy, one can get an expression for thermal conductivity. The expression for thermal conductivity either $k_{el}$ or $k_{ph}$ in its simplified form is

$$k = \frac{1}{3} C \, \nu \, \lambda_{mfp} \qquad (1\text{-}6)$$

The parameters in the expression are defined according to the energy carrying particles. For example if we have metals which are conductors and have free electrons, $C$ is the specific heat of the electrons per unit volume ($J/m^3 \times K$), $\nu$ is the mean electron velocity (m/s) and $\lambda_{mfp}$ is the mean free path of the electrons (m). For nonconductors, $C$ is the specific heat of the phonons, $\nu$ is the phonon velocity (velocity of sound), and $\lambda_{mfp}$ is the mean free path of the phonons. The treatment of these parameters requires molecular dynamic simulations or extensive integral studies of the lattice vibrations (e.g., phonons) and determining the mean free paths.

For most engineering applications, the heat conduction phenomenon is described by Fourier's law which is based on the continuum assumption of the material and from a macroscopic continuum sense. It is an empirical law based on experimental observations which originates from Biot. Since the mechanisms of transport by heat conduction deals with random movement of a large number of such heat carriers, during a finite time period, the statistical movement of the individual heat carriers has been mostly considered and does not significantly effect the heat conduction phenomenon at temperatures higher than the Debye temperature. For the purpose of most practical engineering applications, from a macroscopic sense, a continuum assumption was made to rule out the heat carriers' movement. This assumption neglects the micro-structure and scales of the media and assumes the media to be a continuum thus restricting the theory to deal with only macroscopic information. Since Fourier's law was derived under this so-called phenomenological approach, it is valid for

$$\frac{L}{\lambda_{mfp}} >> 1 \ and \ \frac{t}{\tau} >> 1$$

where L is the physical characteristic length dimension, $\lambda_{mfp}$ is the heat carriers' mean free path, t is the physical time, and $\tau$ is the mean relaxation time of the heat carriers.

For a stationary system. the dimensionless number Knudsen number $Kn$, is given as the ratio of the particle mean free path and the characteristic length scale of the system,

$$Kn = \frac{\lambda_{mfp}}{L}.$$

If we consider a homogeneous but non-stationary system, the Knudsen number, now expressed in the form

$$Kn = \frac{\tau}{t},$$

where the Knudsen number becomes the ratio of the collision time and the macroscopic time scale, characterizing the dynamical evolution of the system. Note that, with $v$ is being the average propagation speed, since $\lambda_{mfp} = v\tau$ and the equality $L = vt$ is always valid up to an order of magnitude, the two above definitions of the Knudsen number are equivalent. Therefore, depending on the value of $Kn$, we specify three regimes as follows:

(i) $Kn$ is much greater than one, the regime is described as rarefied;

(ii) $Kn$ is about one, we are in an intermediate regime and for both of these scales the thermal transport phenomena will be in micro and nanoscale;

(iii) $Kn$ is much less than one, the regime is said to be collisional. This is the regime considered in fluid mechanics and classical heat transfer, where the macroscopic laws such as Fourier law, are valid. In this regime, the system is close to local thermodynamic equilibrium.

**EXAMPLE 1-6** A wide area of current fluid mechanics and heat transfer research is on micro- and smaller scale behaviors. One subset of this area is on the use of microchannels which can be thought of as micron-sized ducts for fluids to flow through. Applications can be electronic chip cooling and micro-heat exchangers, among other things. Knowing the mean free path of air and water is on the order of 0.1 μm and 1 nm, respectively, determine what physical realities must be accounted for when using each of air and water as the working fluid in a microchannel problem.

**SOLUTION**  Assuming a characteristic length of 1 μm for the microchannel diameter, we begin by calculating the Knudsen number for each fluid.

$$Kn_{Air} = \frac{\lambda_{mfp}}{L}$$
$$= \frac{0.1 \ \mu m}{1 \ \mu m} = 0.1$$
$$Kn_{H_2O} = \frac{\lambda_{mfp}}{L}$$
$$= \frac{1 \ nm}{1 \ \mu m} = 0.001$$

Based on the Knudsen numbers and the criteria outlined, the case of air as the working fluid results in $Kn$ closer to unity, meaning micro- and smaller scale effects must still be taken into account. However, using water as the working fluid we see $Kn$ is much less than one, indicating the use of more traditional continuum-based methods are more applicable for studying fluid dynamic and heat transfer effects in a fluid. It may be necessary to account for micro-scale effects in the solid, but the use of liquids as working fluids simplifies a portion of the analysis.

## 1.1.6 Non-Fourier Heat Conduction

As we have discussed, the classical heat conduction theory presented by the Fourier conduction equation completely ignores such nano/micro scale levels of heat conduction mechanisms. First of all, it was derived from macro-scale heat conduction experiments. Also, the measurable experimental transient duration can be considered to be comparable to the macro time duration. In the macro-scale and around room temperature the microscopic effects of the conduction mechanisms to the global conduction phenomenon are neglected. The Fourier model is cited to agree well with experimental results under the macroscopic space/time scale and at the operating conditions at about room temperature. However, for operating conditions at low temperatures, the Fourier model of heat conduction does not govern the observed conduction phenomenon. In contrast to the macroscopic viewpoint, the continuum assumption is cited to be inapplicable in the microscopic scales, and hence, modifications to the Fourier model were necessary by replacing it with another constitutive relation.

Fourier's model of heat conduction applies only for certain regimes or scales of dimensions, times, and temperature regimes. The advent of modern technology and high powered lasers with applications to small scale structures has also led to widespread research activity and general interest. In fact, the wave type energy transport in metals such as thin gold films upon sudden laser heating are observed. Recently created nanostructured materials with non-homogeneous inner structures provide observable support. Recent evidence validating the model has been obtained from temperature propagation data in materials with non-homogeneous inner structures (porous-capillary bodies). It was observed that this propagation was of the wave type at room temperature due to the cumulative effect of the heat transfer mechanisms. The experimental temperature histories seem not to be predicted by Fourier's diffusion model but are in aggreement with the Cattaneo propagative model for the calculated relaxation times.

Since heat conduction mechanisms and energy transport from a microscopic sense are not accounted by the Fourier model, it cannot predict the heat propagation speed in a medium in the transient state. Cattaneo is credited as the first to note that the heat transport for the Fourier model has an infinite propagation speed in the transient state and is credited for formalizing and introducing the non-Fourier heat conduction phenomenon based on the general notion of relaxing the heat flux presented in the classical Fourier heat conduction equation. For example, in an idealized solid, as discussed previously, the thermal energy can be transported by different mechanisms: by quantized electronic excitations (free electrons), by the quanta of lattice vibrations (phonons), and by the electron-phonon or phonon-electron interactions. These quanta undergo collisions of a dissipative nature, causing a thermal resistance in the medium. A relaxation time is associated with the average communication time between these collisions. Thus the one dimensional Cattaneo model which is based on the notion of relaxing the heat flux is given as

$$q_x + \tau \frac{\partial q_x}{\partial t} = -k\frac{\partial T}{\partial x} \qquad (1\text{-}7a)$$

where $\tau$ is the relaxation time (Cattaneo originally developed this model for gases), $k$ is the conductivity, and $q_x$ is the heat flux in $x$ direction.

Another model involving relaxation/retardation is also presented as in terms of the *relaxation time* ($\tau$) and also the *retardation time* (K) constants as

$$q_x + \tau\frac{\partial q_x}{\partial t} = -k\left[\frac{\partial T}{\partial x} + K\frac{\partial^2 T}{\partial t \partial x}\right] \qquad (1\text{-}7b)$$

The main limitations of the macroscopic approach to conduction correspond to length and time scales comparable with the phonon mean free path and the phonon relaxation time, respectively. For example if we consider geometrical dimensions comparable with the phonon wavelength. In this situation, mode quantisation effects become relevant. Consider the case of a wire a few nanometers in diameter. The number of modes that can propagate is discrete and heat conduction is no longer correctly described by the Fourier law in submicron scale objects (10 to 100 nm). One must go back to the basic physics of the phenomenon which, in non-metallic materials, is the physics of vibrations in a crystal lattice. In this case, the main energy carriers are phonons.

## 1.2. CONVECTION

When a fluid flows over a solid, and the temperatures are different, heat transfer takes place between the fluid and the solid surface as a result of the motion of the fluid. This mechanism of heat flow is called *convection*, since the motion of the fluid plays a significant role in augmenting the heat transfer rate. Clearly, if there were no fluid motion, heat transfer would be by conduction. If the fluid motion is caused externally by a forcing mechanism, such as a fan, blower, pump, or wind, the mechanism of heat flow is said to be *forced convection*. If the fluid motion is set up by the buoyancy resulting from density differences caused by the temperature difference within the fluid, the mechanism of heat flow is said to be *free* (or *natural*) *convection*. Here the word *fluid* is used to describe both liquids and gases; for example, air and water are both fluids.

### 1.2.1 Continuum concept

A fluid is composed of molecules which are in constant motion. Due to the large number of particles in close proximity to one another, each molecule can only travel a finite distance before colliding with another molecule. As we discussed, since the average distance a molecule can travel between collisions is called the *mean free path, $\lambda_{mfp}$* and the *Knudsen number, $Kn$*, is defined as $1/Kn = L/\lambda_{mfp}$ . For $1/Kn >> 1$, the fluid can be treated as an infinitely divisible *continuum* rather than a collection of individual molecules. If $1/Kn < 1$, the characteristic length is on the order of the mean free path. Here, the properties are affected by the movement of individual fluid molecules. The fluid in this case is called a *statistical fluid* and must be studied using the techniques of statistical mechanics rather than using the *macroscopic approach* which employs differential calculus. Describing the behavior of a fluid by specifying the motions of individual molecules, as in this case, constitutes a *microscopic approach*.

### 1.2.2 Thermal Properties of Nanofluids

Nanofluids are defined by the nano-sized particles suspended in fluids. These fluids hold desirable thermophysical properties and have recently attracted the attention of many researchers. and resulting very desirable thermophysical properties. With this in mind, scientists have focussed their studies on producing a good model that can accurately predict the effective properties of nanofluids. The fluid properties, such as viscosity, thermal conductivity, and specific heat could be altered by adding nanosize particles. For the following discussion, the property of interest is the thermal conductivity of nanofluids.

The nano-sized particles suspended in the fluids have been observed to enhance the fluids effective thermal conductivity. Unlike microfluids, the particles suspended in the nanofluids do not settle to the bottom of the fluid or clog up passages. There has been

**TABLE 1.1** Thermal conductivity of $Al_2O_3$ and $H_2O$ for various temperatures.

| T, K | $Al_2O_3$, W/(m · K) | $H_2O$, W/(m · K) |
|---|---|---|
| 293 | 40.0 | 0.603 |
| 298 | 37.1754 | 0.6066 |
| 300 | 36.9601 | 0.6098 |
| 373 | 30.2503 | 0.679 |
| 400 | 27.209 | 0.6837 |
| 473 | 22.5099 | 0.663 |
| 500 | 20.93 | 0.6437 |
| 600 | 16.3045 | 0.495 |

vast interest about using nanofluids to meet new challenges in cooling and thermal management, potentially make nanofluids ideal coolants in electronic applications and as a coolant in Heating, Ventilating and Air Conditioning (HVAC) systems. For example in order to enchance the convective heat transfer performance, nanoparticles made of materials like carbon, metals, or metal oxides are combined with heat transfer fluids to increase their thermal conductivity. Argonne National Laboratory researchers in 1995 first demonstrated that dilute liquid-particle mixtures would have thermal conductivity values of about $20 - 150\%$ higher than their base fluids. There are several modes of heat transfer in nanofluids. More complicated models began to include the influences of the *Brownian motion* and *thermophoresis* on the effective thermal conductivity.

Collisions between the fluid molecules is a form of heat transfer in all fluids. Additionally, there is thermal diffusion in the nanoparticles that are suspended in the fluid, diffusion from collision between nanoparticles, and the thermal interactions of dynamic or dancing nanoparticles. The last of these is known as *Brownian motion*. The *Brownian Motion* theory describes how particles suspended in a liquid or gas have random movement. In the case of nanofluids, nanoparticles exhibit random motion, which can be intensified with an increase in temperature. As the particles transfer energy through collisions, at high temperatures these collisions will occur more frequently. This results in greater energy transfer and an enhancement in the thermal conductivity of the material.

*Thermophoresis* is another phenomenon, and it takes place when a nanofluid is subjected to a temperature gradient. During this process, the nanoparticles travel in the direction of decreasing temperature resulting in a decrease in the bulk density. As a consequence the nanoparticle has more surface area available, which allows for increased heat transfer.

It has also been hypothesized that the fluid particles would layer in an ordered manner around the surface of the nanoparticles due to a *no slip* condition at the particles surface. This ordered layering of the fluid would enhance the effective thermal conductivity.

The nano fluids are also known to change the nanostructure of the walls, which intern may cause enhancement to heat transfer.

There are many combinations of nanoparticle materials and base fluids. Thermal conductivities of $Al_2O_3$ and $H_2O$ at several temperatures are given in Table 1.1. Coupled with the effect of size of the nanoparticles, particle volume fraction, and method of creation, a large portion of research has been done on how a specific particle material changes a base fluid. Nanofluids produced for the sake of improved thermal conductivity often have water or ethylene glycol as the base fluid. Common nanoparticles include aluminum oxide, copper oxide, titanium oxide, copper, gold, silver and iron.

Two models were developed to quantify the thermal properties of the nanofluids in terms of the nanoparticle and base fluid properties, volume fraction of its constituents, size of the nanoparticles and their shapes, and operation temperature range. They are *single phase* and *two phase* models. The single phase approach relies on the various mixture models to find out the effective properties of the nanofluids. And hence it relies on how accurate these properties describe the fluids. It assumes that the continuum assumption is still considered valid for nanofluids.

When looking into the single phase model, you must have the effective properties for density, specific heat, dynamic viscosity, and thermal conductivity. All of these thermal properties are concentration dependent. Define $\phi$ as the nanoparticle volume concentration. The specific equation for the specific heat of the nanofluid $c_{nf}$ is given by

$$c_{nf} = (1 - \phi)c_f + \phi c_p \qquad (1\text{-}8a)$$

where the subscripts $nf$, $f$, and $p$ are nanofluid, fluid, and particle respectively. Similarly, the formula for density of the nanofluid $\rho_{nf}$ is given by

$$\rho_{nf} = (1 - \phi)\rho_f + \phi \rho_p \qquad (1\text{-}8b)$$

Brinkman's model, was used to calculate the effective viscosity of the nanofluid $\mu_{nf}$ and is given by the expression

$$\mu_{nf} = \mu_f(1 + 2.5\phi) \qquad for \quad \phi < 5\%. \qquad (1\text{-}8c)$$

## Thermal Conductivity of Nanofluids

Most thermal conductivity models obey the effective medium theory developed by the Maxwell over 100 years ago. Maxwell's model for spherical and well dispersed particles culminates in a simple equation giving the ratio of the nanofluid thermal conductivity $k_{nf}$ to the thermal conductivity of the basefluid $k_f$.

In 1962, Hamilton and Crasser produced their own model for predicting the effective thermal conductivity of nanofluids. Their model takes into account the shape of the particles in the nanofluid and predicts that the effective thermal conductivity should increase with the particle surface area to volume ratio. According to the Hamilton and Crasser model

$$\frac{k_{nf}}{k_f} = \frac{k_p + (n-1)k_f - (n-1)\phi(k_f - k_p)}{k_p + (n-1)k_f + \phi(k_f - k_p)} \qquad (1\text{-}9a)$$

where $k_{nf}$ is the thermal conductivity of the nanofluid, $k_f$ is the thermal conductivity of the base fluid, $k_p$ is the particle thermal conductivity, $\phi$ is the particle volumetric fraction and $n$ is the empirical shape factor

$$\phi = \frac{V_p}{V_p + V_f} .$$

Here $V_p$ and $V_f$ are the particle and fluid volume fractions. The emprical shape factor $n$ is defined as

$$n = \frac{3}{\eta}$$

where $\eta$ is the ratio of the surface area of a sphere with a volume equal to that of the particle to the surface area of the particle, i.e. defined as the sphericity of the particle. It has been confirmed that nonspherical particles do indeed increase the effective thermal conductivity more than spherical particles. However, a requirement of the model is that the conductivity ratio between the two phases must be above 100.

Another model commonly used to predict the effective conductivity of a fluid with particles suspended in the base fluid, was developed by Wasp. This is essentially a simplification of the Hamilton-Crasser model given above but doesn't include particle sphericity.

Wasp's model based on Maxwell's original work for the thermal conductivity is given as

$$\boxed{\frac{k_{nf}}{k_f} = \frac{k_p + 2k_f - 2\phi(k_f - k_p)}{k_p + 2k_f + \phi(k_f - k_p)}} \tag{1-9b}$$

where $k_p$ is the particle's thermal conductivity and $\phi$ is the particle's volumetric fraction. In this equation at the limit of $k_p \gg k_f$, and $\phi \ll 1$, the dependence on particle loading is linear,

$$\frac{k_{nf}}{k_f} = 1 + 3\phi.$$

**EXAMPLE 1-7** For a heat exchanger fluid we need to calculate the thermal conductivity of copper and water nanofluid at 300 K. At this temperature the water thermal conductivity and the copper thermal conductivity are $k_f = 0.60785$ W/(mK) and $k_p = 401$ W/(mK), respectively. Assume the particle volume fraction is 5%.

(a) Estimate the thermal conductivity of the nanofluid by assuming the particle sphericity to be equal to one.

(b) Compare the nanofluid conductivity of copper to Alumina particles. (Hint: Use Table 1.1 to find nanofluid thermal conductivity of Alumina.)

**SOLUTION (a):** Since the particle sphericity is equal to one, we can use the Wasp model

$$\frac{k_{nf}}{k_f} = \frac{k_p + 2k_f - 2\phi(k_f - k_p)}{k_p + 2k_f + \phi(k_f - k_p)}$$

$$\frac{k_{nf}}{0.60785} = \frac{401 + 2(0.60785) - 2(5/100)(0.60785 - 401)}{401 + 2(0.60785) + (5/100)(0.60785 - 401)}$$

$$k_{nf} = 0.705\,\mathrm{W/(mK)}$$

**SOLUTION (b):** According to Table 1.1, the thermal conductivity of $Al_2O_3$ at 300 K is $k_p = 36.901$ W(mK). Again using Wasp model

$$\frac{k_{nf}}{k_f} = \frac{k_p + 2k_f - 2\phi(k_f - k_p)}{k_p + 2k_f + \phi(k_f - k_p)}$$

$$\frac{k_{nf}}{0.60785} = \frac{36.901 + 2(0.60785) - 2(5/100)(0.60785 - 36.901)}{36.901 + 2(0.60785) + (5/100)(0.60785 - 36.901)}$$

$$k_{nf} = 0.699\ \mathrm{W/(mK)}$$

## 1.2.3 Heat transfer coefficient

In macroscale engineering applications, in order to simplify the heat flow calculations, a quantity called the *heat transfer coefficient*, $h$ is defined. To illustrate the concept, consider the flow of a cold fluid at a temperature $T_f$ over a hot body at temperature $T_w$, as illustrated in Fig. 1.6.

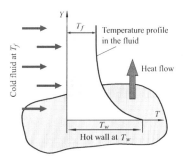

**FIG. 1.6.** Heat transfer by convection from a hot wall at $T_w$ to a cold fluid.

Let $q$ be the heat flux (in watts per square meter) *from the wall to the fluid*. Then the heat transfer coefficient $h$ is defined as

$$\boxed{q = h(T_w - T_f)} \tag{1-10a}$$

where $q$ is the heat flux (in watts per square meter) from the hot wall to the cold fluid. Alternatively, for heat transfer *from the hot fluid to the cold wall*, Eq. (1-10a) is written as

$$\boxed{q = h(T_f - T_w)} \tag{1-10b}$$

where $q$ represents the heat flux from the hot fluid to the cold wall. Historically, the form given by Eq. (1-10a) was first used as a law of cooling. As heat is removed from a body to a liquid flowing over it, it is generally referred to as *Newton's law of cooling*. If the heat flux in Eqs. (1-10a) and (1-10b) is given in watts per square meter and the temperatures are in degrees Celsius (or kelvins), then the heat transfer coefficient $h$ in Eqs. (1-10a) and (1-10b) must have the dimensions $W/(m^2 \cdot {}^\circ C)$ if the equations are dimensionally correct.

The heat transfer coefficient $h$ varies with the type of flow (i.e., laminar or turbulent), the geometry of the body and flow passage area, the physical properties of the fluid, the average temperature, and the position along the surface of the body. It also depends on whether the mechanism of heat transfer is by forced convection or by natural convection. When the heat transfer coefficient varies with the position along the surface of the body, for convenience in engineering applications, its *mean (average)* value $h_m$ over the surface is considered. Equations (1-10a and 1-10b) are also applicable in such cases if the local heat transfer coefficient $h$ is replaced by its mean value $h_m$ and the local heat flux $q$ by its mean value $q_m$. The heat transfer coefficient has a wide range of values for various applications. Table 1.2 lists typical values of $h$ encountered in various applications. The coefficient can be determined analytically for simple configurations, but for complex geometries, an experimental approach becomes necessary. More recently, elaborate computer codes have been prepared that use purely numerical approaches to determine heat transfer coefficients, and some success has been recorded.

**EXAMPLE 1-8**   An electrically heated plate dissipates heat by convection at a rate of $q = 6000 \ W/m^2$ into the ambient air at $T_f = 30^\circ C$. If the surface of the hot plate is at $T_w = 130^\circ C$, calculate the heat transfer coefficient for convection between the plate and the air.

**SOLUTION**   Heat is being transferred from the plate to the fluid, so Eq. (1-10b) is applied:

$$
\begin{aligned}
q &= h(T_w - T_f) \\
6000 &= h(130 - 30) \\
h &= 60 \ W/(m^2 \cdot {}^\circ C)
\end{aligned}
$$

**EXAMPLE 1-9**   Hot air at $T_f = 150^\circ C$ flows over a flat plate maintained at $T_w = 50^\circ C$. The forced convection heat transfer coefficient is $h = 80 \ W/(m^2 \cdot {}^\circ C)$. Calculate the heat transfer rate into the plate through an area of $A = 4 \ m^2$.

**TABLE 1.2  Typical values of the convective heat transfer coefficient $h$**

| Type of flow | $h$, W/(m$^2 \cdot$ °C) |
|---|---|
| *Free convection, $\Delta T = 25$°C* | |
| • 0.25-m vertical plate in: | |
| Atmospheric air | 5 |
| Engine oil | 37 |
| Water | 440 |
| • 0.02-m-OD* horizontal cylinder in: | |
| Atmospheric air | 8 |
| Engine oil | 62 |
| Water | 606 |
| • 0.02-m-diameter sphere in: | |
| Atmospheric air | 9 |
| Engine oil | 60 |
| Water | 606 |
| | |
| *Forced convection* | |
| • Atmospheric air at 25°C with $U_\infty = 10$ m/s over a flat plate: | |
| $L = 0.1$ m | 39 |
| $L = 0.5$ m | 17 |
| • Flow at 5 m/s across 1-cm-OD cylinder of: | |
| Atmospheric air | 85 |
| Engine oil | 1,800 |
| • Water at 1 kg/s inside 2.5-cm-ID† tube | 10,500 |
| | |
| *Boiling of water at 1 atm* | |
| • Pool boiling in a container | 3,000 |
| • Pool boiling at peak heat flux | 35,000 |
| • Film boiling | 300 |
| | |
| *Condensation of steam at 1 atm* | |
| • Film condensation on horizontal tubes | 9,000–25,000 |
| • Film condensation on vertical surfaces | 4,000–11,000 |
| • Dropwise condensation | 60,000–120,000 |

\* OD = outer diameter.
† ID = inner diameter.

**SOLUTION**  For heat transfer from the hot fluid to the plate, Eq. (1-10b) is applied:

$$q = h(T_f - T_w)$$
$$q = 80(150 - 50) = 8 \times 10^3 \text{ W/m}^2$$
$$Q = qA = (8 \times 10^3)(4) = 32 \text{ kW}$$

## 1.3. RADIATION PHENOMENA

The energy emitted by a body due to its temperature is called *thermal radiation*. The radiation energy leaving a body through its bounding surfaces actually originates from the interior region. Radiation energy incident on the surface of a body penetrates into the depths of the body, where it is absorbed. If emission of radiation and absorption of radiation take place within a very short distance from the surface, e.g., a few angstroms, then process is called *surface radiation* and the body is said to be *opaque* to thermal radiation. For example, materials such as metals, wood, stone, paper, and numerous others are considered opaque to thermal radiation. On the other hand, a sheet of glass is said to be *semi-transparent* to the solar radiation incident upon it, because part of the solar radiation is absorbed, part reflected, and the remainder transmitted by the glass. The solar radiation incident on a body of water is gradually attenuated by water as the beam penetrates to the depths of water. Similarly, the solar radiation incident on a sheet of glass is partially absorbed and partially reflected and the remaining is transmitted. Therefore, water and glass are considered semitransparent to the solar radiation.

A *vacuum* is considered *completely transparent* to radiation since radiation propagates with no weakening (attenuation) at all. The atmospheric air contained in a room is also considered transparent to thermal radiation for all practical purposes, because the weakening of radiation by air is insignificant unless the air layer is several kilometers thick. However in most other medium propagating radiation is weakened by absorption of the medium.

The origin of radiation is electromagnetic. It is presented analytically by means of the Maxwell equation and experimentally confirmed by Hertz . The main thrusts of electromagnetic behavior are explained by the Ampere law, Faraday law, and the Lorentz force. Electromagnetic radiation propagating in an arbitrary medium is characterized by various length scales: wavelength, coherence length, mean free path (of scattering, transport, or absorption), and skin depth. Several aspects of these concepts would be needed for the micro and nano heat transfer studies but not necessarily for the macro radiation heat transfer. A wide range of radiation phenomena can be explained in terms of electromagnetic waves, such as radio waves, optics, X-rays, thermal radiation, etc. Thermal radiation is provided by the waves from about 0.1 to 100 micrometers and is divided into ultraviolet, the visible and the infrared ranges. Wavelength dependency for radiation and radiative properties is described as spectral. Photons of a particular wavelength arise from discrete changes in energy levels, or quanta, as described in a basic physics course.

During thermal transport at the nanoscale, the behavior of phonons and photons are similar in many aspects. In particular, they are both bosons, i.e., their equilibrium distribution is the Bose-Einstein distribution. These quasi-particles are treated as classical particles beyond a certain length scale, i.e., the coherence length for phonons and the wavelength for photons, and their propagation is described in each case by a Boltzmann equation. For example the effects of microstructural parameters on thermal performance for fibrous materials at high temperatures can be studied by radiative heat transfer analysis. However, if the fiber has a diameter $D$ less than about ten times the wavelength of the propagating light, then $\lambda$ cannot be modeled using geometric optics ($\pi \times D/\lambda < 10$). That is, the wavelength of the radiative energy should be smaller than $9.42\ \mu m$ when the fiber diameter is taken to be $30\ \mu m$. Otherwise it must be analyzed as an electromagnetic structure, by solution of Maxwell's equations. In this book we will not be studying the nanoscale radiative heat transfer problems. That is the dimensions of our systems will be much greater that the wavelength of the thermal radiation.

It is apparent from the previous discussion that a body at a temperature $T$ emits radiation owing to its temperature, but a body absorbs radiation incident on it. Here we briefly discuss the emission and absorption of radiation by a body.

### 1.3.1 Emission of Radiation:Stefan-Boltzmann law

The maximum quantity of radiation per unit area (called radiation flux) emitted by a body at temperature $T$ is given by the *Stefan–Boltzmann law*

$$\boxed{E_b = \sigma T^4} \quad \text{W/m}^2 \tag{1-11a}$$

where $T$ is the *absolute temperature* in kelvins, $\sigma$ the *Stefan–Boltzmann constant*, $\sigma = 5.6697 \times 10^{-8}$ W/(m$^2 \cdot$ K$^4$), and $E_b$ is called the *blackbody emissive power*. J. Stefan discovered the Stefan-Boltzmann constant in 1879 and L. Boltzmann derived it analytically in 1884. Hence the law is named after both scientists. For English System of units, the *Stefan–Boltzmann constant* is $\sigma = 0.1714 \times 10^{-8}$ Btu/(ft$^2 \cdot$ R$^4$).

It should be noted that only an *ideal radiator* or so-called *blackbody* can emit radiation flux according to Eq. (1-11a). The radiation flux emitted by a *real body* at an absolute temperature $T$ is always less than that of the blackbody emissive power $E_b$; it is given by

$$\boxed{q = \epsilon E_b = \epsilon \sigma T^4} \tag{1-11b}$$

where the *emissivity* $\epsilon$ lies between zero and unity; for all real bodies it is always less than unity.

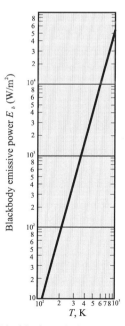

**FIG. 1.7.** Blackbody emissive power $E_b = \sigma T^4$.

A plot of the blackbody emissive power $E_b$ defined by Eq. (1-11a) versus the absolute temperature is given in Figure 1.7. The radiation flux emitted rapidly increases with rising temperature. For example, the emissive power around room temperature, $T = 300$ K is $E_b = 461$ W/m$^2$. The value increases to $E_b = 3562$ W/m$^2$ at $T = 500$ K and further increases to $E_b = 56,700$ W/m$^2$ at $T = 1000$ K.

### 1.3.2 Absorption of Radiation

If a radiation flux $q_{inc}$ is incident on a blackbody, it is completely absorbed by the blackbody. If the radiation flux $q_{inc}$ incident on a real body is given, then the energy absorbed $q_{abs}$ by the body is determined by

$$q_{abs} = \alpha q_{inc}$$

where the *absorptivity* $\alpha$ lies between zero and unity; for all real bodies it is always less than unity.

The absorptivity $\alpha$ of a body is generally different from its emissivity $\epsilon$. However, to simplify the analysis in many practical applications, $\alpha$ is assumed to equal $\epsilon$.

### 1.3.3 Thermal Radiation Heat Exchange

When two bodies at different temperatures "see" each other, heat is exchanged between them by radiation. If the intervening medium is filled with a substance such as air which is transparent to radiation, the radiation emitted from one body travels through the intervening medium with no attenuation and reaches the other body, and vice versa. Then the hot body experiences a net heat loss, and the cold body a net heat gain, as a result of the radiation heat exchange. The analysis of *radiation heat exchange among surfaces* is generally complex. The material covering the fundamentals of the surface radiation will be discussed in Chapter 11. Here we examine some very special cases with illustrative examples.

Figure 1.8 shows a small, hot, opaque plate of surface area $A_1$ and emissivity $\epsilon_1$ that is maintained at an absolute temperature $T_1$ and exposed to a large surrounding area $A_2$ (i.e., $A_1/A_2 \to 0$) at an absolute temperature $T_2$. The space between them contains air which is transparent to thermal radiation. The radiation energy emitted by the surface $A_1$ is given by

$$A_1 \epsilon_1 \sigma T_1^4 .$$

The large surrounding area can be approximated as a blackbody in relation to the small surface $A_1$. Then the radiation flux emitted by the surrounding area is $\sigma T_2^4$, which is also the radiation flux incident on the surface $A_1$. Hence, the radiation energy absorbed by the surface $A_1$ is

$$A_1 \alpha_1 \sigma T_2^4 .$$

The *net radiation loss* at the surface $A_1$ is the difference between the energy emitted and

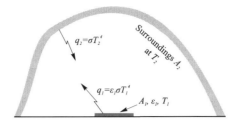

**FIG. 1.8.** Radiation exchange between a surface $A_1$ and its surroundings.

the energy absorbed:

$$Q_1 = A_1 \epsilon_1 \sigma T_1^4 - A_1 \alpha_1 \sigma T_2^4 .$$ (1-12a)

For $\epsilon_1 = \alpha_1$, this result simplifies to

$$\boxed{Q_1 = A_1 \epsilon_1 \sigma (T_1^4 - T_2^4)}$$ (1-12b)

which provides the expression for calculating the radiation heat exchange between a small surface element $A_1$ and its surroundings at $T_2$. Clearly, the positive value of $Q_1$ implies heat loss from the surface $A_1$, and the negative value implies heat gain.

We now consider two finite surfaces $A_1$ and $A_2$ as illustrated in Fig. 1.9. The surfaces

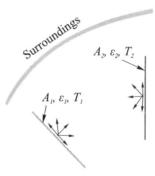

**FIG. 1.9.** Radiation exchange between surfaces $A_1$ and $A_2$.

are maintained at absolute temperatures $T_1$ and $T_2$, respectively, and have emissivities $\epsilon_1$ and $\epsilon_2$. The physical situation implies that part of the radiation leaving surface $A_1$ reaches surface $A_2$ while the remaining is lost to the surroundings. Similar considerations apply for the radiation leaving surface $A_2$. The analysis of radiation heat exchange between the two surfaces for such a case should include the effects of the orientation of the surfaces, the contribution of radiation from the surroundings and the reflection of radiation at the surfaces. For the arrangement shown in Fig. 1.9 if we assume that the radiation flux from the surroundings is negligible compared to those from surfaces $A_1$ and $A_2$, then the net radiation heat transfer $Q_1$ at the surface $A_1$ can be expressed in the form

$$Q_1 = \mathcal{F}_{12} A_1 \sigma (T_1^4 - T_2^4)$$ (1-13)

where $\mathcal{F}_{12}$ is a factor that includes the effects of both orientation of the surfaces and their emissivities.

## 1.3.4 Radiation Heat Transfer Coefficient

To simplify the heat transfer calculations, it may be possible, *under very restrictive conditions*, to define a radiation heat transfer coefficient $h_r$, analogous to the convection heat transfer coefficient, as

$$\boxed{q_1 = h_r(T_1 - T_2)} \ . \tag{1-14}$$

This concept can be applied to the result given by Eq. (1-12b) as now described.

Equation (1-12b) is written as

$$Q = A_1 \epsilon_1 \sigma (2T_1^2)(2T_1)(T_1 - T_2) \ . \tag{1-15a}$$

If $|\, T_1 - T_2 \,| \ll T_1$, this result is linearized as

$$Q_1 \simeq A_1 \epsilon_1 \sigma 4 T_1^3 (T_1 - T_2) \tag{1-15b}$$

or

$$\boxed{q_1 \equiv \frac{Q_1}{A_1} = (4T_1^3 \epsilon_1 \sigma)(T_1 - T_2)} \ . \tag{1-16}$$

A comparison of Eqs. (1-14) and (1-16) reveals that for the specific case given by Eq. (1-12b), a radiation heat transfer coefficient $h_r$ can be defined as

$$\boxed{h_r = 4T_1^3 \epsilon_1 \sigma} \ . \tag{1-17}$$

**EXAMPLE 1-10**  A heated plate of $D = 0.2$ m diameter has one of its surfaces insulated, and the other is maintained at $T_w = 550$ K. If the hot surface has an emissivity $\epsilon_w = 0.9$ and is exposed to a surrounding area at $T_s = 300$ K with atmospheric air being the intervening medium, calculate the heat loss by radiation from the hot plate to the surroundings.

**SOLUTION**  Assuming $\epsilon_1 = \alpha_1$, we can apply Eq. (1-12b):

$$
\begin{aligned}
Q_w &= A_w \epsilon_w \sigma (T_w^4 - T_s^4) \\
&= \left[ \frac{\pi}{4}(0.2)^2 \right] (0.9)(5.67 \times 10^{-8})[(5.5)^4 - 3^4] \times 10^8 \\
&= 134.5 \ \text{W} \ .
\end{aligned}
$$

**EXAMPLE 1-11**  A small hot surface at temperature $T_1 = 430$ K having an emissivity $\epsilon_1 = 0.8$ dissipates heat by radiation into a surrounding area at $T_2 = 400$ K. If this radiation transfer process is characterized by a radiation heat transfer coefficient $h_r$ calculate the value of $h_r$.

**SOLUTION** For this particular case, the requirement $T_1 - T_2 \ll T_1$ is satisfied. Then Eq. (1-17) is applied as follows

$$
\begin{aligned}
h_r &= 4T_1^3 \epsilon_1 \sigma \\
&= 4[(4.3)^3 \times 10^6](0.8)(5.67 \times 10^{-8}) = 14.4 \text{ W}/(\text{m}^2 \cdot {}^\circ\text{C}) .
\end{aligned}
$$

## 1.4. COMBINED MECHANISMS OF HEAT TRANSFER

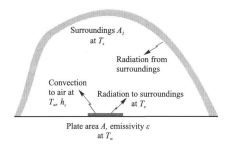

**FIG. 1.10.** Simultaneous convection and radiation from a plate.

We have considered the heat transfer mechanism, conduction, convection, and radiation separately. Now we will take a look at the combined modes of heat transfer mechanism. For example in many practical situations heat transfer from a surface takes place simultaneously by convection to the ambient air and by radiation to the surroundings.

Figure 1.10 illustrates a small plate of area $A$ and emissivity $\epsilon$ that is maintained at $T_w$ and exchanges energy by convection with a fluid at $T_\infty$ with a heat transfer coefficient $h_c$ and by radiation with the surroundings at $T_s$. The heat loss per unit area of the plate, by the combined mechanism of convection and radiation, is given by

$$
q_w = h_c(T_W - T_\infty) + \epsilon\sigma(T_w^4 - T_s^4) . \tag{1-18}
$$

If $| T_w - T_s | \ll T_w$, the second term can be linearized. We obtain

$$
q_w = h_c(T_w - T_\infty) + h_r(T_w - T_s) \tag{1-19a}
$$

where

$$
h_r \equiv 4\epsilon\sigma T_w^3 . \tag{1-19b}
$$

The thermal resistance circuit of this problem is illustrated in Fig. 1-11 for a unit surface area. Here

$$
q = q_w = q_{con} + q_{rad} \tag{1-20}
$$

and

$$
R_{con} = 1/h_c \quad and \quad R_{rad} = 1/h_r \tag{1-21}
$$

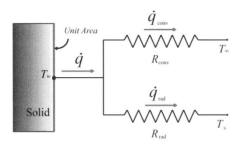

**FIG. 1.11.** Thermal Resistance Concept of Combined Convection and Radiation from a unit surface area

**EXAMPLE 1-12** A small, thin metal plate of area $A$ m$^2$ is kept insulated on one side and exposed to the sun on the other side. The plate absorbs solar energy at a rate of 500 W/m$^2$ and dissipates it by convection into the ambient air at $T_\infty = 300$ K with a convection heat transfer coefficient $h_c = 20$ W/(m$^2 \cdot$ $^\circ$C) and by radiation into a surrounding area which may be assumed to be a blackbody at $T_{sky} = 280$ K. The emissivity of the surface is $\epsilon = 0.9$. Determine the equilibrium temperature of the plate.

**SOLUTION** The energy balance per unit area of the exposed surface is written as

$$500 = 20(T_w - 300) + 0.9 \times 5.67 \times 10^{-8} \left[ \left( \frac{T_w}{100} \right)^4 - (2.8)^4 \right] 10^8$$

or

$$25 = T_w - 300 + 0.255 \left( \frac{T_w}{100} \right)^4 - 15.68$$

or

$$T_w = 340.68 - 0.255 \left( \frac{T_w}{100} \right)^4 .$$

The solution of this equation by trial and error yields the plate temperature as

$$T_w = 315.5 \text{ K} .$$

### 1.4.1 Earth

There are many combined heat transfer problems and the Earth also provides an interesting one, as illustrated in Fig. 1.12. The generated heat is mostly by radioactivity. The Earth looses heat at a total rate of around $42 \times 10^{12} W$ via two modes: conduction and convection. Heat loss occurs primarily through two geological regions of the Earth; the convecting mantle and the continental lithosphere. Consequently, heat lost from the core is transmitted mostly by either conduction or convection. In the case of convection, the convecting mantle moves heat generated from the radioactive decay of elements in the core upward through the interior regions of the Earth. This occurs through dikes, volca-

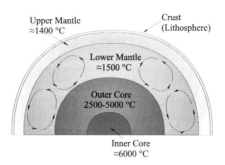

**FIG. 1.12.** A simplified cross section of the Earth.

noes, and hydrothermal activity. Conduction is the main method of heat transfer at the surface regions, including the lithosphere.

The thermal state and heat budget of the Earth is an ongoing study of thermodynamics that scientists are still investigating and requires a thorough knowledge of heat transfer concepts. One may think that heat from the Sun adds heat to the Earth, but this is negligible because it hardly penetrates into the ground at all. It can warm the air on the surface and perhaps the ground, but a kilometer beneath the surface, the incoming radiation from the sun has no effect. This may seem incorrect because everyone knows if the Sun were to vanish, we would all freeze to death in a matter of days. This is once again only so because we live on the surface. If we lived in a cave a mile beneath the surface, it would be as if nothing happened. The light from the Sun is absorbed, stored, and emitted in only the very top layer of the Earth's crust, so its effects are insignificant compared to the overall heat loss from the Earth.

## 1.4.2 Light Bulb

In another example of combined heat transfer, consider the lightbulb. The components making up the light bulb are surprisingly few. Two metal ends at the base of the bulb connect the device to an electrical circuit, allowing current to flow into the bulb. These ends are connected to two stiff wires, which in turn are connected to the metal filament. All of this is contained in a glass bulb, which is either evacuated or filled with an inert gas such as argon. The process through which light (and heat) are given off is actually quite simple, but becomes much more interesting if we look at the mechanisms in greater detail.

As electric current flows through the wire, the moving electrons collide with the tungsten atoms, resulting in a transfer of energy from the former to the latter. At this point, the tungsten wire becomes incredibly hot conducting some of this energy the full length of the tungsten wire, reaching temperatures of around 2200 degrees Celsius. The light bulb, while simple in operation, is great in the context of this class because it makes use of the three means of heat transfer. Assuming a non-reacting gas surrounds the hot tungsten wire, convection will occur between the tungsten and the gas surrounding it. Natural convective currents will transfer energy within the gas and lead to convection between the gas and the glass bulb. It is this convected heat that will then be conducted through the glass, heating up the bulb making it hot to the touch.

It should be apparent that only fraction of the heat will be conducted through the bulb: the wire heats up to 1000's of degrees, yet even though the bulb gets hot, it thankfully gets nowhere near this. Lastly, we have to consider radiation. Indeed, in an incandescent light bulb, about 80 percent of the supplied electric power becomes thermal radiation, while only about 10-12 percent of that is visible light. Clearly, then, heat transfer through radiation will be considerable.

### 1.4.3 Building Climate

In designing modern buildings, environmental concerns are becoming more important every day. In response to threats of global warming, depleting natural resources, and the rising costs of energy production, architects and engineers are developing ways to operate buildings at maximum efficiency to both burn less energy and save money.

One major expense of running a building is incurred in heating and cooling costs. The three major heat transfer methods that affect the climate of a building are conduction, radiation, and forced convection. Green buildings are designed with these three factors in mind to preserve optimal temperatures. With proper insulation, the effects of conduction can be decreased by preserving desired temperatures inside. With a predetermined emissive materials and special shading techniques, designers are able to manage the effects of solar radiation to windows, roofs, and sides of building with direct sun contact, and also still utilizing natural sunlight as a free method of lighting.

The United States Green Building Council (USGBC) has outlined the Leadership in Energy and Environmental Design (LEED) Green Building Rating System, which sets standards for energy consumption based on the size and purpose of a new building. The new LEED certified buildings employ many of the creative methods of reducing their dependence on heating and cooling systems through basic heat transfer concepts. For example using proper insulation is an obvious and long practiced method of keeping buildings at moderate and consistent temperatures. Having proper insulation also stops the energy spent on heating or cooling from being wasted. When designating insulation material, a designer must also consider different areas of the building, like outer walls, windows, doors, roofs, ground, etc. In material selection, a low thermal conductivity constant, k, is desirable. Some classic materials that are commonly used are fiberglass, foam, cellulose, and mineral wool. (Cellulose is also very popular in buildings that are LEED certified because it is made primarily of recycled newspaper.)

If the cooling is needed, solar radiation heating can be an extreme concern for building designers. Thus, engineers have created ways of *insulating* against solar rays. The first method by which solar radiation heating can be combated is by carefully choosing the emissivity of the building surfaces. Many modern buildings today are shiny and reflective. A method alleviating both the need to stop radiation and still let in sunlight is to have grated shading structures on the sides of buildings that incur the most direct sunlight. Thus, a first consideration for these gratings is the site of the building, or the direction in which it is oriented.

## 1.5. UNITS, DIMENSIONS, AND CONVERSION FACTORS

When the dimensions of a physical quantity are to be expressed numerically, a consistent system of units is preferred. In engineering the two most commonly used system of units include (1) the *SI system (Système International d'Unités)* and (2) the *English engineering system.* The basic units for length, mass, time, and temperature in each of these systems are listed in Table 1.3. In this book the SI system is used throughout.

In the SI system, one newton (that is, 1 N) is a force that accelerates a mass of one kilogram to one meter per second per second; or 1 N force is equal to $1 \, \mathrm{kg} \cdot m/s^2$. This is apparent from Newton's second law of motion,

$$\text{Force} = \text{mass} \times \text{acceleration}$$

$$1 \, \mathrm{N} = 1 \, \mathrm{kg} \times 1 \, \mathrm{m/s^2} = 1 \, \mathrm{kg} \cdot \mathrm{m/s^2} \tag{1-22a}$$

**TABLE 1.3  Systems of units**

| Quantity | SI | English engineering system |
|----------|-----|---------------------------|
| Length | m | ft |
| Mass | kg | lb |
| Time | s | s |
| Temperature | K | R |
| Force | N | $\mathrm{lb_f}$ |
| Energy | J or N · m | Btu or ft · $\mathrm{lb_f}$ |

Energy is measured in joules (J) or newton-meters (N · m). Thus

$$1 \, \mathrm{J} = 1 \, \mathrm{N} \cdot \mathrm{m} = 1 \, \mathrm{kg} \cdot \mathrm{m^2/s^2} \; . \tag{1-22b}$$

Power is measured in watts (W) or kilowatts (kW), or joules per second. Then

$$1 \, \mathrm{W} = 1 \, \mathrm{J/s} = 1 \, \mathrm{N} \cdot \mathrm{m/s} = 1 \, \mathrm{kg} \cdot \mathrm{m^2/s^3} \; . \tag{1-22c}$$

and

$$1 \, \mathrm{kW} = 1000 \, \mathrm{W} \; . \tag{1-22d}$$

Pressure is measured in bars,

$$1 \, \mathrm{bar} = 10^5 \, \mathrm{N/m^2} = 10^5 \, \mathrm{kg/(m \cdot s^2)} \tag{1-22e}$$

and

$$1 \text{ atm} = 0.98066 \text{ bar.} \tag{1-22f}$$

When the size of units becomes too large or too small, multiples in powers of 10 are formed using certain prefixes. Some of them are listed in Table 1.4.

### TABLE 1.4 Prefixes for multiplying factors

$10^{-12}$ = pico (p)      $10$ = deca (da)
$10^{-9}$ = nano (n)      $10^2$ = hecto (h)
$10^{-6}$ = micro (μ)    $10^3$ = kilo (k)
$10^{-3}$ = milla (m)    $10^6$ = mega (M)
$10^{-2}$ = centi (c)     $10^9$ = giga (G)
$10^{-1}$ = deci (d)      $10^{12}$ = tera (T)

## PROBLEMS

*Conduction Phenomena*

**1-1.** Estimate the constant volume specific heat of a block of boron at room temperature. The Debye temperature for boron is $\theta_D = 1250$ K. Compare this result to the published experimentally-determined value of $1.026 \frac{\text{J}}{\text{g K}}$.

**1-2.** Estimate the constant volume specific heat of pure copper rod at 300 K. The Debye temperature of our copper is $\theta_D = 315$ K. Compare this result to the experimentally determined value of $0.385 \frac{\text{J}}{\text{g K}}$. for copper at 300 K and 1 atm.

**1-3.** Determine the heat flux across a 0.05-m-thick iron plate [with thermal conductivity of 70 W/(m · °C)] if one of its surfaces is maintained at 60°C and the other at 10°C. What is the heat flow rate across the plate over a surface area of $2 \, m^2$?
*Answer*: 140 kW.

**1-4.** A temperature difference of 100°C is applied across a cork board 5 cm thick with thermal conductivity of 0.04 W/(m · °C). Determine the heat flow rate across a 3-$m^2$ area per hour.

**1-5.** Two large plates, one at 80°C and the other at 200°C, are 12 cm apart. If the space between them is filled with loosely packed rock wool of thermal conductivity 0.08 W/(m · °C), calculate the heat flux across the plates.

**1-6.** The hot surface of a 5-cm-thick insulating material of thermal conductivity 0.1 W/(m · °C) is maintained at 200°C. If the heat flux across the material is 120 W/$m^2$, what is the temperature of the cold surface?

**1-7.** The heat flow through a 4-cm-thick insulation layer for a temperature difference of 200°C across the surfaces is 500 W/$m^2$. What is the thermal conductivity of the insulating material?

**1-8.** A brick wall 30 cm thick with thermal conductivity 0.5 W/(m · °C) is maintained at 50°C at one surface and 20°C at the other surface. Determine the heat flow rate across a 1-m$^2$ surface area of the wall.
*Answer*: 50 W.

**1-9.** A window glass 0.5 cm thick with thermal conductivity 0.8 W/(m · °C) is maintained at 30°C at one surface and 20°C at the other surface. Determine the heat flow rate across a 1-m$^2$ surface area of the glass.
*Answer*: 1.6 kW.

**1-10.** The heat flow through a 4-cm-thick cork board for a temperature difference of 100°C across the surfaces is 0.1 kW/$m^2$. What is the thermal conductivity of the cork board?

**1-11.** The heat flux through a 10-cm-thick layer of loosely packed rock wool for a temperature difference of 100°C is 75 W/m$^2$. What is the thermal conductivity of the packed rock wool?

*Convection*

**1-12.** Estimate the thermal conductivity of alumina-water nanofluid having a particle volume fraction of 1% at room temperature (293 $K$). Assume the particle sphericity to be equal to one.
*Answer*: 0.62 W/(mK).

**1-13.** Water at 20°C flows over a flat plate at 80°C. If the heat transfer coefficient is 200 W/($m^2$ · °C), determine the heat flow per square meter of the plate (heat flux).
*Answer*: 12 kW m$^2$.

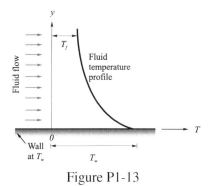

Figure P1-13

**1-14.** Air at 200°C flows over a flat plate maintained at 50°C. If the heat transfer coefficient for forced convection is 300 W/(m$^2$ · °C), determine the heat transferred to the plate through 5 m$^2$ over a period of 2 h.

**1-15.** Water at $50°C$ flows through a 5-cm-diameter, 2-m-long tube with an inside surface temperature maintained at $150°C$. If the heat transfer coefficient between the water and inside surface of the tube is $1000\,W/(m^2 \cdot °C)$, determine the heat transfer rate between the tube and the water.

**1-16.** Cold air at $10°C$ flows over a 2-cm-OD tube, as illustrated in Fig. P1-13. The outside surface of the tube is maintained at $110°C$. If the heat transfer coefficient between the outside surface of the tube and the air is $100\,W/(m^2 \cdot °C)$, determine the rate of heat flow to the air over the 5-m length of the tube.

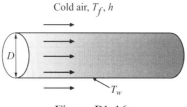

Figure P1-16

**1-17.** A 20-cm-diameter sphere with a surface temperature of $70°C$ is suspended in a stagnant gas at $20°C$. If the free convection heat transfer coefficient between the sphere and the gas is $10\,W/(m^2 \cdot °C)$, determine the rate of heat loss from the sphere.

**1-18.** A 2-cm-diameter sphere with a surface temperature maintained at $50°C$ is suspended in water at $25°C$. Determine the heat flow rate by free convection from the sphere to the water.

**1-19.** Cold air at $0°C$ is forced to flow over a flat plate maintained at $30°C$. The mean heat transfer coefficient is $50\,W/(m^2 \cdot °C)$. Find the heat flow rate from the plate to the air per unit plate area.

**1-20.** Hot air at $75°C$ is forced to flow over a flat plate maintained at $20°C$. The mean heat transfer coefficient is $60\,W/(m^2 \cdot °C)$. Find the heat flow rate from the air to the plate.

**1-21.** A 25-cm vertical plate with a surface temperature maintained at $50°C$ is suspended in atmospheric air at $25°C$. Determine the heat flow rate by free convection from the plate to the air.
*Answer*: 32.5 W/m.

**1-22.** A 5-cm-diameter sphere dissipates heat by convection from its outer surface into ambient air. Calculate the convection heat transfer coefficient between the air and the sphere if the sphere is heated internally with a 50-W electric heater and the temperature difference between the sphere surface and the air is $25°C$.

**1-23.** A 2-cm-diameter sphere with a surface temperature maintained at $40°C$ is suspended in atmospheric air at $15°C$. Determine the rate of heat loss from the sphere by free convection.

*Radiation Phenomena*

**1-24.** A hot surface at a temperature of 400 K has an emissivity of 0.8. Calculate the radiation flux emitted by the surface.

**1-25.** A radiation flux of 1000 W/m$^2$ is incident upon a surface that absorbs 80 percent of the incident radiation. Calculate the amount of radiation energy absorbed by a 4-m$^2$ area of the surface over a period of 2 h.

**1-26.** The temperature $T$ of a plate changes with time $t$ as $T = T_o t^{1/4}$ where the constant $T_o$ is in absolute temperature. How does the blackbody emissive power of the plate change with time?

**1-27.** A blackbody at 30°C is heated to 80°C. Calculate the increase in its emissive power.

*Combined Mechanism of Heat Transfer*

**1-28.** A thin metal plate is insulated at the back surface and exposed to the sun at the front surface, as shown in Fig. P1-27. The front surface absorbs the solar radiation of 800 W/m$^2$ and dissipates it by convection to the ambient air at 20°C. If the convection heat transfer coefficient between the plate and the air is 10 W/(m$^2 \cdot$ °C), what is the temperature of the plate?
*Answer*: $100°C$.

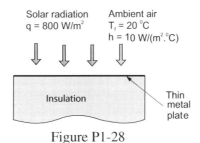

Figure P1-28

**1-29.** The inside surface of an insulation layer is maintained at 150°C and the outside surface dissipates heat by convection into air at 15°C. The insulation layer has a thickness of 10 cm and a thermal conductivity of 1 W/(m $\cdot$ °C). What is the minimum value of the heat transfer coefficient at the outside surface, it the temperature at the outside surface should not exceed 75°C?
Calculate the increase in its emissive power.
*Answer*: $12.5\frac{W}{m^2 °C}$.

**1-30.** A 2 $m$ long un-insulated portion of 5 cm OD hot water pipe looses heat both by convection and radiation into an external environment at 0 °C. The convection heat transfer coefficient is 10 W/(m $\cdot$ °C), and for the radiation heat loss calculations the emissivity is equal to one (blackbody). Determine the heat loss from the unisulated portion of the pipe with a wall temperature of 100 °C.

Calculate the increase in its emissive power.
*Answer*: Q= 559.73 W.

*Units, Dimensions, and Conversion Factors*

**1-31.** Calculate the force of a mass of 10 kg attracted to the earth at a point where the gravitational acceleration is 9.6 m/s$^2$.

**1-32.** A steady force of 10 kN acts on a mass of 5 kg. What is the acceleration of this mass?

**1-33.** Consider a manometer containing a fluid with a density of 1000 kg/m$^3$. The difference in height of the two columns is 500 mm. Calculate the pressure difference in kilopascals.

**1-34.** A plastic plate with an area of 0.1 m$^2$ and a thickness of 2 mm is found to conduct heat at a rate of 1 cal/s at steady-state with surface temperatures 29°C and 31°C. What is the thermal conductivity of plastic in W/(m · °C) at 30°C?
*Answer*: 0.041868 W/(m · °C).

# CHAPTER 2

# *Transient Lumped Systems*

The objective of this chapter is to introduce the concept of time-dependent behavior of temperature in a system. If the surface temperature of a solid body is suddenly altered, the temperature within the body begins to change with both position and time. However, there are many practical applications in which the variation of temperature within the body with position is negligible and the temperature is considered to vary only with time. Analysis of unsteady heat flow under such an assumption, generally referred to as *lumped system analysis,* greatly simplifies the handling of time-dependent problems. Obviously, the range of applicability of such a simple analysis is very limited, but it is helpful in understanding the concept of time-dependent behavior of temperature in a system, as well as being applicable in many practical situations. Therefore, in this chapter we explain the use of lumped system analysis to predict the variation of temperature of a solid body with time during transients and discuss the criterion for the validity of the concept.

## 2.1. LUMPED SYSTEM CONCEPT

Consider a cold solid of arbitrary shape, with mass $m$, initially at a uniform temperature $T_i$, suddenly immersed into a higher-temperature environment. As heat flows from the hot environment into the cold body, the temperature of the solid increases. It is assumed that the lumped system approximation is applicable, namely, that the distribution of temperature within the solid at any instant can be regarded as almost uniform (i.e., the temperature gradients within the solid are neglected). Figure 2.1 illustrates such a system. The energy balance on the system over a time interval dt can be stated as

$$\begin{pmatrix} \text{Increase of the internal} \\ \text{energy of the solid} \\ \text{over the time interval } dt \end{pmatrix} = \begin{pmatrix} \text{Heat flow into the solid} \\ \text{through the outer surfaces} \\ \text{over the time interval } dt \end{pmatrix}. \qquad (2\text{-}1)$$

Let $dT$ be the average temperature rise of the solid over the time interval $dt$ resulting from the heat flow through the boundary surfaces. The left-hand side of Eq. (2-1) is determined as

$$\begin{pmatrix} \text{Increase of the} \\ \text{internal energy} \\ \text{of the solid over} \\ \text{the time interval } dt \end{pmatrix} = (\text{mass})\, c \, dT = \rho V c \, dT \qquad (2\text{-}2)$$

where $\rho$ is the density, $c$ is the specific heat, $V$ is the volume, and $T \equiv T(t)$ is the temperature of the body.

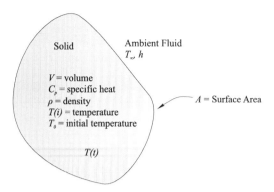

**FIG. 2.1.** Lumped system of transient heat flow.

Let $Q(t)$ be the total rate of heat flowing into the body through its boundary surfaces at any instant $t$. Then the right-hand side of Eq. (2-1) becomes

$$\left(\begin{array}{l} \text{Heat flow into the solid} \\ \text{from the outer surfaces} \\ \text{over the time interval } dt \end{array}\right) = Q(t)\,dt. \tag{2-3}$$

Introducing Eqs. (2-2) and (2-3) into (2-1), we obtain

$$\rho V c\,dT = Q(t)\,dt$$

or

$$\frac{dT(t)}{dt} = \frac{Q(t)}{\rho V c}. \tag{2-4}$$

We derived this equation with reference to a cold solid in a hot fluid, as illustrated in Fig. 2.1.

Equation (2-4) forms the basis for generating an ordinary differential equation for predicting the temperature $T(t)$ of the solid body as a function of time. That is, once the specific expression defining $Q(t)$ has been established, Eq. (2-4) provides an ordinary differential equation in the time variable for determining $T(t)$. The functional form of $Q(t)$ depends on the types of heat transfer process at the outer surface of the body. In the following sections we discuss the development of specific expressions for $Q(t)$ for various situations and determine the temperature $T(t)$ of the solid as a function of time.

## 2.2. EXAMPLES OF LUMPED SYSTEMS

In this section, we illustrate the use of lumped system analysis to predict the variation of the temperature of a solid with time. Our starting point in the analysis is Eq. (2-4). Once the functional form of $Q(t)$ is established for a specific problem, the resulting ordinary differential equation (2-4) can be solved and the variation of the temperature $T(t)$ of the solid as a function of time is determined. Here we examine two simple situations:

(1) a solid subjected to convection over its entire boundary surface, and (2) a solid subjected to convection over part of its boundary surface, with a prescribed heat flux over the remaining portion of the boundary surface.

## 2.2.1 Convection Over All Boundary Surfaces

We consider a physical situation as illustrated in Fig. 2.l. That is, a cold body initially at a uniform temperature $T_i$ is suddenly immersed into a large volume of well-stirred fluid maintained at a uniform temperature $T_\infty$. The mechanism of heat transfer between the fluid and the entire boundary surface of the solid is convection. We assume that the heat transfer coefficient $h$ remains constant and uniform over the entire surface of the solid. Then, the total rate of heat flow $Q(t)$ from the fluid into the solid is given by the expression

$$Q(t) = Ah[T_\infty - T(t)] . \tag{2-5}$$

When this expression is introduced into Eq. (2-4), the following ordinary differential equation for the temperature $T(t)$ results:

$$\frac{dT(t)}{dt} = \frac{Ah}{\rho V c} [T_\infty - T(t)] . \tag{2-6}$$

The solid is at a temperature $T_i$ when it is immersed in the fluid. This information provides the *initial condition* for this differential equation.

Hence, the mathematical formulation of the problem becomes

$$\frac{dT(t)}{dt} + \frac{Ah}{\rho V c} [T(t) - T_\infty] = 0 \quad \text{for} \ \ t > 0 \tag{2-7a}$$

$$T(t) = T_i \quad \text{for} \ \ t = 0 . \tag{2-7b}$$

For convenience in the analysis, we measure the temperature in excess of the ambient temperature $T_\infty$; that is, we choose $T_\infty$ as the reference temperature. Then the following new temperatures are defined:

$$\theta(t) = T(t) - T_\infty \tag{2-8a}$$

$$\theta_i = T_i - T_\infty \tag{2-8b}$$

and a quantity $m$ is introduced:

$$m = \frac{Ah}{\rho V c} \tag{2-8c}$$

where $m$ has the dimension of $(\text{time})^{-1}$. Then Eq. (2-7) becomes

$$\boxed{\frac{d\theta(t)}{dt} + m\theta(t) = 0 \quad \text{for} \ \ t > 0} \tag{2-9a}$$

$$\boxed{\theta(t) = \theta_i \quad \text{for} \ t = 0} \tag{2-9b}$$

where

$$\boxed{m = \frac{Ah}{\rho V c}} \ . \tag{2-9c}$$

Equations (2-9a to 2-9c) govern the variation of the temperature $\theta(t)$ of the solid as a function of time. They can now be solved as described below.

The fundamental solution of Eq. (2-9a) is an exponential in the form

$$e^{-mt} \ .$$

Then the solution for $\theta(t)$ is constructed by multiplying this solution by a constant:

$$\theta(t) = Ce^{-mt}. \tag{2-10a}$$

The unknown constant $C$ is determined by applying the initial condition (2-9b), namely, $\theta(0) = \theta_i$ for $t = 0$, to give

$$\theta_i = C. \tag{2-10b}$$

Introducing the value of $C$ into Eq. (2-10a), the solution for $\theta(t)$ becomes

$$\boxed{\frac{\theta(t)}{\theta_i} = e^{-mt}} \ . \tag{2-11a}$$

Recalling the definitions of $\theta(t)$ and $\theta_i$ given by Eq. (2 8a and b), this solution is written as

$$\boxed{\frac{\theta(t)}{\theta_i} \equiv \frac{T(t) - T_\infty}{T_i - T_\infty} = e^{-mt}} \tag{2-11b}$$

where

$$m = Ah/\rho V c \ . \tag{2-11c}$$

Solution (2-11) is developed for the heating of a cold body immersed in a hot environment. It is also applicable to the cooling of a hot body immersed in a cold environment.

Figure 2.2 shows a plot of the dimensionless temperature $\theta(t)/\theta_i$ given by Eq. (2-11) as a function of time. The temperature decays with time exponentially, and the rate of decay is dependent upon the magnitude of the exponent $m$, The larger the value of m, the faster the rate of decay. An examination of the definition of the parameter $m = hA/\rho c_p V$ reveals that increasing the surface area for a given volume or increasing the heat transfer coefficient increases $m$, which in turn increases the temperature response of a body for a change in environment temperature. On the other hand, increasing the density, specific heat, or volume decreases $m$, which in turn reduces the temperature response of the solid.

For certain common body shapes, the ratio $A/V$ is readily determined; then we have the following specific formulae for the temperature $\theta(t)$ as obtained from Eq. (2-11).

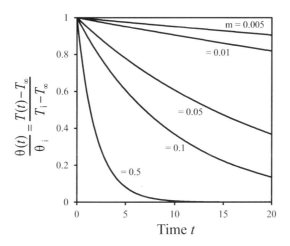

**FIG. 2.2.** The dimensionless temperature $\theta(t)/\theta_i$ given by Eq. (2-11) as a function of time.

For a solid sphere of radius $R$:

$$\frac{A}{V} = \frac{4\pi R^2}{\frac{4}{3}\pi R^3} = \frac{3}{R}$$

$$\boxed{\frac{\theta(t)}{\theta_i} = \exp\left(-\frac{3h}{\rho c R}t\right)} \quad . \qquad (2\text{-}12)$$

For a solid cylinder of radius $R$, length $L$:

$$\frac{A}{V} = \frac{2\pi R(L+R)}{\pi R^2 L} = \frac{2(L+R)}{RL}$$

$$\boxed{\frac{\theta(t)}{\theta_i} = \exp\left(-\frac{2h(L+R)}{\rho c R L}t\right)} \quad . \qquad (2\text{-}13a)$$

For a long cylinder, $L \gg R$, this expression reduces to

$$\boxed{\frac{\theta(t)}{\theta_i} = \exp\left(-\frac{2h}{\rho c R}t\right)} \quad . \qquad (2\text{-}13b)$$

For a cube of side $L$:

$$\frac{A}{V} = \frac{6L^2}{L^3} = \frac{6}{L}$$

$$\boxed{\frac{\theta}{\theta_i} = \exp\left(-\frac{6h}{\rho c L}t\right)} \quad . \qquad (2\text{-}14)$$

For a large plate of thickness $L$:

Let $A^*$ denote the surface area of one side of the plate. Then

$$\frac{A}{V} = \frac{2A^*}{LA^*} = \frac{2}{L}$$

$$\boxed{\frac{\theta(t)}{\theta_i} = \exp\left(-\frac{2h}{\rho c L} t\right)} . \qquad (2\text{-}15)$$

## 2.2.2 Criteria for Lumped Systems

The conditions under which lumped system analysis is applicable are discussed in the next section. Here we simply introduce the *criteria for lumped systems* for solids having shapes such as a slab, a cylinder, or a sphere. Lumped system analysis is applicable if the *Biot number* Bi is less than about 0.1; that is, if

$$\boxed{\text{Bi} \equiv \frac{hL_s}{k_s} < 0.1} . \qquad (2\text{-}16\text{a})$$

where $h$ is the heat transfer coefficient, $k_s$ is the thermal conductivity of the solid, and $L_s$ is the characteristic length of the solid body, defined as

$$L_s = \frac{\text{volume}}{\text{surface area}} . \qquad (2\text{-}16\text{b})$$

**EXAMPLE 2-1** Using lumped system analysis, determine the time required for a solid steel ball of radius $R = 2.5$ cm, $k = 54$ W/(m $\cdot$ °C), $\rho - 7833$ kg/m$^3$, and $c = 0.465$ kJ/(kg $\cdot$ °C) to cool from 850°C to 250°C if it is exposed to an air stream at 50°C having a heat transfer coefficient $h = 100$ W/(m$^2$ $\cdot$ °C).

**SOLUTION** This problem is similar to the problem illustrated earlier in Fig. 2.1. Now the solid is hot and it is exposed to a cold environment. From Eq. (2-11) we have

$$\frac{T(t) - T_\infty}{T_i - T_\infty} = e^{-mt}$$

where $T(t) = 250$°C, $T_\infty = 50$°C, and $T_i = 850$°C.

The volume-to-area ratio is

$$\frac{V}{A} = \frac{\frac{4}{3}\pi R^3}{4\pi R^2} = \frac{R}{3}$$

and

$$m = \frac{hA}{\rho V c} = \frac{h}{\rho c R/3} = \frac{100 \text{ W/(m}^2 \cdot °\text{C})}{(7833 \text{ kg/m}^3)\,[465 \text{ J/(kg} \cdot °\text{C})]\,[0.025/3 \text{ m}]}$$

$$= 1/303.529 \text{ s}^{-1} .$$

Then,

$$\frac{(250-50)°C}{(850-50)°C} = \exp(-t/303.529)$$

or

$$4 = \exp(t/303.529)$$

$$t = \ln(4) \times 303.529$$

$$t \cong 420.78\,\text{s} \cong 7\,\text{min}.$$

We compute the Biot number in order to check the validity of the lumped analysis.

$$\text{Bi} = \frac{hL_s}{k} = \frac{h}{k}\frac{R}{3} = \frac{100 \times (2.5 \times 10^{-2})}{54 \times 3} = 0.016 < 0.1$$

Hence, the analysis is valid.

**EXAMPLE 2-2** A long steel bar of radius $R = 2.5$ cm, $k = 50$ W/(m $\cdot$ °C), $\rho = 7800$ kg/m$^3$, and $c = 0.5$ kJ/(kg $\cdot$ °C) is to be annealed by cooling slowly from 800°C to 100°C in an environment at temperature 50°C. If the heat transfer coefficient between the environment and the surface of the bars is $h = 45$ W/(m$^2 \cdot$ °C), determine the time required for the annealing process using lumped system analysis.

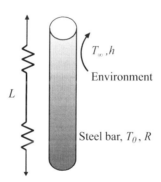

**FIGURE EXAMPLE 2-2  Long steel bar exposed to a cold environment.**

**SOLUTION**  The problem is illustrated in the accompanying figure. From Eq. (2-11) we have

$$\frac{T(t) - T_\infty}{T_i - T_\infty} = e^{-mt}$$

where $T(t) = 100$°C, $T_\infty = 50$°C, and $T_i = 800$°C. As discussed previously, for a long cylinder the volume-to-area ratio is

$$\frac{V}{A} \simeq \frac{\pi R^2 L}{2\pi R L} = \frac{R}{2}$$

$$m = \frac{hA}{\rho V c} = \frac{h}{\rho c(R/2)} = \frac{45 \ \text{W}/(\text{m} \cdot {}^\circ\text{C})}{(7800 \ \text{kg}/\text{m}^3) \ [500 \ \text{J}/(\text{kg} \cdot {}^\circ\text{C})] \ [0.025/2 \ \text{m}]}$$

$$= 1/1083.33 \ \text{s}^{-1} \ .$$

Then,

$$\frac{(100 - 50)^\circ\text{C}}{(800 - 50)^\circ\text{C}} = \exp(-t/1083.33)$$

or

$$15 = \exp(t/1083.33)$$

$$t = \ln(15) \times 1083.33$$

$$t = 2933.7 \ s \cong 49 \ \text{min}.$$

A check of the Biot number indicates that the criterion $\text{Bi} < 0.1$ is also satisfied.

**EXAMPLE 2-3.** A large aluminum plate $[k = 204 \ \text{W}/(\text{m} \cdot {}^\circ\text{C})$, $\rho = 2707 \ \text{kg}/\text{m}^3$, and $c = 0.896 \ \text{kJ}/(\text{kg} \cdot {}^\circ\text{C})]$ of thickness $L = 0.1 \ \text{m}$, that is initially at a uniform temperature of $250^\circ\text{C}$ is cooled by exposing it to an air stream at temperature $50^\circ\text{C}$. Using lumped system analysis, determine the time required to cool the aluminum plate to $100^\circ\text{C}$ if the heat transfer coefficient between the air stream and the plate surface is $h = 80 \ \text{W}/(\text{m}^2 \cdot {}^\circ\text{C})$.

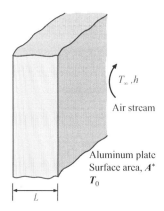

**FIGURE EXAMPLE 2-3 A large aluminum plate exposed to a cold air stream**

**SOLUTION** The problem is illustrated in the accompanying figure. $T(t) = 100^\circ\text{C}$, $T_\infty = 50^\circ\text{C}$, and $T_i = 250^\circ\text{C}$ are given.

The volume-to-area ratio is

$$\frac{V}{A} \cong \frac{A^* L}{2A^*} = \frac{L}{2}$$

where $A^*$ is the surface area of one side of the plate. Then

$$m = \frac{hA}{\rho V c} = \frac{h}{\rho c L/2} = \frac{80 \text{ W}/(\text{m}^2 \cdot {}^\circ\text{C})}{(2707 \text{ kg/m}^3) [896 \text{ J}/(\text{kg} \cdot {}^\circ\text{C})] [0.1/2 \text{ m}]}$$

$$= 1/1515.92 \text{ s}^{-1}.$$

and the time required for cooling is determined as

$$\frac{(100 - 50)^\circ\text{C}}{(250 - 50)^\circ\text{C}} = \exp(-t/1515.92).$$

Then,

$$t = \ln(4) \times 1515.92$$

$$t = 2101.5 \text{ s} = 35 \text{ min}.$$

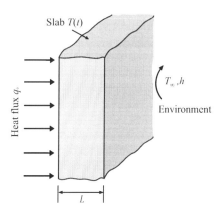

**FIG. 2.3.** A slab with convection on one surface and or prescribed heat flux on the other.

## 2.2.3 Convection Over Part of the Boundary Surface

The lumped system analysis described previously is also applicable to situations involving a body having a part of its surface subjected to convection and the remainder to prescribed heat flux. To illustrate such applications, we consider below two specific problems, one involving a solid shaped as a slab and the other as a cube.

**SLAB.** Consider a slab of thickness $L$, initially at a uniform temperature $T_i$. Suddenly one of its surfaces is subjected to a uniform heat flux $q_o$, while the other surface is exposed to a cool environment at temperature $T_\infty$ with a heat transfer coefficient $h$. Figure 2.3 illustrates the physical problem. Assuming that lumped system analysis is applicable, an equation for determining the temperature $T(t)$ of the plate as a function of time is now developed.

An energy balance on the slab results in an expression exactly the same as that given by Eq. (2-4), namely,

$$\frac{dT(t)}{dt} = \frac{Q(t)}{\rho V c} . \tag{2-17a}$$

Here $Q(t)$ is the total rate of heat transfer into the body; for the specific problem considered here, it is determined as

$$Q(t) = \left( \begin{array}{c} \text{heat flow rate into} \\ \text{the body due to the} \\ \text{prescribed heat flux } q_o \end{array} \right) + \left( \begin{array}{c} \text{heat flow rate into the} \\ \text{body due to convection} \\ \text{from the environment} \end{array} \right)$$

or

$$Q(t) = A^* q_o + A^* h [T_\infty - T(t)] \tag{2-17b}$$

where $A^*$ is the surface area on one side of the plate, $q$ is the prescribed heat flux, and $T_\infty$ is the environment temperature. Introducing Eq. (2-17b) into Eq. (2-4), we obtain

$$\frac{dT(t)}{dt} + \frac{A^* h}{\rho V c} [T(t) - T_\infty] = \frac{A^* q_0}{\rho V c} \quad \text{for } t > 0 \tag{2-17c}$$

subject to the initial condition

$$T(t) = T_i \quad \text{at } t = 0 . \tag{2-17d}$$

Equations (2-17c and 2-17d) represent the mathematical formulation of lumped system analysis for the determination of the temperature $T(t)$ of a slab under the conditions specified above.

We now measure the temperature in excess of the environment temperature $T_\infty$ and define new temperatures $\theta(t)$ and $\theta_i$ as

$$\theta(t) = T(t) - T_\infty \tag{2-18a}$$

$$\theta_i = T_i - T_\infty \tag{2-18b}$$

and introduce a quantity $m^*$, defined as

$$m^* = \frac{h A^*}{\rho c V} = \frac{h}{\rho c L} . \tag{2-18c}$$

For the slab geometry considered here, we have

$$\frac{A^*}{V} = \frac{A^*}{A^* L} = \frac{1}{L}$$

where $L$ is the plate thickness. Then Eqs. (2-17c and 2-17d) become

$$\boxed{\frac{d\theta(t)}{dt} + m^*\theta(t) = m^* \frac{q_o}{h} \quad \text{for } t > 0}$$ (2-19a)

$$\boxed{\theta(t) = \theta_i \quad \text{at } t = 0}$$ (2-19b)

where

$$\boxed{m^* \equiv \frac{h}{\rho c L}}.$$ (2-19c)

The difference between Eqs. (2-19a) and (2-9a) is the constant term on the right-hand side of Eq. (2-19a). Therefore, the solution for Eq. (2-19a) is written as a sum of the *homogeneous solution*, given by Eq. (2-10a) and a *particular solution* as

$$\theta(t) = C\,e^{-m^*t} + \frac{q_o}{h}$$ (2-20)

where $q_o/h$ is a particular solution.

The unknown constant $C$ is determined by the application of the initial condition (2-19b) as

$$\theta_i = C + q_o/h$$

or

$$C = \theta_i - \frac{q_o}{h}.$$ (2-21)

Substitution of Eq. (2-21) into Eq. (2-20) gives the solution to temperature $\theta(t)$ of the plate as a function of time as

$$\boxed{\theta(t) = \theta_i e^{-m^*t} + (1 - e^{-m^*t})\frac{q_o}{h} \quad \text{for } t > 0}.$$ (2-22)

The steady-state temperature of the plate is obtained by setting $t \to \infty$.

$$\boxed{\theta(\infty) = \frac{q_o}{h}}$$ (2-23)

since the exponential terms in Eq. (2-22) vanish for $t \to \infty$.

**EXAMPLE 2-4**  A large aluminum plate $[k = 204\,\text{W}/(\text{m}\cdot{}^\circ\text{C}), \rho = 2707\,\text{kg}/\text{m}^3$, and $c = 0.896\,\text{kJ}/(\text{kg}\cdot{}^\circ\text{C})]$ of thickness 3 cm is initially at a uniform temperature of $50^\circ\text{C}$. Suddenly one of its surfaces is subjected to a uniform heat flux of $8000\,\text{W}/\text{m}^2$, while the other surface is exposed to a cool air at a temperature of $20^\circ\text{C}$. The heat transfer coefficient between the air stream and the surface is $50\,\text{W}/(\text{m}^2\cdot{}^\circ\text{C})$. Assuming that lumped system analysis is applicable, determine the temperature of the plate as a function of time and plot the temperature against time. Also calculate the steady-state temperature of the plate.

**SOLUTION** From Eq. (2-22) we have

$$\theta(t) = \theta_i e^{-m^* t} + (1 - e^{m^* t}) \frac{q_o}{h} \quad \text{for } t > 0$$

where

$$\theta_i \equiv T_i - T_\infty = 50 - 20 = 30°\text{C}$$

$$q_o = 8000 \text{ W/m}^2$$

$$h = 50 \text{ W/(m}^2 \cdot °\text{C)}$$

$$m^* = \frac{hA^*}{\rho V c} = \frac{h}{\rho c L} = \frac{50}{2707 \times 896 \times 0.03}$$

$$= 1/1455.3 \text{ s}^{-1} .$$

Then,

$$
\begin{aligned}
\theta(t) &= 30 \exp(-t/1455.3) + (1 - \exp(-t/1455.3)) \frac{8000}{50} \\
&= -130 \exp(-t/1455.3) + 160°\text{C}
\end{aligned}
$$

and $T(t)$ is determined as

$$
\begin{aligned}
T(t) &= \theta(t) + T_\infty \\
&= 180 - 130 \exp(-t/1455.3)°\text{C} \quad \text{for } t \geq 0 .
\end{aligned}
$$

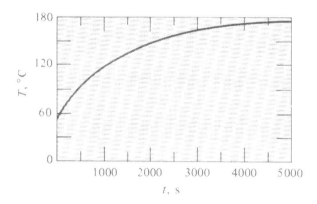

**FIGURE EXAMPLE 2-4 The temperature of the plate as a function of time.**

The accompanying figure shows a plot of the temperature $T(t)$ as a function of time. The steady-state temperature is obtained by setting $t \to \infty$, namely $T(\infty) = 180°\text{C}$.

**CUBE.** Consider a solid cube of side $L$ that is initially at a uniform temperature $T_i$. At times when $T > 0$, two of the boundary surfaces are kept insulated, two are subjected to uniform heating at a rate of $q_o$, and the remaining two dissipate heat by convection into a cool environment at temperature $T_\infty$ with a heat transfer coefficient $h$. The problem is illustrated in Fig. 2.4. Assuming that lumped system analysis is applicable, an energy balance on the cube results in the expression given by Eq. (2-4).

$$\frac{dT(t)}{dt} = \frac{Q(t)}{\rho V c} \tag{2-24a}$$

where $Q(t)$ is the total heat transfer rate into the body through the boundary surfaces. For the specific boundary conditions of the cube shown in Fig. 2.4, $Q(t)$ is determined as:

$$Q(t) = \begin{pmatrix} \text{heat flow rate into the} \\ \text{body due to applied} \\ \text{heated flux } q_o \end{pmatrix} + \begin{pmatrix} \text{heat flow rate into the} \\ \text{body due to convection} \end{pmatrix} \tag{2-24b}$$

$$= 2A_1 q_o + 2A_1 h [T_\infty - T(t)]$$

where $A_1$ is the surface area of one side of the cube and $q_o$ is the prescribed surface heat

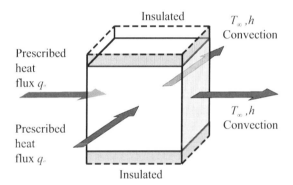

**FIG. 2.4.** A solid cube subject to convection, prescribed heat flux and insulated boundary conditions.

flux. Introducing Eq. (2-24b) into Eq. (2-24a), we obtain

$$\frac{dT(t)}{dt} + \frac{2A_1 h}{\rho V c} [T(t) - T_\infty] = \frac{2A_1 q_o}{\rho V c} \quad \text{for } t > 0 \tag{2-25a}$$

subject to the initial condition

$$T(t) = T_i \quad \text{at } t = 0 . \tag{2-25b}$$

We measure the temperature in excess of the environment temperature $T_\infty$ and define new temperatures

$$\theta(t) = T(t) - T_\infty \tag{2-26a}$$

$$\theta_i = T_i - T_\infty \tag{2-26b}$$

and also introduce a quantity $m_1$:

$$m_1 = \frac{hA_1}{\rho cV} = \frac{h}{\rho cL} \qquad (2\text{-}26c)$$

since for the cube geometry we have

$$\frac{A_1}{V} = \frac{L^2}{L^3} = \frac{1}{L}$$

where $L$ is the length of a side of the cube. Then Eq. (2-25) becomes

$$\boxed{\frac{d\theta(t)}{dt} + 2m_1\theta(t) = 2m_1\frac{q_o}{h} \quad \text{for } t > 0} \qquad (2\text{-}27a)$$

$$\boxed{\theta(t) = \theta_i \quad \text{at } t = 0} \qquad (2\text{-}27b)$$

where

$$m_1 = \frac{h}{\rho cL}. \qquad (2\text{-}27c)$$

This problem is exactly of the same form as Eq. (2-19) except that $m^*$ is replaced by $2m_1$. Therefore, the solution can be immediately obtained from Eq. (2-22) by replacing $m^*$ by $2m_1$ in that equation. We find

$$\boxed{\theta(t) = \theta_i\, e^{-2m_1t} + (1 - e^{-2m_1t})\frac{q_o}{h} \quad \text{for } t > 0}. \qquad (2\text{-}28)$$

**EXAMPLE 2-5** Consider an aluminum cube $[k = 204 \text{ W}/(\text{m}\cdot{}^\circ\text{C})$, $\rho = 2700 \text{ kg/m}^3$, and $c = 0.896 \text{ kJ}/(\text{kg}\cdot{}^\circ\text{C})]$ of side 5 cm that is initially at a uniform temperature of 20°C. For times $t > 0$, two of the boundary surfaces are kept insulated, two are subjected to uniform heating at a rate of 10,000 W/m$^2$, and the remaining two dissipate heat by convection into an environment at a temperature of 20°C with a heat transfer coefficient of 50 W/(m$^2\cdot{}^\circ$C). Using lumped system analysis, determine the time required for the cube to reach 100°C. What is the steady-state temperature of the cube?

**SOLUTION** Given: $T_i = 20°\text{C}$, $T_\infty = 20°\text{C}$, $q_o = 10,000 \text{ W/m}^2$, $V/A = L = 0.05 \text{ m}$, and $h = 50 \text{ W}/(\text{m}^2\cdot{}^\circ\text{C})$. We have

$$\theta_i = T_i - T_\infty = 0$$

$$m = \frac{h}{\rho cL} = \frac{50}{2/00 \times 896 \times 0.05} = \frac{1}{2419}\text{s}^{-1}.$$

Then, using Eq. (2-28), the temperature of the cube as a function of time becomes

$$T(t) = T_\infty + (1 - e^{-2m_1t})\frac{q_o}{h} \quad \text{for } t > 0.$$

Substituting the numerical values, we have

$$T(t) = 20 + (1 - \exp(-2t/2419)) \, \frac{10,000}{50}$$

or

$$T(t) = 220 - 200 \exp(-2t/2419) \; ^\circ\text{C} \; .$$

Then the time required for the cube temperature to reach $T(t) = 100^\circ\text{C}$ becomes

$$t = \frac{2419}{2} \, \ln(10/6) \cong 618 \, \text{s} = 10 \, \text{min} \, 18 \, \text{s} \; .$$

The steady-state temperature of the cube is obtained by letting $t \to \infty$ :

$$T_i = 220 \, ^\circ\text{C} \; .$$

## 2.2.4 Physical Meaning of the Biot Number

The lumped system analysis described previously is applicable only under very restricted conditions. As is the case with all approximate methods of analysis, the range of validity and the accuracy of the results obtained from lumped system analysis cannot be assessed without making comparisons with the exact solutions. Since the principal concept for the development of this method is the uniformity of temperature within the solid during transients, it is necessary to determine the conditions under which the temperature distribution within the solid during transients can be regarded as uniform. Such conditions can be established by examining the behavior of the temperature distribution in solids as a function of time and position as obtained from the exact solutions of the problem. For example, consider temperature transients in a solid that has a simple geometry, such as a slab, a long solid cylinder, or a sphere, initially at a uniform temperature $T_i$ and for times $t > 0$, is subjected to convection with a heat transfer coefficient $h$ into an ambient at a temperature $T_\infty$.

At any instant the maximum temperature difference within the solid occurs between the center and surface temperatures. It is found that this temperature difference remains less than about 5 percent of the center temperature if the *Biot number* remains less than about 0.1, that

$$\boxed{\text{Bi} = \frac{hL_s}{k_s} < 0.1} \tag{2-29}$$

where $k_s$ is the thermal conductivity of the solid, $h$ is the heat transfer coefficient at the outer surface, and $L_s$ is the characteristic length of the solid body, defined as

$$\boxed{L_s = \frac{\text{volume}}{\text{surface area}}} \; . \tag{2-30}$$

For example, for a solid sphere of radius $R$. the characteristic length becomes

$$L_s = \frac{\frac{4}{3}\pi R^3}{4\pi R^2} = \frac{R}{3} . \tag{2-31}$$

Therefore, for solids having geometries that are not significantly different from a slab, sphere, or cylinder, the assumption of uniform temperature within the body is considered valid and lumped system analysis becomes applicable if the criterion given by Eq. (2-29) is satisfied. However, the physical significance of the Biot number is better envisioned if it is arranged in the form

$$\text{Bi} = \frac{h}{k_s/L_s} = \frac{\left( \begin{array}{c} \text{heat-transfer coefficient} \\ \text{at surface of solid} \end{array} \right)}{\left( \begin{array}{c} \text{internal unit conductance of} \\ \text{solid across length } L_s \end{array} \right)} . \tag{2-32}$$

That is, the Biot number is the ratio of the heat transfer coefficient to the internal unit conductance of the solid in terms of the characteristic length.

In order to illustrate the role of the Biot number as the criterion for the validity of lumped system analysis, we rearrange Eq. (2-32) in the form

$$\text{Bi} = \frac{L_s/k_s}{1/h} = \frac{\left( \begin{array}{c} \text{specific internal resistance} \\ \text{of the solid to heat flow} \\ \text{across length } L_s \end{array} \right)}{\left( \begin{array}{c} \text{specific skin resistance} \\ \text{to heat flow at the outer} \\ \text{surface of the solid} \end{array} \right)} . \tag{2-33}$$

Clearly, the criterion $\text{Bi} < 0.1$ implies that the specific internal resistance of the solid to heat flow should be small in comparison to the skin resistance to heat flow at the outer surface of the body. This can be achieved with a small value of $L_s$, a large value of $k_s$, or a small value of $h$. The schematic lumped temperature distribution for a slab is shown in Fig. 2.5b. For Fig. 2.5c, temperature distribution corresponds to very large values of the Biot numbers, $\text{Bi} >> 0.1$ and Fig. 2.5a corresponds to moderate values of the Biot numbers.

**EXAMPLE 2-6** A 6-cm-diameter steel ball $[k = 61 \text{ W}/(\text{m} \cdot {}^\circ\text{C})$, $\rho = 7865 \text{ kg/m}^3$, and $c = 0.46 \text{ kJ}/(\text{kg} \cdot {}^\circ\text{C})]$ is at a uniform temperature of $800^\circ\text{C}$. It is to be hardened by suddenly dropping it into an oil bath at a temperature of $50^\circ\text{C}$. If the quenching occurs when the ball reaches a temperature of $100^\circ\text{C}$ and the heat transfer coefficient between the oil and the sphere is $500 \text{ W}/(\text{m}^2 \cdot {}^\circ\text{C})$, determine how long the ball should be kept in the oil bath.

If 100 balls are to be quenched per minute, determine the rate at which heat must be removed from the oil bath in order to maintain the bath temperature at $50^\circ\text{C}$.

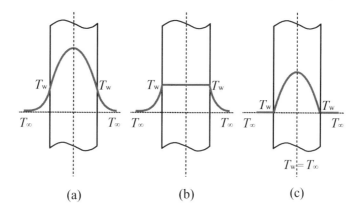

**FIG. 2.5.** The temperature distributions corresponding to three Biot numbers where $T_\infty$ is the surroundings temperature and $T_w$ is the wall temperature. The cases (a) Moderate, (b) lumped, Bi < 0.1 and (c) Bi >> 0.1.

**SOLUTION** The problem can be solved with lumped system analysis with sufficient accuracy if Bi < 0.1. Therefore, we first check the magnitude of the Biot number. The characteristic length $L_s$ is determined using Eq. (2-30) as

$$L_s = \frac{\text{volume}}{\text{area}} = \frac{V}{A} = \frac{R}{3} = 1 \text{ cm}.$$

Then the Biot number becomes

$$\text{Bi} = \frac{hL_s}{k}$$

$$= \frac{500 \text{ W/(m}^2 \cdot {}^\circ\text{C})(0.01 \text{ m})}{61 \text{ W/(m} \cdot {}^\circ\text{C})} = 0.082$$

which is less than 0.1; hence, lumped system analysis is applicable. From Eq. (2-11) we have

$$\frac{T(t) - T_\infty}{T_i - T_\infty} = e^{-mt}$$

where $T(t) = 100^\circ\text{C}$, $T_\infty = 50^\circ\text{C}$, $T_i = 800^\circ\text{C}$, and

$$m = \frac{hA}{\rho V c}$$

$$= \frac{h}{\rho c L_s}$$

$$= \frac{500}{7865 \times 460 \times 0.01} = \frac{1}{72.358} \text{s}^{-1}.$$

Results

$$\frac{100 - 50}{800 - 50} = \exp(-t/72.358)$$

or

$$t = 195.95\,\text{s} \cong 3.3\,\text{min}.$$

The rate of heat removed from one ball is

$$
\begin{aligned}
Q_1 &= mc\Delta T \\
&= \rho V c \Delta T \\
&= 7865 \times 0.46 \times \tfrac{4}{3}\pi (0.03)^3 \times (800 - 100) \\
&= 286.42\,\text{kJ/ball}.
\end{aligned}
$$

For 100 balls, we have

$$Q = 286.42 \times 100 = 28,642\,\text{kJ/min}.$$

**EXAMPLE 2-7** A thermocouple is to be used to measure the temperature in a gas stream. The junction is approximated as a sphere as illustrated in the accompanying figure with thermal conductivity of 25 W/(m · °C), density of 9000 kg/m$^3$, and specific heat of 0.35 kJ/(kg · °C). The heat transfer coefficient between the junction and the gas is 250 W/(m$^2$ · °C). Calculate the diameter of the junction if the thermocouple should measure 95 percent of the applied temperature difference in 3 s.

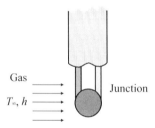

**FIGURE EXAMPLE 2-7 The Thermocouple Junction.**

**SOLUTION** The characteristic length in terms of diameter $D$ is

$$L_s = \frac{V}{A} = \frac{R}{3} = \frac{D}{6}.$$

From Eq. (2-11) we have

$$\frac{\theta(t)}{\theta_i} = \frac{T(t) - T_\infty}{T_i - T_\infty} = e^{-mt}$$

when $T_\infty$ is regarded as the actual gas stream temperature, then $|\,T_i - T_\infty\,|$ becomes the applied temperature difference. If the thermocouple should measure 95 percent of this difference, we should have

$$\frac{\theta(t)}{\theta_i} = \frac{95}{100}$$

and the coefficient $m$ becomes

$$m_1 = \frac{h}{\rho c L_s} = \frac{250}{9000 \times 350(D/6)} = \frac{0.000476}{D} \, \text{s}.$$

Then

$$\frac{5}{100} = \exp(-0.000476/D \times 3)$$

or

$$\frac{0.000476 \times 3}{D} = \ln 20 = 2.9957$$

$$D = \frac{0.000476 \times 3}{2.9957} = 0.000476 \, \text{m} = 0.476 \, \text{mm}.$$

Here we applied lumped system analysis before checking the magnitude of the Biot number. For the diameter we calculated above, the Biot number becomes

$$
\begin{aligned}
Bi &= \frac{hL_s}{k} \\
&= \frac{250 \times 0.000476/6}{25} \\
&= 0.00079 = 0.000476 \, \text{m} = 0.476 \, \text{mm} < 0.1.
\end{aligned}
$$

since the calculated Biot numbers is much less than 0.1, lumped system analysis is valid.

**EXAMPLE 2-8** Check the validity of the lumped system analysis used in Example 2-4.

**SOLUTION** The characteristic length is

$$
\begin{aligned}
L_s &= \frac{\text{volume}}{\text{surface area}} = \frac{A^*L}{2A^*} = \frac{L}{2} \\
&= \frac{0.03 \, \text{m}}{2} = 0.015 \, \text{m}
\end{aligned}
$$

where $A^*$ is the surface area of one side of the plate. Then the Biot number becomes

$$Bi = \frac{hL_s}{k} = \frac{50 \times 0.015}{204} = 0.003675 < 0.1$$

therefore, the lumped system analysis is applicable.

## PROBLEMS

*Lumped system concept*

**2-1.** A solid steel ball of radius $3\,\mathrm{cm}$ $[k = 54\,\mathrm{W}/(\mathrm{m \cdot {}^\circ C})]$ is exposed to an air stream having a heat transfer coefficient of $75\,\mathrm{W}/(\mathrm{m^2 \cdot {}^\circ C})$. Calculate the Biot number. *Answer*: Bi=0.014.

**2-2.** A long solid steel bar of radius $3\,\mathrm{cm}$ $[k = 54\,\mathrm{W}/(\mathrm{m \cdot {}^\circ C})]$ is exposed to an air stream having a heat transfer coefficient of $75\,\mathrm{W}/(\mathrm{m^2 \cdot {}^\circ C})$. Calculate the Biot number.

**2-3.** A large steel plate of thickness $3\,\mathrm{cm}$ $[k = 54\,\mathrm{W}/(\mathrm{m \cdot {}^\circ C})]$ is exposed to an air stream having a heat transfer coefficient of $75\,\mathrm{W}/(\mathrm{m^2 \cdot {}^\circ C})$. Calculate the Biot number.

**2-4.** Check whether lumped system analysis is suitable for Examples 2-2 and 2-3.

*Examples of Lumped Systems*

**2-5.** A solid copper sphere of diameter $10\,\mathrm{cm}$, initially at a uniform temperature of $250^\circ C$ is suddenly immersed in a well-stirred fluid that is maintained at a uniform temperature of $50^\circ C$. The heat transfer coefficient between the sphere and the fluid is $200\,\mathrm{W}/(\mathrm{m^2 \cdot {}^\circ C})$. *(a)* Check whether lumped system analysis is applicable. *(b)* If it is applicable, determine the temperature of the copper block at times $t = 1\,\mathrm{min}$, $t = 2\,\mathrm{min}$, and $t = 5\,\mathrm{min}$ after immersion in the cold fluid. [For copper, $k = 386\,\mathrm{W}/(\mathrm{m \cdot {}^\circ C})$, $\rho = 8954\,\mathrm{kg/m^3}$, and $c = 383\,\mathrm{J}/(\mathrm{kg \cdot {}^\circ C})$.] *Answers*: $T(60) = 213^\circ C$  $T(120) = 183^\circ C$;  $T(300) = 122^\circ C$.

**2-6.** A solid copper cylinder of diameter $10\,\mathrm{cm}$, initially at a uniform temperature of $200^\circ C$. is suddenly immersed in a well-stirred fluid that is maintained at a uniform temperature of $20^\circ C$. The heat transfer coefficient between the cylinder and the fluid is $150\,\mathrm{W}/(\mathrm{m^2 \cdot {}^\circ C})$. *(a)* Check whether lumped system analysis is applicable. *(b)* If applicable, determine the temperature of the copper cylinder at time $t = 2\,\mathrm{min}$ after immersion in the cold fluid. [For copper, $k = 386\,\mathrm{W}/(\mathrm{m \cdot {}^\circ C})$, $\rho = 8954\,\mathrm{kg/m^3}$, and $c = 383\,\mathrm{J}/(\mathrm{kg \cdot {}^\circ C})$.]

**2-7.** A solid iron sphere of diameter $5\,\mathrm{cm}$, initially at a uniform temperature of $700^\circ C$, is exposed to a cool air stream at $100^\circ C$. The heat transfer coefficient between the air stream and the surface of the iron sphere is $80\,\mathrm{W}/(\mathrm{m^2 \cdot {}^\circ C})$. *(a)* Check whether lumped system analysis is applicable. *(b)* If applicable, determine the time required for the temperature of the sphere to reach $300^\circ C$. [For iron, $k = 60\,\mathrm{W}/(\mathrm{m \cdot {}^\circ C})$, $\rho = 7800\,\mathrm{kg/m^3}$, and $c = 460\,\mathrm{J}/(\mathrm{kg \cdot {}^\circ C})$.]

**2-8.** A long cylindrical iron bar of diameter $5$ cm, initially at a uniform temperature of $700^\circ C$, is exposed to a cool air stream at $100^\circ C$. The heat transfer coefficient between the air stream and the surface of the iron bar is $80\,\mathrm{W}/(\mathrm{m^2 \cdot {}^\circ C})$. *(a)* Check whether lumped system analysis is applicable. *(b)* If applicable, determine the time required for the temperature of the rod to reach $300°C$. [For iron, $k = 60\,\text{W}/(\text{m} \cdot °C)$, $\rho = 7800\ \text{kg}/\text{m}^3$, and $c = 460\ \text{J}/(\text{kg} \cdot °C)$.]

**2-9.** A large aluminum plate of thickness $3\,\text{cm}$ is initially at a uniform temperature of $50°C$. Suddenly it is subjected (both surfaces) to a cool air stream at a temperature of $20°C$. The heat transfer coefficient between the air stream and the surface is $50\,\text{W}/(\text{m}^2 \cdot °C)$. *(a)* Check whether lumped system analysis is applicable. *(b)* If applicable, determine the time required for the temperature of the plate to reach $40°C$. [For aluminum, $k = 204\,\text{W}/(\text{m} \cdot °C)$, $\rho = 2707\ \text{kg}/\text{m}^3$, and $c = 896\ \text{J}/(\text{kg} \cdot °C)$.]

**2-10.** A household electric iron has an aluminum base that weighs $1.5\,\text{kg}$. The base has an ironing surface of $0.03\ \text{m}^2$ that is heated from the inner surface with a 300-W heating element and dissipates heat from the outer surface by convection into the air. Initially the iron is at the same temperature as the ambient air at $20°C$. How long will it take for the iron to reach a temperature of $120°C$ after it is turned on, if the heat transfer coefficient between the iron and the ambient air is $20\,\text{W}/(\text{m}^2 \cdot °C)$? [For aluminum, $k = 204\,\text{W}/(\text{m} \cdot °C)$, $\rho = 2707\ \text{kg}/\text{m}^3$, and $c = 896\ \text{J}/(\text{kg} \cdot °C)$.] What is the steady-state temperature of the iron if the control does not cut off the power supply?

**2-11.** A household electric iron has a steel base that weighs $1\,\text{kg}$. The base has an ironing surface of $0.02\ \text{m}^2$ that is heated from the inner surface with a 300-W heating element and dissipates heat from the outer surface by convection into the ambient air at $20°C$. Initially the iron is at a uniform temperature of $30°C$. Suddenly the heating starts. The heat transfer coefficient between the iron and the ambient air is $40\,\text{W}/(\text{m}^2 \cdot °C)$. Calculate the temperature of the iron 3min after the start of heating. [For steel, $k = 70\ \text{W}/(\text{m} \cdot °C)$, $\rho = 7840\ \text{kg}/\text{m}^3$, and $c = 450\ \text{J}/(\text{kg} \cdot °C)$.]

**2-12.** A large steel frying pan of thickness $0.5\,\text{cm}$, initially at $10°C$, is placed on the stove. The bottom of the pan is subjected to a uniform heat flux of $300\,\text{W}/\text{m}^2$ and the top exposed to cool ambient air at $10°C$. The heat transfer coefficient between the pan and the ambient air is $30\,\text{W}/(\text{m}^2 \cdot °C)$. Calculate the temperature of the pan at 3 and 8 min after the start of heating. [For steel, $k = 70\ \text{W}/(\text{m} \cdot °C)$, $\rho = 7840\ \text{kg}/\text{m}^3$, and $c = 450\ \text{J}/(\text{kg} \cdot °C)$.]

**2-13.** A large aluminum frying pan of thickness $1\,\text{cm}$, initially at room temperature $(20°C)$, is placed on the stove. The bottom of the pan is subjected to a uniform heat flux of $500\,\text{W}/\text{m}^2$ and the top exposed to cool air at $20°C$. The heat transfer coefficient between the pan and the air is $50\,\text{kW}/(\text{m}^2 \cdot °C)$. Calculate the time required for the temperature of the pan to reach $200°C$. [For aluminum, $k = 204\ \text{W}/(\text{m} \cdot °C)$, $\rho = 2707\ \text{kg}/\text{m}^3$, and $c = 896\ \text{J}/(\text{kg} \cdot °C)$.]

**2-14.** A 3-cm-diameter aluminum sphere is initially at a temperature of $175°C$. It is suddenly immersed in a well-stirred fluid at a temperature of $25°C$. The temperature of the sphere is lowered to $100°C$ in $42\,s$. Calculate the heat transfer coefficient. Check whether lumped system analysis is applicable. [For aluminum, $k = 204\,W/(m \cdot °C)$, $\rho = 2707\,kg/m^3$, and $c = 896\,J/(kg \cdot °C)$.]

**2-15.** A grape of 1-cm diameter, initially at a uniform temperature of $20°C$, is placed in a refrigerator in which the air temperature is $5°C$. If the heat transfer coefficient between the air and the grape is $20\,W/(m^2 \cdot °C)$, determine the time required for the grape to reach $10°C$. [For the grape, $k = 0.6\,W/(m \cdot °C)$, $\rho = 1100\,kg/m^3$, and $c = 4200\,J/(kg \cdot °C)$.]
*Answer* 7.00 *min.*

**2-16.** A 6-cm-diameter potato at a uniform temperature of $80°C$ is taken out of the oven and suddenly exposed to ambient air at $20°C$. If the heat transfer coefficient between the air and the potato is $25\,W/(m^2 \cdot °C)$, determine the time required for the potato to reach $50°C$. [For the potato, $k = 7\,W/(m \cdot °C)$, $\rho = 1300\,kg/m^3$, and $c = 4300\,J/(kg \cdot °C)$.]

**2-17.** A metal water immersion heater $[k = 300\,W/(m \cdot °C)$. $\rho = 8900\,kg/m^3$, and $c = 400J/(kg \cdot °C)]$ dissipates electric energy at a rate of 50 W. The total volume of the heater is $1.5 \times 10^{-5}\,m^3$, and the outside area is $0.003m^2$. The heater, initially at a uniform temperature of $20°C$ is plugged in while in air. The heat transfer coefficient between the air and the heater is around $10\,W/(m^2 \cdot °C)$. Calculate the time required for the heater to reach its melting temperature, $500°C$.

**2-18.** A large aluminum plate of thickness 3 cm is initially at a uniform temperature of $50°C$. Suddenly one of its surfaces is subjected to a uniform heat flux of $7500\,W/m^2$ and the other surface is exposed to a cool air stream at a temperature of $30°C$. The heat transfer coefficient between the air stream and the surface is $60\,W/(m^2 \cdot °C)$. Using lumped system analysis, determine the temperature of the plate as a function of time and plot it against time. Calculate the steady-state temperature of the plate as time approaches infinity. [For aluminum, $k = 204W/(m \cdot °C)$, $\rho = 2707kg/m^3$, and $c = 896\,J/(kg \cdot °C)$.]

**2-19.** Consider an aluminum cube of side $3\,cm$ that is initially at a uniform temperature of $50°C$. Suddenly all its surfaces are exposed to cool air at $20°C$. The heat transfer coefficient between the air stream and the surfaces is $50\,W/(m^2 \cdot °C)$. Assuming that lumped system analysis is applicable. develop an expression for the temperature $T(t)$ of the cube as a function of time and plot the temperature of the solid against time. [For aluminum, $k = 204\,W/(m \cdot °C)$, $\rho = 2707\,kg/m^3$, and $c = 896\,J/(kg \cdot °C)$.]

**2-20.** Consider the aluminum cube of Problem 2-19, which is initially at a uniform temperature of $50°C$. For times $t > 0$, one of the boundary surfaces is kept insulated, one is subjected to uniform heating at a rate $8000\,W/m^2$, and the remaining four dissipate heat by convection into an environment whose temperature is $20°C$ with a heat transfer coefficient of 50 W/(m$^2$ · °C). Using lumped system analysis, develop an expression for the temperature of the cube as a function of time.

**2-21.** Consider a copper block of sides 2 cm × 2 cm × 3 cm, initially at a uniform temperature of 300°C, that is immersed in a fluid at 25°C. The heat transfer coefficient between the fluid and the surfaces is 80 W/(m$^2$ · °C). Calculate the time required for the cube to cool to 50°C. Check the validity of the lumped system analysis. [For copper, $k = 386$ W/(m · °C), $\rho = 8954$ kg/m$^3$, and $c = 383$ J/(kg · °C).]

**2-22.** A solid copper cylindrical rod of 1 cm diameter and 2 cm height is initially at a uniform temperature of 300°C. Suddenly the surfaces are subjected to convection with a heat transfer coefficient of 20 W/(m$^2$ · °C) into an ambient fluid at 25°C. Determine the temperature of the rod 2 min after the start of the cooling. [For copper, $k = 386$ W/(m · °C), $\rho = 8954$ kg/m$^3$, and $c = 383$ J/(kg · °C).]

**2-23.** A soldering iron has an outside area of 0.01 m$^2$, a mass of 0.6 kg, and a 100-W heating element. The iron, initially at 25°C, is covered with insulation and plugged in. Assuming that lumped system analysis is adequate, estimate the time required for the iron to reach 300°C. [For soldering iron, $k = 75$ W/(m · °C), $\rho = 8000$ kg/m$^3$, and $c = 418$ J/(kg · °C).]

**2-24.** A 0.1-cm-diameter long wooden stick at 15°C is suddenly exposed to 500°C gases with a surface heat transfer coefficient of 15 W/(m$^2$ · °C) between the stick and the gases. If the ignition temperature of the wood is 315°C, find the exposure time before possible ignition. [For wood, $k = 0.14$ W/(m · °C), $\rho = 600$ kg/m$^3$, and $c = 250$ J/(kg · °C).]

**2-25.** A short, cylindrical aluminum bar of 1 cm diameter and 2 cm height is initially at a uniform temperature of 150°C. Suddenly the surfaces are subjected to convective cooling with a heat transfer coefficient of 15 W/(m$^2$ · °C) into an ambient fluid at 30°C. Calculate the temperature of the cylinder 1 min after the start of the cooling. [For aluminum, $k = 204$ W/(m · °C), $\rho = 2707$ kg/m$^3$, and $c = 896$ J/(kg · °C).]

**2-26.** A clay column with cross section 2 cm by 2 cm is initially at a uniform temperature of 200°C. Suddenly, the surfaces are subjected to convective cooling with a heat transfer coefficient of 10 W/(m$^2$ · °C) into ambient air at 25°C. Calculate the temperature of the column 10 min after the start of the cooling. Compare this temperature with that of a plane wall 5 cm thick of the same material and under the same conditions. [For the clay column, $k = 1.28$ W/(m · °C), $\rho = 1458$ kg/m$^3$, and $c = 880$ J/(kg · °C).]

**2-27.** A thermocouple junction, approximated as a sphere of constantan, is to be used to measure the temperature of a gas. The heat transfer coefficient between the gas and the thermocouple is 400 W/(m$^2$ · °C). Calculate the maximum allowable diameter of the junction if the thermocouple should measure 95 percent of the applied temperature difference in 5 s. [For constantan, $k = 22.7\,\text{W}/(\text{m} \cdot {}^\circ\text{C})$, $\rho = 8920\,\text{kg}/\text{m}^3$, and $c = 410\,\text{J}/(\text{kg} \cdot {}^\circ\text{C})$.]

# CHAPTER 3

# Diffusion of Heat and Mass—Governing Equations

In this chapter we first develop the three-dimensional, unsteady heat conduction equation in the rectangular, cylindrical, and spherical coordinate systems and discuss the appropriate boundary conditions. The objective is to provide a good basis for understanding the physical significance of the steady and unsteady governing equation of heat conduction and its boundary conditions, and hence prepare the necessary background for the mathematical formulation for the unsteady and spatial temperature distribution. Numerous illustrative examples are presented to demonstrate the mathematical formulation of typical physical problems. Bioheat equation is given. Similarities in the governing equations for diffusion of heat and diffusion of mass are presented.

## 3.1. DERIVATION OF ONE-DIMENSIONAL TIME-DEPENDENT HEAT CONDUCTION EQUATION

The transient temperature distribution in solids can be determined from the solution of the heat conduction equation subject to a set of appropriate boundary and initial conditions. We need to develop a mathematical formulation of heat conduction in solids that allows for both spatial and time variation of temperature within the body. For simplicity in the analysis, we assume that temperature varies with *time* and only in *one direction*; and we consider the formulation in the rectangular cylindrical, and spherical coordinate systems. We need to develop the heat conduction equation in different coordinate systems because of geometrical considerations arising from the body shapes. For example, for bodies in the form of a slab (i.e., plate), the equation is needed in the rectangular coordinate system. Similarly, for bodies in the form of a cylinder and sphere, the equations are needed in the cylindrical and spherical coordinate systems, respectively. The reason for using different coordinate systems is to ensure that the boundary surfaces of the region coincide with the coordinate surfaces. For example, in the cylindrical coordinate system, one of the coordinate surfaces is a cylinder; hence, it coincides with the cylindrical surface of a body in the form of a cylinder.

The governing equation of heat conduction is obtained from the first law of thermodynamics. The first law of thermodynamics is a general law and depends on the selection of a system or control volume. In this chapter we will work with the *systems*, that means our medium will not be in motion. The system we choose will not have any flow of mass in and out from its boundaries.

To develop the heat conduction equation, we consider a solid whose temperature $T(X, t)$ depends on time $t$ and varies only in one direction, say along the $X$ *coordinate*. For generality in the analysis, it is assumed that the coordinate $X$ represents the

$x$ axis in the rectangular coordinate system or the $r$ axis in the cylindrical and spherical coordinate systems.

The first law requires a relation between heat flux and temperature distribution. The Fourier law, which is a particular law (or also called a constitutive equation), given in Chap. 1, can be written in the $X$ coordinate as

$$q = -k\frac{\partial T(X, t)}{\partial X} \qquad \text{W/m}^2 \tag{3-1}$$

where $q$ is the heat flux in the $X$ direction in W/m$^2$ and $k$ is the thermal conductivity of the solid in W/(m $\cdot$ °C). For generality, we assume an energy source within the solid of strength $g(X, t)$, W/m$^3$ that varies with the position $X$ and time $t$. Here $g(X, t)$ is a specified quantity. For example, for a fuel element of a nuclear reactor, it represents the rate of energy generation within the fuel element due to nuclear fission. In the case of an electric current passing through a wire, it represents the ohm heating. When radioactive elements are present within a solid, it represents the rate of energy generation within the body due to the disintegration of the radioactive elements.

For the one-dimensional heat conduction equation, we consider a volume element of thickness $\Delta x$, and having an area $A$ normal to the coordinate axis $X$, as illustrated in Fig. 3.1. The energy balance equation for this volume element is stated as

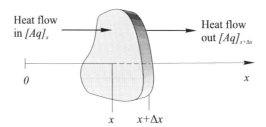

**FIG. 3.1.** Nomenclature for the derivation of one-dimensional heat conduction equation.

$$\begin{pmatrix} \text{Rate of} \\ \text{increase of} \\ \textbf{internal energy} \end{pmatrix} = \begin{pmatrix} \text{Net rate of} \\ \text{heat gain} \\ \textbf{by conduction} \end{pmatrix} + \begin{pmatrix} \text{Rate of} \\ \text{energy} \\ \textbf{generation} \end{pmatrix}. \tag{3-2}$$

Each of the terms in this statement is now evaluated. The rate of increase of internal energy of the volume element resulting from the change of temperature with time is

$$\begin{pmatrix} \text{Rate of} \\ \text{increase of} \\ \text{internal energy} \end{pmatrix} \equiv A\Delta X \rho c\,\frac{\partial T}{\partial t} \tag{3-3a}$$

where   $A$   = surface area normal to the $X$ axis,
   $\Delta X$ = thickness,
   $\rho$   = density of the material, kg/m$^3$,

$c$ = specific heat of the material, J/(kg · °C),

$T$ = temperature of the volume element, °C,

$t$ = time, s .

The rate of heat flow into the element by conduction through area $A$ at location $X$ in the $X$ direction is

$$(Aq)_X$$

where $q$ is the conduction heat flux defined previously. Similarly, the rate of the heat flow out of the element by conduction at location $X + \Delta X$ in the $X$ direction is written as

$$(Aq)_{X+\Delta X} \, .$$

Then, the net rate of heat gained by conduction is the difference between the energy entering and leaving the element, that is,

$$\begin{pmatrix} \text{Net rate of} \\ \text{heat gain} \\ \text{by conduction} \end{pmatrix} \equiv \underbrace{(Aq)_X}_{\text{IN}} - \underbrace{(Aq)_{X+\Delta X}}_{\text{OUT}} \, . \qquad \text{(3-3b)}$$

The rate of energy generation in the volume element $A\Delta X$, for a specified energy generation rate per unit volume $g \equiv g(X, t)\text{W/m}^3$, is given by

$$\begin{pmatrix} \text{Rate of} \\ \text{energy} \\ \text{generation} \end{pmatrix} \equiv A\Delta X \, g \, . \qquad \text{(3-3c)}$$

Introducing Eqs. (3-3a to c) into Eq. (3-2), we have

$$A\Delta X \rho c \, \frac{\partial T}{\partial t} = (Aq)_X - (Aq)_{X+\Delta X} + A\Delta X g$$

which is rearranged in the form

$$\rho c \, \frac{\partial T}{\partial t} = -\frac{1}{A} \, \frac{(Aq)_{X+\Delta X} - (Aq)_X}{\Delta X} + g \, . \qquad \text{(3-4a)}$$

As $\Delta X \to 0$ the first term on the right-hand side becomes the derivative of $Aq$ with respect to $X$, that is,

$$\frac{(Aq)_{X+\Delta X} - (Aq)_X}{\Delta X} = \frac{\partial(Aq)}{\partial X} \, . \qquad \text{(3-4b)}$$

Hence, Eq. (3-4a) takes the form

$$\rho c \, \frac{\partial T}{\partial t} = \frac{1}{A} \, \frac{\partial}{\partial X} \left( Ak \, \frac{\partial T}{\partial X} \right) + g \qquad \text{(3-5)}$$

where $T \equiv T(X, t)$

$\quad\quad A \equiv A(X)$

$$k \equiv k(X)$$
$$g \equiv g(T, t).$$

In the above derivation of Eq. (3-5), we have not specified any particular coordinate system. Equation (3-5) is applicable in the rectangular, cylindrical, and spherical coordinate systems if proper cognizance is given to the variation of area $A$ with the coordinate axis, as described below.

*Rectangular Coordinates*

We replace the coordinate $X$ by the $x$ *variable* and note that the area in the rectangular coordinate system does not vary with $x$. Then, $A$ cancels out, and Eq. (3-5) takes the form

$$\rho c \frac{\partial T(x, t)}{\partial t} = \frac{\partial}{\partial x} \left[ k(x) \frac{\partial T}{\partial x} \right] + g(x, t), \tag{3-6}$$

which is the one-dimensional, time-dependent heat conduction equation in the rectangular coordinate system.

For constant thermal conductivity $k(x) \equiv k$, Eq. (3-6) reduces to

$$\rho c \frac{\partial T(x, t)}{\partial t} = k \frac{\partial^2 T}{\partial x^2} + g(x, t). \tag{3-7}$$

*Cylindrical Coordinates*

We replace the coordinate $X$ by the $r$ *variable* and note that area $A$ varies linearly with the $r$ variable (i.e., $A = 2\pi r H$, where $H$ is the cylinder length). Then, Eq. (3-5) becomes

$$\rho c \frac{\partial T(r, t)}{\partial t} = \frac{1}{r} \frac{\partial}{\partial r} \left[ r k(r) \frac{\partial T}{\partial r} \right] + g(r, t) \tag{3-8}$$

which is the one-dimensional, time-dependent heat conduction equation in the cylindrical coordinate system.

For constant thermal conductivity $k(r) \equiv k$, Eq. (3-8) reduces to

$$\rho c \frac{\partial T(r, t)}{\partial t} = \frac{k}{r} \frac{\partial}{\partial r} \left( r \frac{\partial T}{\partial r} \right) + g(r, t) \tag{3-9a}$$

or

$$\rho c \frac{\partial T(r, t)}{\partial t} = k \left( \frac{\partial^2 T}{\partial r^2} + \frac{1}{r} \frac{\partial T}{\partial r} \right) + g(r, t). \tag{3-9b}$$

*Spherical Coordinates*

In the spherical coordinate system, area $A$ is proportional to the square of the $r$ variable in the form $A = 4\pi r^2$. Introducing this into Eq. (3-5) and replacing $X$ by $r$, we obtain

$$\rho c \, \frac{\partial T(r,t)}{\partial t} = \frac{1}{r^2} \frac{\partial}{\partial r} \left[ r^2 k(r) \frac{\partial T}{\partial r} \right] + g(r,t) \qquad (3\text{-}10)$$

which is the one-dimensional, time-dependent heat conduction equation in the spherical coordinate system.

For constant thermal conductivity $k(r) \equiv k$, Eq. (3-10) reduces to

$$\rho c \, \frac{\partial T(r,t)}{\partial t} = \frac{k}{r^2} \frac{\partial}{\partial r} \left( r^2 \frac{\partial T}{\partial r} \right) + g(r,t) \qquad (3\text{-}11a)$$

or

$$\rho c \, \frac{\partial T(r,t)}{\partial t} = k \left[ \frac{\partial^2 T}{\partial r^2} + \frac{2}{r} \frac{\partial T}{\partial r} \right] + g(r,t) \quad . \qquad (3\text{-}11b)$$

**EXAMPLE 3-1**   Write the heat conduction equation for one-dimensional, steady-state heat flow in a solid having a constant $k$ and a constant rate of energy generation $g_0$ W/m$^2$, within the medium for *(a)* a slab, *(b)* a cylinder, and *(c)* a sphere.

**SOLUTION**   The results are immediately obtainable from the given equations as:

*(a)* By setting $n = 0$ and $r \equiv x$,

$$\frac{d^2 T}{dx^2} + \frac{1}{k} g_0 = 0$$

*(b)* By setting $n = 1$,

$$\frac{1}{r} \frac{d}{dr} \left( r \frac{dT}{dr} \right) + \frac{1}{k} g_0 = 0$$

*(c)* By setting $n = 2$,

$$\frac{1}{r^2} \frac{d}{dr} \left( r^2 \frac{dT}{dr} \right) + \frac{1}{k} g_0 = 0$$

## 3.2. COMPACT FORM OF ONE-DIMENSIONAL TIME-DEPENDENT HEAT CONDUCTION EQUATION

The heat conduction Eqs. (3-7), (3-9), and (3-11) can be written more compactly in the form of a single equation as

$$\rho c \, \frac{\partial T(X,t)}{\partial t} = \frac{1}{X^n} \frac{\partial}{\partial X} \left[ X^n k(X) \frac{\partial T}{\partial X} \right] + g(X,t) \qquad (3\text{-}12a)$$

and for the case of constant thermal conductivity $k(X) = k = \text{constant}$, this equation reduces to

$$\frac{1}{\alpha} \frac{\partial T(X,t)}{\partial t} = \frac{1}{X^n} \frac{\partial}{\partial X} \left( X^n \frac{\partial T}{\partial X} \right) + \frac{1}{k} g(X,t) \qquad (3\text{-}12b)$$

where $X \equiv r$ and $n = 0$ for rectangular coordinates
$\qquad X \equiv r$ and $n = 1$ for cylindrical coordinates
$\qquad X \equiv r$ and $n = 2$ for spherical coordinates.

and $\alpha = k/\rho c$ is the *thermal diffusivity* of the material in meters squared per second.

## One Dimensional Steady-State Heat Conduction Equation

The steady-state condition implies that the temperature within the solid does not vary with time, but may vary with the position. For such situations, the time derivative of temperature vanishes and the heat conduction Eq. (3-12a) reduces to

$$\frac{1}{X^n} \frac{d}{dX} \left[ X^n k(X) \frac{dT(X)}{dX} \right] + g(X) = 0 \quad . \qquad (3\text{-}13)$$

As discussed previously, this equation is of interest in different coordinate systems.

For rectangular coordinates, we set $X = x$ and $n = 0$:

$$\frac{d}{dx} \left[ k(x) \frac{dT(x)}{dx} \right] + g(x) = 0 \quad . \qquad (3\text{-}14)$$

For cylindrical coordinates, we set $X = r$ and $n = 1$:

$$\frac{1}{r} \frac{d}{dr} \left[ r k(r) \frac{dT(r)}{dr} \right] + g(r) = 0 \quad . \qquad (3\text{-}15)$$

For spherical coordinates, we set $X = r$ and $n = 2$:

$$\frac{1}{r^2} \frac{d}{dr} \left[ r^2 k(r) \frac{dT(r)}{dr} \right] + g(r) = 0 \quad . \qquad (3\text{-}16)$$

For the case of constant thermal conductivity, $k(X) = k$, Eqs. (3-14) to (3-16) become:

For rectangular coordinates:

$$\frac{d^2 T(x)}{dx^2} + \frac{g(x)}{k} = 0 \qquad (3\text{-}17a).$$

For cylindrical coordinates:

$$\frac{1}{r} \frac{d}{dr} \left[ r \frac{dT(r)}{dr} \right] + \frac{g(r)}{k} = 0 \qquad (3\text{-}17b).$$

For spherical coordinates:

$$\frac{1}{r^2}\frac{d}{dr}\left[r^2\frac{dT(r)}{dr}\right] + \frac{g(r)}{k} = 0 \qquad (3\text{-}17c).$$

For steady-state heat conduction with no energy sources within the body and constant thermal conductivity, Eqs. (3-17a) to (3-17c) simplify to:

For rectangular coordinates:

$$\frac{d^2T(x)}{dx^2} = 0 \qquad (3\text{-}18a).$$

For cylindrical coordinates:

$$\frac{d}{dr}\left[r\frac{dT(r)}{dr}\right] = 0 \qquad (3\text{-}18b).$$

For spherical coordinates:

$$\frac{d}{dr}\left[r^2\frac{dT(r)}{dr}\right] = 0 \qquad (3\text{-}18c).$$

## 3.3. ONE-DIMENSIONAL NON-FOURIER (CATTANEO'S) HEAT CONDUCTION EQUATION

The Fourier heat conduction equation is diffusive and the resulting transient temperature equations are of the parabolic type. Under certain special heating durations of time and special scales of applications and temperature regimes, the Fourier model fails to predict the temperature propagation speed in transient situations. To account for the temperature propagation speed, and to account for the other anomalies associated with the Fourier model, the Cattaneo model was introduced. In Chapter 1, the heat flux of Cattaneo model for non-Fourier heat conduction was given as

$$q_x = -\tau\frac{\partial q_x}{\partial t} - k\frac{\partial T}{\partial x} \qquad (3\text{-}19a).$$

One dimensional energy equation in rectangular coordinate system without the energy generation term from equation (3-6) in terms of the heat flux, prior our substitution of the Fourier law becomes

$$\rho c_p\frac{\partial T}{\partial t} + \frac{\partial q_x}{\partial x} = 0 \qquad (3\text{-}19b)$$

and differentiating this equation with respect to time t results

$$\rho c_p\frac{\partial^2 T}{\partial t^2} + \frac{\partial^2 q_x}{\partial t\partial x} = 0 \qquad (3\text{-}19c).$$

If the heat flux $q_x$ from the Cattaneo equation (3-19a) is substituted into equation (3-19b), and then the resultant term

$$\frac{\partial^2 q_x}{\partial t \partial x}$$

is eliminated by using equation (3-19c) which results in the hyperbolic (telegraph) equation for the temperature:

$$\rho c_p \frac{\partial T}{\partial t} + \tau \rho c_p \frac{\partial^2 T}{\partial t^2} = k \frac{\partial^2 T}{\partial x^2}$$

dividing the equation by $\tau \rho c_p$ we have:

$$\boxed{\frac{1}{\tau} \frac{\partial T}{\partial t} + \frac{\partial^2 T}{\partial t^2} = \frac{k}{\tau \rho c_p} \frac{\partial^2 T}{\partial x^2}} \qquad (3\text{-}20)$$

The associated temperature propagation speed, $c_T$ is given as

$$c_T = \frac{k}{\rho c_p \tau} \qquad (3\text{-}21)$$

It is clear that in the above expression as $c_T$ approaches infinity, the limiting case of zero relaxation time (as $\tau$ approaches zero), which is the case of infinite speed of heat propagation, the hyperbolic heat conduction equation reverts back to the classical parabolic heat conduction equation. At steady state, the Cattaneo model reverts to the Fourier model, although the relaxation parameter $\tau$ is not equal to zero. As a consequence, the temperature results for the two models differ only during the transient state. In summary, the Fourier equation has infinite heat propagation speed and the Cattaneo equation has a finite heat propagation speed.

## 3.4. SIGNIFICANCE OF THERMAL DIFFUSIVITY

The physical significance of thermal diffusivity is associated with the propagation of heat into the medium during changes of temperature with time. The higher the thermal diffusivity, the faster the propagation of heat into the medium.

Table 3.1 lists the thermal diffusivities of typical materials. There are orders of magnitude differences in the values of thermal diffusivity for different materials. For example, $\alpha$ varies from about $170 \times 10^{-6} \mathrm{m}^2/\mathrm{s}$ for silver to $0.077 \times 10^{-6} \mathrm{m}^2/\mathrm{s}$ for soft rubber. The larger the thermal diffusivity, the shorter the time required for heat to penetrate into the solid. Therefore, under a given applied temperature condition, the penetration of heat into silver is much faster than the penetration into soft rubber.

Next, consider, for example, a semi-infinite medium extending from $x = 0$ to $x \to \infty$ and initially at a uniform temperature $T_0 = 100°\mathrm{C}$. Suddenly the temperature of the surface at $x = 0$ is lowered to $0°\mathrm{C}$ and maintained at that temperature. The temperature in the interior of the solid will vary continuously with position and time. Table 3.2 lists the time required for the temperature to be lowered to $\frac{1}{2}T_0 = 50°\mathrm{C}$ at a location 30 cm from the boundary surface for materials having different thermal diffusivities. It is apparent from this table that the larger the thermal diffusivity, the less time is required for heat to penetrate into the solid.

If we know the specific heat $c_p$ and density $\rho$, it is a common practice to experimentally determine the thermal diffusivity of materials $\alpha$ using transient methods and to calculate indirectly the conductivity, $k$ using the definition of thermal diffusivity $\alpha = \frac{k}{\rho c_p}$. The laser flash method, the thermal wave interferometry method and the thermographic methods are commonly known techniques to measure thermal diffusivities.

**TABLE 3.1 Thermal diffusivity of typical materials.**

| | Average temperature, | | Diffusivity $\alpha$ | $\alpha$ |
|---|---|---|---|---|
| | °C | °F | m²/s | ft²/s |
| **Metals** | | | | |
| Aluminum | 0 | 32 | $85.9\times10^{-6}$ | $924.6\times10^{-6}$ |
| Copper | 0 | 32 | $114.1\times10^{-6}$ | $1228.2\times10^{-6}$ |
| Gold | 20 | 68 | $120.8\times10^{-6}$ | $1300.3\times10^{-6}$ |
| Iron, pure | 0 | 32 | $18.1\times10^{-6}$ | $194.8\times10^{-6}$ |
| Cast iron ($c \simeq 4\%$) | 20 | 68 | $17.0\times10^{-6}$ | $183.0\times10^{-6}$ |
| Lead | 21 | 69.8 | $25.5\times10^{-6}$ | $274.5\times10^{-6}$ |
| Mercury | 0 | 32 | $4.44\times10^{-6}$ | $47.8\times10^{-6}$ |
| Nickel | 0 | 32 | $15.5\times10^{-6}$ | $166.8\times10^{-6}$ |
| Silver | 0 | 32 | $170.4\times10^{-6}$ | $1834.2\times10^{-6}$ |
| Steel, mild | 0 | 32 | $12.4\times10^{-6}$ | $133.5\times10^{-6}$ |
| Tungsten | 0 | 32 | $61.7\times10^{-6}$ | $664.1\times10^{-6}$ |
| Zinc | 0 | 32 | $41.3\times10^{-6}$ | $444.5\times10^{-6}$ |
| **Nonmetals** | | | | |
| Asbestos | 0 | 32 | $0.258\times10^{-6}$ | $2.777\times10^{-6}$ |
| Brick, fireclay | 204 | 399.2 | $0.516\times10^{-6}$ | $5.554\times10^{-6}$ |
| Cork, ground | 38 | 100.4 | $0.155\times10^{-6}$ | $1.668\times10^{-6}$ |
| Glass, Pyrex | | | $0.594\times10^{-6}$ | $6.394\times10^{-6}$ |
| Granite | 0 | 32 | $1.291\times10^{-6}$ | $13.896\times10^{-6}$ |
| Ice | 0 | 32 | $1.187\times10^{-6}$ | $12.777\times10^{-6}$ |
| Oak, across grain | 29 | 84.2 | $0.160\times10^{-6}$ | $1.722\times110^{-6}$ |
| Pine, across grain | 29 | 84.2 | $0.152\times10^{-6}$ | $1.636\times10^{-6}$ |
| Quartz sand, dry | | | $0.206\times10^{-6}$ | $2.217\times10^{-6}$ |
| Rubber, soft | | | $0.077\times10^{-6}$ | $0.829\times10^{-6}$ |
| Water | 0 | 32 | $0.129\times10^{-6}$ | $1.388\times10^{-6}$ |

**TABLE 3.2 Effect of thermal diffusivity on the rate of heat propagation.**

| Material | Silver | Copper | Steel | Glass |
|---|---|---|---|---|
| $\alpha$, m²/s | $170\times10^{-6}$ | $103\times10^{-6}$ | $12.9\times10^{-6}$ | $0.59\times10^{-6}$ |
| Time | 9.5 min | 16.5 min | 2.2 h | 2.00 days |

## 3.5. THREE-DIMENSIONAL TIME-DEPENDENT HEAT CONDUCTION EQUATION

In Sec. 2-1 we derived the one-dimensional, time-dependent heat conduction equation. By following a similar approach but allowing for heat conduction in the three dimensions, the general equation can be derived also. Such derivations are explained in various texts on heat conduction. Here we directly present the resulting equations in the rectangular, cylindrical, and spherical coordinate systems for the case of *constant thermal conductivity*.

For the rectangular coordinate system $(x, y, z)$, the heat conduction equation becomes

$$\frac{\partial^2 T}{\partial x^2} + \frac{\partial^2 T}{\partial y^2} + \frac{\partial^2 T}{\partial z^2} + \frac{1}{k}g = \frac{1}{\alpha}\frac{\partial T}{\partial t} \tag{3-22}$$

where $T \equiv T(x, y, z, t)$.

For the *cylindrical coordinate system* $(r, \phi, z)$, illustrated in Fig. 3.2,

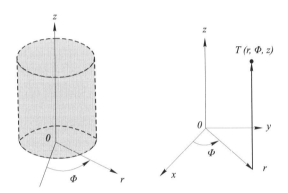

**FIG. 3.2.** Cylindrical coordinate system $(r, \phi, z)$.

it is given

$$\frac{1}{r}\frac{\partial}{\partial r}\left(r\frac{\partial T}{\partial r}\right) + \frac{1}{r^2}\frac{\partial^2 T}{\partial \phi^2} + \frac{\partial^2 T}{\partial z^2} + \frac{g}{k} = \frac{1}{\alpha}\frac{\partial T}{\partial t} \tag{3-23}$$

where $T \equiv T(r, \phi, z, t)$.

Finally, for the *spherical coordinate system* $(r, \phi, \theta)$, illustrated in Fig. 3.3,

it is given by

$$\frac{1}{r^2}\frac{\partial}{\partial r}\left(r^2\frac{\partial T}{\partial r}\right) + \frac{1}{r^2 \sin\theta}\frac{\partial}{\partial \theta}\left(\sin\theta\frac{\partial T}{\partial \theta}\right) + \frac{1}{r^2 \sin^2\theta}\frac{\partial^2 T}{\partial \phi^2} + \frac{g}{k} = \frac{1}{\alpha}\frac{\partial T}{\partial t} \tag{3-24}$$

where $T \equiv T(r, \phi, \theta, t)$.

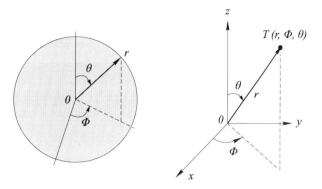

**FIG. 3.3.** Spherical coordinate system $(r, \phi, \theta)$.

Using the vectorial notation presented in Table 3 of Appendix E, the three dimensional equation becomes

$$\nabla(k\nabla \cdot T) + \frac{g}{k} = \frac{1}{\alpha}\frac{\partial T}{\partial t}$$

Clearly, for the special case of temperature depending on time and only the space variable $r$ (or $x$ in the rectangular coordinates), Eqs. (3-22) to (3-24) reduce to Eq. (3-7) to (3-11).

**EXAMPLE 3-2**  By simplifying the three-dimensional equation (3-24), obtain the heat conduction equation for a sphere in which there is energy generation and the temperature varies with time and the radial coordinate $r$ only.

**SOLUTION**  Since the temperature depends on $r$ and $t$ only, we have $T \equiv T(r, t)$. Then the derivatives with respect to $\theta$ and $\phi$ vanish, and Eq. (3-24) reduces to

$$\frac{1}{r^2}\frac{\partial}{\partial r}\left(r^2\frac{\partial T}{\partial r}\right) + \frac{1}{k}g = \frac{1}{\alpha}\frac{\partial T}{\partial t}$$

## 3.6. BOUNDARY AND INITIAL CONDITION CONCEPTS

When the temperature varies with the space variable and time, the energy equation involves a second derivative in the space variables and first derivative in the time variable, as is apparent from the equations given above. In three dimensional, unsteady problems, six boundary conditions are needed in addition to an initial condition to solve the heat conduction problem. The initial condition specifies the distribution of temperature at the origin of the time coordinate, $t = 0$. The boundary conditions specify the thermal condition at the boundary surfaces of the region. For example, at a given boundary surface, the distribution of temperature may be prescribed, or the distribution of the heat flux may be specified, or there may be heat transfer by convection into the ambient fluid at a specified temperature with a known heat transfer coefficient.

Therefore, in the analysis of heat conduction problems, such physical boundary conditions should be represented with appropriate mathematical expressions. We now discuss the mathematical representation of three commonly used, different types of boundary conditions, namely, the *prescribed temperature*, *prescribed heatflux*, and *convection boundary conditions.*

### 3.6.1 Prescribed Temperature Boundary Condition (B.C. First Kind)

There are numerous applications in which the temperature of the boundary surface is considered known. For example, a boundary surface in contact with melting ice is said to be maintained at a uniform temperature $0°C$, or the distribution of temperature at the boundary surface may be known as a function of time.

Consider a plate of thickness $L$ as illustrated in Fig. 3.4.

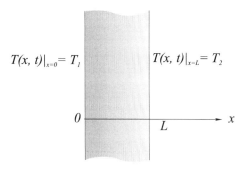

**FIG. 3.4.** Prescribed temperature at the boundary (boundary condition of the *first kind*).

Suppose the boundary surface at $x = 0$ is maintained at a uniform temperature $T_1$ and that at $x = L$, there is a uniform temperature $T_2$. The plate is said to be subjected to prescribed temperature boundary conditions at both surfaces, and these boundary conditions are written as

$$T(x,t)\,|_{x=0} \equiv T(0,t) = T_1 \qquad (3\text{-}25a)$$

$$T(x,t)\,|_{x=L} \equiv T(L,t) = T_2 \qquad (3\text{-}25b)$$

Suppose that the boundary surface at $x = 0$ is maintained at $T_1 = 0°C$ and the boundary surface at $x = L$ is maintained at $T_2 = 100°C$ (e.g., boiling water temperature at atmospheric pressure). These boundary conditions are expressed as

$$T(0,t) = T_1 = 0\,°C$$

$$T(L,t) = T_2 = 100\,°C$$

In more general cases, the distribution of temperature at the boundary surface may be specified as a function of position and time. When the value of temperature is prescribed at the boundary surface, the boundary condition is said to be of the *first kind*.

Similar considerations are applicable for boundary conditions at the surfaces of a cylinder and sphere.

## 3.6.2 Prescribed Heat Flux Boundary Condition (B.C. Second Kind)

In some situations, the rate of heat supply to a boundary surface is considered known. For example, on an electrically heated surface the rate of heat flow entering the solid is known. Such boundary conditions are called *prescribed* heat flux boundary conditions.

Consider a plate of thickness $L$ as illustrated in Fig. 2.5a.

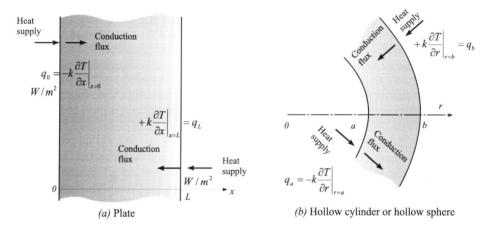

*(a)* Plate        *(b)* Hollow cylinder or hollow sphere

**FIG. 3.5.** Prescribed heat flux at the boundaries (boundary condition of the *second kind*).

Suppose there is a heat supply into the medium at a rate of $q_0$ W/m$^2$, through the boundary surface at $x = 0$ and another heat supply into the medium at a rate of $q_L$ W/m$^2$ through the boundary surface at $x = L$. The mathematical representation of such boundary conditions is now described.

At the boundary surface $x = 0$, the external heat supply $q_0$ W/m$^2$ is equated to the conduction heat flux into the solid:

$$\begin{pmatrix} \text{Heat flow by} \\ \text{conduction} \\ \text{into the body} \\ \text{at } x = 0 \end{pmatrix} = \begin{pmatrix} \text{External heat} \\ \text{supply, } q_0 \text{ W/m}^2 \\ \text{at } x = 0 \end{pmatrix}$$

$$\boxed{-k \left. \frac{\partial T}{\partial x} \right|_{x=0} = q_0} \,. \tag{3-26a}$$

Next, we consider a heat supply at a rate of $q_L$ W/m$^2$ at the surface $x = L$:

$$+k\left.\frac{\partial T}{\partial x}\right|_{x=L} = q_L .$$
(3-26b)

In these prescribed heat flux boundary conditions a positive value for $q_0$ and $q_L$ implies heat supply into the medium. Equations (3-26a) and (3-26b) are the mathematical representation of the prescribed heat flux boundary condition for heat supply into the body. If heat is to be removed from the body, $q_0$ and $q_L$ assume negative values, for example: $q_0 = -100$ W/m$^2$ and $q_L = -200$ W/m$^2$. Then Eqs. (3-26a) and (3-26b) become

$$-k\left.\frac{\partial T(x,t)}{\partial x}\right|_{x=0} = -100 \text{ W/m}^2$$
$$+k\left.\frac{\partial T(x,t)}{\partial x}\right|_{x=L} = -200 \text{ W/m}^2 .$$

The prescribed heat flux boundary condition at the surface is also called *second kind*. The results given by Eqs. (3-26a) and (3-26b) are developed with reference to a slab geometry. Similar results are applicable at the boundary surfaces of a cylinder or sphere as illustrated in Fig. 2.5b for a hollow cylinder or sphere. For such cases the coordinate $x$ is replaced by the radial variable $r$.

### 3.6.3 Convection Boundary Condition (B.C. Third Kind)

In most practical problems, heat flow at the boundary surface takes place by convection with a known heat transfer coefficient $h$ in an environment at a specified temperature. Consider again a plate of thickness $L$ as illustrated in Fig. 3.6a.

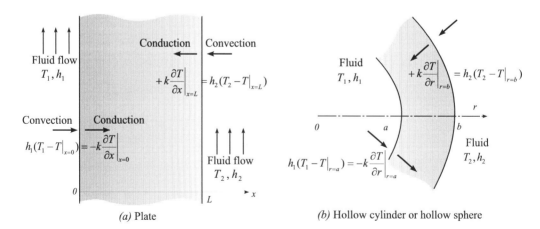

(a) Plate          (b) Hollow cylinder or hollow sphere

**FIG. 3.6.** Convection at the boundaries (boundary condition of the *third kind*).

A fluid with a heat transfer coefficient $h_1$ at a temperature $T_1$ flows over the surface of the plate at $x = 0$ as illustrated at Fig. 3.6a. The mathematical representation of this convection boundary condition is obtained by considering an energy balance at the surface $x = 0$, where

$$
\begin{pmatrix}
\text{Convection heat flux} \\
\text{from the fluid at } T_1 \\
\text{to the surface at } x = 0
\end{pmatrix}
=
\begin{pmatrix}
\text{Convection heat flux} \\
\text{from the surface at} \\
x = 0 \text{ into the plate}
\end{pmatrix}
$$

or

$$
h_1[T_1 - T(x,t)\,|_{x=0}] = -k \left. \frac{\partial T(x,t)}{\partial x} \right|_{x=0}, \tag{3-27a}
$$

which is the convection boundary condition at the surface $x = 0$.

At the other surface, we consider a fluid with a heat transfer coefficient $h_2$ at a temperature $T_2$ flowing over the surface $x = L$, as illustrated in Fig. 3.6. The energy balance for this surface becomes

$$
\begin{pmatrix}
\text{Convection heat flux} \\
\text{from the fluid at } T_2 \\
\text{to the surface at } x = L
\end{pmatrix}
=
\begin{pmatrix}
\text{Conduction heat flux} \\
\text{from the surface at} \\
x = L \text{ into the plate}
\end{pmatrix}
$$

or

$$
h_2[T_2 - T(x,t)\,|_{x=L}] = +k \left. \frac{\partial T(x,t)}{\partial x} \right|_{x=L}, \tag{3-27b}
$$

which is the convection boundary condition at the surface $x = L$.

Similar expressions are applicable for convection boundary conditions at the surfaces of a hollow cylinder or sphere, as illustrated in Fig. 2.6b. Convection boundary conditions are also called of the *third kind*.

The convection boundary conditions given by Eqs. (3-27a) and (3-27b) are rewritten in the form

$$
-k \left. \frac{\partial T(x,t)}{\partial x} \right|_{x=0} + h_1 T(0,t) = h_1 T_1
$$

$$
+k \left. \frac{\partial T(x,t)}{\partial x} \right|_{x=L} + h_2 T(L,t) = h_2 T_2
$$

or

$$
-k \frac{\partial T(x,t)}{\partial x} + h_1 T(x,t) = h_1 T_1 \quad \text{at } x = 0 \tag{3-28a}
$$

$$
+k \frac{\partial T(x,t)}{\partial x} + h_2 T(x,t) = h_2 T_2 \quad \text{at } x = L \tag{3-28b}
$$

where the left-hand sides are in terms of the unknown surface temperature of the body and the right-hand sides are in terms of the known fluid temperatures.

Clearly, the prescribed temperature boundary conditions are obtainable from these results by dividing both sides of the equations above by $h_1$ and by $h_2$, and then letting $h_1 \to \infty$ and $h_2 \to \infty$.

Similarly, the prescribed heat flux boundary conditions are also obtainable from these equations by setting

$$h_1 T_1 \equiv q_0 \quad \text{and} \quad h_2 T_2 \equiv q_L$$

on the right-hand sides of Eqs. (3-28a) and (3-28b) and then letting $h_1 = h_2 = 0$ on the left-hand sides. Finally, the convection boundary conditions for a hollow cylinder or sphere having an inside radius $a$ and an outside radius $b$ are written, according to Fig. 2.6b, in the form

$$\left[-k\frac{\partial T}{\partial r} + h_1 T\right]_{r=a} = h_1 T_1 \quad \text{at } r = a \tag{3-29a}$$

$$\left[+k\frac{\partial T}{\partial r} + h_2 T\right]_{r=b} = h_2 T_2 \quad \text{at } r = b \tag{3-29b}$$

**EXAMPLE 3-3**  A thick-walled tube has inside radius $r_1$ and outside radius $r_2$. A hot gas at temperature $T_1$ flows inside the tube, and a cold gas at temperature $T_2$ flows outside. The heat transfer coefficients for flow inside and outside the tube are specified as $h_1$ and $h_2$, respectively. Write the boundary conditions.

**SOLUTION**  The convection boundary conditions for this problem, are illustrated in Fig. 3.6b. From equation (3-29), we obtain

$$-k\frac{\partial T}{\partial r} = h_1(T_1 - T) \quad \text{at } r = r_1$$

$$+k\frac{\partial T}{\partial r} = h_2(T_2 - T) \quad \text{at } r = r_2$$

where $T$ is the temperature and $k$ is the thermal conductivity of the tube.

### 3.6.4 Thermal and Geometric Symmetry

If a thermal and geometric symmetry coexist about a common symmetry axis (or plane), the temperature distribution is symmetrical about the same axis (or plane). Then, the temperature gradient at the symmetry axis in the direction perpendicular to the axis vanishes, and hence we have

$$\frac{\partial T}{\partial X} = 0 \quad \text{at the symmetry axis.} \tag{3-30}$$

When such a symmetry condition exists within the medium, the mathematical formulation of the heat conduction problem is simplified, as illustrated below.

Consider a slab of thickness $L$ which is initially (i.e., at time $t = 0$) at a specified temperature and for times $t > 0$ is subjected to convection at the boundaries. The heat transfer coefficient $h_\infty$ and the environment temperature $T_\infty$ are the same for both boundary surfaces. If we take the $x$ - axis starting at the center. The boundary conditions at $x = -L/2$ and $x = L/2$ become

$$-k\,\frac{\partial T}{\partial x} = h_\infty(T_\infty - T) \quad \text{at } x = -L/2 \tag{3-31a}$$

$$+k\,\frac{\partial T}{\partial x} = h_\infty(T_\infty - T) \quad \text{at } x = +L/2. \tag{3-31b}$$

To determine the temperature distribution within the solid, the heat conduction equation for this problem should be solved within the region $-L/2 < x < L/2$ subject to the boundary conditions (3-31) and a specified initial condition.

Suppose the initial distribution within the medium is symmetrical about $x = 0$. Then the problem has both geometrical and thermal symmetry at $x = 0$, and the gradient of temperature at $x = 0$ vanishes, that is,

$$\frac{\partial T}{\partial x} = 0 \quad \text{at } x = 0. \tag{3-32}$$

When the problem has both geometrical and thermal symmetry about $x = 0$, it is more convenient to solve the problem over the half of the region $0 < x < L/2$ subject to the boundary conditions given by

$$\frac{\partial T}{\partial x} = 0 \quad \text{at } x = 0 \tag{3-33a}$$

$$k\,\frac{\partial T}{\partial x} = h_\infty(T_\infty - T) \quad \text{at } x = +\frac{L}{2} \tag{3-33b}$$

rather that solving it over the full domain $-L/2 < x < L/2$ subject to the boundary conditions given by Eqs. (3-31). Clearly, solving the heat conduction problem subject to the boundary conditions given by Eqs. (3-33a) and (3-33b) and solving the half domain is much easier than solving the problem over the entire region.


**EXAMPLE 3-4**   Consider a solid bar of radius $r = R$ in which energy is generated at a constant rate $g_0$ W/m$^3$. The bar is cooled by convection from its lateral surfaces into ambient air at a temperature $T_\infty$ with a heat transfer coefficient $h_\infty$. Write the boundary conditions needed for the solution of this problem.


**SOLUTION**   The problem possesses both geometric and thermal symmetry about the axis of the bar. Therefore, we have the symmetry boundary condition at $r = 0$ and the convection boundary condition at $r = R$. Then the heat conduction equation for this problem is to be solved in the region $0 \le r \le R$, subject to the boundary conditions

$$\frac{\partial T}{\partial r} = 0 \qquad\qquad \text{at } r = 0$$

$$+k\,\frac{\partial T}{\partial r} = h_\infty(T_\infty - T) \qquad \text{at } r = R$$

.

## 3.7. GOVERNING EQUATIONS OF HEAT CONDUCTION PROBLEMS

The analysis of heat conduction problems begins with the development of an appropriate mathematical model to represent the actual physical situation under consideration. The solution of the heat conduction equation subject to appropriate boundary and initial conditions gives the distribution of temperature within the solid as a function of time and position. Once the temperature distribution $T(X, t)$ in the solid is known, the heat flow rate anywhere in the medium can be determined from the Fourier law, given previously. Therefore, the first step in the mathematical formulation of the heat conduction problem is choosing the appropriate heat conduction equation according to whether the problem is a steady-state or a transient one.

The geometry of the body establishes the coordinate system to be used. The appropriate heat conduction equation can readily be obtained from the equations developed previously. One-dimensional problems require only two boundary conditions. The physical situation at any one of the surfaces may be a prescribed temperature, a prescribed heat flux, or convection into a ambient at a specified temperature. Such boundary conditions can readily be formulated as discussed previously. In the case of a time-dependent problem, an initial condition is also needed.

In this section we illustrate with examples the mathematical formulation of typical steady-state and transient heat conduction problems, but the solutions are not considered. The development of solutions is the subject of the following chapters.

**EXAMPLE 3-5**   Consider one-dimensional, steady-state heat conduction in a plate with constant thermal conductivity in a region $0 \le x \le L$. Energy is generated in the medium at a rate of $g_0\, e^{-\beta x}\ \mathrm{W/m^3}$, while the boundary surfaces at $x = 0$ are kept insulated and at $x = L$ dissipate heat by convection into a medium at temperature $T_\infty$ with a heat transfer coefficient $h\ \mathrm{W/(m^2 \cdot {}^\circ C)}$. Write the mathematical formulation of this heat conduction problem.

**SOLUTION**   The heat conduction equation is immediately available from Eq. (3-17a) by setting in that equation $g = g_0 e^{-\beta x}$ and considering $k$ constant. The boundary condition at $x = 0$ is obtainable from Eq. (3-26a) by setting $q_0 = 0$ and that at $x = L$ from Eq. (3-28b). Then the mathematical formulation is given by

$$\frac{d^2 T(x)}{dx^2} + \frac{1}{k}\, g_0\, e^{-\beta x} = 0 \quad \text{in } 0 < x < L$$

$$\frac{dT(x)}{dx} = 0 \quad \text{at } x = 0$$

$$k\frac{dT(x)}{dx} + hT(x) = hT_\infty \quad \text{at } x = L$$

**EXAMPLE 3-6**   Energy is generated at a constant rate of $g_0$ W/m$^3$ in a copper hollow cylinder with constant thermal conductivity in the region $a \leq r \leq b$ by the passage of an electric current. The Heat is dissipated by convection into fluids flowing inside and outside the cylindrical tube. Heat transfer coefficients for the inside and outside fluids are $h_a$ and $h_b$, respectively, and temperatures of the inside and outside fluids are $T_a$ and $T_b$, respectively. Write the mathematical formulation of this heat conduction problem.

**SOLUTION**   The heat conduction equation is obtainable from Eq. (3-17b) by setting $n = 1$ and $g = g_0$. The boundary conditions at $r = a$ and $r = b$ are convective boundary conditions and can be written according to Eqs. (3-29). Then the formulation of the problem becomes

$$\frac{1}{r}\frac{d}{dr}\left(r\frac{dT}{dr}\right) + \frac{g_0}{k} = 0 \quad \text{in } a < r < b$$

subject to the boundary conditions

$$-k\frac{dT}{dr} + h_a T = h_a T_a \quad \text{at } r = a$$

$$k\frac{dT}{dr} + h_b T = h_b T_b \quad \text{at } r = b$$

where $T \equiv T(r)$.

**EXAMPLE 3-7**   Develop the mathematical formulation of one-dimensional, steady-state heat conduction for a hollow sphere with constant thermal conductivity in the region $a \leq r \leq b$, when heat is supplied to the sphere at a rate of $q_0$ W/m$^2$ from the boundary surface at $r = a$ and dissipated by convection from the boundary surface at $r = b$ into a medium at zero temperature with a heat transfer coefficient $h$.

**SOLUTION**   This is a one-dimensional, steady-state heat conduction problem in the spherical coordinate system with no energy generation in the medium and constant thermophysical properties. The heat conduction equation is obtained from Eq. (3-18c) by setting $n = 2$. Then, the mathematical formulation becomes

$$\frac{d}{dr}\left(r^2\frac{dT}{dr}\right) = 0 \quad \text{in } a < r < b$$

subject to the boundary conditions

$$-k\frac{dT}{dr} = q_0 \quad \text{at } r = a$$

$$k\frac{dT}{dr} + hT = 0 \quad \text{at } r = b$$

where $T \equiv T(r)$.

the basic equations given in this chapter.

## 3.8. ONE-DIMENSIONAL MASS DIFFUSION EQUATION

Mass transfer processes occur in a variety of applications in mechanical, chemical, and aerospace engineering; physics; chemistry; and biology. Typical examples include the transpiration cooling of jet engines and rocket motors, the ablative cooling of space vehicles during reentry into the atmosphere, the mass transfer from laminar and turbulent streams onto the surfaces of a conduit, and evaporation or condensation on the surface of a tube or plate.

Processes such as absorption, desorption, distillation, solvent extraction, drying, humidification, sublimation, and many others involve mass transfer. In absorption, a gas is brought into direct contact with a liquid solvent in order to remove the soluble components of the gas. The reverse process occurs in desorption; that is, the transfer of solute takes place from the liquid to the gas. In solvent extraction, one or more components of a liquid mixture are extracted by solution in a selective solvent. In humidification, water is transferred from the liquid to the air. The biological applications include oxygenation of blood, food and drug assimilation, respiration mechanism, and numerous others.

When mass transfer takes place in a fluid at rest, the mass is transferred by purely molecular diffusion resulting from concentration gradients; the process is analogous to heat diffusion resulting from temperature gradients. When the fluid is in motion, mass transfer takes place by both molecular diffusion and convective motion of the bulk fluid; then a knowledge of the velocity field is needed to solve the mass transfer problem.

For low concentrations of the mass in the fluid and low mass transfer rates, the convective heat and mass transfer processes are analogous, and many of the results derived in connection with convective heat transfer are applicable to convective mass transfer. Therefore, the mass transfer equations and coefficients can be obtained by analogy directly from the corresponding heat transfer equations. However, under high-mass flux conditions and with chemical reactions there are significant differences between heat and mass transfer processes; such situations exceptions.

### 3.8.1 Definitions of Mass Flux

We consider a fluid mixture of two components, say $A$ and $B$, the composition of which is characterized by the *molal concentration* of the components. The molal concentration $c_A$

of component $A$ is defined as the number of molecules of component $A$ per unit volume of the mixture and may be given in the units $lb \cdot mol/ft^3$ or $kg \cdot mol/m^3$. Various other definitions are also in use in the literature for expressing the composition. For example, the *mole traction* $\chi_A$ of component $A$ is defined as $\chi_A = c_A/c$, where $c$ is the total molal concentration of the mixture. The *mass concentration* $\rho_A$ of component $A$ is the mass of component $A$ per unit volume and may be given in the units $lb/ft^3$ or $kg/m^3$. The *mass fraction* $w_A$ of component $A$ is defined as $w_A = \rho_A/\rho$, where $\rho$ is the total mass density of the mixture.

### 3.8.2 Fick's First Law

In a binary mixture due to the nonuniformity of composition the composition varies in the $x$ direction and molecular diffusion occurs within the fluid. Fick's first law gives the relation between the molal fluxes $J_A$ and $J_B$ in the $x$ direction of species $A$ and $B$ to the concentration gradients by:

$$J_A = -D^*{}_{AB} \frac{dc_A}{dx} \tag{3-36a}$$

$$J_B = -D^*{}_{BA} \frac{dc_B}{dx} \tag{3-36b}$$

where $D^*{}_{AB}$ is the *mass diffusivity* (or *the diffusion coefficient*) of $A$ in $B$ and $D^*{}_{BA}$ is the *mass diffusivity* of $B$ in $A$; they are equal to each other:

$$D^*{}_{AB} = D^*{}_{BA} \equiv D^* \tag{3-37}$$

Because mass diffusion takes place in the direction of decreasing concentration, a minus sign is included to make the mass flux in the positive $x$ direction a positive quantity when the concentration decreases in the positive $x$ direction. Therefore, *when $J_A$ as positive, the mass flux of species A is in the positive x direction, and vice versa.*

$c_i$ = concentration of component $i$ in mixture, $i = A$ or $B$, $kg \cdot mol/m^3$ or $(lb \cdot mol/ft^3)$

$D^*$ = mass diffusivity, or diffusion coefficient, $m^2/s$ or $(ft^2/h)$

$J_i$ = molal flux of component $i$ in $x$ direction, $i = A$ or $B$, $kg \cdot mol/(m^2 \cdot s)$ or $lb \cdot mol/(ft^2 \cdot h)$

$x$ = distance in $x$ direction, m or ft

The mass flux relation given above by Fick's first law is similar to the heat flux expression given by the Fourier law as

$$q = -k\frac{dT}{dx} = -\alpha \frac{d}{dx}(\rho c_p T) \tag{3-38}$$

Clearly, the mass diffusivity $D^*$ listed in Table 3.3 and the heat diffusivity $\alpha$ listed in Table 3.1 have the same units, $ft^2/h$ or $m^2/s$.

**TABLE 3.3  Mass diffusivities of binary gas systems at atmospheric pressure.**

| System | $T$, K | Mass diffusivity $D^*$ | |
|---|---|---|---|
| | | cm$^2$/s | ft$^2$/h |
| Air-ammonia | 273 | 0.198 | 0.769 |
| Air-aniline | 298 | 0.0726 | 0.282 |
| Air-benzene | 298 | 0.0962 | 0.374 |
| Air carbon dioxide | 273 | 0.136 | 0.528 |
| Air-carbon disulfide | 273 | 0.0883 | 0,343 |
| Air-chlorine | 273 | 0.124 | 0.482 |
| Air ethylalcohol | 298 | 0.132 | 0.513 |
| Air-iodine | 298 | 0.0834 | 0.524 |
| Air–mercury | 614 | 0.473 | 1.837 |
| Air-naphthalene | 298 | 0.0611 | 0.237 |
| Air oxygen | 273 | 0.175 | 0.680 |
| Air–sulfur dioxide | 273 | 0.122 | 0.474 |
| Air-toluene | 298 | 0.0844 | 0.328 |
| Air-water | 298 | 0.260 | 1.010 |
| $CO_2$-benzene | 318 | 0.0715 | 0.278 |
| $CO_2$-carbon disulfide | 318 | 0.0715 | 0.278 |
| $CO_2$-ethyl alcohol | 273 | 0.0693 | 0.269 |
| $CO_2$-hydrogen | 273 | 0.550 | 2.136 |
| $CO_2$-nitrogen | 298 | 0.158 | 0.614 |
| $CO_2$-water | 298 | 0.164 | 0.637 |
| Oxygen-ammonia | 293 | 0.253 | 0.983 |
| Oxygen-benzene | 296 | 0.039 | 0.365 |

Compiled from Reid and Sherwood, (1966).

If the mixture is considered to be a perfect gas, the molal concentrations $c_A$ and $c_B$ are related to the partial pressures $\rho_A$ and $\rho_B$ of the species $A$ and $B$ in the mixture by

$$p_i = c_i \mathcal{R} T \quad i = A \ \text{or} \ B \qquad (3\text{-}39)$$

Therefore

$$J_i = \frac{D^*}{\mathcal{R} T} \frac{dp_i}{dx} \quad i = A \ \text{or} \ B \quad \text{kg} \cdot \text{mol}/(\text{m}^2 \cdot \text{s})[\text{lb} \cdot \text{mol}/(\text{ft}^2 \cdot \text{h})] \qquad (3\text{-}40)$$

where
$c_i$ = molal concentration of component $i$ in mixture, kg $\cdot$ mol/m$^3$ or (lb $\cdot$ mol/ft$^3$)

$p_i$ = partial pressure of component $i$ in mixture, atm

$\mathcal{R}$ = gas constant

= 0.730 ft$^3$ $\cdot$ atm/(lb $\cdot$ mol $\cdot$ °R) = 0.08205 m$^3$ $\cdot$ atm/(kg $\cdot$ mol $\cdot$ K)

Consideration is now given to the application of the previous relations for flux in the prediction of concentration distribution for the *steady-state equimolal counter diffusion* in a binary gas mixture composed of components $A$ and $B$. In this mass transfer process, gases $A$ and $B$ diffuse simultaneously in opposite directions through each other. That is, component $A$ diffuses through component $B$, and vice versa, and they diffuse at the same molal rate but in opposite directions. This process is approximated in the distillation of a binary system.

Consider that two large vessels containing uniform mixtures of $A$ and $B$ at different concentrations are suddenly connected by a small pipe. It is assumed that both vessels are at the same total pressure $p$ and uniform temperature $T$. Component $A$ will diffuse from the higher concentration to the lower concentration, and component $B$ will diffuse at the same rate but in the opposite direction through the connecting pipe. Since the vessels are sufficiently large, steady-state equimolal counterdiffusion takes place in the connecting pipe; that is, *the total molal flux with respect to stationary coordinates is zero*, and we have

$$N_A + N_B = 0 \quad \text{or} \quad N_A = -N_B \tag{3-41}$$

For this type of mass diffusion process, the molal fluxes of species $A$ and $B$ relative to stationary coordinates are equal and in the opposite directions resulting

$$J_A = N_A = -N_B = -J_B \tag{3-42}$$

Substitution of this result into Fick's law for $i = A$ gives

$$N_A = -\frac{D^*}{\mathcal{R}T}\frac{dp_A}{dx} \tag{3-43}$$

At steady state $N_A$ and $N_B$ are constant. Then constant $D^*$ implies that the distribution of the partial pressure $p_A$ of component $A$ along the connecting pipe is linear with the distance. The sum of the partial pressures $p_A$ and $p_B$ is equal to the total pressure $p$, which remains constant, i.e.,

$$p_A + p_B = p = \text{const} \tag{3-44}$$

Let $p_{A_1}$ and $p_{A_2}$ be the partial pressures of component $A$ at the two ends of the connecting pipe $x = x_1$ and $x = x_2$, respectively. The integration from $x = x_1$ to $x = x_2$ gives

$$N_A = -\frac{D^*}{\mathcal{R}T}\frac{p_{A_2} - p_{A_1}}{x_2 - x_1} \quad \text{kg} \cdot \text{mol}/(\text{m}^2 \cdot \text{s}) \tag{3-45}$$

A similar relation can be written for $N_B$. If it is assumed that $p_{A_1} > p_{A_2}$, then for component $B$ we must have $p_{B_2} > p_{B_1}$, where $p_{B_1}$ and $p_{B_2}$ are the partial pressures of component $B$ at $x = x_1$ and $x = x_2$, respectively. Figure 3.7 shows schematically the distribution of partial pressures of the two components as a function of distance for $p_{A_1} > p_{A_2}$. Clearly, component $A$ diffuses in the direction from $x_1$ to $x_2$, and component $B$ in the opposite direction.

**EXAMPLE 3-8** Consider two large vessels, each containing uniform mixtures of nitrogen

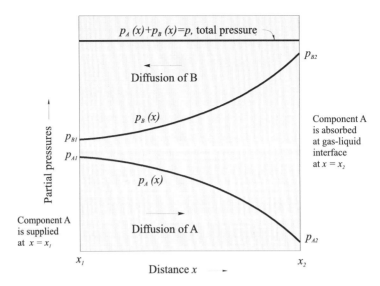

**FIG. 3.7.** Distribution of partial pressures $p_A$ and $p_B$ in equimolal counterdiffusion of a binary gas mixture.

($A$) and carbon dioxide ($B$) at 1 atm, $T = 288.9$ K, but at different concentrations. Vessel 1 contains 80 mole percent $N_2$ and 20 mole percent $CO_2$. Vessel 2 contains 10 mole percent $N_2$ and 90 mole percent $CO_2$. The two vessels are connected with a pipe of $d = 0.1524$ m inside diameter and $L = 1.5$ m long. Assume a steady-state mass transfer. Determine the rate of mass transfer of air between these two vessels. (The mass diffusivity for the $N_2$–$CO_2$ mixture at 1 atm and 288.9 K can be taken as $D^* = 0.16 \times 10^{-4}$ m²/s.)

**SOLUTION** In this mass transfer process, nitrogen, the component $A$ is transferred from vessel 1 containing a higher concentration of nitrogen to vessel 2 containing a lower concentration of nitrogen. In the early stages of the mass transfer, the partial pressure of nitrogen in both vessels is considered to remain constant, hence a steady-state transfer can be assumed. Then the mass transfer process can be characterized as an *equimolal counterdiffusion* as described above, and the mass flux of nitrogen through the connecting duct can be determined by:

$$N_A = \frac{D^*}{RT} \frac{p_{A_1} - p_{A_2}}{x_2 - x_1} \quad \text{kg} \cdot \text{mol}/(\text{m}^2 \cdot \text{s})$$

The total mass transfer rate $Q_A$ of nitrogen is given by

$$Q_A = \text{area} \times N_A = \left(\frac{\pi}{4}d^2\right) \frac{D^*}{RT} \frac{p_{A_2} - p_{A_1}}{x_2 - x_1} \quad \text{kg} \cdot \text{mol/s}$$

and where $x_2 - x_1 = L = 1.5$ m, $\mathcal{R} = 0.08205$ m³ atm/(kg $\cdot$ mol $\cdot$ K),

$p_{A_1} = 0.9 \times 1$ atm $= 0.9$ atm and $p_{A_2} = 0.2 \times 1$ atm $= 0.2$ atm.

The mass transfer rate $Q_A$ is determined by

$$Q_A = \frac{\pi}{4} \times 0.1524^2 \frac{0.16 \times 10^{-4}}{0.08205 \times 288.9} \frac{0.8 - 0.1}{1.5} = 0.5775 \times 10^{-8} \text{ kg} \cdot \text{mol/s}$$

where $d = 0.1524$ m, $D^* = 0.16 \times 10^{-4}$ m$^2$/s and $T = 288.9$ K.

### 3.8.3 Mass Diffusivity

The prediction of mass diffusivity $D^*$ has been the subject of extensive investigations, and the mass diffusivity for gases, liquids, and solids requires different considerations. Various models have also been proposed for the determination of mass diffusivity $D^*_{AB} = D^*_{BA}$ for a binary mixture of gases $A$ and $B$. Here we only present in Table 3.3 measured values of mass diffusivities for typical binary gas systems at 1 atm.

A number of semi empirical relations have been proposed for the determination of mass diffusivity in liquids. The theoretical prediction of mass diffusivity in solids containing pores and capillaries is an extremely complicated matter. When a solid contains capillaries and pores, in some situations the capillary forces are opposed to the concentration gradient; as a result, the mass flux may not even be proportional to the concentration gradient. Describing diffusion inside the tortuous void passages in such a medium by taking into consideration the interaction between different mechanisms of transport appears not to be possible analytically. Therefore, an experimental approach is the only means to determine an *effective mass diffusivity* for a given solid structure and fluid combination.

### PROBLEMS

*One Dimensional Steady-State Heat Conduction Equation*

**3-1.** Consider a plate fuel element of thickness $2L$ for a gas-cooled nuclear reactor. The energy generation in the fuel element can be approximated by a cosine distribution $g = g_0 \cos x/L$, where $x$ is the coordinate measured from the plate center. Thermal conductivity of the plate material is assumed constant. Write the steady-state heat conduction equation governing the temperature distribution in the fuel element.

**3-2.** A plate fuel element of thickness $2L$ has thermal conductivity that varies with temperature, $k(T)$. The following two different types of energy generation are considered: (a) $g = g_0$; (b) $g = g_0 \cos x/L$, where $x$ is the coordinate measured from the plate center. Write the steady-state heat conduction governing the temperature distribution in the fuel element for each of these types of energy generation.

*One Dimensional Time-dependent Heat Conduction Equation*

**3-3.** Consider a plate fuel element of thickness $2L$, initially at a uniform temperature $T_\infty$, in which one of the following three different types of energy generation in the element is suddenly possible: (a) uniform, $g = g_0$; (b) increasing exponentially,

$g = g_0(1 - e^{-bt})$; (c) oscillating as $g = g_0(1 + \alpha \sin \cot)$. Write the unsteady heat conduction equation for the temperature distribution for each of these three cases.

**3-4.** Consider a long tube of inside radius $\alpha$ and outside radius $b$. Suddenly, energy is generated in the tube at a constant rate $g_0$ W/m$^3$ by the passage of electric current. Write the heat conduction equation for the determination of the unsteady temperature distribution in the tube.

**3-5.** Consider a hollow sphere of inside radius $\alpha$ and outside radius $b$. Suddenly, energy is generated in the sphere at a constant rate $g_0$ W/m$^3$. Write the heat conduction equation for the determination of the unsteady temperature distribution in the sphere.

**3-6.** A copper bar of radius $b$ is suddenly heated by the passage of electric current, which generates heat in the rod at a rate $g_0 e^{-\gamma t}$. The thermal conductivity of the rod varies with the radius, $k = k(r)$. Write the unsteady heat conduction equation governing the temperature distribution in the rod.

*Physical Significance of Thermal Diffusivity*

**3-7.** Consider two very thick solids, which can be regarded as semi-infinite mediums extending from $x = 0$ to $x \to \infty$. Initially they are at a uniform temperature $100°C$. Suddenly the temperature of the surfaces at $x = 0$ is lowered to $0°C$ and maintained at that temperature while the temperatures at locations 30 cm from the boundary surfaces are monitored. It takes 10 min. for one of the solids and 120 min. for the other to reach a temperature of $50°C$ at this location. Which solid has larger thermal diffusivity?

**3-8.** The thermal conductivity $k$, the density $\rho$, and the specific heat $c$ of steel are $61$ W/(m · °C), 7865 kg/m$^3$, and 0.46 kJ(kg · °C), respectively. Calculate the thermal diffusivity $\alpha$ m$^2$/s. Compare the calculated value with the thermal diffusivity value given in Table 3.1 for mild steel at $0°C$.

**3-9.** The thermal conductivity $k$, the density $\rho$, and the specific heat $c$ of an aluminum plate are $160$ W/(m · °C), 2790 kg/m$^3$, and 0.88 kJ(kg · °C), respectively. Calculate the thermal diffusivity $\alpha\, m^2$/s. Compare the calculated value with the thermal diffusivity value given in Table 3.1 at $0°C$.

**3-10.** Consider three plates of the same thickness $L$ made of copper, lead, and asbestos. Initially the three plates are at the same uniform temperature $T_0$. Suddenly, each plate is subjected to a uniform heat flux $q_0$ W/m$^2$ at one of its boundary surfaces while the other surface is kept insulated. Which plate will give rise to a faster increase in temperature at the insulated surface? Explain the reason.

*Boundary and Initial Condition Concepts*

**3-11.** Consider a tube of inside radus $r_1$ and outside radius $r_2$. Boiling water at a saturation temperature of $100°C$ flows inside the tube while heat is dissipated from the outside surface by convection with a heat transfer coefficient of $15\,\mathrm{W/(m^2 \cdot °C)}$ into ambient air at a temperature of $20°C$. Write the boundary conditions for the boundary surfaces at $r_1$ and $r_2$.

**3-12.** A spherical shell has an inside radius $r_1$ and an outside radius $r_2$. The inside surface is electrically heated at a rate of $q_1\,\mathrm{W/m^2}$, while the outside surface dissipates heat by convection with a heat transfer coefficient $h_2$ into ambient air at a temperature $T_{\infty 2}$. Write the boundary conditions for the inner and outer surfaces.

**3-13.** Consider a slab of thickness $L$. The boundary at $x = 0$ is subjected to forced convection with a heat transfer coefficient $h$ into an ambient at temperature $T_\infty$. The boundary at $x = L$ is absorbing solar radiation at a rate of $q_0\,\mathrm{W/m^2}$. Write the boundary conditions for both surfaces.

**3-14.** One of the surfaces of a marble slab [with $k = 2\,\mathrm{W/(m \cdot °C)}$] is maintained at $200°C$, while the other boundary is subjected to a constant heat flux of $5000\,\mathrm{W/m^2}$. Write the boundary conditions.

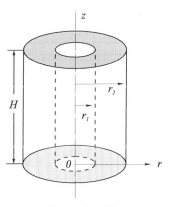

Figure P3-15

**3-15.** Consider a hollow cylinder with inside radius $r_1$, outside radius $r_2$, and height $H$, as illustrated in the accompanying figure, Figure P3-14. The boundary conditions for each of the boundary surfaces are as stated below,
    *(i)* The lower surface at $z = 0$ is kept insulated.
    *(ii)* The upper boundary surface at $z = H$ dissipates heat by convection with a heat transfer coefficient $h_3$ into an ambient at temperature $T_\infty$.
    *(iii)* The inner boundary surface at $r = r_1$ is heated uniformly with an electric heater at a constant rate of $q_0\,\mathrm{W/m^2}$.
    *(iv)* The outer boundary surface at $r = r_2$ dissipates heat by convection, with

a heat transfer coefficient $h_2$, into an ambient at constant temperature $T_\infty$.
Write the mathematical formulation of each boundary condition.

*Governing Equations of Heat Conduction Problems*

**3-16.** Consider a slab of thickness $L$ in which energy is generated at a constant rate of $g_0\,\mathrm{W/m^3}$. The surfaces of the slab are kept at a fixed temperature $T_\infty$. Does the problem have both geometric and thermal symmetry?

Develop the mathematical formulation of this heat conduction problem by taking into account the symmetry condition at the center.

**3-17.** A wood board of thickness 1 cm, initially at a uniform temperature of $20°C$, is suddenly dropped into boiling water. Develop the mathematical formulation of the problem of determining the temperature distribution within the plate for times $t > 0$.

**3-18.** A long cylindrical iron bar of diameter 30 cm, initially at a temperature of $20°C$, is exposed to a hot fluid at $90°C$. The heat transfer coefficient between the hot fluid and surface of the iron bar is $200\,\mathrm{W/(m^2 \cdot °C)}$. (a) Check whether lumped system analysis is suitable. (b) If it is not, develop the mathematical formulation of the problem of determining the temperature distribution within the bar for times $t > 0$. [For iron, $k = 60\,\mathrm{W/(m \cdot °C)}$, $\rho = 7800\,\mathrm{kg/m^3}$, and $c = 460\,\mathrm{J/°C}$.]

**3-19.** One surface of a plate of thickness $L$ is suddenly subjected to radiant heat flux $q_0$, as illustrated in the accompanying figure. The initial temperature of the plate is equal to the ambient temperature $T_\infty$. The heat transfer coefficient $h$ is the same for both surfaces. Develop the mathematical formulation of the problem of determining the unsteady temperature distribution in the plate.

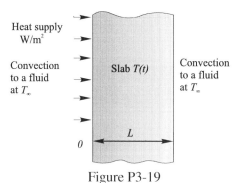

Figure P3-19

**3-20.** An orange of diameter $D$ and thermal conductivity $k$ is initially at a uniform temperature $T_i$. It is placed in a refrigerator in which the air temperature is $T_\infty$. The heat transfer coefficient between the air and the surface of the orange is $h_\infty$. Develop the mathematical formulation of the problem of determining the temperature distribution within the orange for times $t > 0$.

**3-21.** A potato with diameter $D$ and thermal conductivity $k$, initially at a uniform temperature $T_i$, is suddenly dropped into boiling water at $T_0$. The heat transfer coefficient between the water and the surface of the potato is very large. Develop the mathematical formulation of the problem of determining the temperature distribution within the potato for times $t > 0$.

**3-22.** Consider a slab of thickness $L$ and thermal conductivity $k$ that is initially at a uniform temperature $T_i$. Suddenly, the boundary at $x = 0$ is subjected to forced convection with a heat transfer coefficient $h$ into an ambient at temperature $T_\infty$, and the boundary at $x = L$ is absorbing solar radiation at a rate of $q_0 \, \mathrm{W/m^2}$. Develop the mathematical formulation of the problem of determining the temperature distribution within the slab for times $t > 0$.

**3-23.** Consider a tube of inside radius $r_1$, outside radius $r_2$, and thermal conductivity $k$. The inside surface is kept at a temperature of $100°\mathrm{C}$ by boiling water, while the outside surface dissipates heat by convection with a heat transfer coefficient of $15 \, \mathrm{W/(m^2 \cdot °C)}$ into ambient air at a temperature of $20°\mathrm{C}$. Develop the mathematical formulation of the problem of determining the steady-state distribution within the tube.

**3-24.** A spherical shell has an inside radius $r_1$, an outside radius $r_2$, and thermal conductivity $k$. The inside surface is electrically heated at a rate $q_1 \, \mathrm{W/m^2}$, while the outside surface dissipates heat by convection with a heat transfer coefficient $h_2$ into the ambient air at temperature $T_{\infty 2}$. Develop the mathematical formulation of the problem of determining the steady-state temperature distribution within the shell.

**3-25.** Consider a plate fuel element of thickness $2L$ and thermal conductivity $k$. The energy generation in the fuel element can be approximated by a cosine distribution $g = g_0 \cos x/L$, with the coordinate x measured from the plate center. The boundaries at $x = \pm L$ are subjected to cooling by forced convection with a heat transfer coefficient $h$ into the cooling liquid at $T_\infty$. Develop the mathematical formulation of the problem of determining the steady-state temperature distribution within the fuel element.

**3-26.** Consider a long cylindrical fuel element of diameter $D$ and thermal conductivity $k$ in which energy is generated at a constant rate $g_0$. The boundary surface is assumed to be maintained at a constant temperature $T_w$. Develop the mathematical formulation of the problem of determining the steady-state temperature distribution within the fuel element.

**3-27.** Consider the steady-state heat conduction in a plate of thickness $L$ in which energy is generated at a constant rate $g_0$. The boundary surface at $x = 0$ is maintained at a constant temperature $T_0$, while the boundary surface at $x = L$ dissipates heat by convection with a heat transfer coefficient $h$ into an ambient at temperature $T_\infty$. Develop the mathematical formulation of the problem.

**3-28.** Consider the steady-state heat conduction in a slab of thickness $L$ in which energy is generated at a constant rate $g_0$ and the thermal conductivity varies with temperature, $k(T)$. The boundary surface at $x = 0$ is insulated, while the boundary surface at $x = L$ is maintained at $T_0$. Develop the mathematical formulation of the problem.

**3-29.** Consider a slab of thickness $L$, initially with a temperature distribution $F(x)$. For $t > 0$ the boundary surfaces at $x = 0$ and $x = L$ dissipate heat by convection with a heat transfer coefficient $h$ into an ambient at temperature $T_\infty$. Develop the mathematical formulation of the problem of determining the steady-state temperature distribution within the plate for times $t > 0$.

*One Dimensional Mass Diffusion Equation*

**3-30.** Two large vessels contain uniform mixtures of air $(A)$ and sulfur dioxide $(B)$ at 1 atm and 273 K but at different concentrations. Vessel 1 contains 85 mole percent air and 15 mole percent sulfur dioxide. Vessel 2 contains 20 mole percent air and 80 mole percent sulfur dioxide. The vessels are connected with a 10-cm-ID, 2.0-m-long pipe. Assume a steady-state mass transfer. Determine the rate of mass transfer of air between these two vessels with a given mass diffusivity in Table 3.3.

**CHAPTER 4**

# Steady Conduction Without Energy Generation: Thermal Resistance Concept

This chapter is devoted to the determination of steady-state temperature distribution and heat flow in solids with such shapes as a plane wall (i.e., a slab), a long hollow cylinder, and a hollow sphere that have constant thermal conductivity and *no energy generation* within the medium. In engineering applications, the *thermal resistance* concept is frequently used for calculating heat transfer through solids under such conditions. Therefore, the physical significance of this concept and its application in the analysis of heat flow through composite parallel layers are discussed. The use of conduction shape factors in the determination of heat flow through bodies having more complicated shapes is presented.

## 4.1. SINGLE LAYER

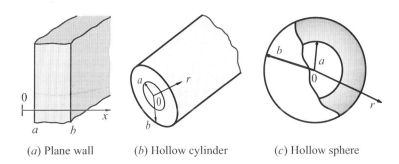

(*a*) Plane wall      (*b*) Hollow cylinder      (*c*) Hollow sphere

**FIG. 4.1.** Coordinates for one dimensional steady heat conduction problems.

The determination of steady-state temperature and heat flow rate through bodies with such shapes as a plane wall, a long hollow cylinder, and a hollow sphere is of interest in numerous engineering applications. Typical examples include heat flow through a window glass, the walls of a building, the wall of a tube, and many others. In such applications there is no energy generation within the solid. Furthermore, the thermal properties of the solid can be regarded as constant, since the temperature variation across the solid is not large. In such situations the temperature distribution within the solid is governed by the heat conduction equations, Eqs. (3-18), which can be written more compactly in the form

$$\frac{d}{dX}\left[X^n \frac{dT(X)}{dX}\right] = 0 \tag{4-1}$$

where

$X \equiv x$ and $n = 0$ for rectangular coordinates

$X \equiv r$ and $n = 1$ for cylindrical coordinates

$X \equiv r$ and $n = 2$ for spherical coordinates.

Figure 4.1 shows the geometry and the coordinates for a plane wall, a hollow cylinder, and a hollow sphere. The solution of Eq. (4-1) over the thickness of the solid subject to appropriate boundary conditions at both surfaces gives the distribution of temperature in the body.

Once the temperature distribution $T(X)$ in the solid has been established, the heat flux $q(X)$ anywhere in the solid can be determined from Fourier's law

$$q(X) = -k \frac{dT(X)}{dX} \quad \text{W/m}^2 \; .$$

(4-2)

When we know the heat flux, the total heat flow rate $Q$ through a surface area $A$ can be readily determined.

In engineering applications the concept of *thermal resistance* is generally used to determine one-dimensional heat flow through solids having such shapes as a plane wall, a long hollow cylinder, or a hollow sphere. In this section we first develop the thermal resistances associated with heat flow through a plane wall and cylindrical and spherical walls, then illustrate the use of this concept in determining the heat flow through a solid.

### 4.1.1 Plane Wall

Consider a slab of thickness $L$, as illustrated in Fig. 4.2. The boundary surfaces at $x = 0$ and $x = L$ are maintained at constant but different temperatures $T_1$ and $T_2$, respectively. There is no energy generation in the solid, and the thermal conductivity is assumed to be constant. To develop the thermal resistance concept for this problem, we first solve the heat conduction problem and determine the expression for the heat flow, then recast this result in a form analogous to *Ohm's law* in electricity in order to establish the equivalent thermal resistance. The procedure is as follows. The mathematical formulation of this heat conduction problem is given by

$$\frac{d^2T(x)}{dx^2} = 0 \quad \text{in } 0 < x < L$$

(4-3a)

$$T(x) = T_1 \quad \text{at } x = 0$$

(4-3b)

$$T(x) = T_2 \quad \text{at } x = L \; .$$

(4-3c)

The integration of Eq. (4-3a) twice yields

$$T(x) = C_1 x + C_2 \; .$$

(4-4)

We have two unknown integration constants $C_1$ and $C_2$ and two boundary conditions, Eqs. (4-3b) and (4-3c), for their determination.

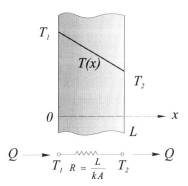

**FIG. 4.2.** One-dimensional steady-state heat flow through a slab and the equivalent thermal resistance concept.

The application of the first boundary condition, Eq. (4-3b), gives

$$C_2 = T_1 \tag{4-5a}$$

and the application of the second boundary condition results in

$$C_1 = \frac{T_2 - C_2}{L} = \frac{T_2 - T_1}{L} . \tag{4-5b}$$

Then the solution becomes

$$T(x) = (T_2 - T_1)\frac{x}{L} + T_1 . \tag{4-6}$$

Equation (4-6) demonstrates that for one-dimensional steady heat conduction through a slab having a constant thermal conductivity and no energy generation, the temperature distribution $T(x)$ is a linear function of $x$.

Knowing the temperature $T(x)$, the heat flux through the slab is determined from the Fourier law. The differentiation of Eq. (4-6) with respect to $x$ gives

$$\frac{dT(x)}{dx} = \frac{T_2 - T_1}{L}$$

and from the Fourier law we have

$$q = -k\frac{dT(x)}{dx} .$$

Then the heat flux becomes

$$q = k\frac{T_1 - T_2}{L} \quad \text{W/m}^2 . \tag{4-7}$$

When $T_1 > T_2$, the right-hand side is positive, and hence the heat flow is in the positive

$x$ direction.

The total heat flow rate $Q$ through an area $A$ of the slab normal to the direction of the heat flow becomes

$$Q = Aq = \frac{T_1 - T_2}{L/Ak} \equiv \frac{\Delta T}{R_{\text{slab}}} \tag{4-8a}$$

where

$$\boxed{R_{\text{slab}} = \frac{L}{Ak}} \tag{4-8b}$$

and

$$\Delta T = T_1 - T_2 \ .$$

The quantity $R_{\text{slab}}$ is called the *thermal resistance* for heat flow through the slab of thickness $L$, area $A$, thermal conductivity $k$ and subjected to prescribed temperature boundary conditions at both surfaces.

The thermal resistance concept developed above can be generalized to include situations involving convection boundary conditions as illustrated below.

## 4.1.2 Plane Wall, Prescribed Temperature at $x = 0$, Convection at $x = L$

We consider a plane wall of thickness $L$, with the boundary surface at $x = 0$ kept at constant temperature $T_1$ and that at $x = L$ subjected to convection with a heat transfer coefficient $h_{\infty 2}$ into an ambient at temperature $T_{\infty 2}$, as illustrated in Fig. 4.3.

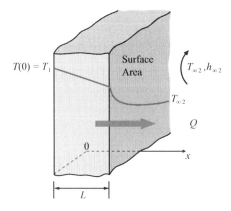

**FIG. 4.3.** Temperature distribution and heat flow for slab with a prescribed temperature at one surface and convection at the other.

An examination of the heat flow path shown in this figure reveals that the heat conducted through the slab $Q$ must be equal to the heat convected from the surface at $x = L$ into the ambient at temperature $T_{\infty 2}$. Therefore, an energy balance equation can be stated as

$$Q = \begin{pmatrix} \text{Conduction through} \\ \text{the solid from the} \\ \text{surface at } x = 0 \\ \text{to } x = L \end{pmatrix} = \begin{pmatrix} \text{Convection from the} \\ \text{surface at } x = L \text{ into} \\ \text{the fluid at } T_{\infty 2} \end{pmatrix} . \qquad (4\text{-}9)$$

We utilize the results given by Eqs. (4-8) and (1-5), respectively, to determine the heat flows by conduction and convection. Then Eq. (4-9) becomes

$$Q = Ak\,\frac{T_1 - T(L)}{L} = Ah_{\infty 2}\left[T(L) - T_{\infty 2}\right] \qquad (4\text{-}10)$$

where $T(L)$ represents the temperature at the boundary surface $x = L$ of the slab. This expression can be rearranged in the form of thermal resistances as

$$Q = \frac{T_1 - T(L)}{L/Ak} = \frac{T(L) - T_{\infty 2}}{1/Ah_{\infty 2}} . \qquad (4\text{-}11)$$

By adding the numerators and denominators, this result can be rewritten as

$$Q = \frac{T_1 - T_{\infty 2}}{L/Ak + 1/Ah_{\infty 2}} \qquad (4\text{-}12)$$

or

$$\boxed{Q = \frac{T_1 - T_{\infty 2}}{R_{\text{slab}} + R_{\infty 2}}} \qquad (4\text{-}13)$$

where we defined

$$\boxed{R_{\text{slab}} = \frac{L}{Ak} \qquad R_{\infty 2} = \frac{1}{Ah_{\infty 2}}} . \qquad (4\text{-}14)$$

The quantity $R_{\text{slab}}$, as discussed previously, is the thermal resistance for the slab itself, and $R_{\infty 2}$ is the *thermal resistance for convective heat flow* from the boundary surface at $x = L$ to the ambient at $T_{\infty 2}$.

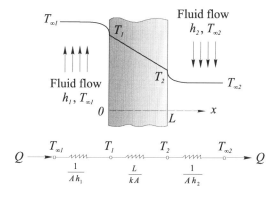

**FIG. 4.4.** Thermal resistance concept for heat flow through a slab with convection at both surfaces.

## 4.1.3 Plane Wall, Convection at Both Boundaries

We consider a slab of thickness $L$ subjected to convection at both boundaries, as illustrated in Fig. 4.4. That is, the boundary surfaces at $x = 0$ and $x = L$ exchange heat by convection with heat transfer coefficients $h_{\infty 1}$ and $h_{\infty 2}$ with fluids at temperatures $T_{\infty 1}$ and $T_{\infty 2}$, respectively. Since there are no energy sources or sinks anywhere in the medium, the heat flow rate $Q$ remains constant throughout the path of heat flow; hence, we write

$$
Q = \begin{pmatrix} \text{Convection} \\ \text{from the fluid} \\ \text{at } T_{\infty 1} \text{ to the} \\ x = 0 \end{pmatrix} = \begin{pmatrix} \text{Conduction} \\ \text{through the} \\ \text{solid from} \\ x = 0 \text{ to } x = L \end{pmatrix} = \begin{pmatrix} \text{Convection from} \\ \text{the surface at} \\ x = L \text{ into the} \\ \text{fluid at } T_{\infty 2} \end{pmatrix}.
$$

$$(4\text{-}15)$$

Equivalent mathematical expressions are written for each term:

$$
Q = A h_{\infty 1}(T_{\infty 1} - T_1) = Ak \frac{T_1 - T_2}{L} = A h_{\infty 2}(T_2 - T_{\infty 2}).
\qquad (4\text{-}16)
$$

This expression is rearranged as

$$
Q = \frac{T_{\infty 1} - T_1}{1/A h_{\infty 1}} = \frac{T_1 - T_2}{L/Ak} = \frac{T_2 - T_{\infty 2}}{1/A h_{\infty 2}}.
\qquad (4\text{-}17)
$$

By adding the numerators and the denominators, we obtain

$$
Q = \frac{T_{\infty 1} - T_{\infty 2}}{(1/A h_{\infty 1}) + (L/Ak) + (1/A h_{\infty 2})}.
\qquad (4\text{-}18)
$$

These results can be rearranged in the form of thermal resistances as

$$
\boxed{Q = \frac{T_{\infty 1} - T_{\infty 2}}{R_{\infty 1} + R_{\text{slab}} + R_{\infty 2}}}
\qquad (4\text{-}19)
$$

where the various thermal resistances are

$$
\boxed{R_{\infty 1} = \frac{1}{A h_{\infty 1}} \qquad R_{\text{slab}} = \frac{L}{Ak} \qquad R_{\infty 2} = \frac{1}{A h_{\infty 2}}}.
\qquad (4\text{-}20)
$$

Clearly, the quantity $R_{\text{slab}}$ is the thermal resistance for the slab itself, and $R_{\infty 1}$ and $R_{\infty 2}$ are the *thermal resistances for convection* at the boundary surfaces $x = 0$ and $x = L$, respectively.

**EXAMPLE 4-1** Determine the steady heat flux through a 0.2-m-thick brick wall [$k = 0.69\,\text{W}/(\text{m} \cdot {}^{\circ}\text{C})$] with one surface at a temperature of $30^{\circ}\text{C}$ and the other at $-20^{\circ}\text{C}$.

**SOLUTION** Given: $L = 0.2$ m, $T_1 = 30^{\circ}\text{C}$, $T_2 = -20^{\circ}\text{C}$, and $k = 0.69\,\text{W}/(\text{m} \cdot {}^{\circ}\text{C})$.

The heat flux is calculated using Eq. (4-7) as

$$q = k\frac{T_1 - T_2}{L}$$

$$= 0.69\,\mathrm{W/(m\cdot {}^\circ C)}\,\frac{[30 - (-20)]^\circ C}{0.2\,\mathrm{m}}$$

$$= 172.5\,\mathrm{W/m^2}\ .$$

**EXAMPLE 4- 2**  A large window glass 0.5 cm thick $[k = 0.78\mathrm{W/(m\cdot {}^\circ C)}]$ is exposed to warm air at 25°C over its inner surface, and the heat transfer coefficient for the inside air is $15\,\mathrm{W/(m^2\cdot {}^\circ C)}$. The outside air is at $-15°C$, and the heat transfer coefficient associated with the outside surface is $50\,\mathrm{W/(m^2\cdot {}^\circ C)}$. Determine the temperatures of the inner and outer surfaces of the glass.

**SOLUTION**  Given: $L = 0.005\,\mathrm{m}$, $k = 0.78\,\mathrm{W/(m\cdot {}^\circ C)}$, $T_{\infty 1} = 25°C$, $h_{\infty 1} = 15\,\mathrm{W/(m^2\cdot {}^\circ C)}$, $T_{\infty 2} = -15°C$, and $h_{\infty 2} = 50\,\mathrm{W/(m^2\cdot {}^\circ C)}$.

Various thermal resistances are determined for $A = 1\,\mathrm{m^2}$. From Eq. (4-20),

$$R_{\infty 1} = \frac{1}{Ah_{\infty 1}} = \frac{1}{15} = 0.06666 \quad {}^\circ C/W$$

$$R_{\infty 2} = \frac{1}{Ah_{\infty 2}} = \frac{1}{50} = 0.02000 \quad {}^\circ C/W$$

$$R_{\mathrm{slab}} = \frac{L}{Ak} = \frac{0.005}{0.78} = 0.00641 \quad {}^\circ C/W\ .$$

Then from Eq. (4-19) we have

$$Q = \frac{T_{\infty 1} - T_{\infty 2}}{R_{\infty 1} + R_{\mathrm{slab}} + R_{\infty 2}} = \frac{25 + 15}{0.09307} = 429.78\,\mathrm{W}\ .$$

Knowing $Q$, Eq. (4-17) can be used to calculate the surface temperatures $T_1$ and $T_2$.

$$T_1 = T_{\infty 1} - QR_{\infty 1} = 25 - (429.78 \times 0.0666) = -3.65°C$$

$$T_2 = T_1 - QR_{\mathrm{slab}} = -3.65 - (429.78 \times 0.00641) = -6.40°C$$

### 4.1.4 Long Hollow Cylinder

We consider a long hollow cylinder of inner radius $r = a$ and outer radius $r = b$. The inner and outer surfaces are kept at uniform temperatures $T_1$ and $T_2$, respectively, as illustrated in Fig. 4.5. There is no energy generation within the solid, and thermal conductivity $k$ is constant.

To develop an expression for the thermal resistance $R_{\mathrm{cyl}}$ of the cylinder wall to heat flow, we solve the heat transfer problem, determine the heat flow rate $Q$, then recast the

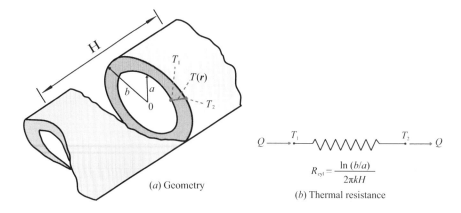

(a) Geometry

$$R_{cyl} \equiv \frac{\ln(b/a)}{2\pi kH}$$

(b) Thermal resistance

**FIG. 4.5.** Thermal resistance concept for heat flow through a hollow cylinder.

result for the heat flow in a form similar to Ohm's law, as described below.

The mathematical formulation of this heat conduction problem is given

$$\frac{d}{dr}\left[r\,\frac{dT(r)}{dr}\right] = 0 \quad \text{in } a < r < b \tag{4-21a}$$

$$T(r) = T_1 \quad \text{at } r = a \tag{4-21b}$$

$$T(r) = T_2 \quad \text{at } r = b. \tag{4-21c}$$

Integration of Eq. (4-21a) twice gives

$$T(r) = C_1 \ln r + C_2 \tag{4-22}$$

and the application of the boundary conditions (4-21b) and (4-21c), respectively, results

$$T_1 = C_1 \ln a + C_2 \tag{4-23a}$$

$$T_2 = C_1 \ln b + C_2. \tag{4-23b}$$

The constants $C_1$ and $C_2$ are obtained from the simultaneous solution of those two equations:

$$C_1 = \frac{T_2 - T_1}{\ln(b/a)} \tag{4-24a}$$

$$C_2 = T_1 - (T_2 - T_1)\,\frac{\ln a}{\ln(b/a)}. \tag{4-24b}$$

Introducing these coefficients into the equation for $T(r)$, the temperature distribution in the wall is expressed as

$$\frac{T(r) - T_1}{T_2 - T_1} = \frac{\ln(r/a)}{\ln(b/a)} \; . \tag{4-25}$$

The heat flux $q(r)$ and the heat flow rate $Q$ over a length $H$ of the cylinder are determined from their definition as

$$q(r) = -k\,\frac{dT(r)}{dr} \tag{4-26}$$

$$= -\frac{k(T_2 - T_1)}{r\ln(b/a)} \quad \text{W/m}^2$$

and

$$Q = A(r)\,q(r) \tag{4-27}$$

$$= (2\pi r H)\left[ -\frac{k(T_2 - T_1)}{r\ln(b/a)} \right]$$

$$= \frac{2\pi k H}{\ln(b/a)}\,(T_1 - T_2) \quad \text{W} \; .$$

This expression for $Q$ is now rearranged in the form

$$\boxed{Q = \frac{T_1 - T_2}{R_{\text{cyl}}}} \tag{4-28}$$

where

$$\boxed{R_{\text{cyl}} = \frac{\ln(b/a)}{2\pi k H}} \; . \tag{4-29}$$

Here $R_{\text{cyl}}$ is called the *thermal resistance to heat fow through the hollow cylinder wall* across a temperature potential $T_1 - T_2$, as illustrated in Fig. 4.5b.

The thermal resistance concept developed above for a hollow cylinder subjected to constant surface temperatures can be generalized to situations involving convection at the boundary surfaces.

*Hollow Cylinder, Convection at Both Boundaries*

We consider a hollow cylinder subjected to convection at both boundary surfaces, as illustrated in Fig. 4.6. That is, a fluid at temperature $T_{\infty 1}$ with a heat transfer coefficient $h_{\infty 1}$ flows over the inner surface at $r = a$, and another fluid at temperature $T_{\infty 2}$ with a heat transfer coefficient $h_{\infty 2}$ flows over the outer surface at $r = b$ of the cylinder. By noting that the total radial heat transfer rate $Q$ through the cylinder wall remains constant, we write the following energy conservation equation:

$$Q = \begin{pmatrix} \text{Convection from} \\ \text{the fluid at } T_{\infty 1} \\ \text{to the inner} \\ \text{surface at } r = a \end{pmatrix} = \begin{pmatrix} \text{Conduction} \\ \text{through the} \\ \text{cylinder wall} \\ \text{from } r = a \\ \text{to } r = b \end{pmatrix} = \begin{pmatrix} \text{Convection from} \\ \text{the outer wall} \\ \text{at } r = b \text{ to the} \\ \text{fluid at } T_{\infty 2} \end{pmatrix} .$$

(4-30a)

We utilize the results given by Eqs. (4-28) and (1-5), respectively, to determine the heat

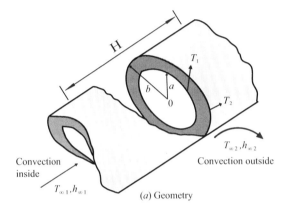

(a) Geometry

**FIG. 4.6.** Thermal resistance concept for radial heat the heat flows by conduction and convection.

flows by conduction and convection. Then Eq. (4-30a) becomes

$$Q = A_a h_{\infty 1} (T_{\infty 1} - T_1) = \frac{2\pi k H}{\ln(b/a)} (T_1 - T_2) = A_b h_{\infty 2} (T_2 - T_{\infty 2}) .$$

(4-30b)

This expression is rearranged as

$$Q = \frac{T_{\infty 1} - T_1}{1/A_a h_{\infty 1}} = \frac{T_1 - T_2}{\ln(b/a)/2\pi k H} = \frac{T_2 - T_{\infty 2}}{1/A_b h_{\infty 2}} .$$

(4-30c)

By adding the numerators and the denominators, we obtain

$$Q = \frac{T_{\infty 1} - T_{\infty 2}}{1/A_a h_{\infty 1} + \ln(b/a)/2\pi k H + 1/A_b h_{\infty 2}} .$$

(4-31)

This result can be rewritten as

$$\boxed{Q = \frac{T_{\infty 1} - T_{\infty 2}}{R_{\infty 1} + R_{\text{cyl}} + R_{\infty 2}}}$$

(4-32)

where various thermal resistances are defined as

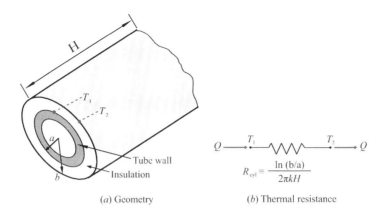

(a) Geometry    (b) Thermal resistance

**FIGURE EXAMPLE 4-3 Thermal insulation for the steam pipe.**

$$R_{\infty 1} = \frac{1}{A_a h_{\infty 1}} = \frac{1}{2\pi a H h_{\infty 1}}$$

$$R_{cyl} = \frac{\ln(b/a)}{2\pi k H}$$  (4-33 a,b,c)

$$R_{\infty 2} = \frac{1}{A_b h_{\infty 2}} = \frac{1}{2\pi b H h_{\infty 2}}$$

**EXAMPLE 4- 3** A cylindrical insulation for a steam pipe has an inside radius of 5 cm, an outside radius of 10 cm, and a thermal conductivity of $0.5 \text{ W}/(\text{m} \cdot \text{°C})$. The inside surface of the insulation is at a temperature of 200°C, and the outside surface is at 20°C. Determine the heat loss per meter length of the insulation.

**SOLUTION** The problem is illustrated in the accompanying figure. Given: $a = 5$ cm, $b = 10$ cm, $k = 0.5 \text{ W}/(\text{m} \cdot \text{°C})$, $T_1 = 200$°C, and $T_2 = 20$°C. The heat loss per meter length, $H = 1$ m, is determined using Eq. (4-29):

$$Q = \frac{T_1 - T_2}{R_{cyl}} = \frac{T_1 - T_2}{\ln(b/a)/2\pi k H}$$

$$= \frac{200 - 20}{\ln(10/5)/(2\pi \times 0.5 \times 1)}$$

$$= 815.8 \text{ W/m length.}$$

**EXAMPLE 4- 4** A long hollow cylinder has an inner radius of 10 cm, an outer radius of 20 cm, and a thermal conductivity $k = 50 \text{ W}/(\text{m} \cdot \text{°C})$. The inner surface is heated uniformly at a constant rate $q_a = 1.16 \times 10^5 \text{ W/m}^2$, and the outer surface is maintained at zero temperature. Calculate the temperature of the inner surface.

**SOLUTION** Given that $q_a = 1.6 \times 10^5 \,\text{W/m}^2$ at the inner surface, the heat flow rate $Q$ over a length $H$ is determined by

$$
\begin{aligned}
Q &= A(r)\, q(r) = A_a q_a \\
&= 2\pi a H q_a
\end{aligned}
$$

and from Eq. (4-27) we have

$$
Q = \frac{2\pi k H}{\ln(b/a)}\,(T_1 - T_2)\,.
$$

By combining these two results, we obtain

$$
2\pi a H q_a = \frac{2\pi k H}{\ln(b/a)}\,(T_1 - T_2)
$$

which is now solved for the inner surface temperature $T_1$ :

$$
\begin{aligned}
T_1 &= \frac{a q_a}{k}\,\ln\left(b/a\right) + T_2 \\
&= \frac{(0.1)(1.16 \times 10^5)}{50}\,\ln\left(\frac{20}{10}\right) + 0 \\
&= 160.8°\text{C}\,.
\end{aligned}
$$

**EXAMPLE 4-5**  A steam pipe of outside diameter 10 cm, maintained at $130°\text{C}$, is covered with a 3-cm-thick asbestos insulation $[k = 0.1 \,\text{W}/(\text{m} \cdot °\text{C})]$. The ambient air temperature is $30°\text{C}$, and the heat transfer coefficient for convection at the outer surface of the asbestos insulation is $25 \,\text{W}/(\text{m}^2 \cdot °\text{C})$. Using the thermal resistance concept, calculate the rate of heat loss from the pipe per meter length of the pipe.

**SOLUTION**  Given: $a = 5$ cm, $b = 8$ cm, $T_1 = 130°\text{C}$, $k = 0.1 \,\text{W}/(\text{m} \cdot °\text{C})$, $T_{\infty 2} = 30°\text{C}$, and $h_{\infty 2} = 25 \,\text{W}/(\text{m}^2 \cdot °\text{C})$. The heat flow rate $Q$ through the pipe is calculated by using Eq. (4-32) and noting that the thermal resistance to heat flow at the inside surface vanishes (i.e., $R_{\infty 1} = 0$). Then

$$
\begin{aligned}
Q &= \frac{T_1 - T_{\infty 2}}{R_{\text{cyl}} + R_{\infty 2}} = \frac{T_1 - T_{\infty 2}}{\ln(b/a)/2\pi k H + 1/2\pi b H h_{\infty 2}} \\
&= \frac{130 - 30}{\ln(8/5)/[(2\pi)(0.1)] + 1/[(2\pi)(0.08)(1)(25)]} \\
&= 120.8 \,\text{W/m length}\,.
\end{aligned}
$$

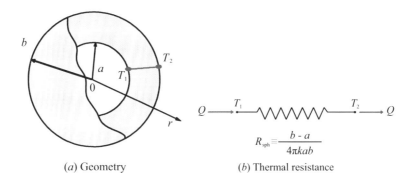

(a) Geometry        (b) Thermal resistance

**FIG. 4.7.** Thermal resistance concept for heat flow through a hollow sphere.

## 4.1.5 Hollow Sphere

We now consider radial heat flow through a hollow sphere of inner radius $r = a$ and outer radius $r = b$, as illustrated in Fig. 4.7. The inner and outer surfaces are maintained at uniform temperatures $T_1$ and $T_2$, respectively. There is no energy generation in the solid, and the thermal conductivity $k$ is constant. To develop the thermal resistance $R_{\text{sph}}$ for the hollow sphere, we first solve this heat conduction problem and determine the expression for radial heat flow rate $Q$ through the hollow sphere. Then this result is recast in a form similar to Ohm's law in order to determine the equivalent thermal resistance for the hollow sphere, as described below.

The mathematical formulation of this heat conduction problem is given by

$$\frac{d}{dr}\left[r^2\,\frac{dT(r)}{dr}\right] = 0 \quad \text{in } a < r < b \tag{4-34a}$$

$$T(r) = T_1 \quad \text{at } r = a \tag{4-34b}$$

$$T(r) = T_2 \quad \text{at } r = b. \tag{4-34c}$$

Equation (4-33a) is integrated twice:

$$T(r) = -\frac{C_1}{r} + C_2 \tag{4-35}$$

and the boundary conditions (4-34b) and (4-34c) are applied:

$$T_1 = -\frac{C_1}{a} + C_2 \tag{4-36a}$$

$$T_2 = \frac{C_1}{b} + C_2. \tag{4-36b}$$

The constants $C_1$ and $C_2$ are determined from the simultaneous solution of these two equations:

$$C_1 = -\frac{ab}{b-a}(T_1 - T_1) \tag{4-37a}$$

$$C_2 = -\frac{bT_1 - aT_1}{b-a}. \tag{4-37b}$$

Then the temperature distribution $T(r)$ becomes

$$T(r) = \frac{a}{r}\left(\frac{b-r}{b-a}\right)T_1 + \frac{b}{r}\left(\frac{r-a}{b-a}\right)T_2. \tag{4-38}$$

The heat flux $q(r)$ is determined from

$$q(r) = -k\frac{dT(r)}{dr} \tag{4-39}$$

$$= \frac{k}{r^2}\frac{ab}{b-a}(T_1 - T_2) \quad \text{W/m}^2$$

and the total heat flow rate $Q$ through the sphere becomes

$$Q = A(r)\,q(r) \tag{4-40}$$

$$= (4\pi r^2)\left[kr^2\frac{ab}{b-a}(T_1 - T_2)\right]$$

$$= 4\pi\frac{k}{b-a}ab(T_1 - T_2) \quad \text{W}.$$

This expression for $Q$ is now rearranged in the form

$$\boxed{Q = \frac{T_1 - T_2}{R_{\text{sph}}}} \tag{4-41}$$

where we defined

$$\boxed{R_{\text{sph}} = \frac{b-a}{4\pi kab}} \tag{4-42}$$

and $R_{\text{sph}}$ is called the *thermal resistance to heat flow for a hollow sphere* across a temperature potential $T_1 - T_2$, as illustrated in Fig. 4.7b.

The thermal resistance concept developed above can be generalized to situations involving convection at the boundary surface.

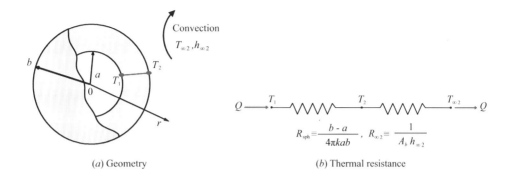

(a) Geometry                    (b) Thermal resistance

**FIG. 4.8.** Thermal resistance concept for a hollow sphere with a prescribed temperature at the inner surface and convection at the outer surface.

## Hollow Sphere, Convection at the Outer Boundary Surface

We consider a hollow sphere maintained at a uniform temperature $T_1$ at the inner surface $r = a$ and subjected to convection with a heat transfer coefficient $h_{\infty2}$ into ambient air of temperature $T_{\infty2}$. The physical situation is illustrated in Fig. 4.8.

Noting that the total radial heat flow rate through the sphere remains constant, we write

$$Q = \begin{pmatrix} \text{Conduction} \\ \text{through the} \\ \text{wall from} \\ r = a \text{ to } r = b \end{pmatrix} = \begin{pmatrix} \text{Convection from} \\ \text{the outer wall at} \\ r = b \text{ to the fluid} \\ \text{at } T_{\infty2} \end{pmatrix} \qquad (4\text{-}43)$$

We utilize the results given by Eqs. (4-40) and (1-5), respectively, to determine the heat flows by conduction and convection. Then Eq. (4-43) becomes

$$Q = r\pi k \, \frac{ab}{b-a} \, (T_1 - T_2) = 4\pi b^2 h_{\infty2} \, (T_2 - T_{\infty2}) \, . \qquad (4\text{-}44)$$

This expression is rearranged as

$$Q = \frac{T_1 - T_2}{(b-a)/4\pi kab} = \frac{T_2 - T_{\infty2}}{1/4\pi b^2 h_{\infty2}} \, . \qquad (4\text{-}45)$$

By adding the numerators and denominators, we obtain

$$Q = \frac{T_1 - T_{\infty2}}{(b-a)/4\pi kab + 1/4\pi b^2 h_{\infty2}} \, . \qquad (4\text{-}46)$$

This result can be rewritten as

$$\boxed{Q = \frac{T_1 - T_{\infty2}}{R_{\text{sph}} + R_{\infty2}}} \qquad (4\text{-}47)$$

where various thermal resistances are defined as

$$R_{\text{sph}} = \frac{b - a}{4\pi kab}, \qquad R_{\infty 2} = \frac{1}{4\pi b^2 h_{\infty 2}}. \qquad (4\text{-}48)$$

**EXAMPLE 4-6** Determine the heat flow rate $Q$ through a copper spherical shell $[k = 386\,\text{W}/(\text{m} \cdot {}^\circ\text{C})]$ of inner radius 2 cm and outer radius 6 cm, if the inner surface is kept at $200^\circ$C and the outer surface at $100^\circ$C.

**SOLUTION** Given: $a = 2$ cm, $b = 6$ cm, $k = 386\,\text{W}/(\text{m} \cdot {}^\circ\text{C})$, $T_1 = 200^\circ$C, and $T_2 = 100^\circ$C. The heat flow rate is calculated by Eq. (4-41):

$$
\begin{aligned}
Q &= \frac{T_1 - T_2}{R_{\text{sph}}} = \frac{T_1 - T_2}{(b - a)/4\pi kab} \\[2mm]
&= \frac{200 - 100}{(0.06 - 0.02)/[(4\pi)(386)(0.06)(0.02)]} \\[2mm]
&= 14.55\,\text{kW}.
\end{aligned}
$$

**EXAMPLE 4-7** Consider an aluminum hollow sphere $[k = 200\,\text{W}/(\text{m} \cdot {}^\circ\text{C})]$ of inside radius 2 cm and outside radius 6 cm. The inside surface is kept at a uniform temperature of $100^\circ$C, and the outside surface dissipates heat by convection with a heat transfer coefficient of $80\,\text{W}/\text{m}^2$ into ambient air at $20^\circ$C. Determine the outside surface temperature of the sphere and the rate of heat flow from the sphere by using thermal resistance concept.

**SOLUTION** Given: $a = 2$ cm, $b = 6$ cm, $k = 200\,\text{W}/(\text{m} \cdot {}^\circ\text{C})$, $T_1 = 100^\circ$C, $T_{\infty 2} = 20^\circ$C, and $h_{\infty 2} = 80\,\text{W}/\text{m}^2$. The heat flow rate $Q$ is calculated using Eq. (4-46):

$$
\begin{aligned}
Q &= \frac{T_1 - T_{\infty 2}}{(b - a)/4\pi kab + 1/4\pi b^2 h_{\infty 2}} \\[2mm]
&= \frac{100 - 20}{(0.06 - 0.02)/[(4\pi)(200)(0.02)(0.06)] + 1/[(4\pi)(0.06)^2(80)]} \\[2mm]
&= 276.3\,\text{W}.
\end{aligned}
$$

Knowing the heat flow rate $Q$, the outside surface temperature $T_2$ is calculated from Eqs. (4-41) and (4-42) as

$$Q = \frac{T_1 - T_2}{R_{\text{sph}}} = \frac{T_1 - T_2}{(b - a)/4\pi kab}$$

$$276.3 = \frac{100 - T_2}{(0.06 - 0.02)/[(4\pi)(200)(0.02)(0.06)]}.$$

Solving for $T_2$ we obtain

$$T_2 = 96.3\,^{\circ}\mathrm{C}\,.$$

## 4.2. MULTILAYERS

In the previous section we considered one-dimensional heat flow through a single layer. However, the problems encountered in most engineering applications involve heat flow through a medium consisting of several parallel layers—for example, the wall of a building consisting of several layers, or a pipe with several layers of insulation. In such problems, we assume no energy generation within the medium and the thermal conductivity of the layers to be constant but different for each layer.

The thermal resistance concept developed in the previous section can readily be applied to determine the heat flow rate through such a multilayer medium. We study this problem for the cases of multilayer plane walls, hollow cylinders, and hollow spheres.

### 4.2.1 Multilayer Plane Wall

Consider a multilayer plane wall consisting of three parallel layers in perfect thermal contact, as illustrated in Fig. 4.9. Let $Q$ be the heat flow rate through a surface area $A$ of this composite medium. Applying the thermal resistance concept to each of the individual layers, including resistance to convection at the outer surfaces, we write

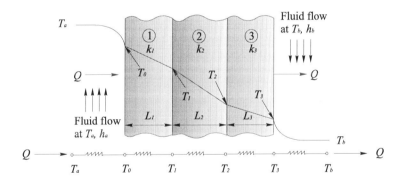

**FIG. 4.9.** A composite of three walls in series paths and the equivalent thermal resistance network.

$$Q = \frac{T_a - T_0}{R_a} = \frac{T_0 - T_1}{R_1} = \frac{T_1 - T_2}{R_2} = \frac{T_2 - T_3}{R_3} = \frac{T_3 - T_b}{R_b} \qquad \text{(4-49a)}$$

where various thermal resistances are defined as

$$R_a = \frac{1}{Ah_a} \quad R_1 = \frac{L_1}{Ak_1} \quad R_2 = \frac{L_2}{Ak_2} \quad R_3 = \frac{L_3}{Ak_3} \quad R_b = \frac{1}{Ah_b}\,. \qquad \text{(4-49b)}$$

Summing the numerators and the denominators of the individual ratios in Eq. (4-49a), the result is written as

$$Q = \frac{T_a - T_b}{R_T} \quad \text{W} \tag{4-50a}$$

where the *total thermal resistance* $R_T$ is defined as

$$R_T = R_a + R_1 + R_2 + R_3 + R_b. \tag{4-50b}$$

This result is analogous to the result for a single-layer slab, except that the quantity $R_T$ represents the sum of all the individual thermal resistances in the path of the heat flow through an area $A$ from the temperature $T_a$ to the temperature $T_b$.

**EXAMPLE 4-8** An industrial furnace is made of fireclay brick of thickness 0.2 m and thermal conductivity $1.0\,\text{W}/(\text{m}\cdot{}^\circ\text{C})$. The outside surface is to be insulated with an insulation material of thermal conductivity $0.05\,\text{W}/(\text{m}\cdot{}^\circ\text{C})$. Determine the thickness of the insulation layer needed to limit the heat loss from the furnace wall to $900\,\text{W}/\text{m}^2$ when the inside surface of the wall is at $930^\circ\text{C}$ and the outside surface is at $30^\circ\text{C}$.

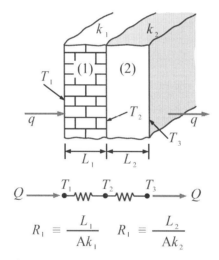

**FIGURE EXAMPLE 4-8 Equivalent thermal resistance network.**

**SOLUTION** The problem is illustrated in the accompanying figure. The equivalent resistance for the two layers is determined from

$$R_T = R_1 + R_2 = \frac{L_1}{Ak_1} + \frac{L_2}{Ak_2}.$$

Then the heat transfer rate $Q$ through an area $A$ is given by

$$Q = \frac{T_1 - T_3}{R_T} = \frac{T_1 - T_3}{L_1/Ak_1 + L_2/Ak_2} = \frac{A(T_1 - T_3)}{L_1/k_1 + L_2/k_2}$$

and the heat flux $q$ becomes

$$q = \frac{Q}{A} = \frac{T_1 - T_3}{L_1/k_1 + L_2/k_2} .$$

Introducing the numerical values, we find

$$900 = \frac{930 - 30}{0.2/1 + L_2/0.05}$$

$$L_2 = 0.04 \text{ m} .$$

**EXAMPLE 4- 9** A thermopane window consists of two 5-mm-thick sheets of glass separated by a stagnant air space of thickness 10 mm. The thermal conductivity of the glass is 0.78 W/(m·°C), and that of air is 0.025 W/(m·°C). The convection heat transfer coefficients for the inside and outside air are 10 W/(m²·°C) and 50 W/(m²·°C), respectively.

(a) Determine the rate of heat loss per square meter of the glass surface for a temperature difference of 60°C between the inside and outside air.

(b) Compare the result with the heat loss if the window had only a single sheet of glass of thickness 5 mm instead of the thermopane.

(c) Compare the result with the heat loss if the window had no stagnant air (i.e., a double sheet of glass of thickness 10 mm).

**SOLUTION** The physical situation is similar to that illustrated in Fig. 4.9. Various quantities are specified as $L_1 = L_3 = 0.005$ m, $L_2 = 0.01$ m, $k_1 = k_3 = 0.78$ W(m·°C), $k_2 = 0.025$ W/(m·°C), $h_a = 10$ W/(m²·°C), $h_b = 50$ W/(m²·°C), and $\Delta T = T_a - T_b = 60$°C.

*(a)* The total thermal resistance, according to Eq. (4-50b), is

$$
\begin{aligned}
R_T &= R_a + R_1 + R_2 + R_3 + R_b \\
&= \frac{1}{Ah_a} + \frac{L_1}{Ak_1} + \frac{L_2}{Ak_2} + \frac{L_3}{Ak_3} + \frac{1}{Ah_b} .
\end{aligned}
$$

Then the rate of heat loss per square meter of the glass surface (i.e., the heat flux) becomes

$$
\begin{aligned}
q &= \frac{Q}{A} = \frac{T_a - T_b}{AR_T} = \frac{\Delta T}{1/h_a + L_1/k_1 + L_2/k_2 + L_3/k_3 + 1/h_b} \\
&= \frac{60}{1/10 + 0.005/0.78 + 0.01/0.025 + 0.005/0.78 + 1/50} \\
&= 112.6 \text{ W/m}^2 .
\end{aligned}
$$

**(b)** If the window has a single sheet of glass with no stagnant air space, the total thermal resistance is

$$
\begin{aligned}
R_T &= R_a + R_1 + R_b \\
&= \frac{1}{Ah_a} + \frac{L_1}{Ak_1} + \frac{1}{Ah_b} .
\end{aligned}
$$

Then the heat flux becomes

$$
\begin{aligned}
q &= \frac{Q}{A} = \frac{T_a - T_b}{AR_T} = \frac{\Delta T}{1/h_a + L_1/k_1 + 1/h_b} \\
&= \frac{60}{1/10 + 0.005/0.78 + 1/50} \\
&= 474.65 \ \mathrm{W/m^2} .
\end{aligned}
$$

The heat loss is about four times larger than that of the previous case.

**(c)** If the sheets of glass are touching each other (i.e., double glass) with no stagnant air layer between them, the total resistance is given by

$$
\begin{aligned}
R_T &= R_a + R_1 + R_3 + R_b \\
&= \frac{1}{Ah_a} + \frac{L_1}{Ak_1} + \frac{L_3}{Ak_3} + \frac{1}{Ah_b} .
\end{aligned}
$$

Then the heat flux becomes

$$
\begin{aligned}
q &= \frac{\Delta T}{1/h_a + L_1/k_1 + L_3/k_3 + 1/h_b} = \frac{\Delta T}{1/h_a + 2L_1/k_1 + 1/h_b} \\
&= 451.74 \ \mathrm{W/m^2} .
\end{aligned}
$$

We note that doubling the glass thickness reduced the heat loss very little; it is the stagnant air space between the two sheets of glass that causes a significant reduction in the heat loss or gain.

### 4.2.2 Multilayer Hollow Cylinder

To illustrate the basic concept in the analysis of heat flow through a multilayer hollow cylinder, we consider a two-layer cylinder, as shown in Fig. 4.10. A hot fluid at temperature $T_a$ with a heat transfer coefficient $h_{\infty l}$ flows inside the tube, while a cold fluid at temperature $T_b$ with a heat transfer coefficient $h_b$ flows outside the tube. Let $Q$ be the total heat flow through the cylinder over a length $H$. Applying the thermal resistance concept to each individual layer, we write

$$
Q = \frac{T_a - T_0}{R_a} = \frac{T_0 - T_1}{R_1} = \frac{T_1 - T_2}{R_2} = \frac{T_2 - T_b}{R_b} , \tag{4-51}
$$

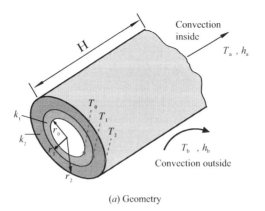

(a) Geometry

$$Q \longrightarrow \underset{R_{\infty 1} \equiv \dfrac{1}{2\pi r_0 H h_a}}{\overset{T_a}{\wedge\!\wedge\!\wedge}} \quad \underset{R_1 \equiv \dfrac{\ln(r_1/r_0)}{2\pi k_1 H}}{\overset{T_0}{\wedge\!\wedge\!\wedge}} \quad \underset{R_2 \equiv \dfrac{\ln(r_2/r_1)}{2\pi k_2 H}}{\overset{T_1}{\wedge\!\wedge\!\wedge}} \quad \underset{R_{\infty 2} \equiv \dfrac{1}{2\pi r_2 H h_b}}{\overset{T_2}{\wedge\!\wedge\!\wedge}} \overset{T_b}{\longrightarrow} Q$$

(b) Thermal resistance

**FIG. 4.10.** Thermal resistance concept for a two-layer hollow cylinder.

where $R_a$ and $R_b$ are the thermal resistances to convection at the inner and outer surfaces, respectively. $R_1$ and $R_2$ are the thermal resistances for the inner and outer cylinders, respectively; they can be determined using relation (4-29). Summing the numerators and the denominators of the individual equalities in Eq. (4-51), we obtain

$$Q = \frac{T_a - T_b}{R_a + R_1 + R_2 + R_b} = \frac{T_a - T_b}{R_T} \quad \text{W} \qquad (4\text{-}52a)$$

where the various thermal resistances are given by

$$R_a = \frac{1}{2\pi r_0 H h_a} \qquad R_1 = \frac{1}{2\pi H k_1} \ln\left(\frac{r_1}{r_0}\right)$$

$$R_2 = \frac{1}{2\pi H k_2} \ln\left(\frac{r_2}{r_1}\right) \qquad R_b = \frac{1}{2\pi r_2 H h_b} \qquad (4\text{-}52b)$$

and $R_T = R_a + R_1 + R_2 + R_b$ is the *total thermal resistance* to heat flow between the temperatures $T_a$ and $T_b$.

**EXAMPLE 4- 10** A steel tube $[k = 15\,\text{W}/(\text{m} \cdot {}^\circ\text{C})]$ of outside diameter 7.6cm and thickness 1.3 cm is covered with an insulation material $[k = 0.2\,\text{W}/(\text{m} \cdot {}^\circ\text{C})]$ of thickness 2 cm. A hot gas at $320^\circ\text{C}$ with a heat transfer coefficient of $200\,\text{W}/(\text{m}^2 \cdot {}^\circ\text{C})$ flows inside the tube. The outer surface of the insulation is exposed to cooler air at $20^\circ\text{C}$ with a heat transfer coefficient of $50\,\text{W}/(\text{m}^2 \cdot {}^\circ\text{C})$. Calculate *(a)*   the heat loss from the tube to the air for a 5-m length of the tube;

*(b)*   the temperature drops due to the thermal resistances of the hot gas flow, the steel tube, the insulation layer, and the outside air.

**SOLUTION**   *(a)*  The radial heat flow through the tube is given by Eq. (4-52) as

$$Q = \frac{T_a - T_b}{R_a + R_1 + R_2 + R_b} \quad W$$

where $R_1$ and $R_2$ are the thermal resistances across the steel tube and the insulation, respectively, and $R_a$ and $R_b$ are the thermal resistances to flow inside and outside the tube.

Given: $r_0 = 0.025\,\text{m}$, $r_1 = 0.038\,\text{m}$, $r_2 = 0.058\,\text{m}$, $H = 5\,\text{m}$, $k_1 = 15\,\text{W}/(\text{m} \cdot {}^\circ\text{C})$, $k_2 = 0.2\,\text{W}/(\text{m} \cdot {}^\circ\text{C})$, $h_a = 200\,\text{W}/(\text{m}^2 \cdot {}^\circ\text{C})$, and $h_b = 50\,\text{W}/(\text{m}^2 \cdot {}^\circ\text{C})$. The various thermal resistances are calculated as

$$R_a = \frac{1}{2\pi r_0 \, H h_a} = \frac{1}{(2\pi)(0.025)(5)(200)} = 6.37 \times 10^{-3}\,{}^\circ\text{C}/\text{W}$$

$$R_1 = \frac{1}{2\pi H k_1} \ln\left(\frac{r_1}{r_0}\right) = \frac{1}{(2\pi)(5)(15)} \ln\left(\frac{3.8}{2.5}\right) = 0.89 \times 10^{-3}\,{}^\circ\text{C}/\text{W}$$

$$R_2 = \frac{1}{2\pi H k_2} \ln\left(\frac{r_2}{r_1}\right) = \frac{1}{(2\pi)(5)(0.2)} \ln\left(\frac{5.8}{3.8}\right) = 67.3 \times 10^{-3}\,{}^\circ\text{C}/\text{W}$$

$$R_b = \frac{1}{2\pi r_2 \, H h_b} = \frac{1}{(2\pi)(0.058)(50)} = 10.98 \times 10^{-3}\,{}^\circ\text{C}/\text{W} \;.$$

Then the total thermal resistance becomes

$$R_T = R_a + R_1 + R_2 + R_b = 85.54 \times 10^{-3}\,{}^\circ\text{C}/\text{W}$$

and the total heat loss from the tube is determined as

$$Q = \frac{320 - 20}{85.54 \times 10^{-3}} = 3.507\,\text{kW} \;.$$

*(b)* Knowing $Q$, various temperature drops are calculated according to Eqs. (4-52a) and (4-52b).

$$\begin{aligned}
\Delta T_{\text{hot gas}} &= Q \times R_a = 22.74^\circ\text{C} \\
\Delta T_{\text{tube wall}} &= Q \times R_1 = 3.18^\circ\text{C} \\
\Delta T_{\text{insulation}} &= Q \times R_2 = 240.27^\circ\text{C} \\
\Delta T_{\text{outside air}} &= Q \times R_b = 39.20^\circ\text{C}
\end{aligned}$$

Clearly, the smallest temperature drop occurs across the steel tube and the largest

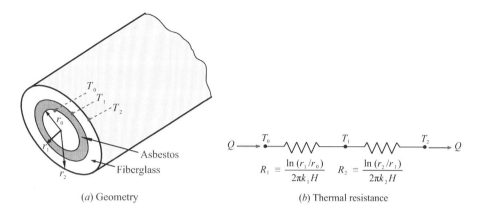

(a) Geometry                    (b) Thermal resistance

**FIGURE EXAMPLE 4-11 Illustration of the physical system.**

across the insulation material.

**EXAMPLE 4- 11**  A steam pipe with an outside radius of 4 cm is covered with a layer of asbestos insulation $[k = 0.15\,\text{W}/(\text{m}\cdot{}^\circ\text{C})]$ 1 cm thick, which is in turn covered with fiberglass insulation $[k = 0.05\,\text{W}/(\text{m}\cdot{}^\circ\text{C})]$ 3cm thick. The outside surface of the steam pipe is at a temperature of 330°C, and the outside surface of the fiberglass insulation is at 30°C. Determine the heat transfer rate per meter length of the pipe and the interface temperature between the asbestos and the fiberglass insulation.

**SOLUTION**  The accompanying figure illustrates the physical situation. The heat flow rate per meter length of the pipe, $Q/H$, can be determined using Eqs. (4-52a) and (4-52b) by noting that $R_a = 0$ and $R_b = 0$. Then we have

$$
\begin{aligned}
\frac{Q}{H} &= \frac{T_0 - T_2}{H(R_1 + R_2)} = \frac{T_0 - T_2}{\ln(r_1/r_0)/2\pi k_1 + \ln(r_2/r_1)/2\pi k_2} \\
&= \frac{330 - 30}{\ln(5/4)/[(2\pi)(0.15)] + \ln(8/5)/[(2\pi)(0.05)]} \\
&= 173.1\ \text{W/m length.}
\end{aligned}
$$

The interface temperature $T_1$ between the asbestos and the fiberglass insulation is determined from the relation

$$
Q = \frac{T_0 - T_2}{R_1 + R_2} = \frac{T_0 - T_1}{R_1}
$$

or

$$
\frac{Q}{H} = \frac{T_0 - T_1}{HR_1} = \frac{T_0 - T_1}{\ln(r_1/r_0)/2\pi k_1}
$$

$$
173.1 = \frac{330 - T_2}{\ln(5/4)/[(2\pi)(0.15)]}.
$$

Hence,

$$T_2 = 289°C.$$

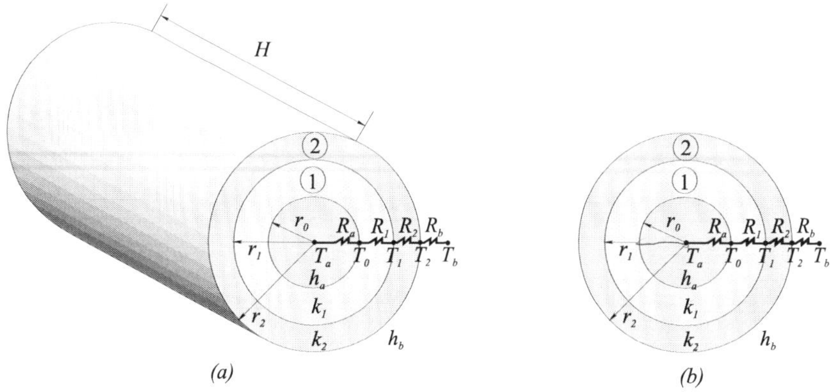

**FIG. 4.11.** Thermal resistances for radial heat flow through *(a)* a hollow composite concentric cylinder, *(b)* a hollow composite concentric sphere

### 4.2.3 Multilayer Hollow Sphere

To illustrate the basic thermal resistance concept in the analysis of heat flow through multilayered hollow spheres, we consider a two-layer hollow sphere, as shown in Fig. 4.11. The radial heat flow $Q$ through the sphere is determined by applying the thermal resistance concept to each individual layer:

$$Q = \frac{T_a - T_0}{R_a} = \frac{T_0 - T_1}{R_1} = \frac{T_1 - T_2}{R_2} = \frac{T_2 - T_b}{R_b}. \qquad (4\text{-}53)$$

Summing the numerators and denominators of these individual equalities, we obtain

$$Q = \frac{T_a - T_b}{R_a + R_1 + R_2 + R_b} \equiv \frac{T_a - T_b}{R_T} \qquad (4\text{-}54)$$

where the various thermal resistances are given by

$$R_a = \frac{1}{4\pi r_0^2 h_a} \qquad\qquad R_1 = \frac{1}{4\pi k_1}\left(\frac{r_1 - r_0}{r_1 r_0}\right)$$

$$R_2 = \frac{1}{4\pi k_2}\left(\frac{r_2 - r_1}{r_2 r_1}\right) \qquad\qquad R_b = \frac{1}{4\pi r_2^2 h_b} \qquad (4\text{-}55)$$

and $R_T = R_a + R_1 + R_2 + R_b$ is called the *total thermal resistance* to heat flow between the temperatures $T_a$ and $T_b$.

**EXAMPLE 4- 12** A spherical container with a thin metallic wall of thickness $t$, and thermal conductivity k, stores Liquid Nitrogen Gas (LNG) at 77 K having a very high heat transfer coefficient (because of phase change). This metal LNG container has an outside diameter of 1.0 m (which is the inside diameter of the insulation material, $d_i = 1.0$ m) and is covered with a 2 cm insulation system composed of glass wool with thermal conductivity, $k_{ins} = 0.04$ W/mK. The outer surface is exposed to ambient air at $T_o$=300 K with a heat transfer coefficient of $h_o$= 10 W/m$^2$K.

**(a)** Draw an equivalent thermal resistance diagram between the air and liquid nitrogen temperatures as potentials, and determine the thermal resistances.

**(b)** Find q, the heat transferred from the outer air into the liquid. Assume that the thermal resistance due to the thin wall is negligible.

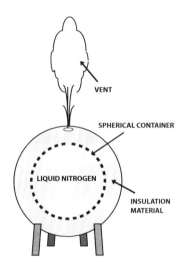

**FIGURE EXAMPLE 4-12 (a) Liquid Nitrogen Gas Storage Tank**

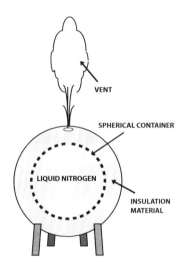

**FIGURE EXAMPLE 4-12 (b) Thermal circuit of Example 4-12a**

**SOLUTION (a)** The thermal circuit with $r_i$ being the inside radius of the spherical tank, $r_i = r_i a = 0.5$ m and $r_0$ is the outside radius of the insulation material.

$$R_1 = \frac{r_{ia} - (r_{ia} - t)}{4\pi k r_i (r_{ia} - t)}; \qquad R_2 = \frac{r_0 - r_{ia}}{4\pi k_{ins} r_0 r_i}; \qquad R_3 = \frac{1}{A h_o} = \frac{1}{h 4\pi r_0^2}$$

Note that $R_1$ can be neglected.

**SOLUTION (b)** Heat transfer to the liquid nitrogen:

$$Q = \frac{-(77 - 300)\ K}{R_2 + R_3}$$

$$Q = \frac{(223)\ \text{K}}{\frac{r_o - r_i}{4\pi k_{ins} r_o r_i} + \frac{1}{h_o 4\pi r_o^2}}$$

$$= \frac{223\ \text{K}}{\frac{(0.52 - 0.50)\ m}{4\pi(0.04\ W/mK)(0.52\ m)(0.50\ m)} + \frac{1}{(10\ W/m^2 K)(4\pi)(0.52\ m)^2}}$$

$$Q = \frac{223\ \text{K}}{(0.1530 + 0.0294)\ \text{K/W}} = 1222.36\ \text{W}$$

$$q = \frac{Q}{A} = \frac{1222.36}{4\pi r^2}$$

$$= \frac{1222.36}{4\pi(0.52)^2} = 360\ \text{W/m}^2$$

Observe that almost the entire thermal resistance is in the insulation.

## 4.2.4 Overall Heat Transfer Coefficient Concept

In engineering applications the heat flow rate $Q$ through multilayer media is also expressed in the form

$$\boxed{Q = (U A)\,\Delta T} \tag{4-56a}$$

where $U$ is called the *overall heat transfer coefficient*. Recalling the definition of the total thermal resistance $R_T$ (i.e., $Q = \Delta T / R_T$) in the path of the heat flow, $U$ is related to $R_T$ by the relation

$$R_T = \frac{1}{U A}\,. \tag{4-56b}$$

For multilayer hollow cylinder and multilayer hollow spherical systems, the area $A$ changes in the radial direction. Therefore, when relating the total thermal resistance to the overall heat transfer coefficient, the surface area on which $U$ is based should be specified. For example, Eq. (4-56b) can be written as

$$R_T = \frac{1}{U_a A_a} = \frac{1}{U_b A_b} \tag{4-57}$$

where $U_a$ is the overall heat transfer coefficient based on the inner surface $A_a$ and $U_b$ is the overall heat transfer coefficient based on the outer surface $A_b$.

Then the total heat flow rate $Q$, in terms of the overall heat transfer coefficient, is written as

$$\boxed{Q = U_a A_a\,\Delta T = U_b A_b\,\Delta T}\ . \tag{4-58}$$

*It does not matter which area the overall heat transfer coefficient $U$ is based on as long* *as it is specified in the definition.*

In the case of heat flow through a composite layer of plane wall, the area does not change in the direction of heat flow, and hence $U$ is the same whether it is based on the outer or inner surface.

For example, the thermal resistance to heat flow through a tube subjected to convection at the inner and outer boundary surfaces, as illustrated in Fig. 4.6, can be obtained from Eq. (4-31) as

$$R = \frac{1}{A_a h_{\infty 1}} + \frac{b-a}{k(A_b - A_a)/\ln(A_b/A_a)} + \frac{1}{A_b h_{\infty 2}} \tag{4-59}$$

since the thermal resistance for the tube given by Eq. (4-33b) is rearranged as

$$\begin{aligned} R_{\text{cyl}} &= \frac{\ln(b/a)}{2\pi k H} = \frac{(b-a)\ln[(2\pi b H)/(2\pi a H)]}{(b-a)(2\pi k H)} = \frac{(b-a)\ln(A_b/A_a)}{k(A_b - A_a)} \\ &= \frac{b-a}{k(A_b - A_a)/\ln(A_b/A_a)} \end{aligned}$$

where $A_a$ and $A_b$ are the inner and outer surface areas of the tube, respectively, and $(b-a)$ represents the tube thickness. Then the *overall heat transfer coefficient* $U_b$ based on the outside surface area, becomes

$$U_b = \frac{1}{A_b R_t} = \frac{1}{(A_b/A_a)(1/h_{\infty 1}) + (A_b/A_{\ln,m})[(b-a)/k] + (1/h_{\infty 2})} \tag{4-60a}$$

where

$$A_{\ln ma} = \frac{A_b - A_a}{\ln(A_b/A_a)} \equiv \text{logarithmic mean area.} \tag{4-60b}$$

Similarly, the overall heat transfer coefficient $U_a$ based on the *inside surface area* of the tube is defined as

$$U_a = \frac{1}{A_a R} = \frac{1}{1/h_{\infty 1} + (A_a/A_{\ln ma})[(b-a)/k] + (A_a/A_b)(1/h_{\infty 2})} \tag{4-61}$$

**EXAMPLE 4- 13** Calculate the overall heat transfer coefficient for Example 4-5, based on the outside surface area of the asbestos insulation.

**SOLUTION** Thermal resistance to the heat flow is

$$\begin{aligned} R &= R_{\text{cyl}} + R_{\infty 2} = \frac{\ln(b/a)}{2\pi k H} + \frac{1}{2\pi b H h_{\infty 2}} \\ &= \frac{\ln(A_b/A_a)(b-a)}{k(A_b - A_a)} + \frac{1}{A_b h_{\infty 2}} = 0.83 \,. \end{aligned}$$

Then the overall heat transfer coefficient based on the outside surface of the asbestos becomes

$$
\begin{aligned}
U_b &= \frac{1}{A_b R} = \frac{1}{2\pi b H R} \\
&= \frac{1}{(2\pi)(0.08)(1)(0.83)} = 2.4 \text{ W}/(\text{m}^2 \cdot {}^\circ\text{C})
\end{aligned}
$$

## 4.3. CONTACT RESISTANCE CONCEPT

Consider two solids, each having a plane flat surface, brought together and one surface pressed against the other. The actual direct contact between the surfaces takes place at only a limited number of spots because the surfaces are not perfectly smooth but possess some micro roughness; as a result, the surfaces are not in perfect thermal contact. The voids between the surfaces are filled with the surrounding fluid, which usually is the air. The heat flow across such an interface takes place by conduction both through the thin fluid layer filling the voids and through the spots in direct metal-to-metal contact. Since the thermal conductivity of the air is less than that of the metal, the thin layer of air filling the voids acts as a thermal resistance to heat flow. Since this resistance is confined to a very thin layer between the surfaces, it is called *thermal contact resistance.*

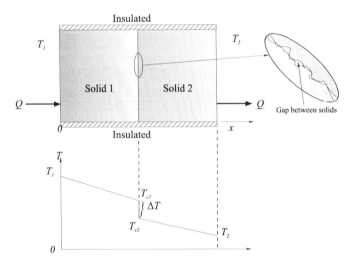

**FIG. 4.12.** Temperature drop across a contact resistance.

Figure 4-12 illustrates the thermal contact resistance concept and the temperature profile through the solids. There is a sudden drop in temperature across the interface. Unless the two metals are welded, there is always a thermal resistance across such an interface. The magnitude of this thermal resistance depends on the surface roughness, the type of material, the interface pressure, the interface temperature, and the type of fluid filling the voids. A considerable amount of experimental work in predicting thermal contact resistance has been done. The inverse of the interface thermal contact resistance is called the *interface thermal conductance,* $h_c$ which has the dimensions of W/(m$^2 \cdot {}^\circ$C).

Figure 4.13 illustrates the effects of surface roughness, the interface pressure, and inter-face temperature on the thermal contact conductance for a stainless steel-to-stainless steel joint with air as the interfacial fluid. The contact conductance increases with increasing interface pressure, increasing interface resistance, and decreasing surface roughness. If an aluminum-to-aluminum joint were used instead of the stainless steel joint, the con-tact conductance would be higher, because aluminum is softer than steel and allows more direct contact between the surfaces. Experimental data for contact conductance, such as those shown in Fig. 4.13, for different surface roughnesses and different combinations of metals are available in the literature. The thermal contact conductance values in vacuum with a few commonl metal interfaces are listed in Table 4.1.

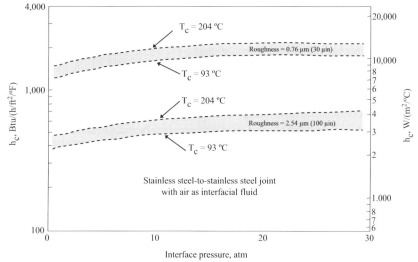

**FIG. 4.13a.** Interface conductance $h_c$ variations.

(*Based on data from Barzelay, Tong, and Holloway (1955).*

**TABLE 4.1  Thermal contact conductance in vacuum at 25 °C temperature.**

| Type of interface | Contact roughness, μm | Contact pressure, atm | $h_c$, W/(m² · °C) |
|---|---|---|---|
| 304 Stainless steel | 0.25 × 0.38 | 0.6 to 75 | 300 to 11,000 |
| 6061-T6 | 1.1 × 1.3 | 0.7 to 75 | 200 to 2100 |
| Aluminum | 0.3 | 0.7 to 75 | 1500 to 32,000 |
| Copper | 0.2 | 0.7 to 75 | 6500 to 14,000 |

(*Based on data from Atkins and Fried (1965).*)

**EXAMPLE 4-14** Consider two stainless steel blocks [$k = 20$ W/(m · °C)], each having a thickness of 1 cm, length of 8 cm, and width of 6 cm, that are pressed together

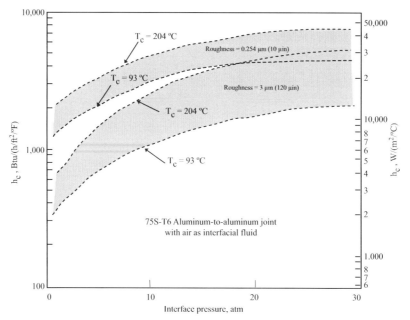

**FIG. 4.13b.** Interface conductance $h_c$ variations.

*(Based on data from Tong, and G.F. Holloway (1955).*

with a pressure of 20 atm. The surfaces have a roughness of about 0.76 μm. The outside surfaces of the blocks are at 120°C and 70°C. Calculate

(a) the heat flow rate across the blocks;

(b) the temperature drop at the interface.

**SOLUTION** (a) The total heat flow rate $Q$ across the blocks is determined by the application of the thermal resistance concept:

$$Q = \frac{\Delta T}{R_1 + R_c + R_2} \quad \text{W}$$

where $\Delta T = T_1 - T_2 = 120 - 70 = 50°C$. The thermal resistances of the blocks are equal, and they are determined by

$$R_1 = R_2 = \frac{L}{kA} = \frac{0.01}{(20)(0.08 \times 0.06)} = 0.1042°C/W .$$

The contact conductance of the interface is determined from Fig. 4-13. For a mean interface temperature of $T_m \cong (120 + 70)/2 = 90°C$, a surface roughness of 0.76 μm, and interface pressure of 20 atm, the contact conductance becomes $h_c = 10,000 \text{ W}/(\text{m}^2 \cdot °\text{C})$. Then the thermal contact resistance of the interface is given by

$$R_c = \frac{1}{h_c A} = \frac{1}{(10,000)(0.08 \times 0.06)} = 0.0208°C/W .$$

Then the heat flow rate across the blocks is

$$Q = \frac{50}{0.1042 + 0.02083 + 0.1042} = 218 \text{ W} .$$

*(b)* The temperature drop across the interface becomes

$$\Delta T_c = \frac{R_c}{R_1 + R_c + R_1} \Delta T$$

$$= \frac{0.0208}{0.1042 + 0.0208 + 0.1042} \times 50 = 4.54°\text{C} .$$

## 4.4. TWO-DIMENSIONAL STEADY-STATE HEAT CONDUCTION: CONDUCTION SHAPE FACTORS

Thus far we have discussed the determination of one-dimensional, steady-state heat flow through bodies having such shapes as a plane wall, cylinder, or sphere. The analysis of heat flow through bodies with more complicated geometries is generally rather involved. However, heat transfer calculations have been performed for a number of specific geometries, and the total heat transfer rate $Q$ through the body is related to the temperature difference $\Delta T$ and a quantity called the *conduction shape factor* $S$ by

$$\boxed{\begin{aligned} Q &= Sk\,\Delta T \\ &= Sk\,(T_1 - T_2) \quad \text{W} \end{aligned}} \tag{4-62}$$

where $k$ is the thermal conductivity of the body and $T_1$ and $T_2$ are the boundary surface temperatures across which heat flow takes place. It is assumed that there is no energy generation within the body.

Clearly, once the conduction shape factor $S$ is known for a specific geometry, the total heat flow rate through the body can be calculated from the simple formula (4-62) for a given thermal conductivity of the solid and temperature difference between the boundary surfaces.

The physical significance of the shape factor $S$ can be better envisioned if Eq. (4-62) is rearranged as

$$Q = \frac{\Delta T}{R} \tag{4-63a}$$

where

$$R = \frac{1}{Sk} . \tag{4-63b}$$

Clearly, the shape factor S is related to the thermal resistance of the body. In the case of one-dimensional heat flow, the shape factors for such geometries as a plane wall, a hollow cylinder, and a hollow sphere are immediately obtained by utilizing the results developed previously. For a plane wall, from Eqs. (4-8b) and (4-63b) we have

$$S = \frac{A}{L}.$$ (4-64a)

For a hollow cylinder, from Eqs. (4-29) and (4-63b) we write

$$S = \frac{2\pi H}{\ln(b/a)}.$$ (4-64b)

For a hollow sphere, Eqs. (4-42) and (4-63b) give

$$S = \frac{4\pi ab}{b - a}.$$ (4-64c)

## TABLE 4.2  Conduction Shape Factors.

| DESCRIPTION | ILLUSTRATION | SHAPE FACTOR | FOR |
|---|---|---|---|
| 1. One dimensional heat conduction through a slab | | $\frac{A}{L}$ | |
| 2. One dimensional heat conduction through a long hollow cylinder | | $\frac{2\pi H}{\ln(r_2/r1)}$ | |
| 3. One dimensional heat conduction through a hollow sphere | | $\frac{4\pi r_1 r_2}{r_2 - r_1}$ | |
| 4. An isothermal sphere at $T_1$ placed in an infinite medium at $T_2$ | | $4\pi R$ | |
| 5. An isothermal sphere at $T_1$ placed in a semi-infinite medium having a surface temperature $T_2$ | | $\frac{4\pi R}{1 - R/(2z)}$ | |

**TABLE 4.2  Conduction Shape Factors** (continued from the previous page).

| PHYSICAL SITUATION | ILLUSTRATION | SHAPE FACTOR | FOR |
|---|---|---|---|
| 6. An isothermal sphere at $T_1$ placed near the insulated boundary of an semi-infinite medium at $T_2$ | | $\frac{4\pi R}{1+R/(2z)}$ | |
| 7. Isothermal cylinder of length, L, at $T_1$ placed horizontally in a semi-infinite medium having a surface temperature $T_2$ | | $\frac{2\pi L}{cosh^{-1}(z/R)}$ | $L \gg R$ |
| 8. Thin, circular disk at $T_1$ placed placed horizontally in a semi-infinite medium having a surface temperature $T_2$ | | $8R$ | $z \gg 2R$ |
| 9. Two parallel, isothermal cylinders of length L at $T_1$ placed in an infinite medium | | $\frac{2\pi L}{cosh^{-1}[(z^2-R_1^2-R_2^2)/(2R_1R_2)]}$ | $L \gg R_1$ $R_2 L \gg z$ |
| 10. Isothermal cylinder of length L at $T_1$ placed vertically in a semi-infinite medium having a surface temperature $T_2$ | | $\frac{2\pi L}{ln(2L/R)}$ | $L \gg 2R$ |
| 11. Circular hole centered in a square solid of length L | | $\frac{2\pi L}{ln(0.54W/R)}$ | $L \gg W$ |
| 12. Eccentric circular hole in a cylindrical solid of length L | | $\frac{2\pi L}{cosh^{-1}[(R_1^2+R_2^2-z^2)/(2R_1R_2)]}$ | $L \gg R^2$ |

These are just a few explicit equations. Various heat transfer calculations have been performed and the corresponding conduction shape factors determined for a number of more complicated geometries. Table 4.2 lists a number of these shape factors. The results in this table can be used in Eq. (4-62) to determine the heat flow rate between surfaces maintained at temperatures $T_1$ and $T_2$.

Consider, for example, Case 5 of Table 4.2. It illustrates an isothermal sphere of radius $R$, maintained at a uniform temperature $T_1$, placed with its center at a distance $z$ from the surface of a semi-infinite domain. The medium has a thermal conductivity $k$, and its surface is maintained at a uniform temperature $T_2$. Using the shape factor concept, the total heat transfer rate $Q$ from the sphere is given by

$$Q = Sk\,(T_1 - T_2) \quad \text{W} \tag{4-65a}$$

where the shape factor $S$ for this particular case is

$$S = \frac{4\pi R}{1 - R/(2z)} . \tag{4-65b}$$

Applications involving other configurations shown in this table are treated in a similar manner.

**EXAMPLE 4- 15**  A spherical tank of radius 1 m containing radioactive material is buried in the earth. The distance between the earth's surface and the tank center is 4 m. Heat release due to radioactive decay in the tank is 500 W. Calculate the steady temperature of the tank's surface if the earth's surface is at 20°C and the thermal conductivity of the earth at this location is $k = 1.0\ W/(\mathrm{m} \cdot {}^\circ\mathrm{C})$.

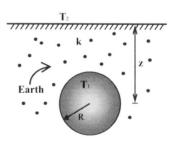

**FIGURE EXAMPLE 4-15 The buried spherical tank.**

**SOLUTION**  The physical situation and the configuration for this problem are similar to Case 4 in Table 4.2. With $R = 1$ m and $z = 4$ m, the shape factor $S$ is determined as

$$
\begin{aligned}
S &= \frac{4\pi R}{1 - R/(2z)} \\
&= \frac{4\pi \times 1}{1 - 1/[(2)(4)]} = 14.36\ \text{m} .
\end{aligned}
$$

For the earth's surface at $T_2 = 20°C$, the steady temperature of the tank's surface $T_1$ is calculated from Eq. (4-62) as

$$Q = Sk\,(T_1 - T_2)$$

$$500 = (14.36)(1)(T_1 - 20)$$

or

$$T_1 = 54.8°C\ .$$

**EXAMPLE 4-16** A hot pipe with an outside radius of 2 cm passes through the hole at the center of a long concrete block 50 cm × 50 cm in cross section, as illustrated in the accompanying figure. The pipe surface is at 80°C, and the outer surface of the concrete block is at 20°C. The thermal conductivity of the concrete may be taken as $k = 0.76\ \text{W}/(\text{m}\cdot°C)$. Determine the rate of heat loss from the pipe per meter of length.

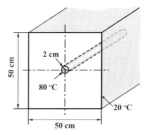

**FIGURE EXAMPLE 4-16 The hot water pipe inside a long square block.**

**SOLUTION** The physical situation and the configuration for this problem are similar to Case 11 in Table 4.2. Given $W = 0.5$ m and $R = 0.02$ m, the shape factor $S$ for a 1-m length of the pipe, $L = 1$ m,

$$
\begin{aligned}
S &= \frac{2\pi L}{\ln(0.54\,W/R)} \\
&= \frac{2\pi \times 1}{\ln[0.54(0.5/0.02)]} = 2.64\ \text{m}\ .
\end{aligned}
$$

For the pipe surface at $T_1 = 80°C$ and the outside surface of the concrete at $T_2 = 20°C$, the heat loss from the pipe is calculated using Eq. (4-62) as

$$
\begin{aligned}
Q &= Sk\,(T_1 - T_2) \\
&= (2.64)(0.76)(80 - 20) \\
&= 120.4\ \text{W}/\text{m}\ \ \text{length.}
\end{aligned}
$$

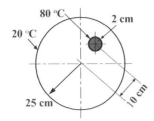

**FIGURE EXAMPLE 4-17 The hot water pipe inside a long cylinder block.**

**EXAMPLE 4-17**  A hot water pipe with an outside radius of 2 cm is embedded eccentrically inside a long cylindrical concrete block of radius 25 cm, as illustrated by the accompanying figure. The distance between the center of the pipe and the center of the cylinder is 10 cm. The surface of the hot water pipe is at 80°C, and the outside surface of the concrete cylinder is at 20°C. The thermal conductivity of concrete may be taken as $k = 0.76$ W/(m·°C). Determine the rate of heat loss from the pipe per meter of length.

**SOLUTION**  The physical situation and the configuration for this problem are similar to Case 12 in Table 4.2. Given $R_1 = 0.02$ m, $R_2 = 0.25$ m, and $z = 0.1$ m, the shape factor $S$ for a 1-m length of the pipe, $L = 1$ m, is

$$
\begin{aligned}
S &= \frac{2\pi L}{\cosh^{-1}[(R_1^2 + R_2^2 - z^2)/(2R_1 R_2)]} \\
&= \frac{(2\pi)(1)}{\cosh^{-1}\{[(0.02)^2 + (0.25)^2 - (010)^2]/(2)(0.02)(0.25)\}} \\
&= \frac{2\pi}{\cosh^{-1}(5.29)} \\
&= 2.67
\end{aligned}
$$

and the heat loss from the pipe is calculated using Eq. (4-62) as

$$
\begin{aligned}
Q &= Sk(T_1 - T_2) \\
&= (2.67)(0.76)(80 - 20) \\
&= 122 \text{ W}.
\end{aligned}
$$

## 4.5. EXTENDED SURFACES

The rate of heat removal by convection from a surface is increased by increasing the surface area for heat transfer by using extended surfaces called *fins*. A familiar example of a finned surface, as illustrated in Fig. 4-14, is a metal spoon in hot water. Heat conducted through the spoon causes the handle to become warmer than the surrounding air. Heat is then transferred from the spoon handle to the air by convection. In industry, fins are used in numerous applications, such as car radiators, double-pipe heat exchangers, electronic equipment cooling, and compressors. The determination of heat flow through a finned surface requires knowledge of the temperature distribution in the fin.

**FIG. 4.14.** A metal spoon in hot water acting as a fin.

## Fins of Uniform Cross Section

Figure 4.15 illustrates the geometry, the coordinates, and the nomenclature for the development of the one-dimensional, steady-state energy equation for fins: of uniform cross section. Consider a small volume element $\Delta x$ and write the: steady-state energy balance for the volume element as

$$
\begin{pmatrix}
\text{Net rate of heat gain} \\
\text{by conduction in} \\
x \text{ direction into} \\
\text{volume element } \Delta x
\end{pmatrix}
+
\begin{pmatrix}
\text{Net rate of heat gain} \\
\text{by convection through} \\
\text{lateral surfaces into} \\
\text{volume element } \Delta x
\end{pmatrix}
= 0
$$

$$
-\frac{d(qA)}{dx}\Delta x + h[T_\infty - T(x)]\,P\Delta x = 0 \tag{4-66a}
$$

$$
\frac{d^2T(x)}{dx^2} - \frac{hP}{Ak}\,[T(x) - T_\infty] = 0 \tag{4-66b}
$$

where the cross-sectional area $A$, the perimeter $P$, the heat transfer coefficient $h$, and the thermal conductivity of the fin material $k$ are constant. This equation is called the *fin equation* and it is written more compactly in the form

$$
\boxed{\frac{d^2\theta(x)}{dx^2} - m^2\theta(x) = 0} \tag{4-67a}
$$

where

$$
m^2 \equiv \frac{hP}{Ak} \qquad \theta(x) = T(x) - T_\infty\,. \tag{4-67b}
$$

Equation (4-67) is a linear, homogeneous, second-order ordinary differential equation with constant coefficients. Its general solution may be taken in the form

$$
\theta(x) = C_1 \cosh m(L - x) + C_2 \sinh m(L - x) \tag{4-68}
$$

where the two constants $C_1$ and $C_2$ are to be determined from the boundary conditions for the problem. The solution given by Eq. (4-68) is more convenient to use in the analysis

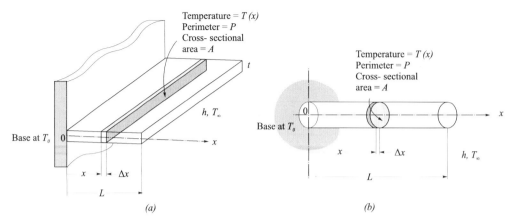

**FIG. 4.15.** Nomenclature for the derivation of one-dimensional fin equation.

of fins of finite length, as will soon be apparent in the solution that follows. Customarily, the temperature distribution at the fin base $x = 0$ is considered known; that is,

$$\theta(0) = T_0 - T_\infty \equiv \theta_0 \qquad (4\text{-}69)$$

where $T_0$ is the fin base temperature. Equation (4-69) provides one of the boundary conditions needed for the determination of the unknown constants in Eq. (4-68). The second boundary condition at the fin tip and the determination of the constants are now described.

**Fins with Negligible Heat Loss at the Tip:**
The heat transfer area at the fin tip is generally small compared with the lateral area of the fin. For such a case, the heat loss from the tip of the fin is negligible, and the boundary condition for the fin tip (i.e., $x = L$) can be taken as no heat loss (i.e., insulated).

$$\frac{d\theta(x)}{dx} = 0 \quad \text{at } x = L . \qquad (4\text{-}70)$$

The boundary condition (4-70) requires that $C_2 = 0$, and the application of the boundary condition (4-69) gives $C_1 = \theta_0/\cosh mL$. Then the solution given by Eq. (4-68) becomes

$$\boxed{\frac{\theta(x)}{\theta_0} = \frac{T(x) - T_\infty}{T_0 - T_\infty} = \frac{\cosh m(L - x)}{\cosh mL}} . \qquad (4\text{-}71)$$

The heat flow $Q$ through the fin is determined by evaluating the conductive heat flow at the fin base according to the relation

$$Q = -Ak \left. \frac{d\theta(x)}{dx} \right|_{x=0}$$

and substituting the temperature distribution given by Eq. (4-71) results,

$$Q = Ak\theta_0 m \tanh mL = \theta_0 \sqrt{PhkA} \tanh mL \quad . \qquad (4\text{-}72)$$

**Fin Efficiency:**

In industrial applications, fins having geometries that are more complicated than those shown in Fig. 4-15 are frequently used. The analysis of heat transfer through such fins is a complicated matter, and the resulting expressions for heat flow are very involved for use in practice. To alleviate this difficulty and simplify the calculation of heat transfer through fins, the concept of *fin efficiency* has been introduced. The fin efficiency $\eta$ is defined by

$$\eta = \frac{\text{actual heat transfer through fin}}{\substack{\text{ideal heat transfer through fin} \\ \text{if entire fin surface were at} \\ \text{fin base temperature } T_0}} = \frac{Q_{\text{fin}}}{Q_{\text{ideal}}} \quad . \qquad (4\text{-}73a)$$

Here $Q_{\text{ideal}}$ is given by

$$Q_{\text{ideal}} = a_f h \theta_0 \qquad (4\text{-}73b)$$

where

$$a_f = \text{surface area of fin}$$
$$h = \text{heat transfer coefficient}$$
$$\theta_0 = T_0 - T_\infty \ .$$

Thus, if the fin efficiency $\eta$ is known, the heat transfer $Q_{\text{fin}}$ through the fin is determined from

$$Q_{\text{fin}} = \eta Q_{\text{ideal}} = \eta a_f h \theta_0 \ . \qquad (4\text{-}73c)$$

To illustrate how $\eta$ can be determined, we consider heat flow through a fin having uniform cross section and negligible heat loss from the fin tip. The heat transfer through the fin is given by Eq. (4-72) as

$$Q_{\text{fin}} = \theta_0 \sqrt{PhkA} \tanh mL \ .$$

For a fin of length $L$ and perimeter $P$, the heat transfer area $a_f$ for the fin is taken as $a_f = PL$. Then $Q_{ideal}$ is determined by Eq. (4-73b) as

$$Q_{\text{ideal}} = PLh\theta_0 \ .$$

Introducing these results into the definition of the fin efficiency $\eta$, we obtain an explicit expression for the efficiency of a fin having a uniform cross section: fin:

$$\eta = \frac{\theta_0 \sqrt{PhkA} \tanh mL}{\theta_0 PLh} = \frac{\tanh mL}{mL} \qquad (4\text{-}74a)$$

where

$$mL = L\sqrt{\frac{Ph}{Ak}} \qquad (4\text{-}74b).$$

For a rectangular fin which has a uniform cross section, $P/A \cong 2/t$ where $t$ is the fin thickness.

Equations for fin efficiency have been developed for fins having other geometries and are available for other geometries.

**EXAMPLE 4-18** Copper-plate fins of rectangular cross section having a thickness $t = 1$ mm, height $L = 10$ mm, and thermal conductivity $k = 380$ W/(m·°C) are attached to a plane wall maintained at a temperature $T_0 = 230$°C. The fins dissipate heat by convection into ambient air at $T_\infty = 30$°C with a heat transfer coefficient $h = 40$ W/(m²·°C). Assuming negligible heat loss from the fin tip, determine the fin efficiency.

**SOLUTION** To determine the fin efficiency η, we first calculate the parameter $mL$ as follows:

$$mL = (14.51)(0.01) = 0.1451$$

where

$$\frac{P}{A} = \frac{2(b+t)}{bt} \cong \frac{2b}{bt} = \frac{2}{t}$$

$$m = \sqrt{\frac{Ph}{kA}} = \sqrt{\frac{2h}{kt}} = \sqrt{\frac{(2)(40)}{380 \times 10^{-3}}} = 14.51 \text{ m}^{-1}.$$

Then, the efficiency η from Eq. (4-74) becomes

$$\eta = \frac{\tanh mL}{mL} = \frac{\tanh 0.1451}{0.1451} = \frac{0.144}{0.1451} = 0.993.$$

**EXAMPLE 4-19** A steel rod of diameter $D = 2$ cm, length $L = 10$ cm, and thermal conductivity $k = 50$ W/(m·°C) is exposed to ambient air at $T_\infty = 20$°C with a heat transfer coefficient $h_\infty = 30$ W/(m²·°C). If one end of the rod is maintained at a temperature of 70°C, calculate the heat loss from the rod.

**SOLUTION** This problem is equivalent to the problem of heat transfer through a fin of constant cross section. The parameter $mL$ is calculated as follows:

$$m^2 = \frac{hP}{Ak} = \frac{h\pi D}{(\pi/4)\,D^2 k} = \frac{4h}{kD} = \frac{(4)(30)}{(50)(0.02)} = 120.$$

Therefore $m = 10.95$ and $mL = (10.95)(0.10) = 1.095$.

Then the heat flow rate is calculated using Eq. (4-72):

$$
\begin{aligned}
Q &= \theta_0 \sqrt{PhkA} \, \tanh mL \\
&= \theta_0 \sqrt{(\pi D)\, hk \left( \frac{\pi}{4}\, D^2 \right)} \, \tanh mL \\
&= (70 - 20)\frac{\pi}{2} \sqrt{(0.02)^3 (50)(30)} \, \tanh(1.095) = 6.8717 \text{ W} .
\end{aligned}
$$

**Overall Surface Efficiency:**

So far we have discussed heat transfer through a single fin. In practice, however, heat transfer through a finned surface consists of heat transfer through the fins and through the bare area between the fins. Let

$a_f$  =  surface area of the fins

$a_b$  =  bare (unfinned) area between the fins

$h$  =  heat transfer coefficient, which is assumed to be the same for both the fin surface and the bare surface.

Then the total heat transfer rate $Q_t$ through the fin assembly is determined from

$$
Q_t = \left( \begin{array}{l} \text{Heat transfer through} \\ \text{the fins} \end{array} \right) + \left( \begin{array}{l} \text{Heat transfer through} \\ \text{the bar surface} \\ \text{between the fins} \end{array} \right) \tag{4-75a}
$$

$$
Q_t = Q_{\text{fin}} + Q_{\text{no}-\text{fin}}
$$
$$
Q_t = \eta a_f h \theta_0 + a_b h \theta_0
$$
$$
Q_t = h \theta_0 \left( \eta a_f + a_b \right) . \tag{4-75b}
$$

Knowing the areas $a_f$ and $a_b$, the fin efficiency $\eta$, the heat transfer coefficient $h$, and the temperature difference $\theta_0$ between the fin base and the ambient, the total heat transfer rate $Q_t$ can be determined from Eq. (4-75b).

$$
Q_t = \eta_{\text{afin}} a h \theta_0 . \tag{4-76}
$$

where

$a$  =  total heat transfer area= $a_f + a_b$

$\beta$  =  $a_f / a$

$\eta_{\text{afin}}$  =  $\beta \eta + (1 - \beta)$

here $\eta_{\text{afin}}$ is the Overall Surface Efficiency or the so called "the Area Weighted Fin Efficiency" or "Surface Area Efficiency".

**Fin Effectiveness:**

$$
\epsilon_f = Q_{\text{fin}}/Q_{\text{withoutfin}} = \eta a_f / a_0
$$

here $\epsilon_f$ is the Fin Effectiveness where $a_0$ is the area fin occupies at the base and $Q_{\text{withoutfin}}$ is,

$$Q_{\text{withoutfin}} = a_0 h \theta_0 .$$

## PROBLEMS

*Single Layer*

**4-1.** Consider a slab of thickness 10 cm. One surface is kept at $20°C$ and the other at $100°C$. Determine the heat flow rate across the slab if the slab is made of pure copper $[k = 387 \text{ W}/(\text{m} \cdot °C)]$, pure aluminum $[k = 202 \text{ W}/(\text{m} \cdot °C)]$, and pure iron $[k = 62 \text{ W}/(\text{m} \cdot °C)]$.

**4-2.** A brick wall $[k = 0.69 \text{ W}/(\text{m} \cdot °C)]$ 5 cm thick is exposed to cool air at $10°C$ with a heat transfer coefficient of $10 \text{ W}/(\text{m}^2 \cdot °C)$ at one of its surfaces, while the other surface is kept at $70°C$. What is the temperature of the surface that is exposed to cool air?

**4-3.** Consider a furnace wall $[k = 1 \text{ W}/(\text{m} \cdot °C)]$ with the inside surface at $1000°C$ and the outside surface at $400°C$. If the heat flow through the wall should not exceed $2000 \text{ W}/\text{m}^2$, what is the minimum wall thickness $L$?

**4-4.** Consider a plane wall 25 cm thick. The inner surface is kept at $400°C$, and the outer surface is exposed to an environment at $800°C$ with a heat transfer coefficient of $10 \text{ W}/(\text{m}^2 \cdot °C)$. If the temperature of the outer surface is $685°C$, calculate the thermal conductivity of the wall. What might the material be?

**4-5.** Consider a pipe with an inner radius of 5 cm and an outer radius of 7 cm. The inner surface is kept at $100°C$, and the outer surface at $80°C$. Determine the heat loss per meter length of the pipe if the pipe is made of pure copper $[k = 387 \text{ W}/(\text{m} \cdot °C)]$, pure aluminum $[k = 200 \text{ W}/(\text{m} \cdot °C)]$, and pure iron $[k = 62 \text{ W}/(\text{m} \cdot °C)]$.

**4-6.** A metal pipe with an outside diameter (OD) of 12 cm is covered with an insulation material $[k = 0.07 \text{ W}/(\text{m} \cdot °C)]$ of 2.5 cm thick. If the outer pipe wall is at $100°C$ and the outer surface of the insulation is at $20°C$, find the heat loss from the pipe per meter length.

**4-7.** A metal pipe of 10 cm OD is covered with a 2-cm-thick insulation $[k = 0.07\text{W}/(\text{m} \cdot °C)]$. The heat loss from the pipe is 100 W per meter of length when the pipe surface is at $100°C$. What is the temperature of the outer surface of the insulation?

**4-8.** Consider a hollow cylinder with inner radius $a$ and outer radius $b$. The inner surface is subjected to a heat supply at a constant rate of $q_1 \text{ W}/\text{m}^2$, while the outer surface is maintained at a uniform temperature $T_2$. Develop an expression for the steady temperature distribution $T(r)$ in the cylinder.

**4-9.** A 5-cm-OD and 0.5-cm-thick copper pipe $[k = 386\,\mathrm{W/(m \cdot {}^\circ C)}]$ has hot gas flowing inside at a temperature of $200{}^\circ C$ with a heat transfer coefficient of $30\mathrm{W/(m^2 \cdot {}^\circ C)}$. The outer surface dissipates heat by convection into the ambient air at $20{}^\circ C$ with a heat transfer coefficient of $15\,\mathrm{W/(m^2 \cdot {}^\circ C)}$. Determine the heat loss from the pipe per meter of length.

**4-10.** A brass condenser tube $[k = 115\,\mathrm{W/(m \cdot {}^\circ C)}]$ with an outside diameter of 2 cm and a thickness of 0.2 cm is used to condense steam on its outer surface at $50{}^\circ C$ with a heat transfer coefficient of $2000\,\mathrm{W/(m^2 \cdot {}^\circ C)}$. Cooling water at $20{}^\circ C$ with a heat transfer coefficient of $5000\,\mathrm{W/(m^2 \cdot {}^\circ C)}$ flows inside.

*(a)* Determine the heat flow rate from the steam to the cooling water per meter of length of the tube.

*(b)* What would be the heat transfer rate per meter of length of the tube if the outer and the inner surfaces of the tube were at $50{}^\circ C$ and $20{}^\circ C$, respectively? Compare this result with *(a)*, and explain the reason for the difference between the two results.

**4-11.** Consider a hollow sphere with an inner radius of 5 cm and an outer radius of 6 cm. The inner surface is kept at $100{}^\circ C$, and the outer surface at $50{}^\circ C$. Determine the heat loss from the sphere if it is made of pure copper $[k = 387\,\mathrm{W/(m \cdot {}^\circ C)}]$, pure aluminum $[k = 200\,\mathrm{W/(m \cdot {}^\circ C)}]$, and pure iron $[k = 62\,\mathrm{W/(m \cdot {}^\circ C)}]$.

**4-12.** Consider a hollow sphere of inner radius $r = a$ and outer radius $r = b$. The inner surface is heated uniformly at a constant rate of $q_a\,\mathrm{W/m^2}$, while the outer surface is exposed to an environment at $T_\infty$ with a heat transfer coefficient $h_\infty$. Develop an expression for the steady temperature distribution $T(r)$ in the sphere.

**4-13.** A 6-cm-OD, 2-cm-thick copper hollow sphere $[k = 386\,\mathrm{W/(m \cdot {}^\circ C)}]$ is uniformly heated at the inner surface at a rate of $150\,\mathrm{W/m^2}$. The outer surface is cooled with air at $20{}^\circ C$ with a heat transfer coefficient of $10\,\mathrm{W/(m^2 \cdot {}^\circ C)}$. Calculate the temperature of the outer surface.

**4-14.** Steam at $150{}^\circ C$ flows inside a pipe $[k = 40\,\mathrm{W/(m \cdot {}^\circ C)}]$ with an inside radius of 4 cm and an outside radius of 5 cm. The heat transfer coefficient between the steam and the inside surface is $2000\,\mathrm{W/(m^2 \cdot {}^\circ C)}$. The outside surface is exposed to atmospheric air at $30{}^\circ C$ with a heat transfer coefficient of $15\,\mathrm{W/(m^2 \cdot {}^\circ C)}$. Find the heat flow rate across the pipe per meter length of the pipe.

*Multilayers*

**4-15.** A container made of 2-cm-thick iron plate $[k = 62\,\mathrm{W/(m \cdot {}^\circ C)}]$ is insulated with a 1-cm-thick asbestos layer $[k = 0.1\,\mathrm{W(m \cdot {}^\circ C)}]$. If the inner surface of the iron plate is exposed to hot gas at $530{}^\circ C$ with a heat transfer coefficient of $100\,\mathrm{W/(m^2 \cdot {}^\circ C)}$ and the outer surface of the asbestos is in contact with cool air at $30{}^\circ C$ with a heat transfer coefficient $20$ W/(m$^2 \cdot$ °C), calculate: (a) the heat flow rate across the layers per square meter of surface area, and (b) the interface temperature between the layers.

*Answer*: $497.8$ °C

**4-16.** Steam at $180$°C flows inside a pipe [$k = 40$ W/(m $\cdot$ °C)] that has an inside radius of 3 cm and an outside radius of 3.5 cm. The heat transfer coefficient between the steam and the inside surface of the pipe is $3000$ W/(m$^2 \cdot$ °C). To reduce the heat loss from the steam pipe to the atmospheric air at $30$°C, a 2-cm-thick layer of magnesia insulation [$k = 0.06$ W/(m $\cdot$ °C)] is added on the outer surface. If the heat transfer coefficient between the atmospheric air and the outside surface of the insulation material is $10$ W/(m$^2 \cdot$ °C), calculate the heat loss to the air.

**4-17.** An industrial furnace is made of fireclay brick 0.3 m thick with a thermal conductivity of $1.5$ W/(m $\cdot$ °C). The outside surface is to be insulated with a material that has a thermal conductivity of $0.01$ W/(m $\cdot$ °C) and a thickness of 0.2 m. The inner surface of the furnace is kept at $600$°C, while the outer surface of the insulation material is exposed to cool air at $30$°C with a heat transfer coefficient of $15$ W/(m$^2 \cdot$ °C). Calculate the heat flow rate across the layers per square meter of surface area and the outer surface temperature of the furnace.

**4-18.** A steel tube [$k = 15$ W/(m $\cdot$ °C)] with an outside diameter of 4 cm and a thickness of 1 cm is covered with insulation material 1.5 cm thick. The inside temperature of the tube is kept at $200$°C, and the outside surface temperature is measured at $199$°C. Calculate the outside surface temperature of the insulation material, if the thermal conductivity of the insulation is $0.2$ W/(m $\cdot$ °C).

**4-19.** A hollow sphere [$k = 15$ W/(m $\cdot$ °C)] with an outside diameter of 8 cm and a thickness of 2 cm is covered with an insulation material [$k = 0.2$ W/(m $\cdot$ °C)] 2 cm thick. Inside the sphere energy is generated at a rate of $3 \times 10^5$ W/m$^3$. The temperature of the interface between the outer surface of the sphere and the insulation is measured to be $300$°C. Calculate the outside surface temperature of the insulation material.

**4-20.** The wall of a building consists of 10 cm of brick [$k = 0.69$ W/(m $\cdot$ °C)], 1.25 cm of Celotex [$k = 0.048$ W/(m $\cdot$ °C)], 8 cm of glass wool [$k = 0.038$ W/(m $\cdot$ °C)], and 1.25 cm of asbestos cement board [$k = 0.74$ W/(m $\cdot$ °C)]. If the outside surface of the brick is at $5$°C and the inside surface of the cement board is at $20$°C, calculate the heat flow rate per square meter of wall surface.

**4-21.** A plane wall of thickness $L$, and thermal conductivity $k_1$ is covered with an insulation layer of thermal conductivity $k_2$. The inside surface of the wall is maintained at a uniform temperature $T_1$, and the outside surface of the insulation layer is exposed to air at temperature $T_b$ with a heat transfer coefficient $h_b$. Develop an expression for determining the thickness $L$ of the insulation layer needed to reduce the heat loss from the uninsulated wall by 30 percent.

**4-22.** A wall of a building is made of 8 cm of building brick $[k = 0.69\,\text{W}/(\text{m} \cdot {}^\circ\text{C})]$, 2 cm of Celotex $[k = 0.048\ \text{W}/(\text{m} \cdot {}^\circ\text{C})]$, and 2 cm of a asbestos cement board $[k = 0.74\,\text{W}/(\text{m} \cdot {}^\circ\text{C})]$. Glass wool $[k = 0.038\ \text{W}/(\text{m} \cdot {}^\circ\text{C})]$ is to be added between the Celotex and Asbestos to reduce the heat flow rate through the wall by 50 percent. Determine the thickness of the cement board.

**4-23.** Determine the interface temperature $T_1$ and the surface temperature $T_3$ of the composite wall shown in Fig. P4-23.

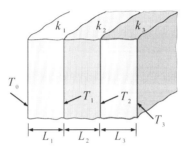

Figure P4-23

**4-24.** A composite wall consisting of three different layers in perfect thermal contact is shown in the accompanying figure, Figure P-4-24. The left and the right outer

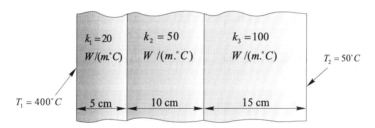

Figure P4-24

surfaces of this composite wall are kept at temperatures $T_1 = 400^\circ\text{C}$ and $T_2 = 50^\circ\text{C}$, respectively. The thickness $L_i$ and the thermal conductivity $k_i$ for $i = 1, 2, 3$ of each layer are also specified. Determine the heat transfer rate per square meter across the composite layer by assuming one-dimensional heat flow and using the thermal resistance concept.

**4-25.** A steel tube $[k = 15\text{W}/(\text{m} \cdot {}^\circ\text{C})]$ with an outside diameter of 7.6cm and a thickness of 1.3cm is covered with an insulation material $[k = 0.2\,\text{W}/(\text{m} \cdot {}^\circ\text{C})]$ 2cm thick. A hot gas at $330^\circ\text{C}$ with a heat trasnsfer coefficient of $400\ \text{W}/(\text{m}^2 \cdot {}^\circ\text{C})$ flows inside the tube. The outer surface of the insulation is exposed to cooler air at $30^\circ\text{C}$ with a heat transfer coefficient of $60\ \text{W}/(\text{m}^2 \cdot {}^\circ\text{C})$. Calculate the heat loss from the tube to the air for a 10-m length of the tube.

**4-26.** Consider a pipe of inside radius $r_1 = 2$ cm, outside radius $r_2 = 4$ cm, and thermal conductivity $k_1 = 10$ W/(m $\cdot$ °C). The inside surface is maintained at a uniform temperature $T_1 = 300$°C, and the outside surface is to be insulated with an insulation material of thermal conductivity $k_2 = 0.1$ W/(m $\cdot$ °C). The outside surface of the insulation material is exposed to an environment at $T_b = 20$°C with a heat transfer coefficient $h_b = 10$ W/(m$^2$ $\cdot$ °C). Develop an expression for determining the thickness $L$ of the insulation material needed to reduce the heat loss by 30 percent of that of the uninsulated pipe exposed to the same environmental conditions.

**4-27.** Consider a steel pipe [$k = 10$ W/(m $\cdot$ °C)] with an inside radius of 5 cm and an outside radius of 10 cm. The outside surface is to be insulated with a fiberglass insulation [$k = 0.05$ W/(m $\cdot$ °C)] to reduce the heat flow rate through the pipe wall by 50 percent. Determine the thickness of the fiberglass.

**4-28.** Consider a hollow sphere with an inside radius $r_1 = 2$ cm, an outside radius $r_2 = 4$ cm, and thermal conductivity $k_1 = 10$ W(m°C). The inside surface is maintained at a uniform temperature of $T_1 = 300$°C, and the outside surface is to be insulated with an insulating material of thermal conductivity $k_2 = 0.1$ W/(m $\cdot$ °C). The outside surface of the insulating material is exposed to an environment at $T_b = 20$°C with a heat transfer coefficient $h_b = 10$ W/(m$^2$ $\cdot$ °C). Develop an expression for determining the thickness of the insulation needed to reduce the heat loss by 30 percent of that of the uninsulated hollow sphere exposed to the same environmental conditions.

**4-29.** Consider a hollow steel sphere [$k = 10$ W/(m $\cdot$ °C)] with an inside radius of 5 cm and an outside radius of 10 cm. The outside surface is to be insulated with a fiberglass insulation [$k = 0.05$ W/(m $\cdot$ °C)] to reduce the heat flow rate through the sphere wall by 50 percent. Determine the thickness of the fiberglass.

**4-30.** A steel tube [$k = 15$ W/(m $\cdot$ °C)] with an outside diameter of 7.6cm and a thickness of 1.3 cm is covered with an insulation [$k = 0.2$ W/(m $\cdot$ °C)] 2 cm thick. A hot gas with a heat transfer coefficient of 400 W/(m$^2$ $\cdot$ °C) flows inside the tube, and the outer surface of the insulation is exposed to cooler air with a heat transfer coefficient of 60 W/(m$^2$ $\cdot$ °C). Calculate the overall heat transfer coefficient $U$ based on the outside surface area of the insulation.

**4-31.** The thickness of the insulation in Problem 4-30 is increased to 4 cm. Calculate the overall heat transfer coefficient $U$ based on the outside surface area of the insulation material.

**4-32.** Calculate the overall heat transfer coefficient $U$ of Problem 4-30 based on the inside surface area of the insulation material.

**4-33.** Consider a composite wall consisting of two layers of different materials $A$ and $B$, as illustrated in Figure P4-33. Layer $A$ is in contact with a hot fluid at $T_a = 200$°C.

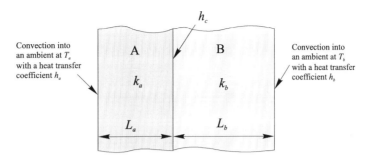

Figure P4-33

The heat transfer coefficient for that surface is $h_a = 15\ \text{W}/(\text{m}^2 \cdot {}^\circ\text{C})$. Layer $B$ is in contact with a cold fluid at $T_b = 30{}^\circ\text{C}$. The heat transfer coefficient for that surface is $h_b = 25\ \text{W}/(\text{m}^2 \cdot {}^\circ\text{C})$. The contact conductance between layers $A$ and $B$ is $h_c = 3\ \text{W}/(\text{m}^2 \cdot {}^\circ\text{C})$. Layer $A$ is $L_a = 2$ cm thick and has a thermal conductivity $k_a = 0.1\ \text{W}/(\text{m} \cdot {}^\circ\text{C})$. Layer $B$ is $L_b = 4$ cm thick and has a thermal conductivity $k_b = 0.05\ \text{W}/(\text{m} \cdot {}^\circ\text{C})$. Determine-the rate of heat transfer through the composite wall per square meter of the surface.

**4-34.** A composite wall consists of four different materials is shown in Figure P4-34. Since the upper and lower surfaces are insulated, the heat flow will be one-dimensional.

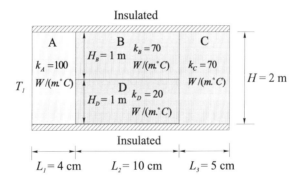

Figure P4-34

The dimensions and the thermal conductivities of each layer are also given. The left outer surface temperature is at $T = 200{}^\circ\text{C}$ and the right outer surface are is at $T = 30{}^\circ\text{C}$. Using the thermal resistance concept, determine the heat flow rate per square meter of the exposed surface.

**4-35.** A 3.5-m-high and 6-m-wide wall consists of long 18-cm $\times$ 24.5-cm cross section horizontal bricks ($k = 0.6\ \text{W}/(\text{m} \cdot {}^\circ\text{C})$) separated by 4-cm-thick plaster layers ($k = 0.22\ \text{W}/(\text{m} \cdot {}^\circ\text{C})$). There are also 2.2-cm-thick plaster layers on each side of the brick and a 3.2-cm-thick rigid foam ($k = 0.2\ \text{W}/(\text{m} \cdot {}^\circ\text{C})$) on the inner side of the wall, as shown in Figure P4-35. The indoor and outdoor temperatures are

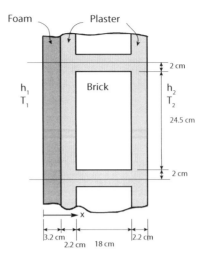

Figure P4-35

27°C and 10°C. The convection heat transfer coeficicents on the inner and outer wall sides are $h_1 = 10$ W/(m² · °C) and $h_2 = 30$ W/(m² · °C), respectively. Assuming one-dimensional heat transfer. Neglect radiation het transfer. (i) Draw the thermal resistance network. (ii) Determine the rate of heat transfer through this wall.

**4-36.** Consider a brass tube [$k = 115$ W/(m · °C)] with an outside radius of 4 cm and a thickness of 0.5 cm. The inside surface of the tube is kept at uniform temperature, and the outside surface is covered with two layers of insulation, each 1 cm thick, with thermal conductivities of 0.1 W/(m · °C) and 0.05 W/(m · °C), respectively. Calculate the overall heat transfer coefficient based on the outside surface area of the outer insulation.

**4-37.** An iron plate 2.5 cm thick [$k = 62$ W/(m · °C)] is in contact with asbestos insulation 1 cm thick [$k = 0.2$ W/(m · °C)] on one side and exposed to hot gas with a heat transfer coefficient of 200W/(m² · °C) on the other surface. If the outer surface of the asbestos is exposed to cool air with a heat transfer coefficient of 40 W/(m² · °C). Calculate the overall heat transfer coefficient $U$ and the heat flow rate across the composite wall per square meter of the surface for a $\Delta T$ of 200°C between the hot gas and cool air.

**4-38.** A brass condenser tube [$k = 115$ W/(m · C)] with an outside diameter of 3 cm and a thickness of 0.25 cm is used to condense steam on its outer surface with a heat transfer coefficient of 4000 W/(m² · °C). Cooling water with a heat transfer coefficient of 5000 W/(m² · °C) flows inside. Find the overall heat transfer coefficient based on the outside surface area of the condenser tube, and calculate the heat transfer rate per 10-m length of the tube for a $\Delta T = 10°C$ between the condensing steam and the cooling water.

**4-39.** A steel tube $[k = 15 \text{ W}/(\text{m} \cdot °\text{C})]$ with an outside diameter of 8 cm and a thickness of 2 cm is covered with an insulation $[k = 0.07 \text{ W}/(\text{m} \cdot °\text{C})]$ 2 cm thick. A hot gas with a heat transfer coefficient of $500 \text{ W}/(\text{m}^2 \cdot °\text{C})$ flows inside the tube. The outer surface of the insulation is exposed to air with a heat transfer coefficient of $50 \text{ W}/(\text{m}^2 \cdot °\text{C})$. Find the overall heat transfer coefficient based on the inside surface area of the steel tube.

**4-40.** Consider a hollow brass sphere $[k = 115 \text{ W}/(\text{m} \cdot °\text{C})]$ with an outside radius of 4 cm and a thickness of 0.5 cm. The outside surface is covered with an insulation $[k = 0.05 \text{ W}/(\text{m} \cdot °\text{C})]$ 1 cm thick. The inside surface of the sphere is kept at a uniform temperature. The outer surface of the insulation is exposed to air with a heat transfer coefficient of $60 \text{ W}/(\text{m}^2 \cdot °\text{C})$. Calculate the overall heat transfer coefficient based on the outside surface area of the insulation and the total heat transfer rate for a $\Delta T = 200°C$ between the inner surface of the sphere and the outside air temperatures.
*Answer*: 23.6 W.

*Contact Resistance Concept*

**4-41.** Two stainless steel pipes are pressed together with a pressure of 10 atm. The surfaces have a roughness of about 2.54 μm and are kept at a mean temperature of 100°C. Determine the interface contact conductance. What would be the contact conductance for a roughness of about 0.76 μm?

**4-42.** Consider two stainless steel plates of thicknesses 0.5 cm and 1 cm, pressed together with a pressure of 10 atm. The surfaces have roughnesses of about 2.54 μm. The outside surfaces of the walls are at 200°C and 100°C. Calculate the heat flow rate per square meter of wall area. What would be the heat flow rate for an interface roughness of 0.76 μm?

**4-43.** Consider two stainless steel slabs $[k = 20 \text{ W}/(\text{m} \cdot °\text{C})]$ with thicknesses of 1 cm and 1.5 cm that are pressed together with a pressure of 20 atm. The surfaces have roughnesses of about 0.76 μm. The outside surfaces of the blocks are at 100°C and 150°C. Calculate the heat flow rate across the slabs and the temperature drop at the interface.

*Two-Dimensional Steady-State Heat Conduction: Conduction Shape Factors*

**4-44.** Consider a spherical heat source with an outside diameter of 0.5 m buried 3 m below the surface of a semi-infinite soil $[k = 0.5 \text{ W}/(\text{m} \cdot °\text{C})]$. If the surface of the source is at 50°C and the surface of the soil is at 20°C, determine the steady heat flow rate from the sphere to the soil.

**4-45.** A spherical heat source with an outside diameter of 30 cm is buried 150 cm below the surface of a semi-infinite soil [$k = 0.5$ W/(m · °C)] at 20°C. If the surface of the source is kept at 50°C, and the surface of the soil is insulated, calculate the steady heat flow from the sphere to the soil.

**4-46.** A pipe with an outer radius of 5 cm, carrying a hot fluid at 200°C, is buried in the earth [$k = 1.3$ W/(m · °C)]. The distance between the pipe center and the earth's surface is 2 m. The pipe is covered with a 2-cm-thick fiberglass layer [$k = 0.04$ W/(m · °C)]. The surface of the earth is at 15°C. Determine the heat loss per meter length of the pipe.

**4-47.** A cylindrical heat source and a cylindrical heat sink, each having a radius of 10 cm and a length of 8m, are buried in an infinite medium of fireclay brick [$k = 1$W/(m · °C)], 15 cm apart and parallel to each other. The surfaces of the cylinders are measured to be 500°C and 400°C, respectively. Determine the steady heat flow from one cylinder to the other.

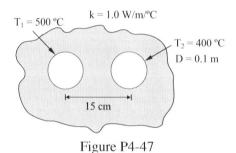

Figure P4-47

**4-48.** A cylindrical storage tank with a radius of 1 m and a length of 3 m is buried in each [$k = 1.3$ W/(m · °C)] with its axis parallel to the surface of the earth. The distance between the tank axis and the earth's surface is 2 m. The tank is kept at 70°C, and the earth's surface is at 15°C. Determine the heat loss from the tank.

**4-49.** A spherical tank with a radius of 2m containing some radioactive material is buried in earth [$k = 1.6$ W/(m · °C)]. The center of the sphere is 5 m from the earth's surface. The tank is at 200°C, and the earth's surface is at 25°C. Determine the heat loss from the sphere.

**4-50.** A hot pipe with an outside radius of 10 cm passes through the hole at the center of a long concrete block [$k = 0.76$ W/(m · °C)] 1 m × 1 m in cross section. The pipe surface is at 100°C, and the outer surface of the block is at 25°C. Determine the heat loss from the pipe per meter length of the pipe.

**4-51.** A hot water pipe with an outside radius of 1 cm is embedded eccentrically inside a long cylindrical concrete block radius of 10 cm. The distance between the center of the pipe and the cylinder is 7 cm. The outside surface of the concrete is maintained at 25°C. The heat loss from the hot water to the concrete is 100 W/m length. Determine the wall temperature of the pipe.

*Extended Surfaces*

**4-52.** Aluminum fins of rectangular profile are attached on a plane wall. The fins have thickness $t = 1\,mm$, length $L = 10\,mm$, and thermal conductivity $k = 200\,W/(m \cdot °C)$. The wall is maintained at a temperature $T_0 = 200°C$, and the fins dissipate heat by convection into the ambient air at $T_\infty = 40°C$ with a heat transfer coefficient $h_\infty = 50\,W/(m^2 \cdot °C)$. Determine the fin efficiency.

**4-53.** Circular aluminum fins of constant rectangular profile are attached to a tube of outside diameter $D = 5\,cm$. The fins have thickness $t = 2\,mm$, height $L = 15\,mm$, and thermal conductivity $k = 200\,W/(m \cdot °C)$. The tube surface is maintained at a uniform temperature $T_0 = 200°C$, and the fins dissipate heat by convection into the ambient air at $T_\infty = 30°C$ with a heat transfer coefficient $h_\infty = 50\,W/(m^2 \cdot °C)$. Determine the fin efficiency.

**4-54.** An iron rod of length $L = 30$ cm, diameter $D = 1$ cm, and thermal conductivity $k = 65\,W/(m \cdot °C)$ is attached horizontally to a large tank at temperature $T_0 = 200°C$, as illustrated in the accompanying figure. The rod is dissipating heat by convection into ambient air at $T_\infty = 20°C$ with a heat transfer coefficient $h_\infty = 15\,W/(m^2 \cdot °C)$. What is the temperature of the rod at distances of 10 and 20 cm from the tank surface?.

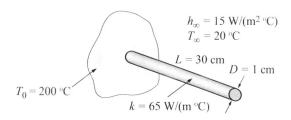

Figure P4-54

**4-55.** An aluminum fin of rectangular profile has a thickness $t = 2$ mm, length $L = 20\,mm$, and thermal conductivity $k = 200\,W/(m \cdot °C)$. Heat is dissipated from the fin by convection into ambient air at $T_\infty = 20°C$ with a heat transfer coefficient $h_\infty = 40\,W/(m^2 \cdot °C)$. If the fin base is at $T_0 = 150°C$, calculate the heat loss from the fin into the ambient air.

**4-56.** An iron rod of length $L = 20$ cm, diameter $D = 2$ cm, and thermal conductivity $k = 65\,W/(m \cdot °C)$ is attached to a large surface at $T_0 = 150°C$. The rod has dissipated heat into the ambient air at $T_\infty = 20°C$ with a heat transfer coefficient

$h_\infty = 15\,\mathrm{W/(m^2 \cdot °C)}$. Calculate the heat transfer rate from the rod to the ambient. *Answers*: (b) 0.25, (c) 11.6 W.

**4-57.** A low carbon steel rod of length $L = 40$ cm, diameter $D = 10$ mm, and thermal conductivity $k = 40\,\mathrm{W/(m \cdot °C)}$ is placed in a medium where one of its end temperatures reaches to $T_\infty = 400°C$ and is kept at that temperature. The ambient is at $T_\infty = 30°C$, and the heat transfer coefficient is $10\,\mathrm{W/(m^2 \cdot °C)}$. Determine *(a)* the temperature profile, *(b)* the fin efficiency, and *(c)* the heat transfer rate from the fin to the ambient.

# CHAPTER 5

## *Steady Conduction with Energy Generation: Analytic and Numerical Solutions*

Heat conduction problems involving energy generation in the solid come up in numerous engineering applications, including heat removal from the fuel elements of nuclear reactors, heat dissipation from an electrically heated source, and many others. In this chapter we present analytic and numerical solution techniques for determining temperature distribution and heat flow in one-dimensional steady-state heat conduction with energy generation in solids having simple shapes, such as a plane wall, a long cylinder, or a sphere. Problems of this type cannot be solved with the thermal resistance concept presented previously.

The methodology for analytic solution of such problems is systematically presented and illustrated with examples. The finite-difference formulation of heat conduction problems is introduced, numerical solution techniques are discussed, and computer applications are illustrated.

## 5.1. ANALYTIC SOLUTIONS

In this section we are concerned with the analytic solution of the one dimensional steady-state heat conduction equation with energy generation and the determination of temperature distribution and/or heat flow rate in the medium. The problem of heat flow in simple geometries, such as a plane wall, a long cylinder, and a sphere, is studied, and illustrative examples are given.

### 5.1.1 Plane Wall with Energy Generation and Constant Surface Temperatures

Consider a plane wall of thickness L, as illustrated in Fig. 5.1a. The boundary surfaces at $x = 0$ and $x = L$ are maintained at constant but different temperatures $T_1$ and $T_2$, respectively. The thermal conductivity of the slab $k$ is constant, and within the slab, energy is generated at a constant rate of $g$ W/m$^3$. The governing differential equation is Eq. (3-17a). Then the mathematical formulation of this heat conduction problem becomes

$$\frac{d^2 T(x)}{dx^2} + \frac{g}{k} = 0 \quad \text{in } 0 < x < L \tag{5-1a}$$

$$T(x) = T_1 \quad \text{at } x = 0 \tag{5-1b}$$

$$T(x) = T_2 \quad \text{at } x = L. \tag{5-1c}$$

The temperature distribution $T(x)$ in the slab can readily be determined by direct integration of the differential equation and then application of the boundary conditions, as now described. Integrating Eq. (5-1a) twice yields

$$T(x) = -\frac{g}{2k} x^2 + C_1 x + C_2. \tag{5-2}$$

The application of the first boundary condition gives

$$C_2 = T_1 \tag{5-3}$$

and the application of the second boundary condition results in

$$T_2 = -\frac{g}{2k} L^2 + C_1 L + C_2 \tag{5-4a}$$

or

$$C_1 = \frac{gL}{2k} + \frac{T_2 - T_1}{L}. \tag{5-4b}$$

Knowing $C_1$ and $C_2$, the temperature distribution in Eq. (5-2) becomes

$$T(x) = \frac{gL^2}{2k} \left[ \frac{x}{L} - \left( \frac{x}{L} \right)^2 \right] + (T_2 - T_1) \frac{x}{L} + T_1 \tag{5-5}$$

which is a *parabolic temperature distribution*. Here, the first term on the right-hand side is the contribution of the energy generation in the medium to the temperature distribution, and the second and third terms are the contributions of the temperatures of the boundary surfaces.

We consider some special cases of the result given by Eq. (5-5).

**(a) No energy generation:**
For the case of no energy generation, we set $g = 0$, and Eq. (5-5) reduces to

$$T(x) = (T_2 - T_1) \frac{x}{L} + T_1 \tag{5-6}$$

which is a *linear temperature distribution*.

**(b) Boundary surface temperatures are equal:**
If the boundary surface temperatures $T_1$ and $T_2$ are equal, $T_1 = T_2 \equiv T_w$, Eq. (5-5) reduces to

$$T(x) = \frac{gL^2}{2k} \left[ \frac{x}{L} - \left( \frac{x}{L} \right)^2 \right] + T_w \tag{5-7}$$

which is a *parabolic and symmetrical temperature* distribution having a maximum temperature at the symmetry axis $x = L/2$, as illustrated in Fig. 5.1b. For this particular case the problem has both geometric and thermal symmetry about the centerline of the plane. In such situations it is convenient to formulate the problem by shifting the origin of the x coordinate to the centerline of the plate, as illustrated in Fig. 5.1c.

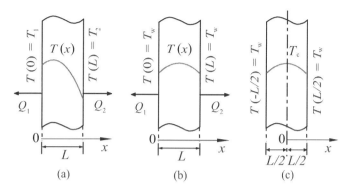

**FIG. 5.1.** A plate with energy generation. (a) Asymmetric temperature distribution, (b) symmetric temperature distribution, and (c) shift of the origin for the symmetric case.

Then the mathematical formulation of the problem is considered only for one-half of the plate, $0 < x < L/2$, as given below:

$$\frac{d^2 T(x)}{dx^2} + \frac{1}{k} g = 0 \quad \text{in } 0 < x < \frac{L}{2} \tag{5-8a}$$

$$\frac{dT(x)}{dx} = 0 \quad \text{at } x = 0 \tag{5-8b}$$

$$T(x) = T_w \quad \text{at } x = \frac{L}{2} \tag{5-8c}$$

This problem is solved by integrating Eq. (5-8a) twice and applying the boundary conditions (5-8b) and (5-8c). The resulting expression for the temperature becomes

$$T(x) = \frac{gL^2}{2k} \left[ \frac{1}{4} - \left( \frac{x}{L} \right)^2 \right] + T_w , \tag{5-9}$$

where the origin of the $x$-coordinate is at the centerline of the slab, as shown in Fig. 5.1c.

The temperature at the centerline, $x = 0$, is obtained from Eq. (5-9) by setting $x = 0$.

$$T = \frac{gL^2}{8k} + T_w \tag{5-10}$$

**Energy Leaving the plate:**
The energy leaving the plate from its boundary surfaces is a quantity of practical interest that can be determined from the definition of the heat flux. We consider the symmetrical problem illustrated in Fig. 5.1c and the corresponding temperature profile given by Eq. (5-9).

The energy leaving the slab from the right boundary surface at $x = L/2$ is determined from

$$q\left(\frac{L}{2}\right) = -k \left. \frac{dT(x)}{dx}\right|_{x=\frac{L}{2}} . \tag{5-11a}$$

Introducing the temperature given by Eq. (5-9) into Eq. (5-11a) and setting $x = L/2$, the heat flux at the boundary surface $x = L/2$ becomes

$$q\left(\frac{L}{2}\right) = \frac{gL}{2} \quad \text{W/m}^2 \tag{5-11b}$$

Since the quantity $gL/2$ is positive, the heat flux $q(L/2)$ is positive. This implies that the heat flow at the boundary surface $x = L/2$ is in the positive $x$ direction, or outward.

Similarly, the heat flux at the left boundary surface $x = -L/2$ is determined from

$$q\left(-\frac{L}{2}\right) = -k \left. \frac{dT(x)}{dx}\right|_{x=-\frac{L}{2}} . \tag{5-12a}$$

Introducing the temperature profile Eq. (5-9) into Eq. (5-12a) and setting $x = -L/2$, the heat flux at $x = -L/2$ becomes

$$q\left(-\frac{L}{2}\right) = -\frac{gL}{2} \quad \text{W/m}^2 . \tag{5-12b}$$

Here, the quantity $-gL/2$ is negative, and so $q(-L/2)$ is also negative. This implies that the heat flow at the boundary surface $x = -L/2$ is in the negative $x$ direction, or outward.

### 5.1.2 Plane Wall with Energy Generation and Convection

To illustrate the solution of a heat conduction problem for a plane wall with energy generation at a constant rate $g$ W/m$^3$ and with a convection boundary condition, we consider the physical problem illustrated in Fig. 5.2. Here, the boundary surface at $x = 0$ is insulated (i.e., adiabatic), and the boundary surface at $x = L$ dissipates heat by convection with a heat transfer coefficient $h_\infty$ into an ambient at temperature $T_\infty$. The mathematical formulation of the problem is given by

$$\frac{d^2T(x)}{dx^2} + \frac{g}{k} = 0 \quad \text{in } 0 < x < L \tag{5-13a}$$

$$\frac{dT(x)}{dx} = 0 \quad \text{at } x = 0 \tag{5-13b}$$

$$-k\frac{dT(x)}{dx} = h_\infty[T(x) - T_\infty] \quad \text{at } x = L . \tag{5-13c}$$

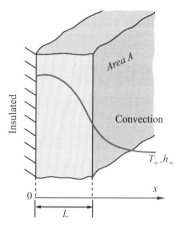

**FIG. 5.2.** A plate with energy generation subject to convective and insulated boundary condition.

To solve this heat conduction problem, Eq. (5-13a) is integrated twice. The first integration gives

$$\frac{dT(x)}{dx} = -\frac{g}{k} x + C_1 \tag{5-14}$$

and the application of the boundary condition Eq. (5-13b) establishes $C_1$ as

$$0 = 0 + C_1 \quad \text{or} \quad C_1 = 0 . \tag{5-15}$$

Then

$$\frac{dT(x)}{dx} = -\frac{g}{k} x . \tag{5-16}$$

The integration of Eq. (5-14) with $C_1 = 0$ results in

$$T(x) = -\frac{g}{2k} x^2 + C_2 \tag{5-17}$$

and the application of the second boundary condition gives

$$-k\left(-\frac{g}{k} L\right) = h_\infty \left(-\frac{g}{2k} L^2 + C_2 - T_\infty\right)$$

or

$$C_2 = \frac{gL^2}{2k} + \frac{gL}{h_\infty} + T_\infty . \tag{5-18}$$

Then the temperature distribution becomes

$$T(x) = \frac{gL^2}{2k} \left[1 - \left(\frac{x}{L}\right)^2\right] + \frac{gL}{h_\infty} + T_\infty . \tag{5-19}$$

We now examine the physical significance of the two limiting cases, $h_\infty \to \infty$ and $h_\infty \to 0$, of the solution (5-19).

**(a)** $h_\infty \to \infty$

For very large values of the heat transfer coefficient, $h_\infty \to \infty$, the second term on the right vanishes and Eq. (5-19) reduces to

$$T(x) = \frac{gL^2}{2k}\left[1 - \left(\frac{x}{L}\right)^2\right] + T_\infty .\qquad(5\text{-}20)$$

This result implies that as $h_\infty \to \infty$, the thermal resistance between the wall surface and the fluid is zero, and hence the surface temperature at $x = L$ equals the ambient temperature $T_\infty$.

**(b)** $h_\infty \to 0$

For very small values of the heat transfer coefficient, $h_\infty > 0$. The solution (5-19) shows that the temperature $T(x)$ becomes infinite. The physical significance of this particular situation is better envisioned by recalling the boundary condition (5-13c). As $h_\infty \to 0$, the boundary conditions (5-13c) reduces to

$$\frac{dT(x)}{dx} \to 0 \qquad h_\infty \to 0 .$$

This result implies that both boundaries of the plate, $x = 0$ and $x = L$, are insulated while energy is continuously generated within the medium. As the generated energy has no way to escape through the insulated boundaries, the temperature of the slab continuously increases, or *the problem does not have a steady-state solution.*

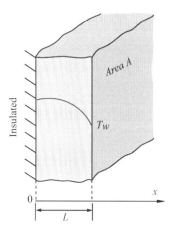

**FIGURE EXAMPLE 5-1**

**EXAMPLE 5-1** Consider a slab of thickness 0.1 m. One of the boundary surfaces, that at $x = 0$, is kept insulated, and the other, at $x = 0.1$ m, is kept at $0°$ C. There is uniform energy generation at a rate of $10^6$ W/m$^3$ in the solid, and the thermal conductivity is constant [$k = 40$ W/(m $\cdot\,°$ C)]. Determine the temperature of the insulated surface.

**SOLUTION** The problem is illustrated in the accompanying figure. Given $L = 0.1$ m, $k = 40$ W/(m $\cdot$ °C), $g = 10^6$ W/m$^3$, and $T_\infty = 0$° C, Eq. (5-20) can be used to determine the temperature distribution in the slab. We find

$$
\begin{aligned}
T(x) &= \frac{gL^2}{2k}\left[1 - \left(\frac{x}{L}\right)^2\right] + T_\infty \\
&= \frac{10^6 \times (0.1)^2}{2 \times 40}\left[1 - \left(\frac{x}{0.1}\right)^2\right] + 0 \\
&= 125(1 - 100x^2)
\end{aligned}
$$

and the temperature of the insulated surface is calculated by setting x = 0:

$$
\begin{aligned}
T(0) &= 125(1 - 100 \times 0) \\
&= 125°\,\mathrm{C}
\end{aligned}
$$

### 5.1.3 Solid Cylinder with Energy Generation and Constant Surface Temperature

Consider a long solid cylinder of radius $r = b$, as illustrated in Fig. 5-3. The boundary surface is maintained at a uniform temperature $T_\infty$. There is energy generation in the solid at a constant rate of $g$ W/m$^3$, and the thermal conductivity is constant. We wish to determine the temperature distribution and the heat flow rate in the solid.

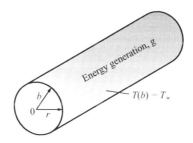

**FIG. 5.3.** A long solid cylinder with energy generation.

The heat conduction equation is given by Eq. (3-17b), and the boundary condition at the outer surface is as specified above. The boundary condition at the center, $r = 0$ is established from the fact that the problem possesses geometric and thermal symmetry about the centerline, and hence $dT/dr$ must be zero at $r = 0$. With this consideration, the mathematical formulation of the problem is given by

$$
\frac{1}{r}\frac{d}{dr}\left[r\,\frac{dT(r)}{dr}\right] + \frac{g}{k} = 0 \quad \text{in } 0 < r < b \tag{5-21a}
$$

$$
\frac{dT(r)}{dr} = 0 \quad \text{at } r = 0 \tag{5-21b}
$$

$$T(r) = T_w \quad \text{at } r = b . \tag{5-21c}$$

This problem can be solved by direct integration, as we did for the case of the plate problem. The first integration of Eq. (5-21a) gives

$$r\,\frac{dT(r)}{dr} = -\,\frac{g}{2k}\,r^2 + C_1$$

or

$$\frac{dT(r)}{dr} = -\,\frac{g}{2k}\,r + \frac{C_1}{r} . \tag{5-22}$$

The application of the boundary condition (5-21b) requires

$$C_1 = 0$$

so that

$$\frac{dT(r)}{dr} = -\,\frac{g}{2k}\,r . \tag{5-23}$$

Integration of Eq. (5-23) gives

$$T(r) = -\,\frac{g}{4k}\,r^2 + C_2 \tag{5-24}$$

and the application of the boundary condition (5-21c) establishes $C_2$ :

$$T_w = -\,\frac{g}{4k}\,b^2 + C_2$$

or

$$C_2 = \frac{gb^2}{4k} + T_w . \tag{5-25}$$

Introducing Eq. (5-25) into (5-24) yields the temperature distribution in the cylinder as

$$T(r) = \frac{gb^2}{4k}\left[1 - \left(\frac{r}{b}\right)^2\right] + T_w . \tag{5-26}$$

The heat flux anywhere in the medium is determined from its definition,

$$q(r) = -k\,\frac{dT(r)}{dr} . \tag{5-27}$$

Introducing the temperature profile equation, Eq. (5-26) into Eq. (5-27), we obtain

$$q(r) = \frac{gr}{2} . \tag{5-28}$$

Generally, the heat flux at the boundary surface is a quantity of practical interest. It is immediately determined by setting $r = b$ in Eq. (5-28),

$$q(b) = \frac{gb}{2} \quad \text{W/m}^2 . \tag{5-29}$$

Here, since $gb/2$ is a positive quantity, the heat flux $q(b)$ is positive, and hence the heat flow is in the positive $r$ direction or outward. This result is expected from physical considerations. In the problem considered here, the highest temperature occurs at the center of the cylinder, and the centerline temperature $T_{\mathrm{\mathlarger{\ell}}}$ is obtained from Eq. (5-26) by setting $r = 0$

$$T_{\mathrm{\mathlarger{\ell}}} = \frac{gb^2}{4k} + T_w . \tag{5-30}$$

Clearly, the larger the radius, the larger the generation rate, or the smaller the thermal conductivity, the larger the center temperature is.

## 5.1.4 Solid Cylinder with Energy Generation and Convection

In the above discussion we considered a problem involving a solid cylinder subjected to a constant temperature boundary condition at the outer surface. However, in most practical applications energy is dissipated by convection from the outer surface into an ambient at a specified constant temperature $T_\infty$, as illustrated in Fig. 5.4. Therefore, we consider heat conduction in a solid cylinder of radius $r = b$ with energy generation at a constant rate of $g$ W/m$^3$, but subjected to convection at the outer surface with a heat transfer coefficient $h_\infty$ into an ambient at a temperature $T_\infty$. The mathematical formulation of this problem is given by

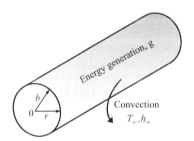

**FIG. 5.4.** A long solid cylinder with energy generation subject to convection boundary condition.

$$\frac{1}{r}\frac{d}{dr}\left[ r\frac{dT(r)}{dr} \right] + \frac{g}{k} = 0 \quad \text{in } 0 < r < b \tag{5-31a}$$

$$\frac{dT(r)}{dr} = 0 \quad \text{at } r = 0 \tag{5-31b}$$

$$-k\frac{dT(r)}{dr} = h_\infty[T(r) - T_\infty] \quad \text{at } r = b . \tag{5-31c}$$

The solution for the temperature distribution $T(r)$ is developed by following the general procedure described previously. That is, the integration of Eq. (5-31a) and the application of the boundary condition (5-31b) gives $C_1 = 0$; then

$$\frac{dT(r)}{dr} = -\frac{g}{2k}\, r \; . \tag{5-32}$$

Integration of this equation gives

$$T(r) = -\frac{g}{4k}\, r^2 + C_2 \tag{5-33a}$$

and then the application of the boundary condition (5-31c) gives the integration constant $C_2$ as

$$C_2 = \frac{g}{4k}\, b^2 + \frac{g}{2h_\infty}\, b + T_\infty \; . \tag{5-33b}$$

Knowing $C_2$ the temperature distribution $T(r)$ in the cylinder becomes

$$T(r) = \frac{gb^2}{4k}\left[1 - \left(\frac{r}{b}\right)^2\right] + \frac{gb}{2h_\infty} + T_\infty \; . \tag{5-34}$$

We now examine the physical significance of two limiting cases, $h_\infty \to \infty$ and $h_\infty \to 0$, of the solution (5-34).

**(a)** $h_\infty \to \infty$

For very large values of the heat transfer coefficient, $h_\infty \to \infty$, the second term on the right-hand side vanishes, and Eq. (5-34) reduces to

$$T(r) = \frac{gb^2}{4k}\left[1 - \left(\frac{r}{b}\right)^2\right] + T_\infty \tag{5-35}$$

which is identical to Eq. (5-26) for the case of constant surface temperature. This is expected, because thermal resistance between the surface and the ambient vanishes as $h_\infty \to \infty$, and the surface temperature is equal to the ambient temperature $T_\infty$.

**(b)** $h_\infty \to 0$

For very small values of the heat transfer coefficient, $h_\infty \to 0$, the solution (5-34) shows that the temperature $T(r)$ becomes infinite. The physical significance of this particular situation becomes apparent from the boundary condition (5-31c), which becomes

$$\frac{dT(r)}{dr} \to 0 \quad \text{as } h_\infty \to 0 \; .$$

Then we have a physical problem involving a solid cylinder with energy generation in the solid and an insulated outer boundary. As the energy generated has no way to escape from the insulated boundary, the temperature continuously increases; hence, *the problem has no steady-state solution.*

The heat flux $q(r)$ anywhere in the cylinder is determined from the definition

$$q(r) = -k \, \frac{dT(r)}{dr} \, . \tag{5-36}$$

Introducing the solution (5-34) into Eq. (5-36), we obtain

$$q(r) = \frac{g}{2} \, r \, , \tag{5-37}$$

which is identical with the result given by Eq. (5-28) for a cylinder with constant surface temperature.

**EXAMPLE 5-2** A 3-mm-diameter chrome-nickel wire of thermal conductivity 20 W/(m · °C) is heated electrically by the passage of electric current, which generates energy within the wire at a uniform rate of $10^9$ W/m$^3$. If the surface of the wire is maintained at $100°$ C, determine the center temperature of the wire.

**SOLUTION** Given: $b = 0.0015$ m, $k = 20$ W/(m · °C), $g = 10^9$ W/m$^3$, and $T_w = 100°$ C. Equation (5-26) or (5-34) with hoax can be used to determine the temperature distribution $T(r)$ as

$$
\begin{aligned}
T(r) &= \frac{gb^2}{4k} \left[ 1 - \left( \frac{r}{b} \right)^2 \right] + T_w \\
&= \frac{10^9 \times (0.0015)^2}{4 \times 20} \left[ 1 - \left( \frac{r}{b} \right)^2 \right] + 100 \, . \\
&= 28.12(1 - 4.44 \times 10^5 \, r^2) + 100
\end{aligned}
$$

The temperature of the center, $r = 0$, becomes

$$T(0) = 128.12° \, \text{C} \, .$$

**EXAMPLE 5-3** In a cylindrical fuel element for a gas-cooled nuclear reactor, the energy generation from within the fuel element due to fission can be approximated by the relation

$$g(r) = g_0 \left[ 1 - \left( \frac{r}{b} \right)^2 \right] \quad \text{W/m}^3$$

where $b$ is the radius of the fuel element and $g_0$ is constant. The boundary surface at $r = b$ is maintained at a uniform temperature $T_w$.

*(i)* Assuming one-dimensional steady heat flow, develop a relation for the temperature drop from the centerline to the surface of the fuel element.

*(ii)* For radius $b = 1$ cm, thermal conductivity $k = 10$ W/(m · °C), and $g = 1.6 \times 10^8$ W/m$^3$, calculate the temperature drop from the centerline to the surface.

**SOLUTION** *(i)* The mathematical formulation of the problem is given as

$$\frac{1}{r}\frac{d}{dr}\left[r\frac{dT(r)}{dr}\right] + \frac{g(r)}{k} = 0 \quad \text{in } 0 < r < b \tag{5-38}$$

$$\frac{dT(r)}{dr} = 0 \quad \text{at } r = 0 \tag{5-39}$$

$$T(r) = T_w \quad \text{at } r = b \tag{5-40}$$

where

$$g(r) = g_0\left[1 - \left(\frac{r}{b}\right)^2\right] \quad \text{W/m}^3 .$$

Substituting the energy generation rate $g(r)$ into the differential equation and rearranging results:

$$\frac{d}{dr}\left(r\frac{dT}{dr}\right) = -\frac{g}{k}\left(r - \frac{r^3}{b^2}\right).$$

The first integration of this equation gives

$$r\frac{dT}{dr} = -\frac{g}{k}\left(\frac{r^2}{2} - \frac{r^4}{4b^2}\right) + C_1$$

and the application of the boundary condition at $r = 0$ results in $C_1 = 0$. Then with $C_1 = 0$. we have

$$\frac{dT}{dr} = -\frac{g}{k}\left(\frac{r}{2} - \frac{r^3}{4b^2}\right).$$

Integration of this equation gives

$$T(r) = -\frac{g}{k}\left(\frac{r^2}{4} - \frac{r^4}{16b^2}\right) + C_2$$

and then the application of the boundary condition at $r = b$ gives $C_2$ as

$$C_2 = \frac{3gb^2}{16k} + T_w .$$

Therefore, the temperature distribution in the fuel element becomes

$$T(r) = -\frac{gr^2}{4k}\left[1 - \left(\frac{r}{2b}\right)^2\right] + \frac{3gb^2}{16k} + T_w .$$

The center temperature $T_\mathbb{C}$ is obtained by setting $r = 0$ in this result. Then the temperature drop from the center to the surface, $T_\mathbb{C} - T_w$, becomes

$$T_\mathbb{C} - T_w = \frac{3gb^2}{16k} .$$

*(ii)* For $b = 1$ cm, $k = 10$ W/(m $\cdot$ °C), and $g = 1.6 \times 10^8$ W/m$^3$, the temperature drop is calculated as

$$T_{\text{¢}} - T_w = \frac{3 \times (1.6 \times 10^8) \times (1 \times 10^{-2})^2}{16 \times 10}$$

$$= 300°\,C\,.$$

**EXAMPLE 5-4** A hollow cylindrical fuel element of inner radius $a$ and outer radius $b$ is heated uniformly within the entire volume at a constant rate of $g$ W/m$^3$ as a result of disintegration of radioactive elements. The inner and outer surfaces of the fuel element are at zero temperature, and the thermal conductivity of the material is constant. Develop an expression for the one-dimensional steady temperature distribution $T(r)$ within the cylinder.

**SOLUTION** The mathematical formulation of the problem is given as

$$\frac{1}{r}\frac{d}{dr}\left[r\,\frac{dT(r)}{dr}\right] + \frac{g}{k} = 0 \quad \text{in } a < r < b$$

$$T(r) = 0 \quad \text{at } r = a$$

$$T(r) = 0 \quad \text{at } r = b\,.$$

Integrating the differential equation twice, we have

$$T(r) = -\frac{g}{4k}\,r^2 + C_1\,\ln r + C_2$$

and the application of the boundary conditions gives the integration constants $C_1$ and $C_2$ as

$$C_1 = \frac{g}{4k}\,\frac{b^2 - a^2}{\ln(b/a)}$$

$$C_2 = \frac{g}{4k}\left[a^2 - \frac{b^2 - a^2}{\ln(b/a)}\,\ln a\right]\,.$$

After rearranging, the temperature distribution $T(r)$ becomes

$$T(r) = \frac{g}{4k}\left[a^2 - r^2 + \frac{(b^2 - a^2)}{\ln(b/a)}\,\ln\frac{r}{a}\right]\,.$$

## 5.1.5 Sphere with Energy Generation and Convection

We are now concerned with the problem of steady-state heat conduction in a solid sphere of radius $b$, having constant thermal conductivity $k$ and uniform energy generation throughout the volume at a constant rate of $g$ W/m$^3$. Heat is dissipated by convection from the outer surface into an ambient at temperature $T_\infty$ with a heat transfer coefficient $h_\infty$. We wish to determine the temperature distribution $T(r)$ in the sphere.

The mathematical formulation of the problem is given by

$$\frac{1}{r^2}\frac{d}{dr}\left[r^2\frac{dT(r)}{dr}\right] + \frac{g}{k} = 0 \quad \text{in } 0 < r < b \tag{5-38a}$$

$$\frac{dT(r)}{dr} = 0 \quad \text{at } r = 0 \tag{5-38b}$$

$$-k\frac{dT(r)}{dr} = h_\infty[T(r) - T_\infty] \quad \text{at } r = b. \tag{5-38c}$$

This problem is readily solved by following the methodology developed previously.

The first integration of the differential equation (5-38a) gives

$$r^2\frac{dT}{dr} = -\frac{g}{3k}r^3 + C_1 \tag{5-39a}$$

and the application of the boundary condition at $r = 0$ yields

$$C_1 = 0. \tag{5-39b}$$

The integration of Eq. (5-39a) with $C_1 = 0$ results in

$$T(r) = -\frac{g}{6k}r^2 + C_2 \tag{5-40a}$$

and the application of the boundary condition at $r = b$ gives the constant $C_2$ as

$$-\frac{gb}{3} + h_\infty\left(-\frac{gb^2}{6k} + C_2\right) = hT_\infty$$

or

$$C_2 = \frac{gb}{3h_\infty} + \frac{g_0 b^2}{6k} + T_\infty. \tag{5-40b}$$

Then the temperature distribution in the sphere becomes

$$T(r) = \frac{bg^2}{6k}\left[1 - \left(\frac{r}{b}\right)^2\right] + \frac{bg}{3h_\infty} + T_\infty. \tag{5-41}$$

The two special cases of this solution for $h_\infty \to \infty$ and $h_\infty \to 0$ are similar to those discussed for the cases of the plate and solid cylinder. That is, as $h_\infty \to \infty$ the solution (5-41) reduces to

$$T(r) = \frac{bg^2}{6k}\left[1 - \left(\frac{r}{b}\right)^2\right] + T_\infty, \tag{5-42}$$

which corresponds to the sphere problem subject to a constant surface temperature $T_{\text{wall}} = T_\infty$ at $r = b$.

For the case of $h_\infty \to 0$, the surface at $r = b$ becomes insulated, and the problem has no steady-state solution because the energy generated has no way to escape from the medium.

**EXAMPLE 5-5**  A solid sphere of radius 5 cm and thermal conductivity $20 \, \mathrm{W(m \cdot {}^\circ C)}$ is heated uniformly throughout its volume at a rate of $2 \times 10^6 \, \mathrm{W/m^3}$, and heat is dissipated by convection to ambient air at $25^\circ \mathrm{C}$ with a heat transfer coefficient of $100 \, \mathrm{W/(m^2 \cdot {}^\circ C)}$. Determine the steady temperatures at the center and the outer surface of the sphere.

**SOLUTION**  Given: $b = 5 \, \mathrm{cm} = 0.05 \, \mathrm{m}$, $k = 20 \, \mathrm{W/(m \cdot {}^\circ C)}$, $g = 2 \times 10^6 \, \mathrm{W/m^3}$, $T_\infty = 25^\circ \mathrm{C}$, and $h_\infty = 100 \, \mathrm{W/(m^2 \cdot {}^\circ C)}$. Equation (5-41) is used to determine the center temperature $T_\mathcal{L}$ by setting $r = 0$:

$$
\begin{aligned}
T_\mathcal{L} &= \frac{gb^2}{6k} + \frac{gb}{3h_\infty} + T_\infty \\
&= \frac{(2 \times 10^6) \times (0.05)^2}{6 \times 20} + \frac{2 \times 10^6 \times 0.05}{3 \times 100} + 25 \\
&= 400^\circ \mathrm{C}
\end{aligned}
$$

and the outer surface temperature $T_w$ is determined by setting $r = b$:

$$
\begin{aligned}
T_w &= \frac{gb}{3h_\infty} + T_\infty \\
&= \frac{2 \times 10^6 \times 0.05}{3 \times 100} + 25 \\
&= 358.33^\circ \mathrm{C}
\end{aligned}
$$

## 5.2. NUMERICAL ANALYSIS

The analytic methods of solution can become very difficult and even impossible to use in many practical problems that arise in engineering applications, such as heat conduction in complex geometries, nonlinear problems, thermal systems involving coupling between the elements, and many others. The numerical techniques are most powerful for solving such complicated problems. In this section we illustrate the basic concepts of numerical analysis for solving simple heat conduction problems using the finite-difference scheme.

When a heat conduction problem is solved exactly by an analytic method, the resulting solution satisfies the governing differential equation at every point in the region as well as at the boundaries. When a numerical scheme such as finite-differences is used, the differential equation of heat conduction is transformed into a set of algebraic equations that are satisfied only at a selected number of discrete nodes over the region.

Therefore, our starting point in finite-difference analysis is the development of the finite-difference equations for the nodes selected over the region. Such equations can be developed either by finite-differencing the derivatives in the differential equation of heat conduction by Taylor series expansion or by writing an energy balance for a differential volume element about a nodal point. Here we prefer the latter approach because it gives better insight into the physical nature of finite-difference formulation of heat conduction problems.

Once the finite-difference form of such equations has been developed, the solution of the heat conduction problem is transformed to the solution of a system of algebraic equations, the number of which is equal to the number of nodal points chosen over the region. Such a system of algebraic equations can readily be solved with a digital computer by using the standard subroutines for solving algebraic equations.

In this section we describe the finite-difference formulation of one- dimensional steady-state heat conduction problems for a plane wall, cylinder, and sphere, and illustrate the application with typical examples.

### 5.2.1 Plane Wall — Finite-Difference Formulation

Consider steady-state heat conduction in a plane wall (slab) of thickness $L$ and constant thermal conductivity $k$, confined to a region $0 \leq x \leq L$ in which energy is generated at a rate of $g(x)\,\mathrm{W/m}^3$, that varies across the thickness of the slab. Figure 5.5 shows the coordinates.

The temperature distribution $T(x)$ in the slab is governed by the steady-state heat conduction equation (3-17a); that is,

$$\frac{d^2 T(x)}{dx^2} + \frac{1}{k}\, g(x) = 0 \quad \text{in } 0 < x < L \,, \tag{5-43}$$

which should be solved subject to appropriate boundary conditions at $x = 0$ and $x = L$.

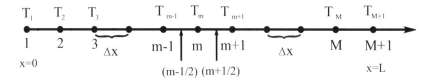

**FIG. 5.5.** Nomenclature for one dimensional finite difference representation of derivatives.

To solve this problem numerically with finite-differences, we need the finite-difference form of this equation written for a selected number of nodal points within the medium. Therefore, the first step in the analysis is to divide the region $0 \leq x \leq L$ into $M$ equal subregions, each of size $\Delta x$, given by

$$\Delta x = \frac{L}{M} \,. \tag{5-44}$$

Hence there are $M + 1$ nodes, from $m = 1$ to $m = M + 1$, as illustrated in Fig. 5.5. In this notation, the node $m$ corresponds to a location whose coordinate $x$ is given by

$$x = (m-1)\Delta x \qquad m = 1, 2, 3, \ldots, M+1 \qquad (5\text{-}45)$$

or $x + \Delta x = m\Delta x$ where $m = 1$ corresponds to the boundary surface at $x = 0$ and $m = M + 1$ corresponds to the boundary surface at $x = L$. Then the temperature $T(x)$ at the node $m$ is denoted by

$$T(x) = T[(m-1)\Delta x] \equiv T_m \qquad (5\text{-}46)$$

The region $0 \le x \le L$ contains $M + 1$ nodes. Those for $m = 2, 3, \ldots, M$ are called the *internal nodes*, and $m = 1$ and $M + 1$ are called the *boundary nodes*.

To develop the finite-difference form of the energy equation (5-43) for an internal node $m$, we consider a differential volume element $\Delta x$ around the node $m$, as illustrated in Fig. 5.6. The steady-state energy balance equation is stated as

$$\begin{pmatrix} \text{Rate of heat} \\ \text{entering} \\ \text{by conduction} \end{pmatrix} + \begin{pmatrix} \text{Rate of} \\ \text{energy} \\ \text{generation} \end{pmatrix} = 0. \qquad (5\text{-}47)$$

The right-hand side of this equation is zero because the steady-state conditions are assumed; hence the rate of increase of internal energy is zero.

The rate at which heat enters the element by conduction through the surfaces of the volume element is given by

$$\begin{pmatrix} \text{Rate of heat} \\ \text{entering} \\ \text{by conduction} \end{pmatrix} = Ak\frac{T_{m-1} - T_m}{\Delta x} + Ak\frac{T_{m+1} - T_m}{\Delta x}$$

$$= \frac{Ak}{\Delta x}(T_{m-1} - 2T_m + T_{m+1}) \qquad (5\text{-}48)$$

and the energy generation term becomes

$$\begin{pmatrix} \text{Rate of} \\ \text{energy} \\ \text{generation} \end{pmatrix} = A\Delta x g_m \qquad (5\text{-}49)$$

where $g_m$ is the energy generation rate per unit volume at the node $m$ corresponding to the location $x = (m-1)\Delta x$.

Introducing Eqs. (5-48) and (5-49) into Eq. (5-47), we obtain

$$\frac{Ak}{\Delta x}(T_{m-1} - 2T_m + T_{m+l}) + A\Delta x g_m = 0$$

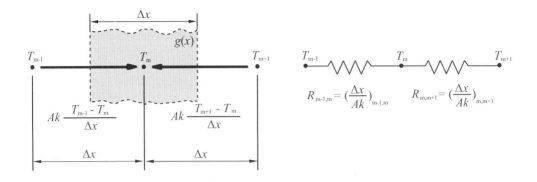

**FIG. 5.6.** Nomenclature for energy balance at an internal node m.

or, after rearranging,

$$(T_{m-1} - 2T_m + T_{m+1}) + \frac{(\Delta x)^2 g_m}{k} = 0 \qquad \text{for} \quad m = 2, 3, \ldots, M. \quad (5\text{-}50)$$

Equation (5-50) is the finite-difference form of the steady-state heat conduction equation (5-43) for an *internal node m*.

Clearly, the region contains $M+1$ unknown node temperatures $T_m$ ($m = 1, 2, \ldots, M+1$), but Eq. (5-50) provides $M - 1$ algebraic equations. To solve such a system, we need two more equations, which are obtained from the consideration of the boundary conditions at the nodes $m = 1$ and $m = M + 1$. We examine below the development of these two additional relations from the boundary conditions for the cases of prescribed temperature, prescribed heat flux, and convection at the boundaries.

**(a) Prescribed Temperature Boundary Condition:**
Suppose the temperatures at the boundaries $x = 0$ and $x = L$ are specified as $f_1$ and $f_{M+1}$ respectively. Then we have

$$T_1 = f_1 \qquad T_{M+1} = f_{M+1} \qquad (5\text{-}51\text{a.b})$$

which provide the two additional relations that are needed to solve the system (5-50), since $f_1$ and $f_{M+1}$ are known quantities.

**(b) Prescribed Heat Flux Boundary Condition.**
Suppose the heat flux $q_0$ W/m$^2$ entering the plane wall through the boundary surface at $x = 0$ is prescribed. To develop an additional finite-difference equation for the node at $x = 0$, we write an energy balance equation for a volume element of thickness $\Delta x/2$ at the node $m = 1$, as illustrated in Fig. 5.7.

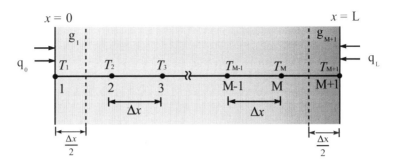

**FIG. 5.7.** Nomenclature for one dimensional finite difference of prescribed heat flux boundary conditions.

$$\left(\begin{array}{c}\text{Rate of heat}\\\text{entering through}\\\text{boundary surface}\end{array}\right) + \left(\begin{array}{c}\text{Rate of heat}\\\text{entering by}\\\text{conduction}\end{array}\right) + \left(\begin{array}{c}\text{rate of}\\\text{energy}\\\text{generation}\end{array}\right) = 0. \qquad (5\text{-}52)$$

If we consider an area A, the mathematical expressions for each of these three terms are written as

$$q_0 A + kA\frac{T_2 - T_1}{\Delta x} + \frac{\Delta x}{2}Ag_1 = 0.$$

This result is rearranged in the form

$$\boxed{2T_2 - 2T_1 + \frac{(\Delta x)^2 g_1}{k} + \frac{2\Delta x q_0}{k} = 0} \qquad \text{for } m = 1 \qquad (5\text{-}53\text{a})$$

which is the finite-difference form of the prescribed heat flux boundary condition at the surface $x = 0$, for the node $m = 1$.

Suppose the heat flux $q_L$ W/m$^2$ entering the wall through the boundary surface at $x = L$ is prescribed. We write an energy balance equation for a differential volume element $\Delta x/2$ at the node $m = M + 1$, as illustrated in Fig. 5.7b, and obtain

$$q_L A + kA\frac{T_M - T_{M+1}}{\Delta x} + \frac{\Delta x}{2}Ag_{M+1} = 0.$$

This result is rearranged in the form

$$\boxed{2T_M - 2T_{M+1} + \frac{(\Delta x)^2 g_{M+1}}{k} + \frac{2\Delta x q_L}{k} = 0} \qquad \text{for } m = M + 1 \qquad (5\text{-}53\text{b})$$

which is the finite-difference form of the prescribed heat flux boundary condition at the node $m = M + 1$.

For the *insulated boundary* (or geometric and thermal symmetry conditions), we have

$$q_0 = 0 \quad \text{or/and} \quad q_L = 0. \tag{5-54}$$

Then Eqs. (5-53a) and (5-53b), respectively, reduce to

$$2T_2 - 2T_1 + \frac{(\Delta x)^2 g_1}{k} = 0$$
$$2T_M - 2T_{M+1} + \frac{(\Delta x)^2 g_{M+1}}{k} = 0. \tag{5-55a,b}$$

Note that Eq. (5-55a) can be obtained from Eq. (5-50) by setting $m = 1$ and taking $T_0 = T_2$, where $T_0$ represents the mirror image of $T_2$ because of symmetry, as illustrated in Fig. 5.8a. Similarly, Eq. (5-55b) can be obtained from Eq. (5-50) by setting $m = M$ and taking $T_M = T_{M+2}$, where $T_M$ represents the mirror image of $T_{M+2}$ because of the symmetry, as illustrated in Fig. 5.8b. It is to be noted that the heat conduction problem in

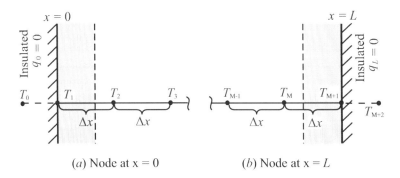

(a) Node at x = 0         (b) Node at x = L

**FIG. 5.8.** Nomenclature for one dimensional finite difference of insulated boundary conditions.

a slab with energy generation in the medium and prescribed heat fluxes at both boundaries *does not have a steady-state solution* unless the sum of the energy generation and the heat entering from one of the boundaries is equal to the heat leaving the slab from the other boundary.

## (c) Convection Boundary Condition:

Suppose the boundary surface at $x = 0$ is subjected to convection with a heat transfer coefficient hail into an ambient at temperature $T_{\infty 1}$, as illustrated in Fig. 5.9a. We consider an energy balance for a volume element of thickness $\Delta x/2$ at the node $m = 1$:

$$\begin{pmatrix} \text{Rate of heat} \\ \text{entering through} \\ \text{the surface} \\ \text{by convection} \end{pmatrix} + \begin{pmatrix} \text{Rate of heat} \\ \text{entering by} \\ \text{conduction} \end{pmatrix} + \begin{pmatrix} \text{Rate of} \\ \text{energy} \\ \text{generation} \end{pmatrix} = 0. \tag{5-56}$$

Considering an area $A$, the mathematical expressions for each of the terms are written

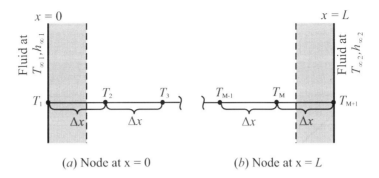

$(a)$ Node at x = 0 $\qquad\qquad$ $(b)$ Node at x = L

**FIG. 5.9.** Nomenclature for one dimensional finite difference of convection boundary conditions.

as

$$h_{\infty 1}A(T_{\infty 1} - T_1) + kA\frac{T_2 - T_1}{\Delta x} + \frac{\Delta x}{2}Ag_1 = 0.$$

After rearrangement, the finite-difference representation of the convection boundary condition at the node $m = 1$ becomes

$$\boxed{2T_2 - \left(2 + \frac{2\Delta x h_{\infty 1}}{k}\right)T_1 + \frac{(\Delta x)^2 g_1}{k} + \frac{2\Delta x h_{\infty 1}}{k}T_{\infty 1} = 0} \quad \text{at } m = 1. \quad \text{(5-57a)}$$

If the boundary surface at $x = L$ is subjected to convection with a heat transfer coefficient $h_{\infty 2}$ into an ambient at temperature $T_{\infty 2}$, the energy balance equation (5-52) is applied to the node $m = M + 1$ to obtain

$$h_{\infty 2}A(T_{\infty 2} - T_{M+1}) + kA\frac{T_M - T_{M+1}}{\Delta x} + \frac{\Delta x}{2}Ag_{M+1} = 0.$$

After rearrangement, the finite-difference form of the convection boundary condition at the node $m = M + 1$ takes the form

$$\boxed{2T_M - \left(2 + \frac{2\Delta x h_{\infty 2}}{k}\right)T_{M+1} + \frac{(\Delta x)^2 g_{M+1}}{k} + \frac{2\Delta x h_{\infty 2}}{k}T_{\infty 2} = 0} \quad \text{at } m = M + 1$$

$$\text{(5-57b)}$$

We now summarize the basic steps discussed above for the finite- difference representation of a steady-state heat conduction problem for a plane wall with energy generation.

The region $0 \le x \le L$ is divided into $M$ equal subregions, containing, in general, $M + 1$ unknown node temperatures $T_m (m = 1, 2, \ldots, M + 1)$. Equation (5-50) provides $M - 1$ equations; the additional two equations are obtained from the boundary conditions for the problem. The finite-difference form of the boundary conditions are given by Eqs. (5-51), (5-53), and (5-57) for the prescribed temperature, prescribed heat flux, and convection boundary conditions, respectively. Then the problem involves $M + 1$ algebraic equations for the $M + 1$ unknown node temperatures $T_m (m = 1, 2, \ldots, M + 1)$, which can readily be solved with a digital computer.

**EXAMPLE 5-6** Consider a slab of thickness $0.1m$ with a thermal conductivity $40 \text{ W}/(\text{m} \cdot {}^\circ \text{C})$ in which energy is generated at a constant rate of $10^6 \text{ W}/\text{m}^3$. The boundary surface at $x = 0$ is insulated, and the one at $x = 0.1$ m is subjected to convection with a heat transfer coefficient of $200 \text{ W}/(\text{m}^2 \cdot {}^\circ \text{C})$ into an ambient at a temperature of $150 \,{}^\circ \text{C}$. The slab is subdivided into five equal subregions, as illustrated in the accompanying figure. Develop the finite-difference equations for the problem.

**SOLUTION** Given: $L = 0.1\text{m}$, $k = 40 \text{ W}/(\text{m} \cdot {}^\circ \text{C})$, $g = 10^6 \text{ W}/\text{m}^3$, and $M = 5$. The size of the subdivision is

$$\Delta x = \frac{L}{M} = \frac{0.1}{5} = 0.02 \text{ m}$$

For the internal nodes, $m = 2$ to $5$, the finite-difference equations are obtained from Eqs. (5-50) as

$$(T_{m-1} - 2T_m + T_{m+l}) + \frac{(0.02)^2 \times 10^6}{40} = 0$$

or

$$(T_{m-1} - 2T_m + T_{m+l}) + 10 = 0 \quad \text{for } m = 2, 3, 4, 5$$

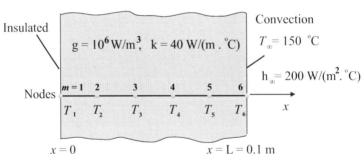

**FIGURE EXAMPLE 5-6**

For the insulated boundary at $x = 0$, the finite-difference equation is obtained from Eq. (5-55a) as

$$2T_2 - 2T_1 + \frac{(0.02)^2 \times 10^6}{40} = 0$$

or

$$2T_2 - 2T_1 + 10 = 0 \quad \text{for } m = 1$$

For the convection boundary at $x = L$, the finite-difference equation is obtained from Eq. (5-57b) as

$$2T_5 - \left(2 + \frac{2 \times 0.02 \times 200}{40}\right)T_6 + \frac{(0.02)^2 \times 10^6}{40} + \frac{2 \times 0.02 \times 200}{40}150 = 0$$

or

$$2T_5 - 2.2T_6 + 40 = 0 \quad \text{for } m = 6$$

Thus we have six algebraic equations for the six unknown node temperatures $T_m (m = 1, 2, \ldots, 6)$. We summarize these equations as

$$
\begin{aligned}
-2T_1 + 2T_2 &= -10 \quad \text{for } m = 1 \\
T_1 - 2T_2 + T_3 &= -10 \quad \text{for } m = 2 \\
T_2 - 2T_3 + T_4 &= -10 \quad \text{for } m = 3 \\
T_3 - 2T_4 + T_5 &= -10 \quad \text{for } m = 4 \\
T_4 - 2T_5 + T_6 &= -10 \quad \text{for } m = 5 \\
2T_5 - 2.2T_6 &= -40 \quad \text{for } m = 6
\end{aligned}
$$

These equations are written in the matrix form as

$$
\begin{bmatrix}
-2 & 2 & 0 & 0 & 0 & 0 \\
1 & -2 & 1 & 0 & 0 & 0 \\
0 & 1 & -2 & 1 & 0 & 0 \\
0 & 0 & 1 & -2 & 1 & 0 \\
0 & 0 & 0 & 1 & -2 & 1 \\
0 & 0 & 0 & 0 & 2 & -2.2
\end{bmatrix}
\begin{bmatrix}
T_1 \\ T_2 \\ T_3 \\ T_4 \\ T_5 \\ T_6
\end{bmatrix}
=
\begin{bmatrix}
-10 \\ -10 \\ -10 \\ -10 \\ -10 \\ -40
\end{bmatrix}
$$

Note that this is a tridiagonal matrix. Summarizing, with the finite-difference approach, the heat conduction equation and its boundary conditions are replaced by a set of algebraic equations. In this example the slab is divided into five subdivisions, resulting in six unknown node temperatures to be determined. If more subdivisions are considered, the result will be a larger number of algebraic equations, which can be solved by a digital computer using the standard subroutines available for solving systems of algebraic equations.

## 5.2.2 Cylinder—Finite-Difference Formulation

The finite-difference formulation of the heat conduction problem for a plane wall, given previously, is not applicable to radial heat flow in cylindrical bodies, because the area A normal to the path of heat flow is not constant but varies linearly with radial position in the cylindrical coordinate system. The general procedure for developing the finite-difference equations for a cylindrical body is essentially similar to that for a plane wall, but the radial variation of the area needs to be included in the analysis.

Consider steady-state radial heat conduction in a long solid cylinder of radius $r = b$, in which energy is generated at a rate of $g(r)\,\mathrm{W/m^3}$. The temperatute distribution $T(r)$ in the cylinder is governed by the heat conduction equation (3-17b), that is,

$$\frac{1}{r}\frac{d}{dr}\left[r\frac{dT(r)}{dr}\right] + \frac{1}{k}g(r) = 0 \quad \text{in } 0 \leq r \leq b \tag{5-58}$$

which should be solved subject to appropriate boundary conditions at $r = 0$ and $r = b$.

To develop the finite-difference form of this energy equation, the region $0 \leq r \leq b$ is divided into $M$ cylindrical subregions, each of thickness $\Delta r$, given by

$$\Delta r = \frac{b}{M} \tag{5-59}$$

as illustrated in Fig. 5.10. Then the region $0 \leq r \leq b$ contains $M+1$ nodes at the locations

$$r = (m-1)\Delta r \quad m = 1, 2, \ldots, M+1 \tag{5-60}$$

with the nodes $m = 1$ and $m = M+1$ corresponding to the center and the outer boundary surface of the solid cylinder, respectively, and the nodes $m = 2, 3, \ldots, M$ being the internal nodes of the region. The problem involves $M + 1$ node temperatures, denoted by

$$T(r) = T[(m-1)\Delta r] \equiv T_m \quad m = 1, 2, \ldots, M+1. \tag{5-61}$$

The finite-difference form of the heat conduction equation for the internal nodes is de-

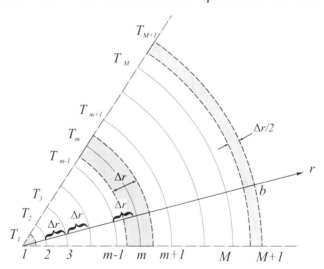

**FIG. 5.10.** Nomenclature for one dimensional finite difference formulation of long solid cylinder

veloped by considering the energy balance equation, Eq. (5-47). We apply this energy balance for a cylindrical volume element of thickness $\Delta r$ about the node $m$ illustrated in Fig. 5.10. The conduction term becomes

$$\begin{pmatrix} \text{Rate of heat} \\ \text{entering} \\ \text{by conduction} \end{pmatrix} = A_{m-1,m}k\frac{T_{m-1}-T_m}{\Delta r} + A_{m+1,m}k\frac{T_{m+1}-T_m}{\Delta r} \qquad (5\text{-}62)$$

$$= 2\pi Hk[(m-1-1/2)T_{m-1} - 2mT_m + (m-1+1/2)T_{m+1}]$$

where

$$A_{m-1,m} = 2\pi\left[(m-1)\Delta r - \frac{1}{2}\Delta r\right]H$$

$$A_{m+1,m} = 2\pi\left[(m-1)\Delta r + \frac{1}{2}\Delta r\right]H$$

with $H$ being the length of the cylinder. The rate of energy generation within the volume element is given by

$$\begin{pmatrix} \text{Rate of} \\ \text{energy} \\ \text{generation} \end{pmatrix} = A_m\Delta r g_m$$

$$= 2\pi H(m-1)(\Delta r)^2 g_m \qquad (5\text{-}63)$$

where $A_m = 2\pi H(m-1)\Delta r$ and $g_m$ are evaluated at the node $m$ corresponding to the location $r = (m-1)\Delta r$.

Introducing Eqs. (5-62) and (5-63) into the energy balance equation (5-47) and rearranging, we obtain the finite-difference form of the heat conduction equation (5-58) for the internal nodes of the cylindrical region

$$\boxed{\left[1 - \frac{1}{2(m-1)}\right]T_{m-1} - 2T_m + \left[1 + \frac{1}{2(m-1)}\right]T_{m+1} + \frac{(\Delta r)^2 g_m}{k} = 0}$$

$$\text{for } m = 2, 3, \ldots, M. \qquad (5\text{-}64)$$

To determine the finite-difference equation for the central node $r = 0$ or $m = 1$, we apply the energy balance equation (5-47) for the volume element of radius $\Delta r/2$ about the node $m = 1$ shown in Fig. 5.10. Various terms are evaluated as

$$\begin{pmatrix} \text{Rate of heat} \\ \text{entering} \\ \text{by conduction} \end{pmatrix} = A_{2,1}k\frac{T_2 - T_1}{\Delta r}$$

$$= \pi Hk(T_2 - T_1). \qquad (5\text{-}65)$$

The rate of energy generation in the volume element is

$$\begin{pmatrix} \text{Rate of} \\ \text{energy} \\ \text{generation} \end{pmatrix} = \pi \left( \frac{\Delta r}{2} \right)^2 H g_1.$$

(5-66)

Introducing Eqs. (5-66) into the energy balance equation (5-47), we obtain the finite-difference equation for the center node $m = 1$ as

$$\boxed{4(T_2 - T_1) + \frac{(\Delta r)^2 g_1}{k} = 0} \quad \text{for } m = 1.$$

(5-67)

The system given by Eqs. (5-65) and (5-67) involves $M + 1$ unknown node temperatures $T_m(m = 1, 2, \ldots, M + 1)$, but only $M$ equations. An additional equation is obtained from the boundary condition at $r = b$, which can be a prescribed temperature, prescribed heat flux, or convection boundary condition. Each of these cases is now examined.

### (a) Prescribed Temperature Boundary Condition:

If the temperature of the boundary surface at the node $M$ is specified as, say, $f_{M+1}$ we have

$$\boxed{T_{M+1} = f_{M+1}} \quad \text{at } m = M + 1$$

(5-68a)

### (b) Prescribed Heat Flux Boundary Condition:

For one-dimensional heat conduction in a solid cylinder, no steady-state can be established under a prescribed heat flux condition at the boundary surface $r = b$. The reason for this is that heat entering the cylinder has no other way to escape; hence it will build up continuously. However, in a hollow cylinder, heat can escape from the inner boundary while entering from the boundary at $r = b$, or vice versa; hence the steady-state solution is possible. For this reason, the finite-difference form of the prescribed heat flux boundary condition at $r = b$ has practical application only for hollow cylinder problems, which will be discussed next. With such a restriction on its application, we now present the finite-difference form of the prescribed heat flux condition at $r = b$.

Let $q_b$ W/m$^2$, the heat flux entering the cylinder from the outer boundary surface at $r = b$, be prescribed. The application of the energy balance equation (5-52) to the boundary node $M + 1$ at $r = b$ yields

$$A_{M,M+1} k \frac{T_M - T_{M+1}}{\Delta r} + A_{M+1} q_b + A_{M+1}^* \frac{\Delta r}{2} g_{M+1} = 0$$

where

$$\begin{aligned} A_{M,M+1} &= 2\pi \left( M\Delta r - \frac{1}{2}\Delta r \right) H \\ A_{M+1} &= 2\pi (M\Delta r) H \\ A_{M+1}^* &= 2\pi \left( M\Delta r - \frac{1}{4}\Delta r \right) H \cong 2\pi (M\Delta r) H \end{aligned}$$

and $H$ is the length of the cylinder.

Here the locations in the r- direction are:

$$
\begin{aligned}
r_{M,M+1} &= (M+1-1-1/2)\Delta r \\
&= (M-1/2)\Delta r \\
r_{M,M+1+1/4} &= (M-1/4)\Delta r
\end{aligned}
$$

Introducing the area terms into the above expression and rearranging, we obtain

$$
\boxed{\left(1-\frac{1}{2M}\right)T_M - \left(1-\frac{1}{2M}\right)T_{M+1} + \frac{\Delta r\, q_b}{k} + \frac{(\Delta r)^2\, g_{M+1}}{2k} = 0} \quad \text{for } m = M+1
$$

$$(5\text{-}68b)$$

## (c) Convection Boundary Condition:

If the outer boundary surface is subjected to convection with a heat transfer coefficient $h_\infty$ into an ambient at temperature $T_\infty$, we apply an energy balance equation similar to that given by Eq. (5-56) for the node $M$ and obtain

$$
A_{M,M+1}k\frac{T_M - T_{M+1}}{\Delta r} + A_{M+1}h_\infty(T_\infty - T_{M+1}) + A^*_{M+1}\frac{\Delta r}{2}g_{M+1} = 0
$$

where

$$
\begin{aligned}
A_{M,M+1} &= 2\pi(M\Delta r - \frac{1}{2}\Delta r)H \\
A_{M+1} &= 2\pi(M\Delta r)H \\
A^*_{M+1} &= 2\pi(M\Delta r - \frac{1}{4}\Delta r)H \cong 2\pi(M\Delta r)H
\end{aligned}
$$

where $H$ is the length of the cylinder.

After introducing the area terms into the energy balance equation and some rearrangement, we obtain

$$
\boxed{\left(1-\frac{1}{2M}\right)T_M - \left[\left(1-\frac{1}{2M}\right) + \frac{\Delta r h_\infty}{k}\right]T_{M+1} + \frac{\Delta r h_\infty}{k}T_\infty + \frac{(\Delta r)^2 g_{M+1}}{2k} = 0}
$$

$$\text{for } m = M+1 \qquad (5\text{-}68c)$$

Summarizing Eqs. (5-65) and (5-67) together with the finite-difference form of the boundary condition at $r = b$ provides $M + 1$ algebraic equations for the determination of $M + 1$ node temperatures $T_m(m = 1, 2, \ldots, M + 1)$ in a solid cylinder.

## HOLLOW CYLINDER:

In the case of a hollow cylinder with an inner radius of $r = a$ and outer radius of $r = b$, in which energy is generated at a rate of $g(r)$ W/m$^3$, the region $a \leq r \leq b$ is divided into $M$ cylindrical subregions, each of thickness $\Delta r$, given by

$$\Delta r = \frac{b - a}{M}$$

as illustrated in Fig. 5.11. Then we have $M + 1$ unknown node temperatures $T_m(m = 1, 2, \ldots, M + 1)$ and we need $M + 1$ relations to determine them. The general procedure for obtaining such relations is similar to that described for the solid cylinder.

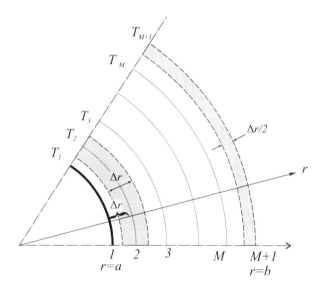

**FIG. 5.11.** Nomenclature for one dimensional finite difference formulation of long hollow cylinder

For the internal nodes $m = 2, 3, \ldots, M$, the energy balance equation (5-47) gives

$$A_{m-1,m}k\frac{T_{m-1} - T_m}{\Delta r} + A_{m+1,m}k\frac{T_{m+1} - T_m}{\Delta r} + A_m \Delta r q_m = 0$$

where

$$A_{m-1,m} = 2\pi \left[ a + (m - 1)\Delta r - \frac{1}{2}\Delta r \right] H$$

$$A_{m+1,m} = 2\pi \left[ a + (m - 1)\Delta r + \frac{1}{2}\Delta r \right] H$$

$$A_m = 2\pi \left[ a + (m - 1)\Delta r \right] H$$

which is rearranged as

$$\left[ \frac{a}{(m-1)\Delta r} + 1 - \frac{1}{2(m-1)} \right] T_{m-1} - 2 \left[ \frac{a}{(m-1)\Delta r} + 1 \right] T_m$$

$$+ \left[ \frac{a}{(m-1)\Delta r} + 1 + \frac{1}{2(m-1)} \right] T_{m+1} + \frac{[(a/(m-1)\Delta r) + 1](\Delta r)^2 g_M}{k} = 0$$

$$\text{for } m = 2, 3, \ldots, M \qquad (5\text{-}69)$$

If the outer boundary surfaces at $r = a$ and $r = b$ are subjected to convection, the finite-difference equations are obtained by the application of the energy balance given by Eq. (5-56).

For the node $m = 1$ at the inner boundary surface $r = a$, we have

$$A_{2,1} k \frac{T_2 - T_1}{\Delta r} + A_1 h_{\infty 1}(T_{\infty 1} - T_1) + A_1^* \frac{\Delta r}{2} g_0 = 0$$

where

$$
\begin{aligned}
A_1 &= 2\pi a H \\
A_{(2,1)} &= 2\pi \left( a + \frac{\Delta r}{2} \right) H \\
A_1^* &\cong 2\pi a H
\end{aligned}
$$

which is rearranged as

$$\frac{a h_{\infty 1}}{k} T_{\infty 1} - \left[ \frac{a}{\Delta r} \left( 1 + \frac{\Delta r h_{\infty 1}}{k} \right) + \frac{1}{2} \right] T_1 + \left( \frac{a}{\Delta r} + \frac{1}{2} \right) T_2 + \frac{a \Delta r}{2k} g_1 = 0 \quad \text{for } m = 1$$

$$(5\text{-}70)$$

For the node $m = M + 1$ at the outer boundary surface $r = b$, we have

$$A_{M,M+1} k \frac{T_M - T_{M+1}}{\Delta r} + A_{M+1} h_{\infty 2}(T_{\infty 2} - T_{M+1}) + A_{M+1}^* \frac{\Delta r}{2} g_{M+1} = 0$$

where

$$
\begin{aligned}
A_{M+1} &= 2\pi b H \\
A_{(M,M+1)} &= 2\pi \left( b - \frac{\Delta r}{2} \right) H \\
A_{M+1}^* &\cong 2\pi b H
\end{aligned}
$$

which is rearranged as

$$\frac{bh_{\infty 2}}{k}T_{\infty 2} - \left[\frac{b}{\Delta r}\left(1 + \frac{\Delta r h_{\infty 2}}{k}\right) - \frac{1}{2}\right]T_{M+1} + \left(\frac{b}{\Delta r} - \frac{1}{2}\right)T_M + \frac{b\Delta r}{2k}g_{M+1} = 0$$

$$\text{for } m = 2, 3, \ldots, M \qquad (5\text{-}71)$$

**EXAMPLE 5-7** A 10-cm-diameter solid chrome-nickel rod with thermal conductivity of 20 W/(m · °C) is heated electrically by the passage of an electric current which generates energy within the rod at a uniform rate of $10^7$ W/m³. The surface of the rod is subjected to convection with a heat transfer coefficient $h = 200$ W/(m² · °C) into an ambient at 30 °C. Determine the finite-difference equations if the radius of the rod is subdivided into five equal intervals.

**SOLUTION** Given: $b = 0.05$ m, $k = 20$ W/(m · °C), $g = 10^7$ W/m, $T_\infty = 30$°C, $h_\infty = 200$ W/(m² · °C) and $M = 5$. Then we have

$$\Delta r = \frac{b}{M} = \frac{0.05}{5} = 0.01m$$

$$\frac{(\Delta r)^2 g}{k} = \frac{(0.01)^2(10^7)}{20} = 50$$

$$\frac{\Delta r h_\infty}{k} = \frac{0.01 \times 200}{20} = \frac{1}{10}$$

The finite-difference equation for the central node $m = 1$ is obtained from Eq. (5-67):

$$4(T_2 - T_1) + 50 = 0 \quad \text{for } m = 1$$

and the finite-difference equations for the internal nodes $m = 2$ to 5 are obtained from Eq. (5-63):

$$\left[1 - \frac{1}{2(m-1)}\right]T_{m-1} - 2T_m + \left[1 + \frac{1}{2(m-1)}\right]T_{m+1} + 50 = 0 \quad \text{for } m = 2, 3, 4, 5$$

Finally, the finite-difference equation for the convection boundary condition at the node $m = M + 1 = 6$ is obtained from Eq. (5-66c):

$$\left(1 - \frac{1}{10}\right)T_5 - \left[\left(1 - \frac{1}{10}\right) + \frac{1}{10}\right]T_6 + \left(\frac{1}{10}\right)(30) + 25 = 0$$

or

$$0.9T_5 - T_6 + 28 = 0 \quad \text{for } m = 6$$

Summarizing, we have six algebraic equations for the six node temperatures $T_m, m =$

1 to 6:

$$
\begin{array}{rclll}
-4T_1 + 4T_2 & = & -50 & \text{for } m = 1 \\
0.5T_1 - 2T_2 + 1.5T_3 & = & -50 & \text{for } m = 2 \\
0.75T_2 - 2T_3 + 1.25T_4 & = & -50 & \text{for } m = 3 \\
0.8333T_3 - 2T_4 + 1.1666T_5 & = & -50 & \text{for } m = 4 \\
0.875T_4 - 2T_5 + 1.125T_6 & = & -50 & \text{for } m = 5 \\
0.9T_5 - T_6 & = & -28 & \text{for } m = 6
\end{array}
$$

which are expressed in the matrix form as

$$
\begin{bmatrix}
-4 & 4 & 0 & 0 & 0 & 0 \\
0.5 & -2 & 1.5 & 0 & 0 & 0 \\
0 & 0.75 & -2 & 1.25 & 0 & 0 \\
0 & 0 & 0.8333 & -2 & 1.1666 & 0 \\
0 & 0 & 0 & 0.875 & -2 & 1.125 \\
0 & 0 & 0 & 0 & 0.9 & -1
\end{bmatrix}
\begin{bmatrix}
T_1 \\ T_2 \\ T_3 \\ T_4 \\ T_5 \\ T_6
\end{bmatrix}
=
\begin{bmatrix}
-50 \\ -50 \\ -50 \\ -50 \\ -50 \\ -28
\end{bmatrix}
$$

### 5.2.3 Sphere — Finite-Difference Formulation

The basic principles of finite-differencing described for the cylinder are applicable for the sphere, except that the radial variation of the area is proportional to the square of the radius. We consider radial heat conduction in a solid sphere of radius $r = b$, in which energy is generated at a rate of $g(r)\mathrm{W/m}^3$. The region $0 \leq r \leq b$ is divided into $M$ spherical shells, each of thickness

$$
\Delta r = \frac{b}{M} \tag{5-72}
$$

The nomenclature for the subdivisions is similar to that shown in Fig. 5.10b for a solid cylinder, except that in this case the geometry is a solid sphere.

For the internal nodes, $m = 2, 3, \ldots, M$, the energy balance equation (5-47) gives

$$
A_{m-1,m} k \frac{T_{m-1} - T_m}{\Delta r} + A_{m+1,m} k \frac{T_{m+1} - T_m}{\Delta r} + A_m \Delta r q_m = 0
$$

where

$$
\begin{aligned}
A_{m-l,m} &= 4\pi \left[ (m-1)\Delta r - \frac{\Delta r}{2} \right]^2 = 4\pi(m-1)^2(\Delta r)^2 \left[ 1 - \frac{1}{2(m-1)} \right]^2 \\
A_{m+l,m} &= 4\pi \left[ (m-1)\Delta r + \frac{\Delta r}{2} \right]^2 = 4\pi(m-1)^2(\Delta r)^2 \left[ 1 + \frac{1}{2(m-1)} \right]^2 \\
A_m &= 4\pi \left[ (m-1)\Delta r \right]^2
\end{aligned}
$$

After rearranging, we obtain

$$\left[1 - \frac{1}{2(m-1)}\right]^2 (T_{m-1} - T_m) + \left[1 + \frac{1}{2(m-1)}\right]^2 (T_{m+1} - T_m) + \frac{(\Delta r)^2 g_m}{k} = 0$$

$$\text{for } m = 2, 3, \ldots, M \qquad (5\text{-}73a)$$

For the values of $m \geq 2$, the following approximations can be made:

$$\left[1 - \frac{1}{2(m-1)}\right]^2 \cong 1 - \frac{1}{(m-1)}$$

$$\left[1 + \frac{1}{2(m-1)}\right]^2 \cong 1 + \frac{1}{(m-1)}$$

Then Eq. (5-73a) reduces to

$$\left[1 - \frac{1}{(m-1)}\right] T_{m-1} - 2T_m + \left[1 + \frac{1}{(m-1)}\right] T_{m+1} + \frac{(\Delta r)^2 g_m}{k} = 0$$

$$\text{for } m = 2, 3, \ldots, M \qquad (5\text{-}73b)$$

For the center node $m = 1$, the energy balance equation (5-47) is also applicable, and yields

$$A_{2,1} k \frac{T_2 - T_1}{\Delta r} + \frac{4}{3}\pi \left(\frac{\Delta r}{2}\right)^3 g_1 = 0 \quad \text{for } m = 1$$

where

$$A_{2,1} = 4\pi \left(\frac{\Delta r}{2}\right)^2$$

and after rearrangement we obtain

$$6(T_2 - T_1) + \frac{(\Delta r)^2 g_1}{k} = 0 \qquad \text{for } m = 1 \qquad (5\text{-}74)$$

For the node $M$ at the boundary surface $r = b$, the finite-difference equation depends on the type of boundary condition. If the boundary surface at $r = b$ is subjected to convection with a heat transfer coefficient $h_\infty$ into an ambient at temperature $T_\infty$, application of the energy balance equation (5-56) gives

$$A_{M,M+1} k \frac{T_{M-1} - T_M}{\Delta r} + A_{M+1} h_\infty (T_\infty - T_{M+1}) + A_{M+1}^* \frac{\Delta r}{2} g_{M+1} = 0$$

where

$$A_{M,M+1} = 4\pi(M\Delta r - \frac{\Delta r}{2})^2$$

$$A_{M+1} = 4\pi(M\Delta r)^2$$

$$A^*_{M+1} \cong 4\pi(M\Delta r)^2$$

After rearrangement we obtain

$$2\left(1 - \frac{1}{2M}\right)^2 T_M - \left[2\left(1 - \frac{1}{2M}\right)^2 + \frac{2\Delta r h_\infty}{k}\right] T_{M+1}$$

$$+ \frac{2\Delta r h_\infty}{k} T_\infty + \frac{(\Delta r)^2 g_{M+1}}{k} = 0$$

for $m = M + 1$

(5-75a)

For $M > 1$, the following approximations can be made:

$$\left(1 - \frac{1}{2M}\right)^2 \cong 1 - \frac{1}{M}$$

$$\left(1 + \frac{1}{2M}\right)^2 \cong 1 + \frac{1}{M}$$

Then Eq. (5-75a) reduces to

$$2\left(1 - \frac{1}{M}\right) T_M - \left[2\left(1 - \frac{1}{M}\right) + \frac{2\Delta r h_\infty}{k}\right] T_{M+1} + \frac{2\Delta r h_\infty}{k} T_\infty + \frac{(\Delta r)^2 g_{M+1}}{k} = 0$$

for $m = M + 1$         (5-75b)

## 5.3. COMPUTER SOLUTIONS

As shown in the previous sections, the finite-differencing of one-dimensional steady-state heat conduction problems results in a tridiagonal system of algebraic equations for the node temperatures $T_m (m = 1, 2, \ldots, M + 1)$. Such a system can be expressed in matrix form as

$$[A]X = D$$

(5-76a)

which can be written more explicitly as

$$\begin{bmatrix} b_1 & c_1 & 0 & & 0 & 0 \\ a_2 & b_2 & c_2 & & & 0 \\ & & & & & \\ 0 & & a_{N-1} & b_{N-1} & c_{N-1} \\ 0 & 0 & 0 & a_N & b_N \end{bmatrix} \begin{Bmatrix} x_1 \\ x_2 \\ \\ x_{N-1} \\ x_N \end{Bmatrix} = \begin{Bmatrix} d'_1 \\ d'_2 \\ \\ d'_{N-1} \\ d'_N \end{Bmatrix} \quad (5\text{-}76b)$$

where $[A]$ is the $N \times N$ coefficient matrix, which is a banded tridiagonal matrix.

## PROBLEMS

*Analytical Solutions*

**5-1** Develop an expression for one-dimensional, steady-state temperature distribution $T(x)$ in a plane wall (slab) of thickness $L$ when the boundary surface at $x = 0$ is kept at a uniform temperature $T_0$ and the boundary surface at $x = L$ dissipates heat by convection with a heat transfer coefficient $h$ into the ambient air at temperature $T_\infty$ The thermal conductivity $k$ is constant, and there is energy generation at a constant rate of $g$ W/m$^3$.

**5-2** Develop an expression for the one-dimensional, steady-state temperature distribution $T(x)$ in a slab of thickness $L$ when the boundary surface at $x = 0$ is kept insulated and the boundary surface at $x = L$ is kept at zero temperature. The thermal conductivity $k$ is constant, and there is energy generation at a rate of $g(x) = g_0 \cos \pi x/2L$ W/m$^3$, where $g_0$ is the energy generation rate per unit volume at $x = 0$. Give the relation for the temperature of the insulated boundary.

**5-3** Consider a slab of thickness $L = 0.l$ m. One of the boundary surfaces, that at $x = 0$ is kept insulated, and the boundary surface at $x = L$ dissipates heat by convection with a heat transfer coefficient of 200 W/(m$^2 \cdot$°C) into the ambient air at 150°$C$. The thermal conductivity of the wall is 10.0 W/(m·°C), and within the wall energy is generated at a constant rate of $10^6$ W/m$^3$. Determine the boundary surface temperatures.
*Answers*: 1150 °C, 650 °C

**5-4** Consider a slab of thickness 0.1 $m$. One of the boundary surfaces, that at $x = 0$, is kept insulated, and the boundary surface at $x = L$ dissipates heat by convection with a heat transfer coefficient $h$ into the ambient air at 150°$C$. The thermal conductivity of the wall is 40 W/(m·°C), and within the wall energy is generated at a constant rate of $10^6$ W/m$^3$. Plot the temperature profiles in the slab for the heat transfer coefficients $h = 200, 350$, and 500 W/(m$^2 \cdot$°C).

**5-5** Develop an expression for the steady-state temperature distribution in a slab of thickness $L$ when the boundary surface at $x = 0$ is kept insulated and the boundary surface at $x = L$ is kept at zero temperature. The thermal conductivity of the wall $k$

is constant, and within the wall energy is generated at a rate of $g(x) = g_0 x^2$ W/m$^3$. Give the expressions for the temperature of the insulated surface at $x = 0$.

**5-6** A nuclear reactor pressure vessel is approximated as a large plane wall of thickness $L$. The inside surface is insulated, the outside surface at $x = L$ is maintained at a uniform temperature $T_2$, and the gamma-ray heating of the plate can be represented as energy generation in the form

$$g(x) = g_0 e^{-\gamma x} \quad \text{W/m}^3$$

where $g_0$ and $\gamma$ are constants and $x$ is measured from the insulated inside surface. Develop an expression for the temperature distribution in the plate.

**5-7** Develop an expression for the steady temperature distribution $T(r)$ in a cylinder of radius $b$ in which energy is generated at a rate of

$$g(r) = g_0 \left(1 - \frac{r}{b}\right) \quad \text{W/m}^3$$

where $g_0$ is a constant, and the boundary surface at $r = b$ is maintained at a uniform temperature $T_w$. Assuming one-dimensional steady heat flow, develop a relation for the temperature drop from the centerline to the surface of the fuel element. For radius $b = 2$ cm, thermal conductivity $k = 10$ W/(m·°C) , and $g_0 = 4 \times 10^7$ W/m$^3$, calculate the temperature drop from the centerline to the surface. *Answer:* $5\,g_0 b^2/36\,k$, 222.2 °C.

**5-8** A hollow cylindrical fuel element of inner radius $a$ and outer radius $b$ is heated uniformly within the entire volume at a constant rate of $g$ W/m$^3$ as a result of disintegration of radioactive material. The inner surface of the element is at zero temperature, and the outer surface is subjected to dissipation of heat by convection with a heat transfer coefficient $h$ into the ambient air at temperature $T_\infty$. The thermal conductivity of the cylinder is constant. Develop an expression for the one-dimensional steady-state temperature distribution $T(r)$ within the cylinder.

**5-9** Determine the one-dimensional temperature distribution in the hollow cylindrical fuel element of Problem 5-8 for the case in which the heat generation rate $g_0(r)$ is a function of the radial position in the form

$$g(r) = g_0(l + Ar) \quad \text{W/m}^2$$

where $g_0$ and $A$ are constants.

**5-10** A long cylindrical rod of radius $b = 5$ cm and $k = 20$ W/(m·°C) contains radioactive material which generates energy uniformly within the cylinder at a constant rate of $g_0 = 2 \times 10^5$ W/m$^3$. The rod is cooled by convection from its cylindrical surface into the ambient air at $T_\infty = 20°$ C with a heat transfer coefficient $h_\infty = 50$ W/(m$^2$·° C) . Determine the temperatures at the center and the outer

surface of this cylindrical rod.
*Answers*: $126.3\,°C$, $120\,°C$

**5-11** A tube of inner radius $r_i$, outer radius $r_0$ and thermal conductivity $k$ is heated by passing an electric current through the tube. The passage of current generates energy at a constant rate of $g_0$ W/m$^3$. The outer surface of the pipe is insulated, and the inner surface is kept at zero temperature. Develop an expression for the steady-state temperature distribution $T(r)$ within the tube and for the temperature of the insulated outer surface.

**5-12** An electric resistance wire of radius $a = 1 \times 10^{-3}$ m with thermal conductivity $k = 25$ W/(m·°C) is heated by the passage of electric current, which generates heat within the wire at a constant rate of $g_0 = 2 \times 10^9$ W/m$^3$. Determine the centerline temperature rise above the surface temperature of the wire if the surface is maintained at a constant temperature.

**5-13** A 3-mm-diameter chrome-nickel wire of thermal conductivity $k = 20$ W/(m·°C) is heated electrically by the passage of an electric current, which generates heat within the wire at a constant rate of $g_0 = 10^7$ W/m$^3$. If the outer surface of the wire is maintained at $50°C$, determine the center temperature of the wire.

**5-14** Heat is generated at a constant rate of $g_0 = 10^6$ W/m$^3$ in a copper rod of radius $r = 0.5\ cm$ and thermal conductivity $k = 386$ W/(m·°C). The rod is cooled by convection from its cylindrical surface into an ambient at $20°C$ with a heat transfer coefficient $h = 1400$ W/(m$^2$·°C). Determine the surface temperature of the rod.
*Answer*: $21.8\,°C$

**5-15** Develop an expression for the steady temperature distribution $T(r)$ in a solid sphere of radius $b$ in which heat is generated at a rate of

$$g(r) = g_0 \left(1 - \frac{r}{b}\right) \quad \text{W/m}^3$$

where $g_0$ is a constant, and the boundary surface at $r = b$ is maintained at a uniform temperature $T_w$.

**5-16** Determine the centerline temperature rise above the surface temperature of the sphere in by Problem 5-15.

**5-17** Heat is generated at a constant rate of $g_0 = 2 \times 10^8$ W/m$^3$ in a copper sphere of radius 1 $cm$ and thermal conductivity $k = 386$ W/(m·°C). The sphere is cooled by convection from its spherical surface into an ambient at $10°C$ with a heat transfer coefficient of $h = 2000$ W/(m$^2$·°C). Determine the surface temperature and the center temperature of the sphere.
*Answers*: $343.3\,°C$, $352\,°C$

**5-18** Determine the temperature distributions in a hollow sphere of inner radius $a$ and outer radius $b$ in which energy is generated: ($a$) at a constant rate of $g_0$ W/m$^3$, and ($b$) as a function of radial position in the form $g(r) = g_0(1 + Ar)$ W/m$^3$, where $g_0$ and $A$ are constants, if the outer surface at $r = b$ is kept at a constant temperature $T_0$ and the inner surface at $r = a$ is insulated.

**5-19** A hollow sphere of inner radius $a$ and outer radius $b$ is heated uniformly within the entire volume at a constant rate of $g_0$ W/m$^3$. The inner surface is at zero temperature, and the outer surface is dissipating heat by convection with a heat transfer coefficient $h$ into the ambient air at temperature $T_0$. The thermal conductivity of the sphere is constant. Develop an expression for the steady temperature distribution within the sphere.

**5-20** A plane wall of thickness $L$ is maintained at a constant temperature $T_0$ at $x = 0$ and $T_L$ at $x = L$ while energy is generated in the medium at a constant rate of $g$ W/m$^3$.

($a$) Develop an expression for the steady-state temperature distribution in the wall.

($b$) Calculate the maximum temperature in the wall for the case in which $T_0 = 50°C$, $T_L = 0°C$, $k = 30$ W/(m·°C), $g = 5 \times 10^4$ W/m$^3$, and $L = 1$ m.

**5-21** A plane wall of thickness $L$ is insulated at the surface $x = 0$ and maintained at a constant temperature $T_L$ at the surface $x = L$. Energy is generated in the wall at a constant rate of $g$ W/m$^3$.

($a$) Develop an expression for the steady-state temperature distribution in the slab.

($b$) Determine the maximum amount of energy that can be generated in the wall if the temperature of the insulated surface should not exceed 200°C when plate thickness $L = 15$ $cm$, plate thermal conductivity $k = 30$ W/(m·°C), and the temperature of the surface at $x = L$ is $T_L = 50°C$.

**5-22** A plane wall of thickness $L = 10$ $cm$ is insulated at the surface $x = 0$ and maintained at a constant temperature $T_L = 200°C$ at the surface $x = L$. The wall has a thermal conductivity $k = 20$ W/(m·°C), and energy is generated at a constant rate $g = 20000$ W/m$^3$. Calculate the temperature of the insulated surface. *Answer*: 205 °C

**5-23** A copper bar of radius $r = 5$ $mm$ and thermal conductivity $k = 360$ W/(m·°C) is heated at a rate of $g = 10^4$ W/m$^3$ by the passage of an electric current. If the outer surface of the wire dissipates heat by convection into an ambient at $T_\infty = 25°C$ with a heat transfer coefficient of $h = 200$ W/(m$^2$·°C), calculate the center temperature of the wire.

*Answer*: 25.1 °C

**5-24** An aluminum wire of radius $r = 2mm$ and thermal conductivity $k = 200$ W/(m·°C) is heated at a rate of $g = 10^5$ W/m$^3$ by the passage of an electric current. If the outer surface of the wire is maintained at a constant temperature $T_\infty = 30°$), calculate the center temperature of the wire.

**5-25** A plane wall of thickness $L$ and constant thermal conductivity $k$ has both its boundary surfaces kept at zero temperature. Energy is generated in the plate at a constant rate of $g = Ax^2$ W/m$^3$, where $A$ is a constant.

($a$) Develop an expression for the temperature distribution $T(x)$ in the slab.

($b$) Calculate the maximum temperature in the slab for $k = 30$ W/(m·°C), $g = (1000)x^2$ W/m$^3$, $L = 50$ cm, and $g = 100$ W/m$^3$.

**5-26** Electric current $I = 500$ $A$ flows through a stainless steel conductor of diameter $D = 5$ $mm$ that has an electric resistance $R = 5 \times 10^{-4}$ $\Omega/m$. Energy generated as a result of the passage of the electric current is dissipated by convection into an ambient at temperature $T_\infty = 0°C$ with a heat transfer coefficient $h = 50$ W/(m$^2$·°C). The thermal conductivity of the conductor is $k = 60$ W/(m·°C). Calculate the center and surface temperatures of the cable.

*Note*:

$$g = \frac{RI^2}{(\pi D^2/4) \times (1)} \quad \text{W/m}^3$$

**5-27** An electric current $I = 200$ $A$ passes through a copper bar with a diameter $D = 2$ $cm$, thermal conductivity $k = 360$ W/(m·°C), and an electric resistance $R = 9 \times 10^{-3}$ $\Omega/m$ that is exposed to air at temperature $T_\infty = 20°C$. The heat transfer coefficient between the surface and the air is $h = 40$ W/(m·°C). Calculate the surface and center temperatures of the bar.

*Note*:

$$g = \frac{RI^2}{(\pi D^2/4) \times (1)} \quad \text{W/m}^3$$

**5-28** Energy is generated at a rate of $g$ W/m$^3$ in a cylindrical fuel element for a nuclear reactor. The fuel element has a diameter $D$ and thermal conductivity $k$, and is cooled by a fluid at a temperature $T_\infty$ with a heat transfer coefficient $h = 1000$ W/(m$^2$·°C).

($a$) Develop an expression for the center temperature of the fuel element,

($b$) Calculate the center temperature for $D = 1$ $cm$, $g = 6 \times 10^8$ W/m$^3$, $T_\infty = 200$ °C, and $k = 40$ W/(m·°C).

*Numerical Analysis*

**5-29** Consider the following one-dimensional, steady-state heat conduction problem:

$$\frac{d^2 T(x)}{dx^2} + \frac{g}{k} = 0 \qquad \text{in } 0 < x < L$$

$$\frac{dT(x)}{dx} = 0 \qquad \text{at } x = 0$$

$$-k\frac{dT(x)}{dx} = h_\infty[T(x) - T_\infty] \quad \text{at } x = L$$

(*a*) Write the finite-difference formulation of this heat conduction problem by dividing the region $O \leq x \leq L$ into five equal parts.

(*b*) Compute the node temperatures for $k = 10$ W/(m·℃), $h_\infty = 200$ W/(m²·℃), $T_1 = 0$℃, $T_\infty = 100$℃, $g = 10^6$ W/m³, and $L = 5$ *cm*.

(*c*) Compare the numerical solution at the nodes with the exact solution.

**5-30** Consider the following one-dimensional, steady-state heat conduction problem:

$$\frac{d^2 T(x)}{dx^2} + \frac{g}{k} = 0 \qquad \text{in } 0 < x < L$$

$$T(x) = T_1 \qquad \text{at } x = 0$$

$$-k\frac{dT(x)}{dx} = h_\infty[T(x) - T_\infty] \quad \text{at } x = L$$

Write the finite-difference formulation of this heat conduction problem by dividing the region $0 \leq x \leq L$ into

(*a*) Four equal parts.

(*b*) Eight equal parts.

(*c*) Compute the node temperatures for $k = 20$ W/(m·℃), $h_\infty = 400$ W/(m²·℃), $T_\infty = 150$℃, $g = 2 \times 10^6$ W/m³, and $L = 10$ *cm*.

(*d*) Compare the numerical solutions at the nodes with the exact solution.

**5-31** Derive the finite-difference formulation for Problem 5-5 by dividing the slab into four equal parts.

(*a*) Evaluate the numerical values for $k = 20$ W/(m·℃), $g_0 = 10^8$ W/m³, and $L = 20$ *cm*.

(*b*) Compare the numerical solution at the nodes with the exact solution.

**5-32** Derive the finite-difference formulation for Problem 5-6 by dividing the slab into four equal parts.

($a$) Evaluate the numerical values for $k = 50$ W/(m·°C), $T_2 = 100$°C, $g_0 = 10^6$ W/m$^3$, $L = 5$ cm, and $\gamma = 0.2m^{-l}$.

($b$) Compare the numerical solution at the nodes with the exact solution.

**5-33** Consider the following one-dimensional steady-state heat conduction problem:

$$\frac{d^2T(x)}{dx^2} + \frac{g_0}{k}\cos\frac{\pi x}{2L} = 0 \qquad \text{in } 0 < x < L$$

$$\frac{dT(x)}{dx} = 0 \qquad \text{at } x = 0$$

$$T(x) = T_w \qquad \text{at } x = L$$

($a$) Write the finite-difference formulation of the problem by dividing the region $0 < x < L$ into five equal parts.

($b$) Compute the node temperatures for $k = 10$ W/(m·°C), $T_w = 500$°C, $g_0 = 10^6$ W/m$^3$, and $L = 0.1$ m.

**5-34** For Problem 5-7, write the finite-difference formulation of the problem by dividing the region $0 < r < b$ into five equal parts, and for $T_w = 0$°C compare the numerical values obtained at the nodes with the exact solutions.

**5-35** Write the finite-difference formulation for Problem 5-10 by dividing the region $0 < r < b$ into five equal parts, and compare the resulting node temperatures with the exact solution.

**5-36** Write the finite-difference formulation for Problem 5-12 by dividing the region $0 < r < b$ into five equal parts, and compare the results with the exact solution.

**5-37** Write the finite-difference formulation for Problem 5-14 by dividing the region $0 < r < b$ into four and eight equal parts and compare these two results for the node temperatures with the exact solution.

CHAPTER 6

# *Transient Heat Conduction*

In the previous two chapters we studied steady-state heat conduction in solids in which temperature within the body varied with position but not with time. We also described a simplified analysis of temperature variation within the solids as a function of time based on the lumped system approach, which assumes uniform temperature within the solid at any instant. However, in many situations the temperature variations within the solid are no longer negligible; hence lumped system analysis is no longer applicable. Then, the analysis of heat conduction problems involves the determination of the temperature distribution within the solid as a function of both time and position, and it is a complicated matter. Various methods of analysis for solving such problems are discussed in advanced texts on heat conduction. Here we are concerned only with the application of the results obtained from such analysis.

Transient heat conduction in solids having simple shapes, such as a semi-infinite region, a plate, a long solid cylinder, and a solid sphere, can be solved analytically, and the transient temperature distribution and heat flow obtained from such solutions can be presented in the form of transient temperature and heat flow charts. In this chapter we present such charts and illustrate their use in predicting temperature variation within a solid as a function of time and position, as well as the heat transfer rate.

There are numerous situations in which either the geometry is complicated or the problem is nonlinear, so that the analytic solution to the problem is either not possible or too elaborate to use in practice. In such situations purely numerical schemes are useful for solving the problem. Therefore, we also describe here a simple explicit finite-difference scheme for solving one-dimensional transient heat conduction problems numerically.

## 6.1. TRANSIENT TEMPERATURE DISTRIBUTION IN A SEMI-INFINITE SOLID

The concept of a one-dimensional semi-infinite solid refers, mathematically, to a region that has a single boundary surface and extends to infinity in one direction. However, in practice, it implies a plate that is sufficiently thick that any temperature disturbance applied to one of its surfaces has negligible effect: for all practical purposes, on the other surface, during the period of observation of temperature transient.

We consider a semi-infinite solid confined to the region $x \geq 0$ and initially at a uniform temperature $T_i$. There is no energy generation within the medium. Suppose, at time $t = 0$, that the thermal condition at the boundary surface $x = 0$ is suddenly changed. The effects of this thermal disturbance will be gradually felt at the interior regions of the body; hence, for times $t > 0$, the temperature of the solid will vary with both position and

187

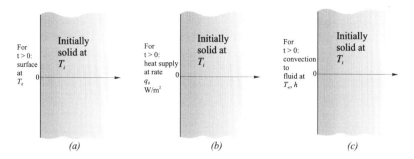

**FIG. 6.1.** Three different boundary conditions for semi-infinite solids.

time. Here we examine the temperature transients within a semi-infinite solid resulting from each of the following three different types of thermal disturbances applied at the boundary surface $x = 0$:

Sudden change in surface temperature
Suddenly imposed surface heat flux
Suddenly imposed convection

### 6.1.1 Sudden Change in Boundary Temperature

Consider a semi-infinite solid that is initially at a uniform temperature $T_i$ and confined to the domain $x \geq 0$. There is no energy generation within the medium. At time $t = 0$, the temperature of the boundary surface at $x = 0$ is suddenly changed to $T_0$. Figure 6.1 illustrates the geometry and coordinates. The mathematical formulation of this one-dimensional heat conduction problem is given by

$$\frac{\partial^2 T(x,t)}{\partial x^2} = \frac{1}{\alpha}\frac{\partial T(x,t)}{\partial t} \quad \text{in } x > 0,\ t > 0 \tag{6-1a}$$

subject to the boundary conditions

$$T(x,t) = T_0 \quad \text{at } x = 0,\ t > 0 \tag{6-1b}$$

$$T(x,t) \to T_i \quad \text{as } x \to \infty,\ t > 0 \tag{6-1c}$$

and the initial condition

$$T(x,t) = T_i \quad \text{for } t = 0,\ \text{in } x \geq 0 \tag{6-1d}$$

The transient heat conduction problem given by Eqs. (6-1a) to (6-1d) has been solved for $T(x,t)$ and the dimensionless temperature $\theta(x,t)$:

$$\theta(x,t) \equiv \frac{T(x,t) - T_0}{T_i - T_0} \tag{6-2a}$$

is expressed in terms of the dimensionless parameter $\xi$,

$$\xi \equiv \frac{x}{2\sqrt{\alpha t}} \tag{6-2b}$$

with the following expression

$$\theta(x,t) = \text{erf}\,(\xi) \tag{6-3}$$

Here *erf($\xi$)* is called the *error function* of argument $\xi$, and its numerical values are tabulated as a function of $\xi$ in Appendix D. It should be noted that erf(0) = 0 and erf($\infty$) = 1. Figure 6.2 shows a plot of the dimensionless temperature $\theta(x,t)$ as a function of the parameter $x/2\sqrt{\alpha t}$. The physical significance of this graph is as follows:

For a given value of $x$, the graph represents the variation in temperature with time at that particular location $x$. Conversely, for a given value of $t$, the graph represents the variation of temperature with position within the solid at a particular time $t$.

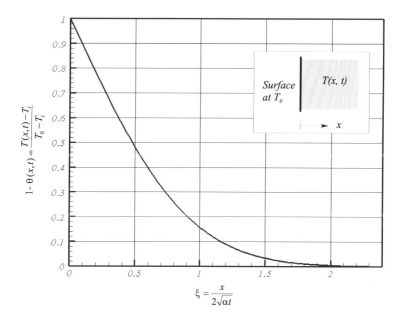

**FIG. 6.2.** Temperature distribution $T(x,t)$ in a semi-infinite solid which is initially at $T_i$; for $t > 0$ the surface at $x = 0$ is maintained at $T_0$.

In engineering applications, the heat flux at the boundary surface $x = 0$ is also of interest. The heat flux at any position is obtained from its definition,

$$q(x,t) = -k\frac{\partial T}{\partial x}. \tag{6-4}$$

Then, the heat flux at the boundary surface $x = 0$ becomes

$$\boxed{q_s(t) = \frac{k(T_0 - T_i)}{\sqrt{\pi \alpha t}}} \quad W/m^2. \tag{6-5}$$

## 6.1.2 Suddenly Imposed Boundary Surface Heat Flux

Consider a semi-infinite solid, initially at a uniform temperature $T = T_i$ and confined to the domain $x \geq 0$. There is no energy generation within the medium. At time $t = 0$, the boundary surface at $x = 0$ is subjected to a constant heat flux $q_0 \ W/m^2$, and maintained so for times $t > 0$.

The mathematical formulation of this heat conduction problem is given by

$$\frac{\partial^2 T(x,t)}{\partial x^2} = \frac{1}{\alpha} \frac{\partial T(x,t)}{\partial t} \quad \text{in } x > 0, \ t > 0 \tag{6-6a}$$

subject to the boundary conditions

$$-k \frac{\partial T(x,t)}{\partial x} = q_0 \quad \text{at } x = 0, \ t > 0 \tag{6-6b}$$

$$T(x,t) \to T_i \quad \text{as } x \to \infty, \ t > 0 \tag{6-6c}$$

and the initial condition

$$T(x,t) = T_i \quad \text{for } t = 0, \text{ in } x \geq 0 \tag{6-6d}.$$

The transient heat conduction problem given by Eqs. (6-6a) to (6-6d) has been solved, and the temperature distribution $T(x,t)$ within the solid is determined as a function of position and time as

$$\boxed{T(x,t) = T_i + \frac{2q_0}{k}(\alpha t)^{1/2} \left[ \frac{1}{\sqrt{\pi}} e^{-\xi^2} + \xi \, \text{erf}(\xi) - \xi \right]} \tag{6-7a}$$

where the parameter $\xi$ is defined as

$$\xi = \frac{x}{2\sqrt{\alpha t}}. \tag{6-7b}$$

We note that the temperature continues to change with time as long as heat flux $q_0$ is maintained at the boundary surface.

## 6.1.3 Suddenly Imposed Convection on the Boundary Surface

We now consider a semi-infinite solid, initially at a uniform temperature $T_i$; for $t > 0$, the boundary surface at $x = 0$ is subjected to convection into a fluid at a constant temperature $T_0$, with a known heat transfer coefficient $h$.

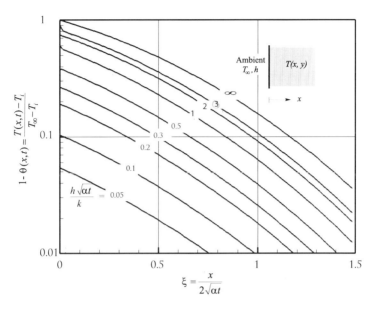

**FIG. 6.3.** Transient temperature $T(x,t)$ in a semi-infinite solid subjected to convection at the boundary surface.

For this case we define a dimensionless temperature $\theta(x,t)$ as

$$\theta(x,t) = \frac{T(x,t) - T_\infty}{T_i - T_\infty} \tag{6-8a}$$

and we obtain the dimensionless temperature distribution as

$$1 - \theta(x,t) = \text{erfc}\,(\xi) - exp(\frac{hx}{k} + \frac{h^2\alpha t}{k^2})\,\text{erfc}\,(\xi + \frac{h\sqrt{\alpha t}}{k}) \tag{6-8b}$$

where

$$\xi = \frac{x}{2\sqrt{\alpha t}} \tag{6-8c}$$

and

$$\text{erfc}\,(\xi) = 1 - \text{erf}\,(\xi). \tag{6-8d}$$

The numerical values of the *error function erf(ξ)* are tabulated as a function of ξ in Appendix D.

Figure 6.3 shows a plot of the quantity

$$1 - \theta(x,t) = \frac{T(x,t) - T_i}{T_\infty - T_i}$$

as a function of the dimensionless parameter $\xi = \frac{x}{2\sqrt{\alpha t}}$ for several different values of the dimensionless parameter $h\sqrt{\alpha t}/k$.

The special case $h \to \infty$ is equivalent to the problem with a constant temperature $T_\infty$ at the boundary surface $x = 0$.

**EXAMPLE 6-1** A thick stainless-steel plate $[\alpha = 1.6 \times 10^{-5} \text{ m}^2/s$ and $k = 61 \text{ W}/(\text{m·°C})]$ is initially at a uniform temperature of 150°C. Suddenly one of its surfaces is lowered to 20°C and maintained at that temperature for times $t > 0$. By treating the plate as a semi-infinite solid, determine the temperature at a depth 2 cm from the surface and the surface heat flux at a time 1 min after lowering the surface temperature.

**SOLUTION** Given $\alpha = 1.6 \times 10^{-5} \text{ m}^2/s$, $x = 0.02$ m, and $t = 60$ s, the parameter $\xi$, becomes

$$\xi = \frac{x}{2\sqrt{\alpha t}} = \frac{0.02}{2\sqrt{1.6 \times 10^{-5} \times 60}} = 0.32.$$

Knowing $\xi$, the dimensionless temperature is obtained either from the analytic expression, Eq. (6-3), or from the graph given in Fig. 6.2. If the analytic expression is used, we have for $\xi = 0.32$, from Appendix D, $\text{erf}(\xi) = 0.34913$. Then Eqs. (6-2a) and (6-3) give

$$\theta(x,t) \equiv \frac{T(x,t) - T_0}{T_i - T_0} = \text{erf}(\xi) = 0.34913.$$

If Fig. 6.2 is used, this result could also be obtained for $\xi = 0.32$, but not so accurately. Now, knowing $T_i = 150$°C and $T_0 = 20$°C, the temperature at 2 cm depth and after 1 min is determined:

$$
\begin{aligned}
T(0.02 \text{ m}, 60 \text{ s}) &= 0.34913(T_i - T_0) + T_0 \\
&= 0.34913(150 - 20) + 20 = 65.4\text{°C}.
\end{aligned}
$$

The heat flux at the surface at time t = 1 min = 60 s is calculated from Eq. (6-5):

$$
\begin{aligned}
q_s(t) &= \frac{k(T_0 - T_i)}{\sqrt{\pi \alpha t}} \\
&= \frac{61(20 - 150)}{\sqrt{\pi \times 1.6 \times 10^{-5} \times 60}} = -144.4 \text{ kW}/\text{m}^2
\end{aligned}
$$

where the minus sign indicates that the heat flow is out from the slab.

**EXAMPLE 6-2** A thick concrete slab $[\alpha = 7 \times 10^{-7} \text{ m}^2/s$ and $k = 1.37 \text{ W}/(\text{m·°C})]$ is initially at a uniform temperature of 340°C. Suddenly one of its surfaces is subjected to convective cooling with a heat transfer coefficient of 100 W/(m²·°C) into an ambient at 40°C. Calculate the temperature at a depth 10 cm from the surface at the time 1 h after the start of cooling.

**SOLUTION** Given $[\alpha = 7 \times 10^{-7} \text{ m}^2/s$, $x = 0.1$ m, and $t = 3600$ $s$, then the parameter $\xi$ becomes

$$\xi = \frac{x}{2\sqrt{\alpha t}} = \frac{0.1}{2\sqrt{7 \times 10^{-7} \times 3600}} = 1.0.$$

Given $h = 100$ W/(m$^2 \cdot$°C) and $k = 1.37$ W/(m·°C), the dimensionless parameter $h\sqrt{\alpha t}/k$ appearing in Fig. 6.3 becomes

$$\frac{h\sqrt{\alpha t}}{k} = \frac{100\sqrt{7 \times 10^{-7} \times 3600}}{1.37} = 3.66.$$

Then from Fig. 6.3 we have

$$1 - \theta(x, t) = 0.11$$

and given $T_i = 340$°C and $T_\infty = 40$°C, the temperature at 10 cm depth after 1 h is determined to be

$$
\begin{aligned}
1 - \theta(x, t) &= \frac{T(x, t) - T_i}{T_\infty - T_i} = 0.11 \\
T(0.1, 3600) &= 0.11(40 - 340) + 340 = 307 \text{ °C}.
\end{aligned}
$$

## 6.2. ONE DIMENSIONAL TRANSIENT TEMPERATURE AND HEAT FLOW: HEISLER CHARTS

Analytic solutions are available for temperature distribution and heat flow as a function of time and position in solids that have simple shapes, such as a slab, a long solid cylinder, or a sphere. Therefore transient temperature and heat flow charts can be constructed from such solutions for ready reference in practical applications.

Here we consider the situation in which the solid is initially at a uniform temperature $T_i$ and there is no energy generation in the medium. At time $t = 0$, the boundary surfaces are suddenly subjected to convection with a known heat transfer coefficient $h$ into an ambient at a specified constant temperature $T_\infty$. The resulting transient-temperature is first solved by *M. P. Heisler* and therefore often referred to as *Heisler Charts*. Next, the transient-temperature and the heat flow charts for slab and for cylinder are presented, and their use is explained with examples.

### 6.2.1 Transient-Temperature Chart for Slab

Consider a slab (i.e., a plane wall) of thickness $2L$, confined to the region $-L \leq x \leq L$. Initially the slab is at a uniform temperature $T_i$. Suddenly, at time $t = 0$, both boundary surfaces of the slab are subjected to convection with a heat transfer coefficient $h$ into ambients at a temperature $T_\infty$ and they are maintained at that condition for $t > 0$.

Figure 6.4a illustrates the geometry coordinates and the boundary conditions for this problem. It is apparent that the problem possesses both geometrical and thermal symmetry about the plane $x = 0$; therefore we need to consider this heat conduction problem for

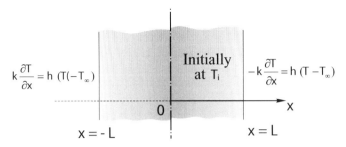

**FIG. 6.4a.** A slab of thickness $2L$ subjected to convection at both boundary surfaces.

only half the region, say $0 \leq x \leq L$. Then, the mathematical formulation of this heat conduction problem over the region $0 \leq x \leq L$ with a symmetry boundary condition at $x = 0$ and a convection boundary condition at $x = L$ becomes

$$\frac{\partial^2 T}{\partial x^2} = \frac{1}{\alpha}\frac{\partial T}{\partial t} \quad \text{in } 0 < x < L, \text{ for } t > 0 \tag{6-9a}$$

$$\frac{\partial T}{\partial x} = 0 \quad \text{at } x = 0, \text{ for } t > 0 \tag{6-9b}$$

$$k\frac{\partial T}{\partial x} + hT = hT_\infty \quad \text{at } x = L, \text{ for } t > 0 \tag{6-9c}$$

$$T = T_i \quad \text{in } 0 \leq x \leq L, \text{ for } t > 0 \tag{6-9d}$$

Scrutiny of this formulation reveals that the temperature $T(x,t)$ depends on too many parameters, that is, $t, x, L, T_i, T_\infty, h, k,$ and $\alpha$; therefore, it is not practical to present the solution for $T(x,t)$ in graphical form if the effects of all these parameters on temperature are to be included. To alleviate such a difficulty, the following dimensionless parameters are introduced:

$$\theta = \frac{T(x,t) - T_\infty}{T_i - T_\infty} = \text{dimensionless temperature} \tag{6-10a}$$

$$X = \frac{x}{L} = \text{dimensionless coordinate} \tag{6-10b}$$

$$\text{Bi} = \frac{hL}{k} = \text{Biot number} \tag{6-10c}$$

$$\tau = \frac{\alpha t}{L^2} = \text{dimensionless time or Fourier number.} \tag{6-10d}$$

Then the above heat conduction problem becomes

$$\frac{\partial^2 \theta}{\partial X^2} = \frac{\partial \theta}{\partial \tau} \quad \text{in } 0 < X < 1, \text{ for } \tau > 0 \tag{6-11a}$$

$$\frac{\partial \theta}{\partial X} = 0 \quad \text{at } X = 0, \text{ for } \tau > 0 \tag{6-11b}$$

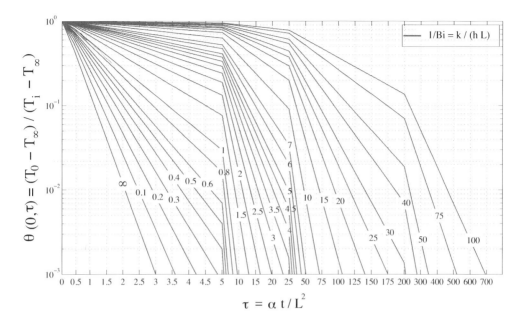

**FIG. 6.4b.** Transient-temperature chart for a slab of thickness $2L$ subjected to convection at both boundary surfaces. Dimensionless temperature $\theta(0, \tau)$ at the center plane, $x = 0$.

$$\frac{\partial\theta}{\partial X} + \text{Bi } \theta = 0 \quad \text{at } X = 1, \text{ for } \tau > 0 \qquad (6\text{-}11c)$$

$$\theta = 1 \quad \text{in } 0 \le X \le 1, \text{ for } \tau = 0. \qquad (6\text{-}11d)$$

In this formulation the number of dimensionless parameters affecting $\theta(X, \tau)$ is reduced to three, namely, $\tau$, Bi and $X$; hence, it becomes practical to present the solution for temperature in graphical form. Before presenting some results, it is instructive to examine the physical significance of the dimensionless parameters $\tau$ and Bi that appear in the above equations. The dimensionless time $\tau$ (i.e., the Fourier number) given by Eq. (6-l0d) is rearranged in the form

$$\tau = \frac{\alpha t}{L^2} = \frac{k(1/L)L^2}{\rho c_p L^3/t} = \frac{\left(\begin{array}{c}\text{rate of heat conduction} \\ \text{across } L \text{ in volume } L^3, \ W/^\circ C\end{array}\right)}{\left(\begin{array}{c}\text{rate of heat storage} \\ \text{in volume } L^3, \ W/^\circ C\end{array}\right)}. \qquad (6\text{-}12a)$$

Thus, the Fourier number is a measure of the rate of heat conduction compared with the rate of heat storage in a given volume element. Therefore, the larger the Fourier number, the deeper the penetration of heat into a solid over a given time.

The physical significance of the Biot number can be better understood if Eq. (6-l0c) is rearranged in the form

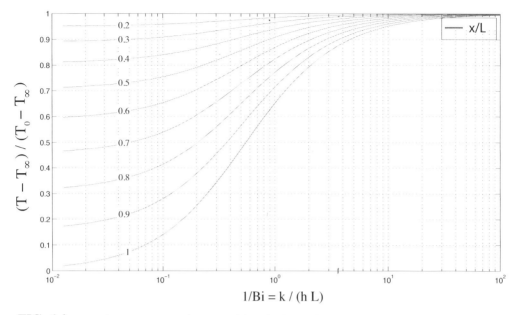

**FIG. 6.4c.** Transient-temperature chart for a slab of thickness $2L$ subjected to convection at both boundary surfaces. Position correction for use with Figure 6.4b.

$$\text{Bi} = \frac{hL}{k} = \frac{h}{k/L} = \frac{\left(\begin{array}{c}\text{heat transfer coefficient} \\ \text{at the surface of the solid}\end{array}\right)}{\left(\begin{array}{c}\text{internal conductance of} \\ \text{solid across length } L\end{array}\right)}. \qquad (6\text{-}12b)$$

That is, the Biot number is the ratio of the heat transfer coefficient to the unit conductance of the solid over the characteristic dimension.

The problem defined by Eqs. (6-11) has been solved, and the results for the dimensionless temperature are presented in Fig. 6.4$b$ and $c$. Figure 6.4$b$ gives the midplane temperature $T_0$ or $\theta(0, \tau)$ at $X = 0$ as a function of the dimensionless time $\tau$ for several different values of the parameter 1/Bi.

The curve for 1/Bi= 0 corresponds to the case in which $h \rightarrow \infty$, or the surfaces of the plate are maintained at the ambient temperature $T_\infty$. For larger values of 1/Bi, the Biot number is small, or the internal conductance of the solid is large in comparison with the heat transfer coefficient at the surface. This, in turn, implies that temperature distribution within the solid is sufficiently uniform, and hence lumped system analysis becomes applicable. To illustrate this we refer to Fig. 6.4$c$, which relates the temperatures at different locations within the slab to the midplane temperature $T_0$. Given $T_0$, temperatures at different locations within the slab can be determined.

An examination of Fig. 6.4$c$ reveals that for values of 1/Bi larger than 10, or Bi< 0.1, the temperature distribution within the slab may be considered uniform with an error of less than about 5 percent. We recall that Bi< 0.1 was used previously as the criterion for lumped system analysis to be applicable.

The amount of heat transfer to or from the plate over a given period of time is also a quantity of practical interest.

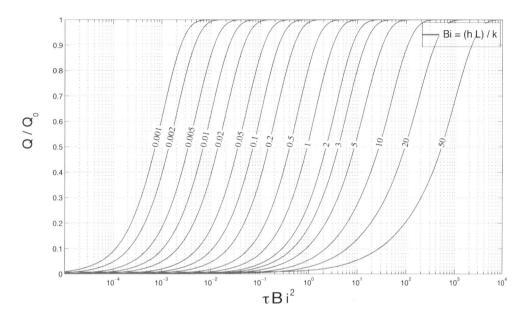

**FIG. 6.5.** Dimensionless heat transferred $Q/Q_0$ for a slab of thickness $2L$.

Figure 6.5 shows the dimensionless heat transferred $Q/Q_0$ as a function of dimensionless time for several different values of the Biot number for a slab of thickness $2L$. Here $Q$ represents the total amount of energy which is lost by the plate up to any time $t$ during the transient heat transfer. The quantity $Q_0$ for the slab volume $V = (2L)(\text{depth})$, defined as

$$Q_0 = \rho c_p V (T_i - T_\infty) \quad W \cdot s \tag{6-13}$$

represents the initial energy of the slab relative to the ambient temperature. Knowing $Q_0$ and determining the ratio $Q/Q_0$ from Fig. 6.5, the amount of heat transfer $Q$ is calculated.

**EXAMPLE 6-3** A steel plate $[\alpha = 1.2 \times 10^{-5} \text{ m}^2/s, k = 43 \text{ W}/(\text{m·°C}) , c_p = 465$ J/(kg·°C), and $\rho = 7833 \text{ kg/m}^3]$ of thickness 10 cm, initially at a uniform temperature of 240°C, is suddenly immersed in an oil bath at 40°C. The convection heat transfer coefficient between the fluid and the surface is 600 W/(m²·°C) ,
$(a)$ How long will it take for the center-plane to cool to 100°C?
$(b)$ What is the temperature at a depth 3 cm from the outer surface?
$(c)$ Calculate the energy removed from the plate during this time.

**SOLUTION** $(a)$ Given $2L = 10\ cm = 0.1$ m or $L = 0.05$ m, $k = 43$ W/(m·℃), and $h = 600$ W/(m²·℃), we have

$$\frac{1}{\text{Bi}} = \frac{k}{hL} = \frac{43}{600 \times 0.05} = 1.43 \quad \text{or} \quad \text{Bi} = 0.7$$

and given $T_0 = 100℃$, $T_\infty = 40℃$, and $T_i = 240℃$, we calculate

$$\theta(0, \tau) = \frac{T_0 - T_\infty}{t_i - T_\infty} = \frac{100 - 40}{240 - 40} = 0.3$$

Hence, Fig. 6.4$b$, for $\theta(0, \tau) = 0.3$ and 1/Bi= 1.43 we read the dimensionless time $\tau \simeq 2.2$. Knowing $\tau$, we calculate the time as

$$\tau = \frac{\alpha t}{L^2} \quad \text{or} \quad t = \frac{2.2(0.05)^2}{1.2 \times 10^{-5}} = 558\ s$$
$$t = 7\ min\ 38\ s.$$

$(b)$ To determine the temperature at a location 3 cm from the surface (i.e., 2 cm from the centerline), we compute the dimensionless location $x/L$ as

$$\frac{x}{L} = \frac{0.02}{0.05} = 0.4.$$

For 1/Bi= 1.43 and $x/L = 0.4$, from Fig. 6.4$c$ we have

$$\frac{T - T_\infty}{T_0 - T_\infty} \cong 0.95.$$

Hence $T$ is determined as

$$T = T_\infty + (T_0 - T_\infty)(0 - 95)$$
$$= 40 + (100 - 40)(0.95) = 97℃.$$

(c) The energy removed from the plate per square meter (including both sides) during $t = 7\ min\ 38\ s$ is determined as follows:

From Fig. 6.5, for Bi= 0.7 and for Bi² · $\tau = (0.7)^2(2.2) = 1.078$, we have

$$\frac{Q}{Q_0} \simeq 0.93.$$

For the plate of thickness $2L = 0.1$ m, $Q_0$ is determined from Eq. (6-13) as

$$Q_0 = \rho c_p V (T_i - T_\infty)$$
$$= (7833)(465)(0.1)(240 - 40)$$
$$= 72.847\ \text{MJ}.$$

Knowing $Q_0$, the energy removed from the plate per square meter in $7\ min\ 38\ s$ becomes

$$Q = 0.93Q_0 = 67.7 \text{ MJ}.$$

## 6.2.2 Transient-Temperature Chart for Long Cylinder

Consider one-dimensional transient heat conduction in a long cylinder of radius $b$ which is initially at a uniform temperature $T_i$. Suddenly, at time $t = 0$, the boundary surface at $r = b$ is subjected to convection with a heat transfer coefficient $h$ into an ambient at temperature $T_\infty$ and maintained so for times $t > 0$. Figure 6.6$a$ illustrates the geometry, the coordinates, and the boundary condition.

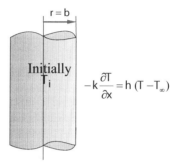

**FIG. 6.6a.** A long solid cylinder of radius $r = b$ subjected to convection at the boundary surface $r = b$.

The mathematical formulation of this cylindrical one-dimensional heat conduction problem is similar to that given by Eqs. (6-9$a$) to (6-9$d$), except that the $x$ variable is replaced by the $r$, and the Laplacian term $\partial^2 T/\partial x^2$ is replaced by $(1/r)(\partial/\partial r)(r\partial T/\partial r)$. For the reasons stated previously, it is desirable to represent the formulation in the dimensionless form. Therefore, the following dimensionless quantities are defined:

$$\text{Bi} = \frac{hb}{k} = \text{Biot number} \qquad (6\text{-}14a)$$

$$\tau = \frac{\alpha t}{b^2} = \text{dimensionless time, or Fourier number} \qquad (6\text{-}14b)$$

$$\theta = \frac{T(r,t) - T_\infty}{T_i - T_\infty} = \text{dimensionless temperature} \qquad (6\text{-}14c)$$

$$R = \frac{r}{b} = \text{dimensionless radial coordinate} \qquad (6\text{-}14d)$$

Then the mathematical formulation of this heat conduction problem, in the dimensionless form, is given by

$$\frac{1}{R}\frac{\partial}{\partial R}\left(R\frac{\partial T}{\partial R}\right) = \frac{\partial \theta}{\partial \tau} \quad \text{in } 0 < R < 1, \text{ for } \tau > 0 \qquad (6\text{-}15a)$$

$$\frac{\partial \theta}{\partial R} = 0 \quad \text{at } R = 0, \text{ for } \tau > 0 \qquad (6\text{-}15b)$$

$$\frac{\partial \theta}{\partial R} + \text{Bi}\,\theta = 0 \quad \text{at } R = 1, \text{ for } \tau > 0 \qquad (6\text{-}15c)$$

$$\theta = 1 \quad \text{in } 0 \leq R \leq 1, \text{ for } \tau = 0 \qquad (6\text{-}15d)$$

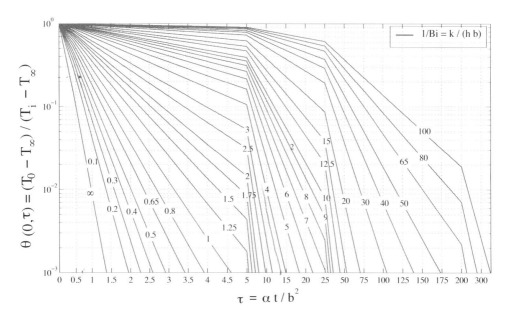

**FIG. 6.6b.** Transient-temperature chart for a long solid cylinder of radius $r = b$ subjected to convection at the boundary surface $r = b$. Dimensionless temperature $\theta(0, \tau)$ at the axis of the cylinder, $r = 0$.

This problem has been solved, and the results for the dimensionless center temperature $\theta(0, \tau)$ (or the center temperature $T_0$) at $R = 0$ are plotted in Fig. 6.6$b$ as a function of the dimensionless time $T$ for several different values of the parameter $1/\text{Bi}$. Figure 6.6$c$ relates the temperatures at different locations within the cylinder to the center temperature $T_0$. Therefore, given $T_0$, temperatures at different locations within the cylinder can be determined from Fig. 6.6$c$.

Figure 6.7 shows the dimensionless heat transferred $Q/Q_0$ as a function of dimensionless time for several different values of the Biot number for the cylinder problem given by Eqs. (6-15$a$) to (6-15$d$). Here $Q_0$ is as defined by Eq. (6-13), and $Q$ represents the total amount of energy lost by the cylinder up to any time $t$ during the transient heat transfer.

**EXAMPLE 6-4** Consider a slab of thickness 10 cm, and a cylinder of diameter 10 cm, each made of steel [$\alpha = 1.6 \times 10^{-5}$ m$^2$/$s$ and $k = 61$ W/(m·℃)] and initially at uniform temperature 300℃. Suddenly, they are all immersed into a well-stirred large bath at 50℃. The heat transfer coefficient between the surfaces and the fluid is 1000 W/(m$^2$·℃). Calculate the time required for the centers of the slab and the cylinder to cool to 80℃.

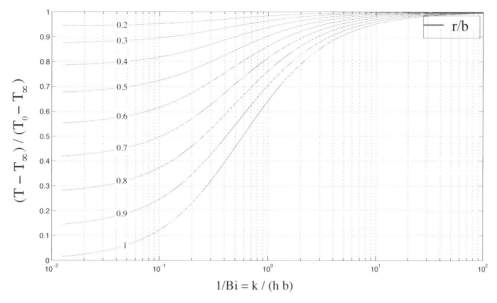

**FIG. 6.6c.** Transient-temperature chart for a long solid cylinder of radius $r = b$ subjected to convection at the boundary surface $r = b$. Position correction for use with Figure 6.6a.

**SOLUTION** Given $k = 61 \ \text{W}/(\text{m·°C})$, $h = 1000 \ \text{W}/(\text{m}^2\text{·°C})$, $L = (r_0)_{cyl} = (r_0)_{sph} = 5 \ cm = 0.05$ m, $T_0 = 80°C$, $T_i = 300°C$, and $T_\infty = 50°C$, we calculate

$$\frac{1}{\text{Bi}} = \frac{k}{hL} = \frac{61}{(1000)(0.05)} = 1.22$$

$$\theta(0, \tau) = \frac{T_0 - T_\infty}{T_i - T_\infty} = \frac{80 - 50}{300 - 50} = 0.12$$

Taking $\theta(0, \tau) = 0.12$ and $1/\text{Bi} = 1.22$, the dimensionless time for the slab is determined from Fig. 6.4$b$ as $\tau = 3.5$. Then the time required $t$ for the slab becomes

$$t = \frac{\tau L^2}{\alpha} = \frac{(3.5)(0.05)^2}{1.6 \times 10^{-5}} = 547 \ s.$$

Similarly, for the cylinder with $r = 0.05$ m we obtain $\theta(0, \tau) = 0.12$ and $1/\text{Bi} = 1.22$. The dimensionless time $\tau$ is determined from Fig. 6.6$b$ as $\tau = 1.7$. Then the time required $t$ for the cylinder becomes

$$t = \frac{\tau r_0^2}{\alpha} = \frac{(1.7)(0.05)^2}{1.6 \times 10^{-5}} = 266 \ s.$$

**EXAMPLE 6-5** A long steel shaft of radius 10 cm [$\alpha = 1.6 \times 10^{-5} \ \text{m}^2/s$ and $k =$

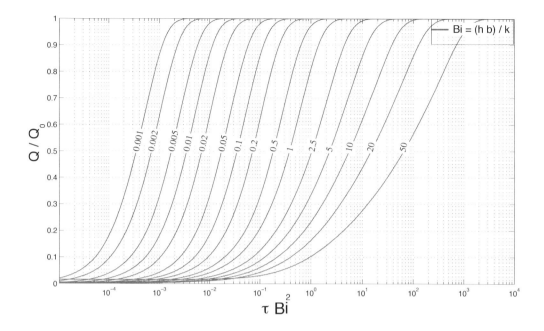

**FIG. 6.7.** Dimensionless heat transferred $Q/Q_0$ for a long cylinder of radius $b$.

61 W/(m·℃)] is removed from an oven at a uniform temperature of 500℃ and immersed in a well-stirred large bath of coolant maintained at 20℃. The heat transfer coefficient between the shaft surface and the coolant is 150 W/(m²·℃) . Calculate the time required for the shaft surface to reach 300℃.

**SOLUTION** Given $k = 61$ W/(m·℃) , $h = 150$ W/(m²·℃) and $r_0 = 10$ $cm = 0.1$ m. In order to use Fig. 6.6, we calculate

$$\frac{1}{Bi} = \frac{k}{hL}$$
$$= \frac{61}{(150)(0.05)} = 4.07$$
$$\frac{r}{r_0} = 1$$

Then, from Fig. 6.6c, for l/Bi= 4.07 and $r/r_0 = 1$, we have

$$\frac{T - T_\infty}{T_0 - T_\infty} \cong 0.87$$

where $T$ is the surface temperature, $T_\infty$ is the ambient temperature, and $T_0$ is the temperature at the axis of the shaft. Knowing the surface temperature $T = 300℃$ and $T_\infty = 20℃$, the temperature at the axis, $T_0$ is determined as

$$T_0 = T_\infty + \frac{T - T_\infty}{0.87}$$

$$= 20 + \frac{300 - 20}{0.87} = 341.84°C.$$

Next, given $T_i = 500°C$ and $T_\infty = 20°C$, and taking $T_0 = 341.84°C$, we determine the dimensionless temperature $\theta(O, \tau)$ to be

$$\theta(O, \tau) = \frac{T_0 - T_\infty}{T_i - T_\infty} = \frac{341.84 - 20}{500 - 20} = 0.67$$

and then read the dimensionless time $\tau$ from Fig. 6.6$b$ for $1/\text{Bi} = 4.07$ to be $\tau = 1$. We calculate the time required for the surface temperature to reach $300°C$ as follows:

$$\tau = \frac{\alpha t}{r_0^2} = 1$$

or

$$t = \frac{r_0^2}{\alpha} = \frac{(1.3)(0.1)^2}{1.6 \times 10^{-5}} = 625 \ s \cong 10\frac{1}{2} \ \text{min}.$$

### 6.2.3 Transient-Temperature Chart for a Sphere

We now consider transient heat conduction for a solid sphere of radius $b$ that is initially at a uniform temperature $T_i$. At time $t = 0$, the boundary surface at $r = b$ is suddenly subjected to convection with a heat transfer coefficient $h$ into an ambient at temperature $T_\infty$ and maintained so for times $t > 0$. Figure 6.8$a$ illustrates the geometry, the coordinates, and the boundary conditions.

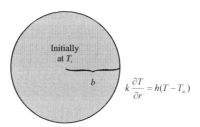

**FIG. 6.8.** A solid sphere of radius $r = b$ subjected to convection at the boundary surface $r = b$.

We introduce dimensionless variables as defined by Eqs. (6-14$a$) to (6-14$d$). Then the mathematical formulation of this heat conduction problem in dimensionless form becomes

$$\frac{1}{R^2}\frac{\partial}{\partial R}\left(R^2\frac{\partial T}{\partial R}\right) = \frac{\partial \theta}{\partial \tau} \quad \text{in } 0 < R < 1, \text{ for } \tau > 0 \qquad (6\text{-}16a)$$

$$\frac{\partial \theta}{\partial R} = 0 \quad \text{at} \ R = 0, \ \text{for} \ \tau > 0 \tag{6-16b}$$

$$\frac{\partial \theta}{\partial R} + \text{Bi} \ \theta = 0 \quad \text{at} \ R = 1, \ \text{for} \ \tau > 0 \tag{6-16c}$$

$$\theta = 1 \quad \text{in} \ 0 \le R \le 1, \ \text{for} \ \tau = 0 \tag{6-16d}.$$

Similarly this problem is solved by the mathematicians and the dimensionless center temperature $T_0$ or $\theta(0, \tau)$ for the sphere as a function of dimensionless time $\tau$ for several different values of the parameter 1/Bi, and the temperatures at different locations within the sphere to the center temperature $T_0$ relation is also plotted. These plots are not presented in this book.

## 6.3. NUMERICAL ANALYSIS AND SOLUTIONS

The transient-temperature and heat flow charts presented in the previous section were constructed using the exact analytic solutions for the corresponding problem. A close scrutiny of these heat conduction problems reveals that they are restricted to bodies having simple shapes, such as a semi-infinite medium, a slab, a long solid cylinder, or a sphere. Furthermore, the thermal properties of the solid are assumed to be constant. When the body has an irregular shape, has temperature-dependent thermal properties, or is subjected to a nonlinear boundary condition, such as radiation to or from the boundary surface, exact analytic solution of the problem is not possible. The transient heat conduction problems for such situations can be solved using purely numerical approaches, such as finite-difference or finite-element methods.

The use of numerical methods in the solution of transient heat conduction in solids has been studied extensively, and there is a vast amount of literature on the subject. Here we present an introductory treatment of the use of the finite-difference method in the solution of one-dimensional transient heat conduction problems in the rectangular coordinate system. There are several different types of finite-difference schemes, each of which has advantages under certain conditions. To introduce the reader to the subject, we consider only the explicit method of finite-differencing, because it is a simple and straightforward approach, and the resulting system of algebraic equations is very easy to solve.

### The Explicit Finite-Difference Scheme

The transient heat conduction problems of this chapter consist of a one-dimensional time-dependent heat conduction equation, two boundary conditions, and an initial condition. The basic idea of the finite-difference representation of such a problem is to transform the differential equation and its boundary conditions into a set of algebraic equations.

To illustrate the application of this concept, we consider a one-dimensional transient heat conduction problem for a slab with constant properties, confined to the region $0 \le x \le L$, that is subjected to some specified boundary conditions at the surfaces $x = 0$ and $x = L$, with an initial temperature distribution over the region.

The heat conduction equation for this problem is given by

$$\frac{\partial T(x,t)}{\partial t} = \alpha \frac{\partial^2 T}{\partial x^2} \quad \text{in } 0 < x < L \tag{6-17}$$

To obtain the finite-difference form of this differential equation, the $x$ and $t$ domains are divided into small steps $\Delta x$ and $\Delta t$, as illustrated in Fig. 6.9. Suppose the region $0 \leq x \leq L$ is divided into $M$ equal intervals, and a time step $\Delta t$ is chosen. Then, we have

$$x = (m-1)\Delta x$$

or

$$x + \Delta x = m\Delta x \quad m = 1, 2, \ldots, M, M+1 \tag{6-18a}$$

$$t = i\Delta t \quad i = 0, 1, 2, \ldots \tag{6-18b}$$

where $M$ is the number of equal subintervals over the region $0 \leq x \leq L$,

$$\Delta x = \frac{L}{M} \tag{6-18c}$$

and the temperature $T(x,t)$ at a location $x$ and time $t$ is denoted by the symbol $T_m^i$; that is,

$$T(x,t) = T[(m-1)\Delta x, i\Delta t] \equiv T_m^i. \tag{6-18d}$$

Note that in the space domain there are $M+1$ nodes (i.e., $m = 1, 2, 3, \ldots, M+1$).

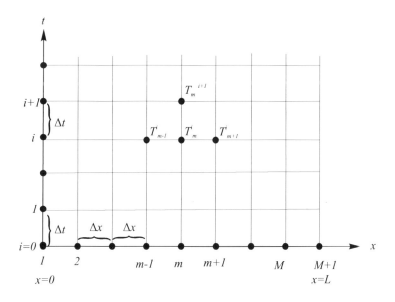

**FIG. 6.9.** Subdivision of space and time domain for finite-difference representation of the one-dimensional heat conduction equation.

To develop the finite-difference equations for each of these nodes, it is desirable to consider them in two distinct groups:

1. The *interior nodes*, consisting of the nodes $m = 2, 3, ..., M$, for which the finite-difference equations are obtained by utilizing the heat conduction equation (6-17).

2. The *boundary nodes*, or the nodes $m = 1$ and $m = M + 1$, for which the finite-difference equations are determined by utilizing the boundary conditions for the problem.

We present below the development of the finite-difference equations for the *interior* and *boundary* nodes.

## INTERIOR NODES:

To develop the finite-difference form of the heat conduction equation (6-17) for an interior node $m$ at time step $i$, we need to discretize the partial derivatives with respect to the space and time variables.

The second derivative of temperature with respect to $x$, at a node $m$ (position $x = (m - 1)\Delta x$) and at time step $i$ (time $i\Delta t$), is represented in the finite-difference form as described previously in Chapter 5. We find

$$\frac{\partial^2 T}{\partial x^2}\bigg|_{m,i} \cong \frac{T_{m-1}^i - 2T_m^i + T_{m+1}^i}{(\Delta x)^2} \tag{6-19a}$$

where $T_{m-1}^i$ and $T_{m+1}^i$ are the two neighboring points to the node $T_m^i$, and all of them are evaluated at the time step $i$.

The first derivative of temperature with respect to the time variable $t$ at a position $m$ and a time step $i$ is represented by

$$\frac{\partial T}{\partial t}\bigg|_{m,i} \cong \frac{T_m^{i+1} - T_m^i}{\Delta t} \tag{6-19b}$$

where $T_m^{i+1}$ represents the temperature at the location $x = (m - 1)\Delta x$ at the time $(i + 1)\Delta t$. The right-hand side of Eq. (6-19b) is a forward finite-difference representation with respect to time.

By introducing Eqs. (6-19) into Eq. (6-17), the finite-difference form of the one-dimensional time-dependent heat conduction equation at an internal node $m$ becomes

$$\frac{T_m^{i+1} - T_m^i}{\Delta T} = \alpha \frac{T_{m-1}^i - 2T_m^i + T_{m+1}^i}{(\Delta x)^2}. \tag{6-20}$$

This equation is rearranged in the form

$$\boxed{T_m^{i+1} = r\left(T_{m-1}^i + T_{m+1}^i\right) + (1 - 2r)T_m^i} \tag{6-21}$$

where

$$i = 0, 1, \ldots$$
$$m = 2, 3, \ldots, M$$
$$r = \frac{\alpha \Delta t}{(\Delta x)^2}. \tag{6-22}$$

Equation (6.21) is called the *explicit finite-difference* form of the one-dimensional time-dependent heat conduction equation (6-17).

The method is called *explicit* because the temperature $T_m^{i+1}$ at node $m$ at a time step $i+1$, is immediately determined from Eq. (6-21) if the temperatures of node $m$ and its two neighboring points at the previous time step $i$ are available and the value of the parameter $r$ is specified.

The system of equations (6-21) provides $M - 1$ algebraic equations, but contains $M + 1$ unknown node temperatures (i.e., $T_1^i, T_2^i, \ldots, T_{M+1}^i$). The additional two relations are obtained by utilizing the boundary conditions at the nodes $m = 1$ and $m = M + 1$, as described below.

## BOUNDARY NODES:

The boundary conditions at the nodes $m = 1$ and $m = M + 1$ may be prescribed temperature, prescribed heat flux, or convection into an ambient at a specified temperature.

When the temperatures are specified at the boundaries, the node temperatures $T_1^i$ and $T_{M+1}^i$ are known for all times; this provides two additional relations, and so Eqs. (6-21) are a complete set for the solution of $M - 1$ unknown interior node temperatures for each time step.

In the case of insulated, prescribed heat flux, or convection boundary conditions at the nodes $m = 1$ and $m = M + 1$, the node temperatures $T_1^i$ and $T_{M+1}^i$ are unknown. Two additional equations are needed in order to make the number of equations equal to the number of unknowns in the system (6-21). These equations are developed by writing an energy balance equation for a differential volume $\Delta V$ of thickness $\Delta x/2$ at node $m = 1$ and/or $m = M + 1$, as illustrated in Fig. 6.10. If the step size $\Delta x$ is sufficiently small, the heat capacity associated with the differential volume element at the boundary node can be neglected. Then the finite-difference equations for the boundary nodes are developed by considering the following steady-state energy balance equation.

$$\left\{ \begin{array}{l} \text{Rate of heat entering } \Delta V \\ \text{from all it's surfaces at} \\ \text{time step } i + 1 \end{array} \right\} + \left\{ \begin{array}{l} \text{Rate of energy generation} \\ \text{in } \Delta V \text{ at time step } i + 1 \end{array} \right\} = 0 \tag{6-23}$$

Suppose we have *convection* at the boundary surface $x = 0$, with a heat transfer coefficient $h_0$ into an ambient at temperature $T_{\infty 0}$, but no energy generation in the medium.

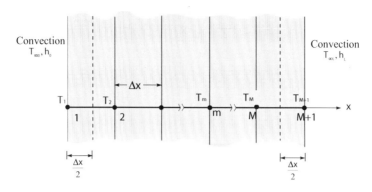

**FIG. 6.10.** Finite-difference equations for nodes on the boundaries.

The application of equation (6-23) to the node $m = 1$ yields

$$h_0 \left( T_{\infty 0} - T_1^{i+1} \right) + k \frac{T_2^{i+1} - T_1^{i+1}}{\Delta x} = 0. \tag{6-24a}$$

Solving for $T_1^{i+1}$, we get

$$\boxed{T_1^{i+1} = \frac{1}{1 + \Delta x h_0 / k} \left( T_2^{i+1} + \frac{\Delta x h_0}{k} T_{\infty 0} \right)} \quad \text{for } m = 1 \tag{6-24b}$$

where the parameter $r$ is defined by Eq. (6-22).

In the case of *convection* at the boundary surface $x = L$, with a heat transfer coefficient $h_L$ into an ambient at temperature $T_{\infty L}$, but no energy generation in the medium, the application of the energy equation (6-23) to the node $m = M + 1$ gives

$$h_L \left( T_{\infty L} - T_{M+1}^{i+1} \right) + k \frac{T_M^{i+1} - T_{M+1}^{i+1}}{\Delta x} = 0. \tag{6-25a}$$

Solving for $T_{M+1}^{i+1}$, we obtain

$$\boxed{T_{M+1}^{i+1} = \frac{1}{1 + \Delta x h_L / k} \left( T_M^{i+1} + \frac{\Delta x h_L}{k} T_{\infty L} \right)} \quad \text{for } m = M + 1. \tag{6-25b}$$

Equations (6-24*b*) and (6-25*b*) are the finite-difference equations for the boundary nodes $m = 1$ and $m = M + 1$, respectively, when these boundary surfaces are subjected to *convection*.

If the boundary surface at $x = 0$ is subjected to constant heat flux $q_0$, then the application of energy balance given by Eq. (6-23) to the node at $m = 1$ yields

$$q_0 + k \frac{T_2^{i+1} - T_1^{i+1}}{\Delta x} = 0 \tag{6-26a}$$

or

$$T_1^{i+1} = q_0 \frac{\Delta x}{k} + T_2^{i+1} \qquad (6\text{-}26b)$$

where $q_0$ is a positive quantity when it is into the wall.

If the boundary surface at $x = L$ is subjected to constant heat flux $q_L$, then the application of energy balance given by Eq. (6-23) to the node at $m = M + 1$ yields

$$q_L + k \frac{T_M^{i+1} - T_{M+1}^{i+1}}{\Delta x} = 0 \qquad (6\text{-}27a)$$

or

$$T_{M+1}^{i+1} = q_L \frac{\Delta x}{k} + T_M^{i+1} \qquad (6\text{-}27b)$$

where $q_L$ is a positive quantity when it is into the wall.

If the boundary surface at $m = 1$ or $m = M + 1$ is *insulated (adiabatic)*, the resulting finite-difference equation for the insulated boundary $m = 1$ or $m = M + 1$ is obtained from Eq. (6-24b) or (6-25b), respectively, by setting $h_0$ or $h_L$ equal to zero.

**RESTRICTION ON THE VALUE OF $r$ :**

We note that the finite-difference equations (6-21) contain a parameter $r$, defined as

$$r = \frac{\alpha \Delta t}{(\Delta x)^2}. \qquad (6\text{-}28)$$

The disadvantage of the simple explicit finite-difference scheme discussed above is that there is a restriction on the permissible value of $r$, imposed by a numerical stability condition. In finite-difference solution, the mesh size $\Delta x$ is generally chosen first, and then the value of the thermal diffusivity $\alpha$ is established by the material property. If the value of $r$ is fixed by the stability criterion, the permissible size of the time step $\Delta t$, according to Eq. (6-28), is restricted to

$$\Delta t \leq \frac{r(\Delta x)^2}{\alpha}. \qquad (6\text{-}29)$$

In general we take the equality in choosing the $\Delta t$ values. This condition implies that, if the mesh size $\Delta x$ is reduced by a factor of $n$ to improve the accuracy, the corresponding decrease in the time step $\Delta t$ is by a factor of $n^2$. Then, a large number of calculations are needed to solve the problem over a given time interval. If this stability criterion is violated, numerical calculations become unstable.

The accompanying figure, Figure 6.11 illustrates what happens to the numerical results if the above stability criterion is violated. This figure shows that the numerical results obtained with the time step satisfying the condition $r = \frac{5}{11} < \frac{1}{2}$ are in good agreement with the exact solution. However, the numerical solution of the same problem with a slightly larger time step, which violates the above stability criterion of $r = \frac{5}{9} > \frac{1}{2}$ results in an unstable solution.

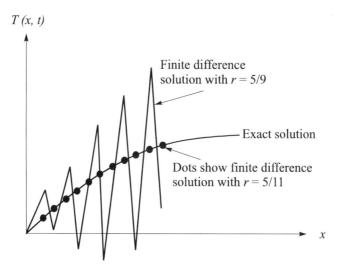

**FIG. 6.11.** Effects of parameter $r = \alpha \Delta t / (\Delta x)^2$ on stability of finite difference solution.

There are various mathematical techniques for determining the stability criterion associated with the finite-difference representation of the time-dependent heat conduction equation. Here we avoid mathematical developments, and instead use a physical argument to establish such a stability criterion, as described below.

Let us examine the stability criterion associated with difference equation (6-21). Suppose that at any time step the temperatures $T_{m-1}^i$ and $T_{m+1}^i$ at nodes $m-1$ and $m+1$ are equal but less than $T_m^i$ at node $m$ between them. If the value of $r$ exceeds $\frac{1}{2}$, the coefficient $(1-2r)$ becomes negative. Then, according to the finite-difference equation (6-21), for $(1-2r)$ negative, the temperature $T_m^{i+1}$ at node $m$ at the next time step should be less than that at the neighboring two nodes. This is not possible thermodynamically, since we assumed that $T_m^i$ was higher than the temperature at the neighboring nodes. Therefore, to obtain meaningful solutions from Eq. (6-21), the coefficient $(1-2r)$ of $T_m^i$ should not be negative; that is,

$$(1 - 2r) \geq 0 \quad \text{or} \quad \boxed{r \leq \frac{1}{2}}. \qquad (6\text{-}30)$$

where

$$r = \frac{\alpha \Delta t}{(\Delta x)^2}$$

**CALCULATION PROCEDURE:**

Having discussed the finite-difference form of the transient heat conduction equation at the internal nodes and that of the boundary conditions at the boundary nodes, we next summarize the mathematical formulation of the heat conduction problem and the corresponding finite-difference equations before discussing the calculational procedure.

Consider transient heat conduction in a slab $0 \leq x \leq L$ that is initially at a prescribed temperature $F(x)$ and for times $t > 0$ is subjected to convection from its boundaries into ambients at a constant temperature $T_\infty$. The mathematical formulation of this heat conduction problem is given by

$$\frac{\partial T(x,t)}{\partial t} = \alpha \frac{\partial^2 T}{\partial x^2} \quad \text{in } 0 < x < L, \ t > 0 \tag{6-31a}$$

$$-k\frac{\partial T}{\partial x} + h_0 T = h_0 T_\infty \quad \text{at } x = 0, \ t > 0 \tag{6-31b}$$

$$k\frac{\partial T}{\partial x} + h_L T = h_L T_\infty \quad \text{at } x = L, \ t > 0 \tag{6-31c}$$

$$T(x,t) = F(x) \quad \text{for } t = 0, \ 0 \le x \le L \tag{6-31d}$$

To write the finite-difference form of this problem, the region $0 \le x \le L$ is divided into $M$ equal subregions, each of thickness $\Delta x$, as illustrated in Fig. 6.9, and the time step $\Delta t$ is chosen to satisfy the stability criterion.

The finite-difference form of the differential equation (6-31a) for the internal nodes $m = 2, 3, ..., M$, using the explicit scheme, is obtained from Eq. (6-21)

$$\boxed{T_m^{i+1} = r\left(T_{m-1}^i + T_{m+1}^i\right) + (1 - 2r)T_m^i \quad \text{for } m = 2, 3, \ldots, M} \tag{6-32a}$$

where

$$r = \frac{\alpha \Delta t}{(\Delta x)^2}.$$

The finite-difference forms of the boundary conditions (6-31b) and (6-31c) at the nodes $m = 1$ and $m = M + 1$ are obtained, respectively, from Eqs. (6-24b) and (6-25b); with $T_{\infty 0} = T_{\infty L} = T_\infty$, we have

$$\boxed{\begin{aligned} T_1^{i+1} &= \frac{1}{1+\Delta x h_0/k}\left(T_2^{i+1} + \frac{\Delta x h_0}{k}T_\infty\right) \quad \text{for } m = 1 \\ T_{M+1}^{i+1} &= \frac{1}{1+\Delta x h_L/k}\left(T_M^{i+1} + \frac{\Delta x h_L}{k}T_\infty\right) \quad \text{for } m = M + 1 \end{aligned}} \tag{6-32b,c}$$

Finally, the finite-difference form of the initial condition, Eq. (6-31d), is written as

$$T_m^0 = F(x + \Delta x) \equiv F_m \quad \text{for } m = 1, 2, \ldots, M + 1 \text{ and } i = 0. \tag{6-32d}$$

Thus Eqs. (6-32a) to (6-32c) provide $M + 1$ relations for the determination of $M + 1$ unknown node temperatures $T_m^i$ $(m = 1, 2, ..., M + 1)$ for each time step $i = 1, 2, 3, ....$

We summarize the calculation procedure as follows:

1.  Choose the number of subdivisions $M$, hence determine the mesh size $\Delta x = L/M$.

2. Choose the value of the parameter $r$ consistent with the stability criterion defined by Eq. (6-30), namely, set

$$r \leq \frac{1}{2}$$

3. The material property establishes the value of the thermal diffusivity, $\alpha$. Knowing $\Delta x$, $\alpha$, and $r$, establish the corresponding time step according to the definition of $r$ given by Eq. (6-28); that is,

$$\Delta t = \frac{r(\Delta x)^2}{\alpha}$$

4. Calculations are started by setting $i = 0$. Then Eq. (6-32a) gives the temperatures $T_m^1$ at all internal nodes $m = 2, 3, ..., M$ at the end of the first time step, $i = 1$ or $t = \Delta t$, since the node temperatures on the right-hand side of Eq. (6-32a) are available from the known initial temperatures.

5. Setting $i = 0$ in Eqs. (6-32b) and (6-32c), the temperatures $T_1^1$ and $T_{M+1}^1$ at the boundary nodes are determined, since $T_2^1$, $T_M^1$ and all the other quantities on the right-hand side of Eqs. (6-32b) and (6-32c) are known.

6. Given the node temperatures $T_m^1$ ($m = 1, 2, 3, ..., M + 1$) at the end of the first time step, we repeat the procedure in steps 4 and 5 by setting $i = 1$ and calculating the node temperatures $T_m^2$ ($m = 1, 2, ..., M + 1$) at the end of the second time step $i = 2$ or at the time $t = 2\Delta t$.

7. The node temperatures for subsequent times are found in a similar manner.

The application of the above calculation procedure is now illustrated with the following example.

**EXAMPLE 6-6** A large brick wall ($\alpha = 5 \times 10^{-7} \ m^2/s$) of thickness $L = 20$ cm is initially at a uniform temperature $T_i = 100°C$. Suddenly both of its surfaces are lowered to 20°C and maintained at that temperature for times $t > 0$. Using four subdivisions (i.e., $M = 4$), corresponding to a mesh size of $\Delta x = 20/4 = 5$ cm, and an explicit finite-difference scheme, calculate the temperature distribution at the nodes for 10 consecutive time steps.

**SOLUTION** The mathematical formulation of this heat conduction problem for the large brick is given by

$$\frac{\partial T}{\partial t} = \alpha \frac{\partial^2 T}{\partial x^2} \quad \text{in } 0 < x < L, \ t > 0$$

subject to the boundary conditions

$$T = 20°C \quad \text{at } x = 0, \ t > 0$$
$$T = 20°C \quad \text{at } x = L, \ t > 0$$

and the initial condition

$$T = 100°C \quad \text{for } t = 0, \ \text{in } 0 \le x \le L.$$

For illustration purposes and to create simplicity in the computations, we have chosen only $M = 4$ equal subdivisions of the given region, which corresponds to a very coarse mesh size.

$$\Delta x = \frac{L}{M} = \frac{20}{4} = 5 \ cm.$$

Thus, over the entire region we have only five nodes, $m = 1, 2, ..., 5$, of which two are the boundary nodes and the remaining three are internal nodes.

The finite-difference equations for the interior nodes are obtained from Eq. (6-21) by setting the value of $r$ such that it does not violate the stability criterion. For $r = \frac{1}{2}$, Eq. (6-21) becomes

$$T_m^{i+1} = \frac{1}{2} \left( T_{m-1}^i + T_{m+1}^i \right) \quad m = 2, 3, 4.$$

For the prescribed temperature boundary conditions considered in this problem, the equations for the boundary nodes $m = 1$ and $M + 1 = 5$ become

$$T_1^{i+1} = 20 \quad m = 1 \qquad T_5^{i+1} = 50 \quad M + 1 = 5$$

Finally, the initial condition for the problem is written as

$$T_m^0 = 200 \quad i = 0, \ m = 1, 2, 3, 4, 5$$

and the corresponding time step $\Delta t$ with $r = \frac{1}{2}$ becomes

$$\Delta t = \frac{r(\Delta x)^2}{\alpha} = \frac{1}{2} \frac{(0.05)^2}{5 \times 10^{-7}} = 2500 \ s.$$

By using the finite-difference equations $(a)$ to $(d)$ and following the computational procedure described previously, the unknown node temperatures $T_m^i$ $(m = 2, 3, 4)$ are readily determined.

Table 6.1 shows the results of such calculations for 10 consecutive time steps. The step $i = 10$ corresponds to the time $t = 10 \times 2500\ s = 6.94\ h$.

In practice, a much finer mesh is needed to obtain sufficiently accurate results. This involves the use of both a large number of node points in the medium and a large number of time steps. In such situations, all the calculations are performed by using a digital computer.

**TABLE 6.1  Numerical solution to nodal temperatures of Example 6-6.**

| | Distance (x), meters | | | | |
|---|---|---|---|---|---|
| Time (t), seconds | 0.00 | 0.05 | 0.10 | 0.15 | 0.20 |
| 0.0 | 100. | 100. | 100. | 100. | 100. |
| 2500.0 | 20.0 | 100.0 | 100.0 | 100.0 | 20.0 |
| 5000.0 | 20.0 | 60.0 | 100.0 | 60.0 | 20.0 |
| 7500.0 | 20.0 | 60.0 | 60.0 | 60.0 | 20.0 |
| 10000.0 | 20.0 | 40.0 | 60.0 | 40.0 | 20.0 |
| 12500.0 | 20.0 | 40.0 | 40.0 | 40.0 | 20.0 |
| 15000.0 | 20.0 | 30.0 | 40.0 | 30.0 | 20.0 |
| 17500.0 | 20.0 | 30.0 | 30.0 | 30.0 | 20.0 |
| 20000.0 | 20.0 | 25.0 | 30.0 | 25.0 | 20.0 |
| 22500.0 | 20.0 | 25.0 | 25.0 | 25.0 | 20.0 |
| 25000.0 | 20.0 | 22.5 | 25.0 | 22.5 | 20.0 |

## 6.3.1 Inclusion of Heat Capacity in Finite-Difference Equations for Boundary Nodes

The finite-difference expressions for the boundary nodes given by Eqs. (6-32$b$) and (6-32$c$) assume steady-state conditions, and hence do not include the effects of the heat capacity of the material in the control volume at the boundaries. If a sufficiently small mesh size $\Delta x$ is used, the effect of heat capacity in the boundary node is negligible; hence Eqs. (6-24$b$) and (6-25$b$) are quite accurate to use for solving transient heat conduction problems. However, if the step size $\Delta x$ is not sufficiently small, it is desirable to include the effects of heat capacitance in the difference equation for the boundary nodes by considering a time-dependent energy balance at the boundary node. The transient energy balance for a volume element $\Delta V$ at the boundaries can be stated as

$$\begin{pmatrix} \text{Rate of heat} \\ \text{entering } \Delta V \\ \text{from all its} \\ \text{surfaces at} \\ \text{time step } i \end{pmatrix} + \begin{pmatrix} \text{rate of energy} \\ \text{generation} \\ \text{in } \Delta V \text{ at} \\ \text{time step } i \end{pmatrix} = \begin{pmatrix} \text{rate of increase} \\ \text{of internal} \\ \text{energy of} \\ \Delta V \end{pmatrix}. \qquad (6\text{-}33)$$

Suppose we have *convection* at the boundary surface $x = 0$, with a heat transfer coefficient $h_0$ into an ambient at temperature $T_{\infty 0}$, but no energy generation in the medium. The application of the energy equation (6-33) to the node $m = 1$ yields

$$h_0 \left( T_{\infty 0} - T_1^i \right) + k \frac{T_2^i - T_1^i}{\Delta x} = \rho c_p \frac{\Delta x}{2} \frac{T_1^{i+1} - T_1^i}{\Delta t}$$

Solving for $T_1^{i+1}$, we get

$$\boxed{T_1^{i+1} = 2r \left( T_2^i + \frac{\Delta x h_0}{k} T_{\infty 0} \right) + \left[ 1 - 2r \left( 1 + \frac{\Delta x h_0}{k} \right) \right] T_1^i} \quad \text{for } m = 1 \quad (6\text{-}34a)$$

where

$$r = \frac{\alpha \Delta t}{(\Delta x)^2}$$

In the case of *convection* at the boundary surface $x = L$, with a heat transfer coefficient $h_L$ into an ambient at temperature $T_{\infty L}$ but no energy generation in the medium, the application of the energy equation (6-33) to the node $m = M + 1$ give

$$h_L \left( T_{\infty L} - T_{M+1}^i \right) + k \frac{T_M^i - T_{M+1}^i}{\Delta x} = \rho c_p \frac{\Delta x}{2} \frac{T_{M+1}^{i+1} - T_{M+1}^i}{\Delta t}.$$

Solving for $T_{M+1}^{i+1}$, we obtain

$$\boxed{T_{M+1}^{i+1} = 2r \left( T_M^i + \frac{\Delta x h_L}{k} T_{\infty L} \right) + \left[ 1 - 2r \left( 1 + \frac{\Delta x h_L}{k} \right) \right] T_{M+1}^i} \quad \text{for } m = M+1$$

$$(6\text{-}34b)$$

Equations (6-34$a$) and (6-34$b$) are the finite-difference equations for the boundary nodes $m = 1$ and $m = M + 1$, respectively, when these boundary surfaces are subjected to convection. These equations include the effects of the heat capacity of the volume element associated with the boundary nodes $m = 1$ and $m = M + 1$; hence they are different from the corresponding equations (6-24$b$) and (6-25$b$), which are developed by neglecting the transient effects at the boundaries.

If Eqs. (6-34$a$) and (6-34$b$) are used as the finite-difference expressions for the boundary nodes $m = 1$ and $m = M + 1$, an additional restriction on the permissible value of the parameter $r$ should be recognized. By following an argument similar to that described previously for the derivation of the stability criterion given by Eq. (6-30), we conclude that the coefficients of $T_1^i$ and $T_{M+1}^i$ in Eqs. (6-34$a$) and (6-34$b$) should be positive; that is,

$$1 - 2r \left( 1 + \frac{\Delta x h_0}{k} \right) \geq 0 \quad \text{for } m = 1 \quad (6\text{-}35a)$$

$$1 - 2r\left(1 + \frac{\Delta x h_L}{k}\right) \geq 0 \quad \text{for} \quad m = M + 1. \tag{6-35b}$$

These conditions imply that the following restrictions should be imposed on the value of $r$ in Eqs. (6-34a) and (6-34b), respectively:

$$\boxed{0 < r \leq \frac{1}{2(1 + \Delta x h_0/k)}} \quad \text{for} \quad m = 1 \tag{6-36a}$$

$$\boxed{0 < r \leq \frac{1}{2(1 + \Delta x h_L/k)}} \quad \text{for} \quad m = M + 1 \tag{6-36b}.$$

Clearly, the stability criteria imposed on the maximum permissible value of $r$ that results from Eqs. (6-36a) and (6-36b) is more severe than that given by Eq. (6-30), which results from the interior modes. Among these three $r$'s, only *the smallest value* should be considered as the stability criterion for the system when performing the numerical calculations.

If the boundary conditions at $x = 0$ and $x = L$ are subjected to constant heat flux $q_0$ and $q_L$, respectively, the application of the energy equation (6-33) to the nodes $m = 1$ and $m = M + 1$ yields, respectively, the following finite difference expressions:

$$q_0 + k\frac{T_2^i - T_1^i}{\Delta x} = \rho c_p \frac{\Delta x}{2}\frac{T_1^{i+1} - T_1^i}{\Delta t} \tag{6-37a}$$

or

$$\boxed{T_1^{i+1} = 2r\left(T_2^i + \frac{\Delta x}{k}q_0\right) + (1 - 2r)T_1^i} \tag{6-37b}$$

and

$$q_L + k\frac{T_M^i - T_{M+1}^i}{\Delta x} = \rho c_p \frac{\Delta x}{2}\frac{T_{M+1}^{i+1} - T_{M+1}^i}{\Delta t} \tag{6-38a}$$

or

$$\boxed{T_{M+1}^{i+1} = 2r\left(T_M^i + \frac{\Delta x}{k}q_L\right) + (1 - 2r)T_{M+1}^i} \tag{6-38b}$$

and the restriction on the permissible value of the parameter $r$ for these boundary nodes becomes

$$0 < r \leq \frac{1}{2} \quad \text{for } m = 1 \text{ and } m = M + 1 \tag{6-39}$$

If the boundary surface at $m = 1$ or $m = M + 1$ is *insulated (adiabatic)*, the resulting finite-difference equation for the insulated boundary $m = 1$ or $m = M + 1$ is obtained from Eq. (6-34a) or (6-34b), respectively, by setting $h_0$ or $h_L$ equal to zero. We find

$$\boxed{T_1^{i+1} = 2rT_2^i + (1 - 2r)T_1^i} \quad \text{for} \quad m = 1 \tag{6-40a}$$

$$\boxed{T_{M+1}^{i+1} = 2rT_M^i + (1 - 2r)T_{M+1}^i} \quad \text{for } m = M + 1. \qquad (6\text{-}40b)$$

The finite-difference form of the heat conduction equation for the internal nodes remains the same as that given by Eq. (6-21).

**EXAMPLE 6-8** A steel plate [ $\alpha = 1.2 \times 10^{-5}$ m$^2/s$ and $k = 43$ W/(m·°C) ] of thickness 10 cm, initially at a uniform temperature $T_i$, is suddenly immersed in an oil bath at $T_\infty = 20$°C. The convection heat transfer coefficient between the fluid and the top surface is $h_0 = 500$ W/(m$^2$·°C) , and that for the bottom surface is $h_L = 300$ W/(m$^2$·°C) . Using five equal subdivisions, or a mesh size $\Delta x = 2$ cm, determine the largest permissible value of time step $\Delta t$, if the heat capacity effects in the finite-difference equations for the boundary nodes are included.

Give the resulting finite-difference equations for all the nodes, using the largest permissible time step.

**SOLUTION** For $M = 5$, we have

$$\Delta x = \frac{L}{M} = \frac{10}{5} = 2 \; cm$$

The nodes, $m = 1, 2, ..., 6$, are shown in the accompanying figure.

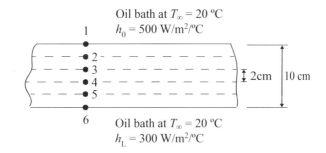

**FIGURE EXAMPLE 6-8.**

Nodes 2, 3, 4, and 5 are interior nodes, and 1 and 6 are the top and bottom boundary surface nodes. To ensure the stability of the finite-difference equations for the interior nodes, we should satisfy the inequality given by Eq. (6-30):

$$r \leq 0.5$$

To ensure the stability of the finite-difference equations at the boundary nodes 1 and 6, we should satisfy the inequalities given by Eqs. (6-36$a$) and (6-36$b$), respectively:

$$r \leq \frac{1}{2(1 + \Delta x h_0/k)} \quad = \quad 0.4057$$

$$r \leq \frac{1}{2(1 + \Delta x h_L/k)} \quad = \quad 0.4388$$

where $\Delta x = 0.02$ m, $k = 43$ W/(m·°C), $h_0 = 500$ W/(m²·°C), and $h_L = 300$ W/(m²·°C). Clearly, the smallest value of $r$ is that imposed by the top boundary node 0, which is $r < 0.4057$. This gives the largest possible time increment $\Delta t$,

$$\Delta t = \frac{r(\Delta x)^2}{\alpha} = \frac{0.4057 \times (0.02)^2}{1.2 \times 10^{-5}} = 13.52\ s$$

The finite-difference equations for the interior nodes 2, 3, 4, and 5 are obtained from Eq. (6-32a):

$$\begin{aligned}
T_2^{i+1} &= r\left(T_1^i + T_3^i\right) + (1 - 2r)T_2^i \\
T_3^{i+1} &= r\left(T_2^i + T_4^i\right) + (1 - 2r)T_3^i \\
T_4^{i+1} &= r\left(T_3^i + T_5^i\right) + (1 - 2r)T_4^i \\
T_5^{i+1} &= r\left(T_4^i + T_6^i\right) + (1 - 2r)T_5^i
\end{aligned}$$

The finite-difference equations for the boundary nodes 1 and 6 are given by Eqs. (6-34a) and (6-34b):

$$\begin{aligned}
T_1^{i+1} &= 2r\left(T_2^i + \frac{\Delta x h_0}{k}T_{\infty 0}\right) + \left[1 - 2r\left(1 + \frac{\Delta x h_0}{k}\right)\right]T_1^i \\
T_6^{i+1} &= 2r\left(T_5^i + \frac{\Delta x h_L}{k}T_{\infty L}\right) + \left[1 - 2r\left(1 + \frac{\Delta x h_L}{k}\right)\right]T_6^i
\end{aligned}$$

where

$$\begin{aligned}
\frac{\Delta x h_0}{k} &= \frac{0.02 \times 500}{43} = 0.2326 \\
\frac{\Delta x h_L}{k} &= \frac{0.02 \times 300}{43} = 0.1395
\end{aligned}$$

and

$$r = 0.3057$$

Using the finite-difference equations the unknown node temperatures $T_m^i$ will be determined.

## 6.4. PRODUCT SOLUTION FOR TRANSIENT MULTIDIMENSIONAL HEAT CONDUCTION

When there is no internal energy generation in the medium, for some special circumstances it is possible to combine the solutions obtained from one-dimensional transient-temperature charts and to construct the solution for a multi-dimensional transient heat conduction problem. Such an approach is called the method of *product solution*. For example this method is applicable if the solution of a two-dimensional, time-dependent heat conduction problem can be shown to be equivalent to the product of the solutions of two one-dimensional, transient heat conduction problems, or if the solution of a three-dimensional, time-dependent heat conduction problem can be shown to be equivalent to the product of the solutions of three one-dimensional, transient heat conduction problems. Here we will demonstrate the concept for only two-dimensional problems.

## Demonstration of the Concept of Product Solution

The basis of the product solution is better envisioned with the following example.

Consider a rectangular bar of sides $2L_1$ and $2L_2$, confined to the region $-L_1 \leq x \leq L_1$ and $-L_2 \leq y \leq L_2$, as illustrated in Fig. 6.12.

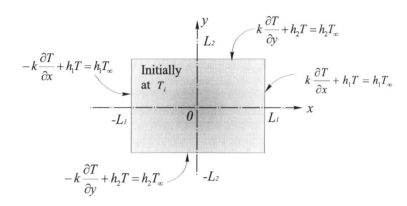

**FIG. 6.12.** Product solution for transient heat conduction in a rectangular bar.

Initially the slab is at a uniform temperature $T_i$. Suddenly at $t = 0$ all boundary surfaces are subjected to convection to an ambient at a constant temperature $T_\infty$. The mathematical formulation of this heat conduction problem, in terms of the dimensionless temperature

$$\theta(x, y, t) = \frac{T(x, y, t) - T_\infty}{T_i - T_\infty}$$

is given by

$$\frac{\partial^2 \theta}{\partial x^2} + \frac{\partial^2 \theta}{\partial y^2} = \frac{1}{\alpha} \frac{\partial \theta}{\partial t} \quad \text{in } -L_1 < x < L_1, \ -L_2 < y < L_2 \text{ for } t > 0 \qquad (6\text{-}41\text{a})$$

$$-k \frac{\partial \theta}{\partial x} + h_1 \theta = 0 \quad \text{at } x = -L_1 \qquad (6\text{-}41\text{b})$$

$$k \frac{\partial \theta}{\partial x} + h_1 \theta = 0 \quad \text{at } x = L_1 \qquad (6\text{-}41\text{c})$$

$$-k \frac{\partial \theta}{\partial y} + h_2 \theta = 0 \quad \text{at } y = -L_2 \qquad (6\text{-}41\text{d})$$

$$k\frac{\partial\theta}{\partial y} + h_2\theta = 0 \quad \text{at } y = L_2 \tag{6-41e}$$

$$\theta = 1 \quad \text{for } t = 0 \tag{6-41f}.$$

It can be shown that the solution of this two-dimensional problem can be expressed as a product of the solutions of two one-dimensional problems $\theta_1(x,t)$ and $\theta_2(y,t)$ in the form

$$\theta(x,y,t) = \theta_1(x,t)\,\theta_2(y,t)$$

where $\theta_1(x,t)$ is the solution of the one-dimensional problem

$$\frac{\partial^2\theta_1}{\partial x^2} = \frac{1}{\alpha}\frac{\partial\theta_1}{\partial t} \quad \text{in } -L_1 < x < L_1, \ t > 0 \tag{6-42a}$$

$$-k\frac{\partial\theta_1}{\partial x} + h_1\theta_1 = 0 \quad \text{at } x = -L_1 \tag{6-42b}$$

$$k\frac{\partial\theta_1}{\partial x} + h_1\theta_1 = 0 \quad \text{at } x = L_1 \tag{6-42c}$$

$$\theta_1 = 1 \quad \text{for } t = 0 \tag{6-42d}$$

and $\theta_2(y,t)$ is the solution of the one-dimensional problem:

$$\frac{\partial^2\theta_2}{\partial y^2} = \frac{1}{\alpha}\frac{\partial\theta_2}{\partial t} \quad \text{in } -L_2 < y < L_2, \ t > 0 \tag{6-43a}$$

$$-k\frac{\partial\theta_2}{\partial y} + h_2\theta_2 = 0 \quad \text{at } y = -L_2 \tag{6-43b}$$

$$k\frac{\partial\theta_2}{\partial y} + h_2\theta_2 = 0 \quad \text{at } y = L_2 \tag{6-43c}$$

$$\theta_2 = 1 \quad \text{for } t = 0 \tag{6-43d}$$

The validity of the above decomposition can be verified by substituting $\theta = \theta_1\theta_2$ in the original two-dimensional problem given by [Eqs. (6-41)].

Clearly, the above one-dimensional problems for the functions $\theta_1(x,t)$ and $\theta_2(y,t)$ are exactly the same as that whose solution is given by the transient-temperature chart in Fig. 6.4.

From the previous illustration we conclude that the solution of the two-dimensional heat conduction problem defined by Eqs. (6-41) for a rectangular region $-L_1 < x < L_1$, $-L_2 < y < L_2$ can be constructed as the product of the solutions of two one-dimensional, time-dependent problems for slabs, whose solutions are obtained from the chart given in Fig. 6.4.

The concept of the product solution described above—decomposing the solution for a rectangular bar to the product of the solutions of two slab problems—is illustrated in Fig. 6.13a.

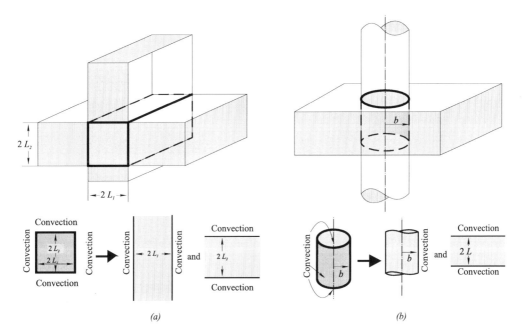

**FIG. 6.13.** Decomposition for product solution.

The basic idea developed here with reference to a rectangular bar can be extended to other configurations. For example, the two-dimensional, transient-temperature distribution $T(r, z, t)$ in a solid cylinder of radius $b$ and finite height $2L$, initially at temperature $T_i$ and subjected to convection at the boundaries, can be expressed in the dimensionless form as

$$\theta(r, z, t) = \frac{T(r, z, t) - T_\infty}{T_i - T_\infty}.$$

Then the solution of this problem can be constructed as the product of the solutions of two one-dimensional problems, that is, one for the slab problem given in Fig. 6.4 and the other for a long, solid cylinder given in Fig. 6.6. Such a decomposition process is illustrated in Fig. 6.13b.

Clearly, there are numerous other configurations to three dimensional problems, which permit decomposition into one-dimensional problems, and their solutions can be constructed by the product solution. Including, but not restricted to a three dimensional semi-infinite rectangular bar, a cube and/or a rectangular parallel piped geometries. Although the computational tools are becoming easily available, the use of the charts gives us quick estimates. Here we present two examples.

**EXAMPLE 6-9** Molybdenum ($k = 123\ W/m \cdot K$, $\alpha = 4.790 \times 10^{-5}\ m^2/s$) is utilized in high temperature situations because of its high melting point. It is silvery white in color, very hard, and has one of the highest melting points of all elements. Molybdenum on Earth is not found free but as a compound. The only pure molybdenum that has ever been found was by the Russian Luna 24 Mission on the moon. Molybdenum is commonly used in rockets. Suppose that pure molybdenum has been mined from the moon. A spacecraft propulsion system is built using a slab of this pure molybdenum in its construction. The pure Molybdenum slab has dimensions 8 $cm$ × 5 cm. Due to energy generation, the bar is maintained at 1250°C. The slab is then subjected to convective heating due to a long burn maneuver. Here it is exposed to an ambient $T_\infty = 2000$°C. Assuming the heat transfer coefficient is $h = 350$ W/(m · °C), calculate the center temperature of the bar at $t = 5\ min$ after the start of heating exposure.

**SOLUTION**  The dimensionless temperature $\theta(x, y, t)$ for this problem is defined as

$$\theta(x, y, t) = \frac{T(x, y, t) - T_\infty}{T_i - T_\infty}$$

The solution for $\theta$ can be constructed as a product of the solutions of two slab problems: $\theta_1(x, t)$, the solution for a slab of thickness $2L_1 = 8$ cm, and $\theta_2(y, t)$, the solution for a slab of thickness $2L_2 = 5$ cm.

For the slab $2L_1 = 8$ cm, we have

$$\tau = \frac{\alpha t}{L_1^2} = \frac{(4.79 \times 10^{-5})(5 \times 60)}{4^2 \times 10^{-4}} = 8.98 = 9$$

and

$$\frac{1}{\text{Bi}} = \frac{k}{hL_1} = \frac{123}{350 \times 4 \times 10^{-2}} = 8.79 = 9$$

Then the center temperature for this slab problem, for $\tau = 9$ and 1/Bi = 9, is obtained from Fig. 6.4b as

$$\theta_{1,0} = 0.4.$$

For the slab $2L_2 = 5$ cm, we have

$$\tau = \frac{\alpha t}{L_2^2} = \frac{(4.79 \times 10^{-5})(5 \times 60)}{0.25^2 \times 10^{-4}} = 23,$$

and

$$\frac{1}{\text{Bi}} = \frac{k}{hL_2} = \frac{123}{350 \times 2.5 \times 10^{-2}} = 14.$$

The center temperature for this problem, for $\tau = 9$ and 1/Bi = 14, is obtained from Fig. 6.4b as

$$\theta_{2,0} = 0.2.$$

Then the dimensionless center temperature $\theta_0$ for the two-dimensional problem is determined by product solution:

$$\theta_0 = \theta_{1,0} \cdot \theta_{2,0} = 0.4 \times 0.2 = 0.08,$$

and the center temperature $T_0$ for the two-dimensional problem becomes

$$\theta_0 = \frac{T_0 - T_\infty}{T_i - T_\infty} = 0.08$$
$$T_0 = T_\infty + (T_i - T_\infty)(0.08)$$
$$= 2000 + (-750)(0.08) = 1940\,°C.$$

**EXAMPLE 6-10** A short, iron cylinder with a diameter $D = 5$ cm and a height $H = 4$ cm is initially at a uniform temperature $T_i = 250°C$. Suddenly it is subjected to an ambient at $\tau_\infty = 20°C$ with a heat transfer coefficient $h = 500\ \text{W}/(\text{m}^2 \cdot °C)$. The iron has $k = 60\ \text{W}/(\text{m} \cdot °C)$, $\alpha = 1.6 \times 10^{-5}\ \text{m}^2/\text{s}$. Calculate the center temperature $T_0$ at $t = 2$ min after the start of cooling.

**SOLUTION** The dimensionless temperature $\theta(r,z,t)$ for this problem is defined as

$$\theta(r,z,t) = \frac{T(r,z,t) - T_\infty}{T_i - T_\infty}.$$

The solution for $\theta$ can be constructed as a product of the solutions of the following two problems: $\theta_1(r,t)$, the solution for a long cylinder of diameter $D = 5$ cm, and $\theta_2(z,t)$, the solution for a slab of thickness $2L_2 = 4$ cm.

For the cylinder with $D = 5$ cm, we have

$$\tau = \frac{\alpha t}{(D/2)^2} = \frac{(1.6 \times 10^{-5})(2 \times 60)}{2.5^2 \times 10^{-4}} = 3.1$$

and

$$\frac{1}{\text{Bi}} = \frac{k}{hD/2} = \frac{60}{500\,(2.5 \times 10^{-2})} = 4.8.$$

The center temperature for this cylinder problem, for $\tau = 3.1$ and $1/\text{Bi} = 4.8$, is obtained from Fig. 6.6b as

$$\theta_{1,0} = 0.31.$$

For the slab with $2L_2 = H = 4$ cm, we have

$$\tau = \frac{\alpha t}{L_2^2} = \frac{(1.6 \times 10^{-5})(2 \times 60)}{(2 \times 10^{-2})^2} = 4.8$$

and

$$\frac{1}{\text{Bi}} = \frac{k}{hL_2} = \frac{60}{500\,(2 \times 10^{-2})} = 6.0.$$

The center temperature for this slab problem, for $\tau = 4.8$ and $1/\text{Bi} = 6$, is obtained from Fig. 6.4b as

$$\theta_{2,0} = 0.45$$

Then the dimensionless center temperature $\theta_0$ for the two-dimensional short cylinder problem is determined by product solution:

$$\theta_0 = \theta_{1,0} \cdot \theta_{2,0} = 0.31\,(0.45) = 0.14$$

Therefore the center temperature $T_0$ becomes

$$
\begin{aligned}
\theta_0 &\equiv \frac{T_0 - T_\infty}{T_i - T_\infty} = 0.14 \\
T_0 &= T_\infty + (T_i - T_\infty)(0.14) \\
&= 20 + (250 - 20)\,(0.14) = 52.2\,^\circ\text{C}.
\end{aligned}
$$

## 6.5. TRANSIENT MASS DIFFUSION

In the previous sections we considered mass transfer problems in which the concentration distribution is a function of one space variable only. In many engineering applications the concentration distribution in the medium varies with both time and position. The mathematical analysis of such unsteady mass transfer problems is complicated because they involve the solution of differential equations with more than one independent variable. However, a large number of unsteady mass transfer problems can be expressed in a form analogous to the one-dimensional, time-dependent heat conduction problems considered in this chapter. Therefore, the same mathematical techniques discussed for the solution of a time-dependent heat conduction equation become applicable to the solution of one-dimensional, unsteady mass diffusion problems. In this section we present the mathematical formulation of the one-dimensional, unsteady mass diffusion equation in the rectangular coordinate system and discuss its solution for typical applications.

When there are no mass sources, sinks, or chemical reactions in the medium and the mass transfer takes place as a result of pure molecular diffusion, the mass conservation equation for a given species may be stated as

$$
\begin{pmatrix} \text{Net rate of diffusion} \\ \text{of species } A \text{ into} \\ \text{medium} \end{pmatrix} = \begin{pmatrix} \text{rate of increase of} \\ \text{of species } A \text{ in} \\ \text{medium} \end{pmatrix}. \qquad (6\text{-}44)
$$

We now consider a one-dimensional mass diffusion in the $x$ direction for a differential volume element of thickness $\Delta x$ and area $a$, as illustrated in Fig. 6.13, and we write the mathematical expressions for various terms in the mass conservation equation (6-44) as

$$
(J_A|_x - J_A|_{x+\Delta x})a = a\,\Delta x \frac{\partial c_A}{\partial t} \qquad (6\text{-}45)
$$

where

$J_A$ = molal diffusion flux
$c_A$ = molal concentration of component $A$
$t$ = time.

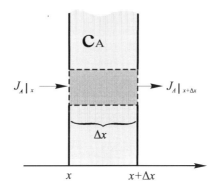

**FIG. 6.14.** Nomenclature for the derivation of the one-dimensional, unsteady mass diffusion equation.

By Fick's law of diffusion, the diffusion flux $J_A$ is related to the concentration gradient by

$$J_A = -D^* \frac{\partial c_A}{\partial x} \tag{6-46}$$

Substituting Eq. (6-47) into Eq. (6-46) and assuming a constant $D^*$, we obtain

$$\frac{\partial^2 c_A}{\partial x^2} = \frac{1}{D^*} \frac{\partial c_A}{\partial t} \tag{6-47}$$

where
$c_A$ = molal concentration of component $A$, $\mathrm{kg \cdot mol/m^3}$
$D^*$ = mass diffusivity for diffusion of component $A$ in medium, $\mathrm{m^2/s}$
$t$ = time, s
$x$ = distance, m

Equation (6-48) is called *the one-dimensional, time-dependent mass diffusion equation* in the rectangular coordinate system for constant mass diffusivity. It is analogous to the heat conduction (or diffusion) equation given previously in the form

$$\frac{\partial^2 T}{\partial x^2} = \frac{1}{\alpha} \frac{\partial T}{\partial t} \tag{6-48}$$

We note that in the mass diffusion equation the mass concentration $c_A$ replaces temperature $T$, and the mass diffusivity $D^*$ replaces the heat diffusivity $\alpha$. This equation can readily be generalized to the three-dimensional case:

$$\nabla^2 c_A = \frac{1}{D^*} \frac{\partial c_A}{\partial t} \tag{6-49}$$

where $\nabla^2$ is the Laplacian operator and in the rectangular coordinate system is given as

$$\nabla^2 \equiv \frac{\partial^2}{\partial x^2} + \frac{\partial^2}{\partial y^2} + \frac{\partial^2}{\partial z^2} \qquad (6\text{-}50)$$

Equation (6-49) is analogous to the three-dimensional, time-dependent heat conduction equation, with no energy generation and constant thermal diffusivity.

The mass transfer problems characterized by the mass diffusion equation as given above are encountered in processes such as drying, vapor penetration through porous media, and numerous other applications. Since the mass conservation equation is of exactly the same form as the one-dimensional, time-dependent heat conduction equation, the same mathematical techniques described previously for the solution of heat conduction problems are applicable.

## 6.6. TRANSIENT BIOHEAT EQUATION

Clinicians are interested in determining deep tissue temperature in a noninvasive manner, and are currently developing temperature control methods to ensure protection of vital organs during sickness, surgery, or after trauma. To achieve these goals, one must create accurate thermal models and use them to determine relationships between core and deep tissue temperature, or in optimization problems to improve therapy and treatment planning.

The bioheat equation is important in the biomedical field because it models the temperature distribution throughout the tissue. For example, extreme heating and cooling is used to destroy certain tissue in surgical procedures, and since we know how much heat is needed to destroy tissue, a knowledge of the temperature distribution will allow for correct heat flux to be applied. The bioheat equation can be used to model the temperature distribution when one is burned, but it can also be used for situations of constant cooling of burn victims in order to save healthy tissue.

Clinical applications in this field are temperature control during hypothermia, hyperthermia, and in subjects under anesthesia, the analysis of burns, cryosurgery, the development of tissue thermal property measurement techniques; and also to determine changes in organ temperature due to energy deposition of electromagnetic waves produced by hand held telecommunication devices, imaging techniques or radiation therapy. Other applications include the treatment of Parkinson's disease, the improvement of drug absorption and delivery, and the treatment of viral diseases such as of HIV using whole body hyperthermia.

Body temperature in mammals and other homeotherms is maintained within a fairly constant range that is compatible with other regulatory systems and cellular physiology. Temperature regulation in animals implies the presence of mechanisms capable of leveling the rate of heat production to the rate of heat transfer to the environment. Temperature regulation, the result of evolution, helps to optimize organ function and serves as an important factor in the development of infection diseases. Some examples of thermoregulatory mechanisms observed in homeotherms are shivering, sweating, panting and selective brain cooling.

Extreme temperature variations in homeotherms can be lethal, and range from heat stroke to coma induced by cold exposure. At the cellular level, a small temperature reduction can decrease the tissue oxygen requirements, and temperatures over 42 $^{\circ}C$ can produce protein break down. As a result, temperature reduction in cases of low blood flow and the use of high temperatures to promote necrosis of specific tissues have promising clinical applications, but require ample physiologic knowledge of temperature control and tissue heat transfer mechanisms.

The tissue thermal model consists in a bioheat type equation (6-51) that incorporates temperature dependent metabolic heat generation and blood flow. The bioheat equation usually used is the well-known Pennes' equation,

$$\rho c_p \left( \frac{\partial T}{\partial t} \right) = \nabla (k \nabla T) + \rho_b c_b W_b \left( T_a - T \right) + g_m, \qquad (6\text{-}51)$$

where $T$ and $T_a$ correspond to the tissue and arterial temperature, respectively; $W_b$ represents the blood perfusion term, and $g_m$ denotes the metabolic heat generated by the tissue. The parameters $\rho$, $c_p$, and $k$ represent the density, heat capacity and thermal conductivity, and are considered constant within each tissue. $\rho_b$ and $c_b$ represent the density and heat capacity of blood. The perfusion term assumes that within a small volume of tissue the blood flowing in the small capillaries enters at an arterial temperature $T_a$ and exists at the local tissue temperature $T$. That is, it assumes that thermal equilibration occurs in the capillary bed.

Pennes' equation has been adapted by many researchers for the analysis of a variety of bioheat transfer applications that range in complexity from thermal regulation of the entire human body to a simple, homogeneous volume of tissue. However it is not the only bioheat equation and researchers have suggested more accurate but complicated models. Despite the erroneous concepts of Pennes model, it has been a useful tool to study the living tissue and is used to accurately predict temperatures.

For a uniform thermal conductivity tissue we have,

$$\rho c_p \left( \frac{\partial T}{\partial t} \right) = k \nabla^2 T + \rho_b c_b W_b \left( T_a - T \right) + g_m, \qquad (6\text{-}52)$$

For the case of a steady state and one dimensional heat transfer problem with temperature, T as a function of the $x$-coordinate we have

$$\frac{\partial^2 T}{\partial x^2} + \frac{\rho_b c_b W_b}{k} \left( T_a - T \right) + \frac{g_m}{k} = 0 \qquad (6\text{-}53)$$

If we define an excess temperature $\theta_1 = T - T_a$, then we have

$$\frac{\partial^2 \theta_1}{\partial x^2} - \frac{\rho_b c_b W_b}{k} \theta_1 + \frac{g_m}{k} = 0 \qquad (6\text{-}54)$$

If we define an excess temperature $\theta_2 = \theta_1 - \frac{g_m}{\rho_b c_b W_b}$, then the Pennes equation becomes

$$\frac{\partial^2 \theta_2}{\partial x^2} - m^2 \theta_2 = 0 \qquad (6\text{-}55)$$

which takes the form of the fin (extended surface) equation in Chapter 4 and requires two boundary conditions in the $x$-direction.

## PROBLEMS

*Transient Temperature and Heat Flow in a Semi-Infinite Solid*

**6-1** A thick stainless-steel slab $[\alpha = 1.5 \times 10^{-5} \ \mathrm{m^2/s}$ and $k = 60 \ \mathrm{W/(m \cdot ℃)}]$ is initially at a uniform temperature of $220℃$. Suddenly one of its surfaces is lowered to $50℃$ and maintained at that temperature. By treating the slab as a semi-infinite solid, determine the temperature at a depth 1 cm from the surface and the heat flux at the surface $2 \ min$ after the surface temperature is lowered.

**6-2** A thick concrete slab $[\alpha = 7 \times 10^{-7} \ \mathrm{m^2/s}$ and $k = 1.4 \ \mathrm{W/(m \cdot ℃)}]$ is initially at a uniform temperature of $400℃$. Suddenly one of its surfaces is subjected to convective cooling with a heat transfer coefficient of $50 \ \mathrm{W/(m^2 \cdot ℃)}$ into an ambient at $50℃$. By treating the slab as a semi-infinite solid, calculate the temperature at a depth 5 cm from the surface and $0.5 \ h$ after the start of cooling.

**6-3** A fireclay brick slab $[\alpha = 5.4 \times 10^{-7} \ \mathrm{m^2/s}$ and $k = 1 \ \mathrm{W/(m \cdot ℃)}]$ 10 cm thick is initially at a uniform temperature of $350℃$. Suddenly one of its surfaces is subjected to convection with a heat transfer coefficient of $100 \ \mathrm{W/(m^2 \cdot ℃)}$ into an ambient at $40℃$. Calculate the temperature at a depth 1 cm from the surface $2 \ min$ after the start of cooling.

**6-4** A thick copper slab $[\alpha = 1.1 \times 10^{-4} \ \mathrm{m^2/s}$ and $k = 380 \ \mathrm{W/(m \cdot ℃)}]$ is initially at a uniform temperature of $10℃$. Suddenly one of its surfaces is raised to $100℃$. Calculate the heat flux at the surface $1 \ min$ and $2 \ min$ after the raising of the surface temperature.

**6-5** A thick aluminum slab $[\alpha = 8.4 \times 10^{-5} \ \mathrm{m^2/s}$ and $k = 200 \ \mathrm{W/(m \cdot ℃)}]$ is initially at a uniform temperature of $20℃$. Suddenly one of its surfaces is raised to $100℃$. Calculate the time required for the temperature at a depth 5 cm from the surface to reach to $80℃$.

**6-6** A thick concrete slab $[\alpha = 7 \times 10^{-7} \ \mathrm{m^2/s}$ and $k = 1.4 \ \mathrm{W/(m \cdot ℃)}]$ is initially at a uniform temperature of $80℃$. One of its surfaces is suddenly lowered to $20℃$. Determine the temperatures at depths 2 and 4 cm from the surface $10 \ min$ after the surface temperature is lowered.

**6-7** A thick stainless steel slab $[\alpha = 1.6 \times 10^{-5} \ \mathrm{m^2/s}$ and $k = 60 \ \mathrm{W/(m \cdot ℃)}]$ is initially at a uniform temperature of $100℃$. One of its surfaces is suddenly lowered to 30℃. Determine the time required for the temperature at a depth 2 cm from the surface to reach 50℃.

**6-8** A thick bronze [$\alpha = 0.86 \times 10^{-5}$ m$^2$/s and $k = 26$ W/(m·℃)] is initially at a uniform temperature of 250℃. Suddenly one of its surface temperatures is lowered to 25℃. Determine the temperature at a location 5 cm from the surface 10 *min* after the surface temperature is lowered.

**6-9** A thick bronze [$\alpha = 0.86 \times 10^{-5}$ m$^2$/s and $k = 26$ W/(m·℃)] is initially at a uniform temperature of 250℃. Suddenly one of its surfaces is exposed to convective cooling by a fluid at 25℃. Assuming that the heat transfer coefficient for convection between the fluid and the surface is 150 W/(m$^2$·℃), determine the temperature at a location 5 cm from the surface 10 *min* after the exposure.

**6-10** A thick wood wall [$\alpha = 0.82 \times 10^{-7}$ m$^2$/s and $k = 0.15$ W/(m·℃)] is initially at a uniform temperature of 20℃. The wood may ignite at 400℃. If the surface is exposed to hot gases at $T_\infty = 500$℃ and the heat transfer coefficient between the gas and the surface is 45W/(m$^2$·℃), how long will it take for the surface of the wood to reach 400℃?
*Answer*: 597.6 sec.

**6-11** A thick wood wall [$\alpha = 0.82 \times 10^{-7}$ m$^2$/s and $k = 0.15$ W/(m·℃)] is initially at a uniform temperature of 20℃. Suddenly one of its surfaces is raised to 80℃. Calculate the temperature at a distance 2 cm from the surface 10 *min* after the exposure.

**6-12** A water pipe is to be buried in soil ($\alpha = 0.2 \times 10^{-6}$ m$^2$/s) at sufficient depth to prevent freezing in winter. When the soil is at a uniform temperature of 5℃, the surface is subjected to a uniform temperature of $-10$℃ continuously for 50 days. What minimum burial depth for the pipe is needed to prevent freezing?
*Answer*: 1.264 m

*One Dimensional Transient Temperature and Heat Flow: Heisler Chart for Slab*

**6-13** A steel plate [$\alpha = 1.2 \times 10^{-5}$ m$^2$/s, $k = 43$ W/(m·℃)], $c_p = 465$ J/(kg·℃), and $\rho = 7833$ $kg/m^3$] thickness 5 cm, initially at a uniform temperature of 200℃, is suddenly immersed in an oil bath at 20℃. The convective heat transfer coefficient between the fluid and the surface is 500 W/(m$^2$·℃). How long will it take for the centerplanc to cool to 100℃? *Answer*: 182.3 *sec*

**6-14** A marble plate [$\alpha = 1.3 \times 10^{-6}$ m$^2$/s and $k = 380$ W/(m·℃)] of thickness 3 cm is initially at a uniform temperature of 130℃. The surfaces are suddenly lowered to 30℃. Determine the center-plane temperature 2 *min* after the lowering of the surface temperature.

**6-15** A marble plate [$\alpha = 1.3 \times 10^{-6}$ m$^2$/s and $k = 380$ W/(m·℃)] of thickness 5 cm is initially at a uniform temperature of 100℃. The surfaces are suddenly immersed in an oil bath at 20℃. The convective heat transfer coefficient between the oil and the marble surface is 400 W/(m$^2$·℃). Calculate the temperature at a depth of 2 cm from one of the surfaces 5 *min* after the exposure. Determine the energy removed from the marble during this time for a marble plate 1 *m* × 1 m in size.

**6-16** A copper plate [$\alpha = 1.1 \times 10^{-4}$ m$^2$/s and $k = 380$ W/(m·℃)] of thickness 2 cm is initially at a uniform temperature of 25℃. Suddenly both of its surfaces are raised to 50℃. Calculate the centerline temperature 10 *min* after the surface temperature is raised.

**6-17** A fireclay brick slab [$\alpha = 5.4 \times 10^{-7}$ m$^2$/s and $k = 1$ W/(m·℃)] of thickness 5 cm is initially at a uniform temperature of 350℃. Suddenly one of its surfaces is subjected to convection with a heat transfer coefficient of 100 W/(m$^2$·℃) into an ambient at 40℃. The other surface is insulated. Calculate the centerline temperature 1 *h* after the start of cooling.

*One Dimensional Transient Temperature and Heat Flow: Heisler Chart for Cylinder*

**6-18** A long steel shaft of radius 20 cm [$\alpha = 1.6 \times 10^{-5}$ m$^2$/s and $k = 60$ W/(m·℃)] is taken out of an oven at a uniform temperature of 500℃ and immersed in a well-stirred large bath of 20℃ coolant. The heat transfer coefficient between the shaft surface and the coolant is 200 W/(m$^2$·℃). Calculate the time required for the shaft surface to reach 100℃. *Answer*: 1.04 *hrs*

**6-19** A long steel bar [$\alpha = 1.6 \times 10^{-5}$ m$^2$/s and $k = 60$ W/(m·℃)] of diameter 5 cm is initially at a uniform temperature of 200℃. Suddenly the surface of the bar is exposed to an ambient at 20℃ with a heat transfer coefficient of 500 W/(m$^2$·℃). Calculate the center temperature 2 *min* after the start of the cooling. Calculate the energy removed from the bar per meter length during this time period.

**6-20** A hot dog can be regarded as a solid having a shape in the form of a long solid cylinder. Consider a hot dog [$\alpha = 1.6 \times 10^{-7}$ m$^2$/s and $k = 0.5$ W/(m·℃)] of diameter 2 cm, initially at a uniform temperature of 10℃, dropped into boiling water at 100℃. The heat transfer coefficient between the water and the surface is 150 W/(m$^2$·℃). If the meat is considered cooked when its center temperature reaches 80℃, how long will it take for the centerline temperature to reach 80℃? Compare the result with that obtainable using lumped system analysis. *Answer*: 207.5 *s*

**6-21** A long chrome-steel rod [$\alpha = 1.1 \times 10^{-5}$ m$^2$/s and $k = 40$ W/(m·℃)] of diameter of 8 cm is initially at a uniform temperature of 225℃. It is suddenly exposed to a convective environment at 25℃ with a surface heat transfer coefficient of 50 W/(m$^2$·℃). Determine the center temperature at 0.1 and 1 *h* after exposure to the cooler ambient. Compare the result with that obtainable using lumped system analysis.

**6-22** A long copper rod [$\alpha = 1.1 \times 10^{-4}$ m$^2$/s and $k = 380$ W/(m·℃)] of diameter 5 cm is initially at a uniform temperature of 100℃. It is suddenly dropped into a coolant pool at 20℃. The heat transfer coefficient between the coolant and the rod is 500 W/(m$^2$·℃). Determine the center temperature of the rod 100 $s$ after exposure to the coolant. Calculate the energy removed from the rod per meter length during this time period.

**6-23** A long aluminum wire [$\alpha = 8.4 \times 10^{-5}$ m$^2$/s and $k = 200$ W/(m·℃)] of diameter 0.5 cm is initially at a uniform temperature of 20℃. Suddenly its surface temperature is increased to 30℃. Calculate the time required for the center temperature to reach 25℃.

*Numerical Analysis and Finite-Difference Solutions*

**6-24** An aluminum plate ($\alpha = 8 \times 10^{-5}$ m$^2$/s) 4 cm thick is initially at a uniform temperature of 20℃. Suddenly its surfaces are raised to 220℃. Using an explicit finite difference scheme and a mesh size $\Delta x = 1$ cm, calculate the center temperature at 5, 10, and 15 $s$ after the surfaces are exposed to high temperature.

**6-25** An aluminum plate ($\alpha = 8 \times 10^{-5}$ m$^2$/s) 4 cm thick is initially at a uniform temperature of 20℃. Suddenly one of its surfaces is raised to 220℃ while the other surface is kept insulated. Using an explicit finite-difference scheme and a mesh size $\Delta x = 1$ cm, calculate the temperature of the insulated surface 5, 10 and 15 $s$ after the other surface is exposed to high temperature.

**6-26** An 8-cm-thick chrome-steel plate [$\alpha = 1.6 \times 10^{-5}$ m$^2$/s, $k = 60$ W/(m·℃)], initially at a uniform temperature of 325℃, is suddenly exposed to a cool airstream at 25℃ at both of its surfaces. The heat transfer coefficient between the air and the surface is 400 W/(m$^2$·℃). Using an explicit finite-difference scheme and a mesh size $\Delta x = 1$ cm, determine the center-plane temperature 5 and 15 $min$ after the start of cooling. Neglect the heat capacity effects of the boundary elements.

**6-27** A large brick wall ($\alpha = 5 \times 10^{-7}$ m$^2$/s) that is 20 cm thick is initially at a uniform temperature of 300℃. Suddenly its surfaces are lowered to 50℃ and maintained at that temperature. Using an explicit finite-difference scheme and a mesh size $\Delta x = 5$ cm, determine the time required for the center temperature to reach 200℃ after the start of cooling.

**6-28** A large brick wall ($\alpha = 5 \times 10^{-7}$ m$^2$/s) that is 20 cm thick is initially at a uniform temperature of 150℃. Suddenly its surfaces are lowered to 30℃ and maintained at that temperature. Using an explicit finite-difference scheme and a mesh size $\Delta x = 5$ cm, determine the center temperature 3 $h$ after the start of cooling.

**6-29** A brick wall [$\alpha = 5 \times 10^{-7}$ m$^2$/s, $k = 1$ W/(m·℃)] 6 cm thick is initially at a uniform temperature of 100℃. Suddenly its surface temperatures are lowered by being exposed to a fluid at 20℃ with a heat transfer coefficient of 150 W/(m·℃). Using an explicit finite-difference scheme and a mesh size $\Delta x = 2$ cm, determine the time required for the surface temperatures to drop to 80℃. Include the heat capacity effects of the boundary elements.
*Answer*: $\Delta t = 0.8964$ *sec*, $\Delta x = 1$ *cmr* $= 0.4347$, $M = 60$, the surface temperature reaches 80℃ in approximately 7 *secs*.

**6-30** Determine the center-plane temperature of the chrome-steel plate of Problem 6-26 5 *min* after the start of cooling by including the heat capacity effects of the boundaries.

**6-31** A steel plate [$\alpha = 1.2 \times 10^{-5}$ m$^2$/s, $k = 43$ W/(m·℃)] 10 cm thick, initially at a uniform temperature $T_0$, is suddenly immersed in an oil bath at $T_\infty$. The convection heat transfer coefficient between the fluid and the surfaces of the plate is 400 W/(m$^2$·℃). Using a mesh size $\Delta x = 2$ cm, determine the largest permissible value of the time step $\Delta t$ if the heat capacity effects in the finite-difference equations for the boundary nodes are included.
*Answer*: 14.05 *secs*

*Product Solution for Transient Multidimensional Heat Conduction*

**6-32** A 6 cm by 3 cm rectangular bar with $k = 50$W/(m · °C) and $\alpha = 1.5 \times 10^{-5}$m$^2$/s is initially at a uniform temperature $T_i = 250$°C. Suddenly the bar is subjected to convective cooling with a heat transfer coefficient $h = 400$ W/(m$^2$ · °C) into an ambient at $T_\infty = 20$°C as shown in Figure P6-32. Determine the center temperature $T_0$ of the bar $t = 3$ min after it starts cooling.
*Answer*: 48.5 °C

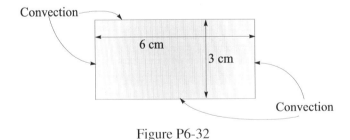

Figure P6-32

**6-33** A short, cylindrical bar with $k = 60$ W/(m · °C) and $\alpha = 1.6 \times 10^{-5}$m$^2$/s and diameter $D = 5$ cm and height $L = 4$ cm is initially at a uniform temperature $T_\infty = 250$°C. Suddenly the cylinder is subjected to ambient convective cooling with a heat transfer coefficient $h = 500$ W/(m$^2$ · °C) at $T_\infty = 20$°C. Determine

the center temperature $T_0$ of the cylinder $t = 2$ min after the start of the cooling.
*Answer*: $52.2\,°\mathrm{C}$

**6-34** A concrete slab corner as shown in Figure P6-34, within $0 \le x < \infty, 0 \le y < \infty$, with $k = 1.3\ \mathrm{W/(m \cdot °C)}$ and $\alpha = 8 \times 10^{-7} \mathrm{m^2/s}$ is initially at a uniform temperature $T_i = 130°\mathrm{C}$. Suddenly this corner is subjected to an ambient convective cooling with a heat transfer coefficient $h = 100\ \mathrm{W/(m^2 \cdot °C)}$ at $T_\infty = 30°\mathrm{C}$. Determine the temperature at a point $P$, $T_p$ at a location $x = 10$ cm, $y = 10$ cm, after $t = 2$ h it starts cooling.

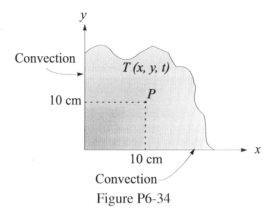

Figure P6-34

**6-35** A fireclay brick in the dimensions of semi infinite strip, $0 < x < \infty$, as shown in Figure P6-35 within $0 < y < 8$ cm is initially at a uniform temperature $T_i = 250°\mathrm{C}$. Suddenly it is subjected to an ambient convective cooling at $T_\infty = 25°\mathrm{C}$, with a heat transfer coefficient $h = 100\ \mathrm{W/(m^2 \cdot °C)}$. Calculate the temperature $T_0$ of a point $P$ located along the midplane at a distance $x = L = 5$ cm from the surface, after $t = 2$ h it starts cooling. The fireclay brick has $k = 1\ \mathrm{W/(m \cdot °C)}$ and $\alpha = 5.4 \times 10^{-7} \mathrm{m^2/s}$
*Answer*: $28.8\,°\mathrm{C}$

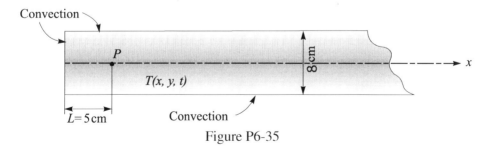

Figure P6-35

**6-36** A semi-infinite cylindrical iron bar with $k = 60\ \mathrm{W/(m \cdot °C)}$ and $\alpha = 1.6 \times 10^{-5} \mathrm{m^2/s}$ is initially at a uniform temperature $T_i = 350°\mathrm{C}$. It has a $D = 4$ cm and it is within the region $0 \le x < \infty$ as shown in Figure P6-36. Suddenly it is subjected to an ambient convective cooling at $T_\infty = 25°C$ with a heat transfer coefficient $h = 200 \text{ W}/(\text{m}^2 \cdot °\text{C})$. Determine the temperature $T_p$ of a point $P$ located along the axis at $x = L = 3$ cm from the flat surface, $t = 2$ min after it starts cooling.

*Answer*: 174 °C

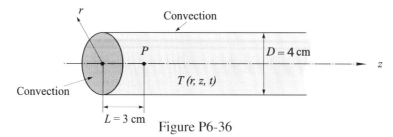

Figure P6-36

# CHAPTER 7

# *External Forced Convection Heat Flow*

A large proportion of heat transfer applications utilize *forced convection*, which involves transfer of heat between the outer surfaces of a solid body and a fluid that is forced to flow over it by some mechanism, such as a pump or a blower. For example, in a liquid-to-liquid heat exchanger, a pump is used to force the fluid to flow over the tube bundles. In a gas-cooled nuclear reactor, the hot gas from the reactor core is circulated over the tubes of the steam generator by special blowers. In the cooling of an automobile radiator, air is forced to flow over the hot radiator tubes as a result of the motion of the car.

The mechanism of heat transfer in forced convection is complicated. The transfer of heat between a solid surface and a fluid takes place through a combination of conduction and fluid motion. Consider a solid that is at a higher temperature than the fluid. Heat flows by conduction from the surface of the solid to the fluid adjacent to the wall. The heated fluid particles are then carried away into the cooler regions of the flow by fluid motion. Therefore, the characteristics of fluid motion govern the temperature distribution and heat transfer between the hot surface and the free stream. An understanding of velocity and temperature distribution in flow is most important in the study of heat transfer by forced convection. In this chapter we present a qualitative discussion of basic concepts pertaining to the distribution of velocity and temperature in the fluid and their consequences for heat transfer without getting involved in the study of equations of motion and energy. The significance of *dimensionless analysis* in the development of heat transfer correlations is illustrated, the velocity and thermal boundary-layer concepts basic to the study of forced convection over surfaces are introduced, and the approximate *integral method* is utilized to determine the velocity and temperature distributions in the flow. Some useful correlations are then presented for the determination of the drag force and heat transfer in both laminar and turbulent flow over solids with simple shapes, such as a flat plate, a circular or noncircular cylinder, and a sphere.

## 7.1. BASIC CONCEPTS

Heat transfer between the fluid and the surface of the solid, and the drag force exerted by the fluid on the body, are closely related to the distribution of temperature and velocity in the flow field. A good understanding of the factors affecting the temperature and velocity distribution is essential in the study of forced convection. Therefore, some qualitative discussion of the *velocity* and *thermal boundary-layer* concepts and the role of dimensionless parameters in the correlation of heat transfer in forced convection are given below.

## 7.1.1 Dimensionless Parameters

Heat transfer in flow over a body is affected by a variety of factors, including the flow pattern characteristics, the fluid properties, the flow passage geometry, and the surface conditions. The fluid flow pattern can be characterized as *laminar, transition*, or *turbulent*. The fluid properties that affect heat transfer include density, thermal conductivity, viscosity, and specific heat. The flow passage geometry may take such forms as flow over a flat plate, a cylinder, a sphere, tube banks or flow inside ducts and many others. Clearly there are too many factors that affect heat transfer between a solid surface and a fluid flowing over it.

Suppose the flow passage geometry and the character of the flow pattern are fixed; suppose, say, that a laminar flow along a flat plate and the local heat transfer coefficient $h_x$ at a distance $x$ from the leading edge of the plate (i.e., from the point where the flow first enters the plate) are considered. The parameters that affect heat transfer are $x$, $k$, $u$, $\rho$, $\mu$, $c_p$, $h_x$ where $k$, $\rho$, $\mu$, and $c_p$ are the thermal conductivity, density, viscosity, and specific heat of the fluid and $u$ is the main flow velocity. For the specific case considered here, the local heat transfer coefficient $h_x$ at a position $x$ depends on six independent variables, and the determination of a correlation among these seven parameters is of practical concern.

For the specific case of flow over a flat plate considered, it can be shown that the following three dimensionless groups can be established among these seven different parameters:

$$\text{Nu}_x = \frac{h_x x}{k} = \text{Nusselt number (local)}$$

$$\text{Pr} = \frac{c_p \mu}{k} = \text{Prandtl number}$$

$$\text{Re}_x = \frac{\rho u x}{\mu} = \text{Reynolds number (local)}$$

Then, one envisions a correlation of heat transfer in the form

$$\text{Nu}_x = f[\text{Re}_x, \ \text{Pr}] \tag{7-1a}$$

or a specific functional form for the correlation may be chosen as

$$\text{Nu}_x = C(\text{Re}_x)^a (\text{Pr})^b \tag{7-1b}$$

where the numerical values for the constant $C$ and the exponents $a$ and $b$ are to be determined by the "best fit" to experimental data. Later in this chapter, the values of $a$, $b$, and $C$ for various flow configurations will be presented.

The principal advantages of correlating heat transfer in terms of dimensionless groups are now apparent. The experimental data is correlated in terms of three variables instead of the original seven variables, and the results of such correlations are applicable to a variety of fluids, flow velocities, and geometrical dimensions, provided that the flow characteristics and geometry considered remain the same.

Clearly, the success of dimensional analysis strongly depends upon the proper choice of the parameters involved, which requires a good insight into the physical nature of the problem. Suppose we had chosen six parameters instead of the seven; the resulting dimensionless groups obtained by dimensionless analysis would have been incorrect.

## 7.1.2 Velocity Boundary Layer

Consider the flow of a viscous fluid over a flat plate, as illustrated in Fig. 7.1. Let $x$ be

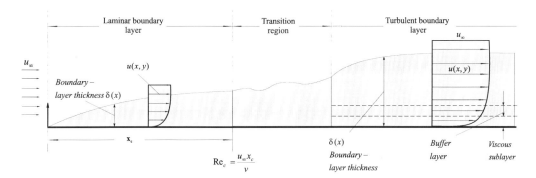

**FIG. 7.1.** Boundary-layer concept for flow over a flat plate.

the coordinate axis measured along the plate in the direction of the flow, and let y be the coordinate axis normal to the surface of the plate. A fluid with a free-stream velocity $u_\infty$, flows along the plate. Immediately before the leading edge of the plate (i.e., $x = 0$), the fluid velocity is uniform everywhere, but a significant change in the velocity profile occurs as fluid moves along the plate. The viscous forces tend to retard the flow in the regions near the surface. The fluid particles in contact with the surface assume zero velocity, whereas in the region sufficiently far away from the surface, the flow velocity $u_\infty$ remains essentially unaffected. Such a situation implies that the flow velocity $u$ parallel to the surface should increase from a value $u = 0$ at $y = 0$ to $u = u_\infty$, for $y$ sufficiently large. Then, at each location $x$, one envisions a point $y = \delta(x)$ in the flow field where the axial velocity $u$ is equal to 99 percent of the free-stream velocity $u_\infty$. The locus of the points where $u = 0.99u_\infty$ is called the *velocity boundary layer*, or simply the *boundary layer*. We use the notation $\delta(x)$ to denote the thickness of the boundary layer.

With these considerations, the flow field can be assumed to be separated into two distinct regions: (1) The *boundary-layer region*, where the flow velocity $u$ increases rapidly with the distance from the wall surface, and (2) the *potential-flow region* outside the boundary layer, where the velocity gradients are negligible. It is the steep velocity gradients in the boundary layer that give rise to shear stress in the fluid, which in turn exerts drag on the plate surface. Therefore an understanding of the behavior of flow in the boundary-layer region is important in the study of flow over surfaces.

We now examine the boundary-layer flow in the $x$ direction along the plate. The characteristics of this flow is governed by a dimensionless quantity called Reynolds number,

$\text{Re}_x$, defined as

$$\boxed{\text{Re}_x \equiv \frac{u_\infty x}{\nu} = \frac{\text{inertia force}}{\text{viscous force}}}$$ (7-2a)

where

$$u_\infty = \text{free-stream velocity}$$
$$x = \text{distance from leading edge}$$
$$\nu = \text{kinematic viscosity of the fluid}$$

Depending on the value of the Reynolds number, the flow in the boundary layer can be *laminar, transitional*, or *turbulent*. When the flow is *laminar*, the fluid particles move along streamlines in an orderly manner. The term *turbulent* is used to indicate that the motion of the fluid is chaotic in nature and involves crosswise mixing or eddying super-imposed on the motion of the mainstream. *Transitional*, as the name implies, indicates the region where the boundary layer flow changes from laminar to turbulent behavior. Figure 7.1 schematically illustrates the laminar, transition, and turbulent boundary layers for flow along a flat plate. The boundary layer starts from the leading edge (i.e., $x = 0$) of the plate as laminar, and the flow stays laminar up to a critical distance $x = x_c$, where the transition from laminar to turbulent flow takes place. For most practical purposes, for flow along a flat plate the transition begins at a value of Reynolds number

$$\boxed{\text{Re}_x \equiv \frac{u_\infty x}{\nu} \cong 5 \times 10^5}$$ (7-2b)

This critical value is strongly dependent on the surface roughness and the turbulence level of the free stream. For example, with very large disturbances in the free stream, the transition may begin at a Reynolds number as low as $10^5$, whereas for flows which are free from disturbances, the transition may not start until a Reynolds number of $10^6$ or more is reached. For flow along a flat plate, the boundary layer is always turbulent for $\text{Re}_x \geq 4 \times 10^6$.

In the *turbulent boundary layer*, next to the wall there is a very thin layer, called the *viscous sublayer*, where the flow retains its viscous-flow character. Adjacent to the viscous sublayer is a region called the *buffer layer*, in which there is fine grained turbulence and the mean axial velocity rapidly increases with the distance from the wall. The buffer layer is followed by the turbulent layer, in which there is a larger-scale turbulence and the velocity changes relatively little with the distance from the wall. These concepts are also illustrated in Fig. 7.1.

The Reynolds number as defined above is based on three distinct parameters: velocity, kinematic viscosity, and a characteristic length. For the flow over a flat plate considered here, the characteristic length is chosen as the distance $x$ measured along the plate. The choice of the characteristic length depends on the geometry of the body. For example, for flow across a sphere or a cylindrical tube, the diameter can be used as the characteristic dimension. Furthermore, the value of the critical Reynolds number at the transition from laminar to turbulent flow for bodies having different geometries is different from that given above.

**DRAG COEFFICIENT**. The presence of steep velocity gradients in the boundary layer gives rise to a drag force exerted on the body as a result of flow over it . The determination of this drag force is of interest in engineering applications. The drag force can be calculated by making use of the *drag coefficient* concept as now described.

The shear stress $\tau_x$ at the wall surface at any location $x$ is related to the velocity gradient by

$$\tau_x = \mu \left. \frac{\partial u(x,y)}{\partial y} \right|_{y=0} \tag{7-3}$$

where $\mu$ is the viscosity of the fluid. However, in engineering practice calculating the shear stress from the knowledge of the velocity gradients at the wall surface is not practical. To alleviate this difficulty, the concept of *local drag coefficient* $c(x)$ is introduced, and the shear stress is related to the drag coefficient in the form

$$\boxed{\tau(x) = c(x) \frac{\rho u_\infty^2}{2}} \quad N/m^2 \tag{7-4}$$

where $\rho$ is the density and $u_\infty$ is the free-stream velocity of the flow. Clearly, knowing $c(x)$, the shear stress (or the drag force per unit area) at the location $x$ is determined from Eq. (7-4).

By equating Eqs. (7-3) and (7-4), the following expression is obtained:

$$c(x) = \frac{2\nu}{u_\infty^2} \left. \frac{\partial u(x,y)}{\partial y} \right|_{y=0} \tag{7-5}$$

where $\nu = \mu/\rho$ is the kinematic viscosity of fluid. Therefore, if the flow problem in the boundary layer can be solved and the velocity distribution $u$ determined, then $c(x)$ is obtained from the definition in Eq. (7-5), and the resulting explicit expression can be used in practical applications.

The average value of $c(x)$ over the distance from $x=0$ to $x=L$ along the plate is also of interest. Knowing the local values of $c(x)$, the *mean drag coefficient* $c_m$ over the distance $x=0$ to $x=L$ is determined from

$$c_m = \frac{1}{L} \int_{x=0}^{L} c(x)dx. \tag{7-6}$$

Once the *mean drag coefficient* $c_m$ is available, the *drag force F* acting on the plate over the length from $x=0$ to $x=L$ and for a width $w$ is determined from

$$\boxed{F = wLc_m \frac{\rho u_\infty^2}{2}} \quad N \tag{7-7}$$

### 7.1.3 Thermal Boundary Layer

Analogous to the concept of velocity boundary layer, one can envision the development of a thermal boundary layer along the flat plate associated with the temperature profile in the fluid. To illustrate the concept, we consider the flow of a fluid at a uniform temperature $T_\infty$ along a flat plate maintained at a constant temperature $T_w$. Let $T(x, y)$ be the temperature of the fluid at a location $(x, y)$, where the coordinates $x$ and $y$ are measured along and perpendicular to the plate surface, respectively. Suppose the fluid is hotter than the wall, that is, $T_\infty > T_w$.

A dimensionless fluid temperature $\theta(x, y)$ is now defined as

$$\theta(x, y) = \frac{T(x, y) - T_w}{T_\infty - T_w} \tag{7-8}$$

That is, we measure the fluid temperature $T(x, y)$ in excess of the wall temperature $T_w$ and divide it by $T_\infty - T_w$. We consider two limiting cases of $\theta(x, y)$, one at the wall surface $y = 0$ and the other at distances sufficiently far away from the wall (i.e., $y$ large). We have

$$\begin{aligned} \theta(x, y) &= 0 &&\text{at } y = 0 \\ \theta(x, y) &\to 1 &&\text{for large } y \end{aligned} \tag{7-9}$$

The dimensionless fluid temperature $\theta(x, y)$ varies from a value of $\theta = 0$ at the wall surface to a value of $\theta = 1$ at sufficiently large distances from the wall. Then at each location $x$ along the plate one envisions a point $y = \delta_t(x)$ in the flow such that $\theta(x, y)$ assumes a value of 0.99. The locus of such points where $\theta(x, y) = 0.99$ is called the *thermal boundary layer*. The concept is analogous to the velocity boundary layer discussed previously; it is illustrated in Fig. 7.2. In the thermal boundary-layer region the temperature

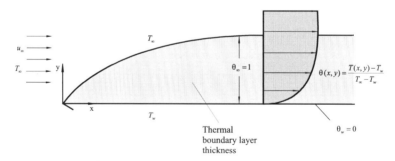

**FIG. 7.2.** Thermal boundary-layer concept for flow of a hot fluid over a cold wall.

gradients are very steep, and so heat transfer between the fluid and the wall is governed by the characteristics of the temperature profile in the thermal boundary layer. Therefore, the relative thickness of the thermal and velocity boundary layers is a factor that affects heat transfer between the fluid and the wall surface. Analytical studies have shown that the relative thickness of boundary layers depends on the Prandtl number of the fluid, defined as

$$\text{Pr} = \frac{\mu c_p}{k} = \frac{\mu/\rho}{k/\rho c_p} = \frac{\nu}{\alpha} = \frac{\text{molecular diffusivity of momentum}}{\text{molecular diffusivity of heat}} \qquad (7\text{-}10)$$

The dependence of the relative thickness of $\delta_t(x)$ and $\delta(x)$ can be stated as

$$\delta_t(x) < \delta(x) \text{ for Pr} > 1 \qquad (7\text{-}11a)$$

$$\delta_t(x) = \delta(x) \text{ for Pr} = 1 \qquad (7\text{-}11b)$$

$$\delta_t(x) > \delta(x) \text{ for Pr} < 1 \qquad (7\text{-}11c)$$

There is a wide difference in the values of the Prandtl number for various types of fluids. Figure 7.3 illustrates approximate ranges of Pr for different fluids. For practical

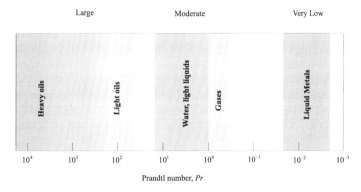

**FIG. 7.3.** Typical ranges of Prandtl number for various types of fluids.

purposes the fluids can be separated into three groups: fluids having very low, moderate, and large Prandtl numbers. Oils have large Prandtl numbers; fluids such as gas, water, and light liquids have moderate Prandtl numbers; and liquid metals have very low Prandtl numbers. Figure 7.3 shows that there is a gap between the very low and moderate values of the Prandtl number where no type of fluid appears to belong. A schematic illustration of the relative thickness of $\delta(x)$ and $\delta_t(x)$ for these three groups of fluids is shown in Fig. 7.4. For liquid metals the thermal boundary layer is much thicker than the velocity boundary layer, whereas for oils the thermal boundary layer is much smaller than the velocity layer.

**HEAT TRANSFER COEFFICIENT.** The concept of heat transfer coefficient is widely used in the determination of heat transfer between the wall surface and the fluid forced to flow over it. To illustrate the physical significance of the heat transfer coefficient in relation to the temperature distribution in the flow, we consider the flow of a hot fluid at a temperature $T_\infty$ over a cold plate at a constant temperature $T_w$. Fluid particles in the immediate vicinity of the wall surface remain stationary. Therefore, heat transfer between the wall surface and the adjacent fluid particles is by pure conduction. Then the conduction heat flux $q(x)$ from the adjacent hot fluid to the wall surface at $y = 0$ (i.e., the plate

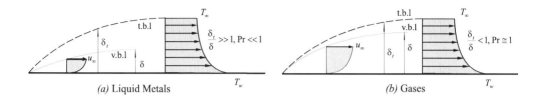

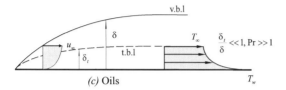

(a) Liquid Metals

(b) Gases

(c) Oils

**FIG. 7.4.** Relative thickness of velocity and thermal boundary layers for different types of fluids.

surface) is given by

$$q(x) = k \left. \frac{\partial T(x, y)}{\partial y} \right|_{y=0} \tag{7-12a}$$

where $k$ is the thermal conductivity of the fluid. Here the negative sign is omitted from the conduction flux, because heat flow from the fluid to the wall, in the negative $y$ direction, is considered.

In engineering applications it is not practical to calculate the derivative of temperature distribution in the fluid in order to determine the heat transfer rate as given by Eq. (7-12a). Instead, the heat transfer between the fluid and the wall surface is related to a local heat transfer coefficient $h(x)$, defined as

$$q(x) = h(x) \left( T_\infty - T_w \right) \tag{7-12b}$$

where $T_\infty$ and $T_w$ are the free-stream and plate surface temperatures, respectively. The definition given by Eq. (7-12b) implies that heat transfer is from the fluid to the wall surface; hence it is consistent with the $q(x)$ defined by Eq. (7-12a) .

The expression defining $h(x)$ is now determined by equating Eqs. (7-12a) and (7-12b).

$$\underbrace{h(x) \left( T_\infty - T_w \right)}_{convection} = \underbrace{k \left. \frac{\partial T(x, y)}{\partial y} \right|_{y=0}}_{conduction} \tag{7-13a}$$

or

$$\boxed{h(x) = k \frac{[\partial T(x, y)/\partial y]_{y=0}}{T_\infty - T_w}} \tag{7-13b}$$

Given the temperature distribution in the flow, the local heat transfer coefficient $h(x)$ can be calculated from Eq. (7-13b). This expression is also used in analytical studies to establish the relation for $h(x)$ by utilizing the solution of the temperature distribution in the thermal boundary layer.

In engineering applications, the mean value of $h_m$ over a distance $x = 0$ to $x = L$ along the surface is of practical interest. The *mean heat transfer coefficient $h_m$* is determined from

$$\boxed{h_m \equiv \frac{1}{L} \int_0^L h(x)dx}$$

(7-14)

Knowing the mean heat transfer coefficient $h_m$, the heat transfer rate $Q$ from the fluid to the wall over the distance from $x = 0$ to $x = L$ and width $w$ is determined from

$$Q = wLh_m(T_\infty - T_w)$$

(7-15)

**EXAMPLE 7-1**  Air at atmospheric pressure and at 300 K flows with a velocity of 1 m/s over a flat plate. The transition from laminar to turbulent flow is assumed to take place at a Reynolds number of $5 \times 10^5$. Determine the distance from the leading edge of the plate at which transition occurs.

**SOLUTION**  The kinematic viscosity $\nu$ of atmospheric air at $T_\infty = 300$ K is $0.168 \times 10^{-4}$ m$^2$/s. The transition is assumed to occur at a distance $x = L$, where $\text{Re}_L = 5 \times 10^5$. Then the distance $L$ is determined from

$$\text{Re}_L = \frac{u_\infty L}{\nu} = \frac{L}{0.168 \times 10^{-4}} = 5 \times 10^5$$

or

$$L = 8.4 \text{ m}$$

**EXAMPLE 7-2**  Air at atmospheric pressure and at 300 K flows over a flat plate with a velocity of 2 m/s. The average drag coefficient $c_m$ over a distance of 3 mfrom the leading edge is $2.22 \times 10^{-3}$. Calculate the drag force acting per 1-m width of the plate over the distance of 3 mfrom the leading edge.

**SOLUTION**  The density of atmospheric air $\rho$ at $300K$ is 1.177 kg/m$^3$. The drag force acting on the plate is determined by Eq. (7-7) as

$$\begin{aligned} F &= wLc_m\frac{\rho u_\infty^2}{2} = (1)(3)(2.22 \times 10^{-3})\frac{(1.177)(2)^2}{2} \\ &= 0.0157 \text{ N} \end{aligned}$$

**EXAMPLE 7-3**  The physical properties of engine oil at 100°C are given by $\rho = 840.01$ kg/m$^3$, $c_p = 2.219$ kJ/(kg $\cdot$°C), $k = 0.137$ W/(m $\cdot$ K), and $\nu = 0.203 \times 10^{-4}$ m$^2$/s. Calculate the Prandtl number.

**SOLUTION**

$$Pr = \frac{\nu}{\alpha} = \frac{\nu}{k/\rho c_p}$$

$$= \frac{0.203 \times 10^{-4}}{0.137/(840.01 \times 2.219 \times 10^3)}$$

$$= 276$$

## 7.2. LAMINAR FLOW OVER A FLAT PLATE

In the previous section we introduced the concepts of *drag* and *heat transfer coefficients* and showed that they are related to the velocity and temperature distributions in the flow, respectively. However, we have not shown how the velocity and temperature profiles in the flow can be determined by analytical means. In our discussion of dimensional analysis, it was shown that the functional form of the correlation of heat transfer coefficient (or the Nusselt number) is expected to be of the form given by Eq. (7-1*b*). The objective of this section is to illustrate, by approximate analytic approaches, the determination of the velocity and temperature profiles in the flow field for laminar flow over a flat plate. Then, by utilizing such information, we develop approximate analytic expressions for both the drag and heat transfer coefficients.

### 7.2.1 Velocity Distribution

The distribution of velocity for flow over bodies is governed by a system of coupled partial differential equations called the *continuity* and *momentum* equations. For the simple situation involving laminar flow along a plate, the flow velocity is characterized by two components. One is $u(x, y)$ in the flow direction parallel to the surface of the plate, and the other is $v(x, y)$ normal to the surface of the plate. The determination of these two velocity components requires two equations, the continuity and the $x$-direction momentum equations. Such equations can be solved exactly by numerical techniques and the velocity component $u(x, y)$ needed for the computation of the drag coefficient can be determined. There is also a relatively simple approximate method of analysis, called the *integral method*, available for solving the velocity problem in flow. To develop the integral form of the equations of motion, the continuity and momentum equations are manipulated by integrating them and then eliminating the normal velocity component $v(x, y)$ between them. Such a procedure results in the following equation, called the *momentum integral equation*:

$$\frac{d}{dx}\left[\int_0^{\delta(x)} u(u_\infty - u)dy\right] = \nu \left.\frac{\partial u}{\partial y}\right|_{y=0} \qquad \text{in } 0 < y < \delta(x) \qquad (7\text{-}16a)$$

where $x$ and $y$ are the coordinates measured, respectively, along the plate in the direction of flow and normal to the plate surface. In addition, $u_\infty$ is the main stream velocity measured at distances away from the plate, and $\nu$ is the kinematic viscosity of the fluid, both of which are considered known. Then the velocity problem governed by Eq. (7-16$a$) involves two unknowns: the velocity component $u(x, y)$ and the boundary-layer thickness $\delta(x)$. We are concerned with the approximate method of solution of the momentum integral equation (7-16$a$). Basic steps in the analysis are as follows :

1. Assume a profile for the distribution of the axial velocity $u(x, y)$ in the boundary layer, $0 < y < \delta(x)$. Here we consider a second-degree polynomial of $y$ in the form

$$u(x, y) = a_0(x) + a_1(x)y + a_2(x)y^2 \quad \text{in } 0 < y < \delta(x) \qquad (7\text{-}16b)$$

where the coefficients $a_i(x)$ are, in general, functions of $x$ and yet to be related to the velocity boundary-layer thickness $\delta(x)$.

2. The next step in the analysis is to relate $a_i(x)$ to $\delta(x)$ by utilizing the actual physical conditions for the variation of $u(x, y)$ within the boundary layer. We have only three such coefficients and consider the following three physically realistic requirements for $u(x, y)$:

$$
\begin{aligned}
u(x, y) &= 0 & \text{at } y = 0 \\
u(x, y) &= u_\infty & \text{at } y = \delta(x) \\
\frac{\partial u(x, y)}{\partial y} &= 0 & \text{at } y = \delta(x).
\end{aligned}
$$

By utilizing these three conditions, three equations are obtained for determining $a_0$, $a_1$, and $a_2$ in terms of the boundary-layer thickness $\delta(x)$. When these expressions are introduced into Eq. (7-16$b$), the following expression is obtained for the velocity profile:

$$u(x, y) = u_\infty \left[ 2\frac{y}{\delta} - \left(\frac{y}{\delta}\right)^2 \right] \qquad (7\text{-}16c)$$

where $\delta \equiv \delta(x)$. Clearly, if the boundary-layer thickness $\delta(x)$ is known, the velocity distribution $u(x, y)$ is determined from Eq. (7-16$c$).

3. The final step in the analysis is the determination of $\delta(x)$. The velocity profile Eq. (7-16$c$) is introduced into the momentum integral equation (7-16a)

$$\frac{d}{dx}\left(\int_0^{\delta(x)} u_\infty\left[2\frac{y}{\delta} - \left(\frac{y}{\delta}\right)^2\right]\left\{u_\infty - u_\infty\left[2\frac{y}{\delta} - \left(\frac{y}{\delta}\right)^2\right]\right\}dy\right) = \frac{2\nu u_\infty}{\delta(x)} \qquad (7\text{-}16d)$$

where we made use of the following expressions at $y = 0$.

$$\frac{\partial u}{\partial y} = u_\infty\left(\frac{2}{\delta} - \frac{2^2}{\delta}y\right)$$

$$\frac{\partial u}{\partial y} = \frac{2u_\infty}{\delta}.$$

When the integration with respect to $y$ is performed, the following ordinary differential equation results for the determination of the velocity boundary-layer thickness $\delta(x)$:

$$\frac{d}{dx}\left[\frac{2}{15}u_\infty^2\delta(x)\right] = \frac{2\nu u_\infty}{\delta(x)}$$

or

$$\delta d\delta = \frac{15\nu}{u_\infty}dx \qquad (7\text{-}17a)$$

and the boundary condition needed to solve this differential equation is determined from the physical situation that the boundary-layer thickness vanishes at $x = 0$, as illustrated in Fig. 7.1. Then we have

$$\delta(x) = 0 \quad \text{for } x = 0. \qquad (7\text{-}17b)$$

The solution of the ordinary differential equation in $(7\text{-}17a)$ subject to the boundary condition of Eq. $(7\text{-}17b)$ gives

$$\delta^2(x) = \frac{30\nu x}{u_\infty}$$

or

$$\delta(x) = \sqrt{\frac{30\nu x}{u_\infty}}. \qquad (7\text{-}17c)$$

This expression for $\delta(x)$ is rearranged in dimensionless form as

$$\frac{\delta(x)}{x} = \sqrt{\frac{30}{\text{Re}_x}}$$

$$= \frac{5.48}{\text{Re}_x^{1/2}} \qquad (7\text{-}17d)$$

where the local Reynolds number $\text{Re}_x$ is defined by

$$\text{Re}_x = \frac{u_\infty x}{\nu}. \qquad (7\text{-}17e)$$

Thus, Eq. $(7\text{-}16c)$ together with $(7\text{-}17d)$ provides an expression for the velocity distribution $u(x, y)$ in the boundary-layer flow over a flat plate.

## 7.2.2 Drag Coefficient

Having established an approximate solution for the velocity distribution $u(x, y)$ in flow, we are now in a position to develop an approximate analytic expression for the drag coefficient $c_x$ for laminar boundary-layer flow along a flat plate. From Eq. (7-5) we have

$$c_x = \frac{2\nu}{u_\infty^2} \frac{\partial u(x,y)}{\partial y}\bigg|_{y=0} \tag{7-18a}$$

where the velocity gradient is evaluated by utilizing the expressions given by Eqs. (7-16c) and (7-17d). That is,

$$\frac{\partial u(x,y)}{\partial y}\bigg|_{y=0} = \frac{2u_\infty}{\delta(x)} = \frac{2u_\infty}{\sqrt{30\nu x/u_\infty}}. \tag{7-18b}$$

Introducing Eq. (7-18b) into Eq. (7-18a), the following approximate expression is determined for the local drag coefficient $c_x$:

$$c_x = \frac{4\nu}{u_\infty \sqrt{30\nu x/u_\infty}} = \frac{0.73}{\text{Re}_x^{1/2}}. \tag{7-18c}$$

Our analysis for the determination of velocity profile being approximate, the resulting expression for the drag coefficient given above is also approximate. One of the shortcomings of approximate analysis is that the accuracy of the result cannot be assessed until the solution is compared with the exact result. For this particular problem, the velocity distribution in flow has been determined exactly by numerical solution of the continuity and momentum equations, and the resulting exact expression for the local drag coefficient is given by

$$c(x) = \frac{0.664}{\text{Re}_x^{1/2}} \quad \text{for Re} \leq 10^5 \tag{7-19a}$$

where $\text{Re}_x = u_\infty x/\nu$. We note that the local drag coefficient $c_x$ decreases with increased distance from the leading edge in the form

$$c(x) \sim x^{-1/2}. \tag{7-19b}$$

Note that our approximate analysis for $c_x$ is within 10 percent of the exact value. The average drag coefficient $c_m$, over the plate length from $x = 0$ to $x = L$, is determined from its definition as

$$c_m = \frac{1}{L} \int_{x=0}^{L} c(x)dx = 2c(x)|_{x=L} \tag{7-20a}$$

Introducing Eq. (7-19a) into Eq. (7-20a), we obtain

$$\boxed{c_m = \frac{1.328}{\text{Re}_L^{1/2}}} \quad \text{for Re} \leq 5 \times 10^5 \tag{7-20b}$$

where

$$\text{Re}_L = \frac{u_\infty L}{\nu}.$$

Given the average drag coefficient $c_m$, the drag force $F$ acting on the plate over the length $x = 0$ to $x = L$ and for a width $w$ is determined according to Eq. (7-7), that is,

$$\boxed{F = wLc_m \frac{\rho u_\infty^2}{2}} \quad N \qquad (7\text{-}20c)$$

### 7.2.3 Temperature Distribution

Previously, it was pointed out that given the temperature distribution in flow, the heat transfer coefficient can be determined from its definition, given by Eq. (7-13b). We are now concerned with the determination of the temperature distribution in the flow field. In general, the temperature distribution in flow is determined from the solution of the energy equation, which is a partial differential equation that contains the velocity components. The solution of such an equation is quite involved and beyond the scope of this work. However, an approximate solution for the temperature distribution $T(x, t)$ can be obtained by considering the integral form of the energy equation, called the *energy integral equation*, given by

$$\frac{d}{dx}\left[\int_0^{\delta_t} u(1 - \theta)dy\right] = \alpha \frac{\partial \theta}{\partial y}\bigg|_{y=0} \quad \text{in } 0 < y < \delta_t \qquad (7\text{-}21a)$$

where

$$\theta(x, y) = \frac{T(x, y) - T_w}{T_\infty - T_w} = \text{dimensionless temperature}$$
$$T(x, y) = \text{temperature distribution}$$
$$\delta_t \equiv \delta_t(x) = \text{thermal boundary-layer thickness}$$

This equation involves three unknowns, namely, $u(x, y)$, $\theta(x, y)$, and $\delta_t(x)$. If suitable profiles can be established for the velocity and temperature distributions, then the integral equation can be solved for the thermal boundary-layer thickness $\delta_t(x)$ by following a procedure similar to that used in the solution of the momentum integral equation. The basic steps are now described.

1. Suitable profiles are chosen for the velocity and temperature distributions. There are numerous possibilities. For simplicity in the analysis and for illustration purposes, we consider a parabolic profile for $u(x, y)$, given previously by Eq. (7-16c) as

$$u(x, y) = u_\infty \left[2\frac{y}{\delta} - \left(\frac{y}{\delta}\right)^2\right] \quad \text{in } 0 < y < \delta \qquad (7\text{-}21b)$$

where

$$\delta = \sqrt{\frac{30\nu x}{u_\infty}}.$$

A parabolic profile is also chosen for the dimensionless temperature $\theta(x, y)$:

$$\theta(x, y) = c_0(x) + c_1(x)y + c_2(x)y^2$$

where the coefficients $c_i(x)$ are functions of $x$ and yet to be related to $\delta_t(x)$.

2. To determine the unknown coefficients $c_0$, $c_1$, and $c_2$, the following three physically realistic boundary conditions are imposed on $\theta(x, y)$:

$$
\begin{aligned}
\theta(x, y) &= 0 & \text{at } y = 0 \\
\theta(x, y) &= 1 & \text{at } y = \delta_t(x) \\
\frac{\partial \theta(x, y)}{\partial y} &= 0 & \text{at } y = \delta_t(x)
\end{aligned}
$$

Note that these conditions are similar to those imposed on the determination of the coefficients for the velocity profile. Therefore, the temperature profile takes the form

$$\theta(x, y) = 2\left(\frac{y}{\delta_t}\right) - \left(\frac{y}{\delta_t}\right)^2 \qquad \text{in } 0 < y < \delta \qquad (7\text{-}21c)$$

Note that this temperature profile is similar to the velocity profile given by Eq. (7-21b).

3. The final step in the analysis is the determination of the thermal boundary-layer thickness $\delta_t(x)$. The velocity profile, Eq. (7-21b), and the temperature profile, Eq. (7-21c), are introduced into the energy integral equation, Eq. (7-21a).

$$\frac{d}{dx}\left\{ u_\infty \int_0^{\delta_t} \left[ 2\left(\frac{y}{\delta}\right) - \left(\frac{y}{\delta}\right)^2 \right]\left[ 1 - 2\left(\frac{y}{\delta_t}\right) + \left(\frac{y}{\delta_t}\right)^2 \right] dy \right\} = \frac{2\alpha}{\delta_t} \qquad (7\text{-}21d)$$

The integration with respect to $y$ is performed:

$$\frac{d}{dx}\left[ \delta\left( \frac{1}{6}\Delta^2 - \frac{1}{30}\Delta^3 \right) \right] = \frac{2\alpha}{u_\infty \delta_t} \qquad (7\text{-}22a)$$

where

$$\Delta = \frac{\delta_t}{\delta}. \qquad (7\text{-}22b)$$

Here we consider the situation in which the thermal boundary-layer thickness $\delta_t$, is smaller than the velocity boundary layer $\delta$. Therefore, $\Delta < 1$, and in Eq. (7-22a) the term $\frac{1}{30}\Delta^3$ can be neglected in comparison to $\frac{1}{6}\Delta^2$. Equation (7-22a) simplifies to

$$\frac{d}{dx}(\delta\Delta^2) = \frac{12\alpha}{u_\infty \delta \Delta} \qquad (7\text{-}22c)$$

Differentiation with respect to $x$ is performed:

$$\delta \frac{d\Delta^2}{dx} + \Delta^2 \frac{d\delta}{dx} = \frac{12\alpha}{u_\infty(\delta\Delta)}$$

or

$$2\delta^2\Delta^2\frac{d\Delta}{dx} + \Delta^3\delta\frac{d\delta}{dx} = \frac{12\alpha}{u_\infty}$$

or

$$\frac{2}{3}\delta^2\frac{d\Delta^3}{dx} + \delta\frac{d\delta}{dx}\Delta^3 = \frac{12\alpha}{u_\infty} \qquad (7\text{-}22\text{d})$$

since

$$\Delta^2\frac{d\Delta}{dx} = \frac{1}{3}\frac{d\Delta^3}{dx}$$

The velocity boundary-layer thickness $\delta$ is

$$\delta^2 = \frac{30\nu x}{u_\infty} \qquad (7\text{-}22\text{e})$$

and differentiation, we obtain

$$2\delta\frac{d\delta}{dx} = \frac{30\nu}{u_\infty} \qquad (7\text{-}22\text{f})$$

Substituting Eqs. (7-22$e$) and (7-22$f$) into Eq. (7-22$d$), we obtain

$$x\frac{d\Delta^3}{dx} + \frac{3}{4}\Delta^3 = \frac{3}{5}\frac{\alpha}{\nu} \qquad (7\text{-}22\text{g})$$

This is an ordinary differential equation of first order in $\Delta^3$, and its general solution is written as (see the note at the end of this chapter for an explanation)

$$\Delta^3 = Cx^{-3/4} + \frac{3/5}{3/4}\frac{\alpha}{\nu} \qquad (7\text{-}22\text{h})$$

The integration constant $C$ is determined by the application of the boundary condition

$$\delta_t = 0 \quad \text{at } x = 0 \qquad (7\text{-}22\text{i})$$

which implies that heat transfer starts at the leading edge of the plate. The application of this boundary condition gives $C = 0$. Therefore, the solution for $\Delta^3$ becomes

$$\Delta^3 = \frac{4}{5}\frac{\alpha}{\nu} = \frac{4}{5\text{Pr}} \qquad (7\text{-}22\text{j})$$

or

$$\Delta = \frac{\delta_t}{\delta} = \left(\frac{4}{5}\right)^{1/3} \mathrm{Pr}^{-1/3} \tag{7-22k}$$

where

$$\mathrm{Pr} = \frac{\nu}{\alpha}$$

The substitution of $\delta(x) = \sqrt{30\nu x/u_\infty}$ into Eq. (7-22k) gives the thermal boundary-layer thickness $\delta_t(x)$ as

$$\delta_t(x) = \left(\frac{4}{5}\right)^{1/3} \mathrm{Pr}^{-1/3} \sqrt{\frac{30\nu x}{u_\infty}}$$

which can be rearranged as

$$\delta_t(x) = 5.085 \frac{x}{\mathrm{Pr}^{1/3}\mathrm{Re}_x^{1/2}} \tag{7-22l}$$

where

$$\mathrm{Re}_x = \frac{u_\infty x}{\nu}$$

Thus, Eq. (7-21c), together with Eq. (7-22l), provides an expression for the dimensionless temperature distribution $\theta(x, y)$ in the flow.

## 7.2.4 Heat Transfer Coefficient

Having established an approximate expression for the temperature distribution in the flow, we are now in a position to develop an approximate analytic expression for the local heat transfer coefficient $h(x)$ for laminar boundary layer flow along a flat plate.

The local heat transfer coefficient $h(x)$ is defined by Eq. (7-13b) as

$$h(x) = k \frac{[\partial T(x, y)/\partial y]_{y=0}}{T_\infty - T_w} \tag{7-23a}$$

or it is related to $\theta(x, y)$ by

$$h(x) = k \left. \frac{\partial \theta(x, y)}{\partial y} \right|_{y=0} \tag{7-23b}$$

Introducing Eq. (7-21c) into Eq. (7-23b), we obtain

$$h(x) = k \frac{2}{\delta_t(x)} \tag{7-23c}$$

For the thermal boundary-layer thickness $\delta_t(x)$ as given by Eq. (7-22l), the local heat transfer coefficient $h(x)$ becomes

$$h(x) = \frac{2}{5.085} \frac{k}{x} \mathrm{Re}_x^{1/2} \mathrm{Pr}^{1/3} \tag{7-23d}$$

or the local Nusselt number $\text{Nu}_x$ is determined as

$$\text{Nu}_x = \frac{xh(x)}{k} = 0.393\text{Re}_x^{1/2}\text{Pr}^{1/3} \qquad (7\text{-}23e)$$

which is valid for laminar flow, $\text{Re}_x < 5 \times 10^5$. Note that the functional form of the local Nusselt number given by Eq. (7-23$e$) is consistent with the functional form established by dimensional analysis and given by Eq. (7-1$b$).

The Nusselt number given by Eq. (7-23$e$) is approximate because it is based on a temperature profile determined by an approximate method of analysis. Its accuracy cannot be established until it is compared with an exact analysis of the problem or verified experimentally. The exact analysis of heat transfer for laminar boundary-layer flow is available, and we present below some of these results. It has been shown that such solutions are dependent upon the range of the Prandtl number. Therefore, in presenting the results for the heat transfer coefficients determined through analytic solutions, we consider them in three groups: $h(x)$ applicable for fluids having moderate, very low, and high Prandtl numbers.

**1. $h(x)$ for moderate Prandtl numbers.** More than half a century ago Pohlhausen developed an analytic solution for the local heat transfer coefficient $h(x)$ for forced laminar convection over a flat plate maintained at a uniform temperature. His result, applicable for moderate Prandtl numbers, can be expressed in dimensionless form as

$$\boxed{\text{Nu}_x = 0.332\text{Re}_x^{1/2}\text{Pr}^{1/3}} \quad \text{for} \quad \begin{matrix} 0.6 < \text{Pr} < 10 \\ \text{Re}_x < 5 \times 10^5 \end{matrix} \qquad (7\text{-}24a)$$

where $\text{Nu}_x$, $\text{Re}_x$, and Pr are defined as

$$\text{Nu}_x = \frac{xh(x)}{k} \quad \text{Pr} = \frac{\nu}{\alpha} \quad \text{Re}_x = \frac{xu_\infty}{\nu} \qquad (7\text{-}24b)$$

and $x$ is the distance measured along the plate, starting from the leading edge. The physical properties of the fluid are to be calculated at the *film temperature* $T_f$, which is the arithmetic mean of the free-stream and wall surface temperatures; that is,

$$T_f = \frac{1}{2}(T_w + T_\infty) \qquad (7\text{-}25)$$

The average value of the heat transfer coefficient over the distance from $x = 0$ to $x = L$ is determined from the definition given by Eq. (7-14). We find

$$h_m = \frac{1}{L}\int_0^L h(x)dx = 2\, h(x)|_{x=L}$$

which yields

$$\boxed{\text{Nu}_m = 0.664\text{Re}_L^{1/2}\text{Pr}^{1/3}} \quad \text{for} \quad \begin{matrix} 0.6 < \text{Pr} < 10 \\ \text{Re}_x < 5 \times 10^5 \end{matrix} \qquad (7\text{-}26a)$$

where

$$\mathrm{Nu}_m = \frac{h_m L}{k} \quad \mathrm{Re}_L = \frac{u_\infty L}{\nu} \tag{7-26b}$$

and all the properties are evaluated at the *film temperature*.

These results are applicable for fluids such as gases, water, and light liquids.

**2. $h(x)$ for large Prandtl numbers.** The Prandtl number is very large for liquids such as oils. Pohlhausen's analysis for the limiting case of Pr→ ∞ gives

$$\boxed{\mathrm{Nu}_x = 0.339\mathrm{Re}_x^{1/2}\mathrm{Pr}^{1/3}} \quad \text{for} \quad \begin{array}{l} \mathrm{Pr} \to \infty \\ \mathrm{Re}_x < 5 \times 10^5 \end{array} \tag{7-27a}$$

The average value of the Nusselt number over the distance $x = 0$ to $x = L$ is determined by Eq. (7-14) as

$$\boxed{\mathrm{Nu}_m = 0.678\mathrm{Re}_L^{1/2}\mathrm{Pr}^{1/3}} \quad \text{for} \quad \begin{array}{l} \mathrm{Pr} \to \infty \\ \mathrm{Re}_x < 5 \times 10^5 \end{array} \tag{7-27b}$$

where the mean $Nu_m$ and $Re_L$ are defined by Eq. (7-26b).

**3. $h(x)$ for very small Prandtl numbers.** The Prandtl number is very low for liquid metals. The limiting case of Pohlhausen's solution for Pr> 0 gives

$$\boxed{\mathrm{Nu}_x = 0.564\mathrm{Pe}_x^{1/2}} \quad \text{for} \quad \begin{array}{l} \mathrm{Pr} \to 0 \\ \mathrm{Re}_x < 5 \times 10^5 \end{array} \tag{7-28}$$

where the local Peclet number $\mathrm{Pe}_x$ is defined as

$$\mathrm{Pe}_x = \mathrm{Re}_x \, \mathrm{Pr} = \frac{u_\infty x}{\alpha}$$

The average value of the Nusselt number, $\mathrm{Nu}_m$, is calculated by Eq. (7-14).

**EXAMPLE 7-4** An approximate expression for the local heat transfer coefficient $h(x)$ in the laminar boundary layer along a flat plate is given by

$$h(x) = 0.393\frac{k}{x}\mathrm{Pr}^{1/3}\mathrm{Re}_x^{1/2}.$$

Develop an expression for the average heat transfer coefficient $h_m$ over a distance from the leading edge of the plate.

**SOLUTION** The average heat transfer coefficient $h_m$ from $x = 0$ to $x = L$ is determined using Eq. (7-14) to be

$$h_m = \frac{1}{L}\int_0^L h(x)dx.$$

Introducing the expression for $h(x)$, we find

$$
\begin{aligned}
h_m &= \frac{1}{L}0.393\mathrm{Pr}^{1/3}\left(\frac{u_\infty}{\nu}\right)^{1/2}\int_0^L \frac{1}{x^{1/2}}dx \\
&= 2(0.393)\frac{k}{L}\mathrm{Pr}^{1/3}\mathrm{Re}_x^{1/2} = 2[h(x)]_{x=L}.
\end{aligned}
$$

That is, the average heat transfer coefficient $h_m$ is twice the value of the local heat transfer coefficient $h_x$ evaluated at $x = L$

**EXAMPLE 7-5**  Consider laminar flow of ordinary fluid at temperature $T_\infty$ over a flat plate maintained at a uniform temperature $T_\infty$ in the region $0 \le x \le x_0$ and at a uniform temperature $T_w$ in the region $x > x_0$. That is, heat transfer between the plate and the fluid does not start until the location $x = x_0$. Determine the thermal boundary-layer thickness by an approximate integral method.

**SOLUTION**  The ratio $\delta_t(x)/\delta(x) = \Delta$ is given by Eq. (7-22h) as

$$
\Delta^3 = Cx^{-3.4} + \frac{3/5}{3/4}\frac{\alpha}{\nu}
$$

The integration constant $C$ is determined by the application of the boundary condition $\delta_t = 0$ for $x = x_0$, which is $\Delta(x) = 0$ at $x = x_0$. We find

$$
\Delta^3 = \frac{4}{5}\mathrm{Pr}^{-1}\left[1 - \left(\frac{x_0}{x}\right)^{3/4}\right]
$$

where

$$
\mathrm{Pr} = \frac{\nu}{\alpha}
$$

**EXAMPLE 7-6**  Air at atmospheric pressure and at $350$ K flows over a flat plate with a velocity of $15$ m/s. Determine the drag force per 1-m width of the plate acting over the distance $0.3$ mfrom the leading edge.

**SOLUTION**  The physical properties of atmospheric air at $350$ K are

$$
\rho = 0.998 \ kg/m^3 \quad \nu = 20.76 \times 10^{-6} \ m^2/s
$$

The Reynolds number at a distance $x = L = 0.3$ mis

$$
\mathrm{Re}_L = \frac{u_\infty L}{\nu} = \frac{(15)(0.3)}{20.76 \times 10^{-6}} = 2.17 \times 10^5
$$

This Reynolds number is less than the critical Reynolds number $\mathrm{Re}_c \cong 5 \times 10^5$; therefore the flow is laminar. The average drag coefficient $c_m$ over the length $x = 0$

to $x = L$ is given by Eq. (7-20$b$):

$$c_m = \frac{1.328}{\text{Re}_L^{1/2}} = \frac{1.328}{(2.17 \times 10^5)} = 2.85 \times 10^{-3}$$

Then the drag force acting on the plate is determined by Eq. (7-7):

$$\begin{aligned} F &= wLc_m \frac{\rho u_\infty^2}{2} = (1)(0.3)(2.85 \times 10^{-3})\frac{(0.988)(15)^2}{2} \\ &= 0.095 \text{ N} \end{aligned}$$

**EXAMPLE 7-7**   Air at atmospheric pressure and at a mean temperature of 77℃ flows over a flat plate with a velocity of 9 m/$s$. Plot the local and average heat transfer coefficients as a function of the distance from the leading edge of the plate for the laminar boundary layer.

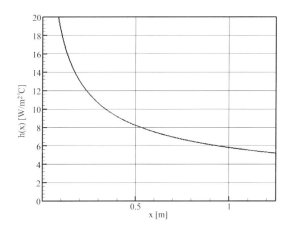

**FIGURE EXAMPLE 7-7**

**SOLUTION**   The physical properties of atmospheric air taken at atmospheric pressure and at 77℃ are as follows:

$$k = 0.03 \text{ W}/(\text{m} \cdot {}^\circ\text{C}) \quad \nu = 2.076 \times 10^{-5} \text{ m}^2/s \quad \text{Pr} = 0.697$$

For $\text{Re}_c = 5 \times 10^5$, the location $x_c$ where the transition occurs is determined as

$$x_c = \frac{\nu \text{Re}_c}{u_\infty} = \frac{(2.076 \times 10^{-5})(5 \times 10^5)}{9} = 1.153 \text{ m}$$

The local heat transfer coefficient for the laminar boundary layer is determined by

Eq. (7-24):

$$\mathrm{Nu}_x = 0.332\mathrm{Pr}^{1/3}\mathrm{Re}_x^{1/2}$$

$$\frac{xh(x)}{k} = 0.332\mathrm{Pr}^{1/3}\left(\frac{xu_\infty}{\nu}\right)^{1/2}$$

or

$$h(x) = 0.332\mathrm{Pr}^{1/3}\left(\frac{u_\infty}{\nu}\right)^{1/2} k\frac{1}{x^{1/2}}$$

$$= 0.332(0.697)\left(\frac{9}{2.076\times 10^{-5}}\right)^{1/2}(0.03)frac1x^{1/2}$$

$$= \frac{5.82}{x^{1/2}}$$

The average heat transfer coefficient over any distance from $x = 0$ to $x = l_x$ is determined by Eq. (7-14) to be

$$h_m(x = l_x) = \frac{1}{l_x}\int_0^{l_x} h(x)dx = 2h(x)|_{x=l_x}$$

or

$$h_m(x = l_x) = 2\left(\frac{5.82}{x^{1/2}}\right)\bigg|_{x=l} = \frac{11.64}{l^{1/2}}$$

A plot of $h_x$ and $h_m(x = l_x)$ is given in the accompanying figure.

**EXAMPLE 7-8** Mercury at 70°C flows with a velocity of 0.1 m/s over a 0.4-m-long flat plate maintained at 130°C. Assuming that the transition from laminar to turbulent flow takes place at $\mathrm{Re}_c = 5 \times 10^5$, determine the average heat transfer coefficient over the length of the plate.

**SOLUTION** The physical properties of the fluid are taken at the film temperature $T_f = (70 + 130)/2 = 100$°C as follows:

$$k = 10.51 \text{ W/(m}\cdot°\text{C)} \quad \nu = 0.0928 \times 10^{-6} \text{ m}^2/s \quad \mathrm{Pr} = 0.0162$$

For $\mathrm{Re}_c = 5 \times 10^5$, the location $x_c$ where the transition occurs is determined to be

$$x_c = \frac{\nu \mathrm{Re}_c}{u_\infty} = \frac{(0.0928 \times 10^{-6})(5 \times 10^5)}{0.1} = 0.464 \text{ m}$$

Hence $L = 0.4$ m $< x_c = 0.464$ mand the flow is laminar over the entire length of the plate.

The local Nusselt number for the laminar boundary layer is determined at $x = L$

by Eq. (7-28):

$$
\begin{aligned}
\mathrm{Nu}|_{x=L} &= 0.564\mathrm{Pe}^{1/2} \\
&= 0.564(\mathrm{Re}_L\mathrm{Pr})^{1/2} \\
&= 0.564\left[\frac{(0.4)(0.1)}{0.0928\times 10^{-6}}(0.0162)\right]^{1/2} = 47.13
\end{aligned}
$$

and the average Nusselt number is calculated from Eq. (7-14):

$$
\begin{aligned}
\mathrm{Nu}_m &= 2\mathrm{Nu}|_{x=L} \\
&= 2(47.13) = 94.26
\end{aligned}
$$

Then the average heat transfer coefficient over the length of the plate $L = 0.4$ m becomes

$$
\begin{aligned}
h_m &= \frac{k}{L}\mathrm{Nu}_m \\
&= \left(\frac{10.51}{0.4}\right)94.26 = 2476.64 \ \mathrm{W}/(\mathrm{m}^2\cdot{}^\circ\mathrm{C})
\end{aligned}
$$

## 7.3. TURBULENT FLOW OVER A FLAT PLATE

For forced flow over a flat plate, a transition from laminar to turbulent flow takes place in the range of Reynolds numbers from $2\times 10^5$ to $5\times 10^5$. The term *turbulent* is used to denote that the motion of the fluid is chaotic in nature and involves crosswise mixing and eddying superimposed on the motion of the mainstream.

The eddying or crosswise mixing is advantageous in that it assists greatly in improving heat transfer between the fluid and the surface of the solid body, but it has the disadvantage of increasing the drag generated by the flow.

The flow patterns in turbulent flow are so complex that most of the correlations of velocity distribution in flow are of a semiempirical nature. The local drag coefficient $c_x$ and the local heat transfer coefficient $h(x)$ are quantities of practical interest in turbulent flow over a flat plate. Here we present some of the recommended expressions for the determination of the drag and heat transfer coefficients.

### 7.3.1 Drag Coefficient

Schlichting examined a vast amount of experimental data and recommended the following correlation for the local drag coefficient $c_x$ for turbulent flow over a flat plate:

$$
\boxed{c(x) = 0.0592\mathrm{Re}_x^{-0.2}} \tag{7-29}
$$

valid for $5\times 10^5 < \mathrm{Re}_x < 10^7$.

At higher Reynolds number, the following correlation is recommended by Schultz-Grunow:

$$c(x) = 0.370(\log \text{Re}_x)^{-2.584}$$

(7-30)

valid for $10^7 < \text{Re}_x < 10^9$.

In many applications, the flow is laminar over the part of the plate surface $0 < x \leq x_c$, where $x_c$ is the location of the transition from laminar to turbulent, and turbulent over the remaining region $x_c < x \leq L$. The drag coefficient for the laminar region was given previously by Eq. (7-19a), and for the turbulent flow region Eq. (7-29) can be used. Then the mean drag coefficient $c_m$ over the entire region $0 < x < L$ can be determined by proper averaging of these two local drag coefficients. The resulting expression for the average drag coefficient $c_m$ becomes

$$c_m = 0.074\text{Re}_L^{-0.2} \frac{B}{\text{Re}_L} \quad \text{for } \text{Re}_c < \text{Re}_L < 10^7$$

(7-31)

which is valid over the entire region of laminar and turbulent flow. The value of $B$ depends on the value of the critical Reynolds number $\text{Re}_c$ chosen for the transition from laminar flow; corresponding values are listed below:

$$
\begin{aligned}
B &= 700 & \text{for } Re_c &= 2 \times 10^5 \\
B &= 1050 & \text{for } Re_c &= 3 \times 10^5 \\
B &= 1740 & \text{for } Re_c &= 5 \times 10^5 \\
B &= 3340 & \text{for } Re_c &= 1 \times 10^6
\end{aligned}
$$

**RELATION BETWEEN $c(x)$ AND $h(x)$.** The drag and heat transfer coefficients for laminar flow over a flat plate can readily be determined by theoretical means; but this is not quite true for the case of turbulent flow. Therefore, the drag and heat transfer coefficients for turbulent flow are generally determined by experimental means. It is easier to measure the drag force than the heat transfer coefficient. Furthermore, correlations are generally available for the determination of the drag coefficient in turbulent flow. Therefore, efforts have been directed toward developing relations between the drag coefficient and the heat transfer coefficient so that $h(x)$ can be determined once $c(x)$ is known.

One such relation is given in the form

$$\text{St}_x \text{Pr}^{2/3} = \frac{1}{2}c(x)$$

(7-32a)

where $\text{St}_x$ is the *local Stanton number*, defined as

$$\text{St}_x = \frac{\text{Nu}_x}{\text{Pr} \, \text{Re}_x}$$

(7-32b)

and $\mathrm{Nu}_x$, Pr, and $\mathrm{Re}_x$ are as given by Eq. (7-24$b$). The relationship in Eq. (7-32$a$) is referred to as the *Reynolds-Colburn* analogy between the drag and heat transfer coefficients.

## 7.3.2 Heat Transfer Coefficient

We now make use of the Reynolds-Colburn analogy to develop expressions for the heat transfer coefficient $h(x)$ from the knowledge of the drag coefficient for turbulent flow over a flat plate.

Equations (7-29) and (7-30) give the local drag coefficient in turbulent flow. They can be used in Eqs. (7-32) to develop expressions for the local heat transfer coefficient for turbulent flow over a flat plate. The use of Eq. (7-29) gives

$$\boxed{\mathrm{Nu}_x = 0.0296\mathrm{Re}_x^{0.8}\mathrm{Pr}^{1/3}} \quad \text{for } 5 \times 10^5 < \mathrm{Re}_x < 10^7 \tag{7-33}$$

and Eq. (7-30) yields

$$\boxed{\mathrm{Nu}_x = 0.185\mathrm{Re}_x(\log\mathrm{Re}_x)^{-2.584}\mathrm{Pr}^{1/3}} \quad \text{for } 10^7 < \mathrm{Re}_x < 10^9 \tag{7-34}$$

where

$$\mathrm{Re}_x = \frac{u_\infty x}{\nu} \quad \mathrm{Pr} = \frac{\nu}{\alpha} \quad \mathrm{Nu}_x = \frac{h(x)x}{k}$$

and all properties are evaluated at the *film temperature*.

The following expression for the local heat transfer coefficient in turbulent flow over a flat plate has been proposed [Whitaker, 1976]:

$$\boxed{\mathrm{Nu}_x = 0.0298\mathrm{Re}_x^{0.8}\mathrm{Pr}^{0.43}} \quad \text{for } 2 \times 10^5 < \mathrm{Re}_x < 5 \times 10^5 \tag{7-35}$$

where all properties are evaluated at the film temperature. A large number of experimental data are found to correlate well with this expression.

In most practical applications the flow is *laminar* over a portion $0 < x < x_c$ of the plate and turbulent over the remaining portion $x_c < x < L$ of the plate, where $x_c$ is the location of the transition from laminar to turbulent flow. The average value of the heat transfer coefficient $h_m$ over the entire region $0 < x < L$ can be determined by properly averaging the local heat transfer coefficients for the laminar and turbulent flow regions. Taking the local heat transfer coefficients from Eqs. (7-24$a$) and (7-35) for the laminar- and turbulent-flow regions, respectively, averaging them properly, and assuming that the transition from laminar to turbulent flow takes place at a critical Reynolds number $\mathrm{Re}_c = 2 \times 10^5$, the following expression is obtained for the average Nusselt number applicable over the entire region $0 < x < L$:

$$\boxed{\mathrm{Nu}_m = 0.036\mathrm{Pr}^{0.43}(\mathrm{Re}_L^{0.8} - 17,400) + 297\mathrm{Pr}^{1/3}} \tag{7-36}$$

The last term on the right-hand side can be approximated as

$$297\text{Pr}^{1/3} \cong 297\text{Pr}^{0.43}$$

and the viscosity correction can be introduced by multiplying the right-hand side of the resulting expression by $(\mu_\infty/\mu_w)^{0.25}$. Then the following equation is obtained:

$$\text{Nu}_m = 0.036\text{Pr}^{0.43}(\text{Re}_L^{0.8} - 9200)\left(\frac{\mu_\infty}{\mu_w}\right)^{0.25} \qquad (7\text{-}37)$$

All physical properties are evaluated at the free-stream temperature except $\mu_w$, which is evaluated at the wall temperature. The viscosity correction factor takes care of the effects of the property variation with temperature in liquids. For gases, the viscosity correction is neglected, and for such a case the physical properties are evaluated at the film temperature.

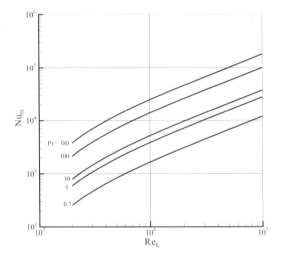

**FIG. 7.5.** Average Nusselt number (Eq. 7-37) for turbulent flow over a flat plate.

The relation given by Eq. (7-37) is plotted in Fig. 7.5 as a function of the Reynolds number $\text{Re}_L$ for several different values of the Prandtl number. This figure also shows the average drag coefficient determined from Eq. (7-13).

Equation (7-37) gives the average Nusselt number over the laminar and turbulent boundary layers over a flat plate for $\text{Re}_L > 2 \times 10^5$. It has been proposed to correlate the experimental data for air, water, and oil covering the following ranges:

$$2 \times 10^5 < \text{Re}_L < 5.5 \times 10^6$$
$$0.70 < \text{Pr} < 380$$
$$0.26 < \left(\frac{\mu_\infty}{\mu_w}\right)^{0.25} < 3.5$$

Equation (7-37) correlates the experimental data reasonably well when the free-stream turbulence is small. If high-level turbulence is present in the free stream, Eq. (7-37) without the constant 9200 correlates the data reasonably well.

**EXAMPLE 7-9** Atmospheric air at $T_\infty = 40°C$ with a free-stream velocity $u_\infty = 8 \text{ m/s}$ flows along a flat plate $L = 3$ mlong which is maintained at a uniform temperature of $100°C$. Calculate the average heat transfer coefficient over the entire length of the plate. Assume that transition occurs at $\text{Re}_c = 2 \times 10^5$.

**SOLUTION** The physical properties of atmospheric air at $T_f = (T_w + T_\infty)/2 = (100 + 40)/2 = 70°C$ are taken as follows:

$$
\begin{aligned}
k &= 0.0295 \text{ W/(m} \cdot \text{K)} \\
\nu &= 2.005 \times 10^{-5} \text{ m}^2/s \\
\text{Pr} &= 0.699
\end{aligned}
$$

The Reynolds number at $L = 3$ mis

$$
\text{Re}_L = \frac{u_\infty L}{\nu} = \frac{8 \times 3}{2.005 \times 10^{-5}} = 1.2 \times 10^6
$$

The average heat transfer coefficient over $L = 3$ m, without the viscosity correction, is determined from Eq. (7-37) as

$$
\begin{aligned}
\text{Nu}_m &= 0.036\text{Pr}^{0.43}[\text{Re}_L^{0.8} - 9200] \\
&= 0.036(0.699)^{0.43}[(1.2 \times 10^6)^{0.8} - 9200] \\
&= 1969
\end{aligned}
$$

$$
\begin{aligned}
h_m &= \frac{k}{L}\text{Nu}_m = \frac{0.0295}{3}1969 \\
&= 19.4 \text{ W/(m}^2 \cdot °\text{C)}
\end{aligned}
$$

Here the physical properties are evaluated at the film temperature because the viscosity correction is neglected. We note that when the viscosity correction needs to be included, the physical properties are evaluated at the free-stream temperature.

**EXAMPLE 7-10** Calculate the total heat transfer rate $Q$ from the plate of Example 7-9 to the air over the length $L = 3$ mand width $w = 1$ m.

**SOLUTION** The heat transfer rate is

$$
\begin{aligned}
Q &= wLh_m(T_w - T_\infty) \\
&= (1)(3)(19.4)(100 - 40) \\
&= 3492 \text{ W}
\end{aligned}
$$

## 7.4. FLOW ACROSS A SINGLE CIRCULAR CYLINDER

Flow across a single circular cylinder is frequently encountered in practice, but the determination of the heat transfer coefficient is a very complicated matter because of the complexity of the flow patterns around the cylinder. Figure 7.6 illustrates with sketches

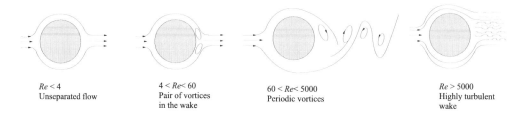

| $Re < 4$ | $4 < Re < 60$ | $60 < Re < 5000$ | $Re > 5000$ |
| Unseparated flow | Pair of vortices in the wake | Periodic vortices | Highly turbulent wake |

**FIG. 7.6.** Flow around a circular cylinder at various Reynolds numbers.

the flow characteristics around a circular cylinder. The magnitude of the Reynolds number,

$$\text{Re} = \frac{u_\infty D}{\nu} \tag{7-38}$$

affects the formation of various types of flow patterns. Here the Reynolds number is based on the diameter $D$ of the cylinder. For a Reynolds number less than about 4, the flow around the cylinder remains unseparated, and the flow patterns are relatively simple. At a Reynolds number of about 4, vortices start to form in the wake region, and for $Re > 4$ the flow patterns become very complicated. The local drag and heat transfer coefficients vary around the circumference of the cylinder.

In most engineering applications the average values of the drag and heat transfer coefficients over the circumference are of interest. Therefore, we focus our attention on the determination of the average drag and heat transfer coefficients.

### 7.4.1 Average Drag Coefficient

Consider the flow of a fluid with a free-stream velocity $u_\infty$ across a single circular tube of diameter $D$ and length $L$. The drag force $F$ acting on the tube is of interest in many engineering applications. To calculate this drag force $F$, an *average drag coefficient* $c_D$ is defined as

$$\boxed{\frac{F}{LD} = c_D \frac{\rho u_\infty^2}{2}} \tag{7-39}$$

Here $LD$ represents the area normal to the flow; the density $\rho$ and the free-stream velocity $u_\infty$ are known. Then, given $c_D$, the drag force $F$ acting over the length $L$ of the tube can be readily determined from Eq. (7-39). The drag coefficients $c_D$ for flow across single cylinder and also other noncircular long cylinder of various geometries are studied in fluid mechanics books [given by Schlichting].

## 7.4.2 Average Heat Transfer Coefficient

The average heat transfer coefficient $h_m$ for flow across a single cylinder has been studied experimentally by various investigators using a variety of fluids, such as air, water, paraffin, transformer oil, liquid sodium, and many others, covering a wide range of Prandtl numbers. Therefore there are several correlations available for the determination of $h_m$.

A sufficiently general correlation for $h_m$ is given in the form

$$\text{Nu}_m = 0.3 + \frac{0.62\text{Re}^{1/2}\text{Pr}^{1/3}}{[1 + (0.4/\text{Pr})^{2/3}]^{1/4}}\left[1 + \left(\frac{\text{Re}}{282,000}\right)^{5/8}\right]^{4/5} \quad \begin{array}{l} \text{for Re Pr} > 0.2 \text{ and} \\ 10^2 < \text{Re} < 10^7 \end{array}$$

(7-40)

Equation (7-40) underpredicts most data by about 20 percent in the range $20,000 < \text{Re} < 400,000$. Therefore, for this particular range of Reynolds numbers, the following modified form of Eq. (7-40) is recommended.

$$\text{Nu}_m = 0.3 + \frac{0.62\text{Re}^{1/2}\text{Pr}^{1/3}}{[1 + (0.4/\text{Pr})^{2/3}]^{1/4}}\left[1 + \left(\frac{\text{Re}}{282,000}\right)^{1/2}\right] \quad \begin{array}{l} \text{for Re Pr} > 0.2 \text{ and} \\ (2 < \text{Re} < 40) \times 10^5 \end{array}$$

(7-41)

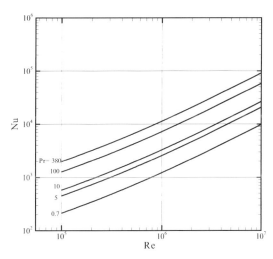

**FIG. 7.7.** Average Nusselt number (Eq. 7-40) as a function of Reynolds number for flow across a single circular cylinder.

For ready reference, the expression given by Eq. (7-40) is plotted in Fig. 7.7 as a function of the Reynolds number $Re$ for several different values of the Prandtl number. For the Peclet number less than 0.2, the following expression can be used:

$$\text{Nu}_m = (0.8237 - \ln\text{Pe}^{1/2})^{-1} \quad \text{for Pe} < 0.2$$

(7-42)

In the above relations all properties are to be evaluated at the *film temperature* $T_f =$

$(T_w + T_\infty)/2$, and the Reynolds and Peclet numbers are defined as

$$\text{Re} = \frac{u_\infty D}{\nu} \tag{7-43a}$$

$$\text{Pe} = \text{Re} \, \text{Pr} = \frac{u_\infty D}{\alpha} \tag{7-43b}$$

where $D$ is the tube diameter, $\alpha$ is the thermal diffusivity of the fluid , and $u_\infty$ is the free stream velocity.

### 7.4.3 Variation of $h(\theta)$ around the Cylinder

In the above discussion we focused our attention on the determination of the average value of the heat transfer coefficient for the cylinder. Actually, the local value of the heat transfer coefficient $h(\theta)$ varies with the angle $\theta$ around the cylinder as illustrated by Fig. 7.8. It has a fairly high value at the *stagnation point* $\theta = 0$ and decreases around the cylinder as the boundary layer thickens. The decrease of the heat transfer coefficient is continuous until the boundary layer separates from the wall surface or the laminar boundary layer changes to turbulent; then an increase occurs with the distance around the cylinder. The an approximate variation of the local heat transfer coefficient $h(\theta)$ with $\theta$ around a circular cylinder has been investigated. In order to give some idea of the variation, $h(\theta)$ plotted against the angle $\theta$ measured from the stagnation point, is presented in Fig. 7.9 for a fixed value of several Reynolds number. The flow mechanism around the cylinder must

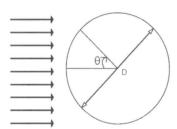

**FIG. 7.8.** Schematics of flow of air around a circular cylinder.

be complicated because $h(\theta)$ exhibits several maxima and minima at different locations which vary with the Reynolds number. For example, in the curve for Re= $140,000$, the first minimum occurs at the transition from the laminar to the turbulent boundary layer at an angle $\theta \cong 80°$; the second minimum occurs at $\theta \cong 130°$, where flow separation takes place.

**EXAMPLE 7-11**   Atmospheric air at $T_\infty = -5°C$ and a free-stream velocity $u_\infty = 6 \text{ m}/s$ flows across a single tube of outside diameter $D = 25$ cm. The tube's surface is kept at a uniform temperature $T_w = 180°C$. Determine the average heat transfer coefficient.

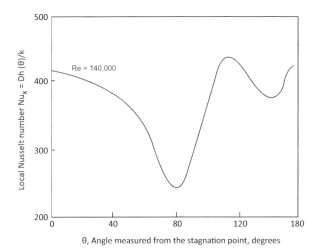

**FIG. 7.9.** Variation of the local heat transfer coefficient $h(\theta)$ around a circular cylinder for flow of air.

**SOLUTION** The physical properties of air at the film temperature $T_f = (T_w + T_\infty)/2 = (-5 + 180)/2 = 87.5°C$ are

$$k = 0.0308 \text{ W}/(\text{m} \cdot °\text{C}) \quad \text{Pr} = 0.695 \quad \nu = 2.184 \times 10^{-5} \text{ m}^2/s$$

The Reynolds number becomes

$$\text{Re} = \frac{u_\infty D}{\nu} = \frac{6 \times 0.25}{2.184 \times 10^{-5}} = 6.868 \times 10^4$$

Equation (7-41) is applied to calculate $h_m$:

$$\begin{aligned}
\text{Nu}_m &= 0.3 + \frac{0.62\text{Re}^{1/2}\text{Pr}^{1/3}}{[1 + (0.4/\text{Pr})^{2/3}]^{1/4}} \left[1 + \left(\frac{\text{Re}}{282,000}\right)^{1/2}\right] \\
&= 188.9
\end{aligned}$$

$$\begin{aligned}
h_m &= \frac{k}{D}\text{Nu}_m = \frac{0.0308}{0.25} \times 188.8 \\
&= 23.3 \text{ W}/(\text{m}^2 \cdot °\text{C})
\end{aligned}$$

**EXAMPLE 7-12** Calculate the rate of heat loss from a 1-m length of the tube of Example 7-11 into the air.

**SOLUTION** The heat loss to the air becomes

$$\begin{aligned}
Q &= h_m(\pi D L)(T_w - T_\infty) \\
&= 23.3(\pi)(-0.25)(1)[180 - (-5)] = 3385 \text{ W}
\end{aligned}$$

## 7.5. FLOW ACROSS A SINGLE NONCIRCULAR CYLINDER

The results of experiments to determine the average heat transfer coefficient $h_m$ for the flow of gases across a single, noncircular, long cylinder of various geometries have been correlated through the following simple relationship [Jacob]:

$$\text{Nu}_m = \frac{h_m D_e}{k} = c\left(\frac{u_\infty D_e}{\nu}\right)^n = c(Re)^n \tag{7-44}$$

where the constant $c$, the exponent $n$, and the characteristic dimension $D_e$ for various geometries are presented in Table 7.1. The physical properties of the fluid are evaluated at the arithmetic mean of the free-stream and wall temperatures.

**EXAMPLE 7-13**   Atmospheric air at $T_\infty = 27°C$ with a free-stream velocity of $u_\infty = 10$ m/s flows across a square duct of 12.5 cm by 12.5 cm cross section oriented such that one of its lateral surfaces is perpendicular to the direction of flow. The duct's surface is kept at a uniform temperature $T_w = 100°C$. Determine the average heat transfer coefficient.

**SOLUTION**   The physical properties of air at the film temperature $T_f = (T_w + T_\infty)/2 = (100 + 27)/2 = 63.5°C$ are

$$k = 0.029 \text{W}/(\text{m} \cdot °\text{C}) \quad \text{Pr} = 0.7 \quad \nu = 1.94 \times 10^{-5} \text{ m}^2/s$$

The Reynolds number becomes

$$\begin{aligned}
\text{Re} &= \frac{u_\infty D}{\nu} = \frac{10 \times 0.125}{1.94 \times 10^{-5}} \\
&= 6443
\end{aligned}$$

We use Eq. (7-44) with Table 7.1 to determine

$$\begin{aligned}
\text{Nu}_m &= c\text{Re}^n = 0.092(6443)^{0.675} \\
&= 34.3 \\
h_m &= \frac{k}{D}\text{Nu}_m = \frac{0.029}{0.125}(34.3) \\
&= 7.96 \text{ W}/(\text{m}^2 \cdot °\text{C})
\end{aligned}$$

**EXAMPLE 7-14**   Calculate the heat transfer rate from the duct to the air per meter length of the duct of Example 7-13.

**SOLUTION**   The heat transfer rate becomes

$$\begin{aligned}
Q &= h_m(4D_e L)(T_w - T_\infty) \\
&= 80.5(4 \times 0.012 \times 1)(100 - 27) \\
&= 282 \text{ W}
\end{aligned}$$

**TABLE 7.1 The constant and the exponent of Eq. (7-44).**

| Flow direction and geometry | $Re = \dfrac{u_\infty D_e}{\nu}$ | $n$ | $c$ |
|---|---|---|---|
| $u_\infty \rightarrow$ ◇ $D_e$ | 5,000–100,000 | 0.588 | 0.222 |
| $u_\infty \rightarrow$ ⬭ $D_e$ | 2,500–15,000 | 0.612 | 0.224 |
| $u_\infty \rightarrow$ ◇ $D_e$ | 2,500–7,500 | 0.624 | 0.261 |
| $u_\infty \rightarrow$ ⬡ $D_e$ | 5,000–100,000 | 0.638 | 0.138 |
| $u_\infty \rightarrow$ ⬡ $D_e$ | 5,000–19,500 | 0.638 | 0.144 |
| $u_\infty \rightarrow$ ☐ $D_e$ | 5,000–100,000 | 0.675 | 0.092 |
| $u_\infty \rightarrow$ ☐ $D_e$ | 2,500–8,000 | 0.699 | 0.160 |
| $u_\infty \rightarrow$ \| $D_e$ | 4,000–15,000 | 0.731 | 0.205 |
| $u_\infty \rightarrow$ ⬡ $D_e$ | 19,500–100,000 | 0.782 | 0.035 |
| $u_\infty \rightarrow$ ◯ $D_e$ | 3,000–15,000 | 0.804 | 0.085 |

## 7.6. FLOW ACROSS A SINGLE SPHERE

The basic characteristics of flow over a single sphere are somewhat similar to those for flow over a single circular tube, shown in Fig. 7.6. Therefore, the variation of the drag and heat transfer coefficients with the Reynolds number is expected to be similar to that for a single circular cylinder. The drag and heat transfer coefficients vary with the position around the sphere. Here we are concerned only with the average values of the drag and heat transfer coefficient over the entire sphere surface, because they are the quantities of interest in most engineering applications.

### 7.6.1 Average Drag Coefficient

Consider a fluid flowing with a free-stream velocity $u_\infty$ over a single sphere of diameter $D$. The drag force $F$ exerted by flow on the sphere is related to the *average drag coefficient* $c_D$ in the form

$$\boxed{\frac{F}{A} = c_D \frac{\rho u_\infty^2}{2}} \tag{7-45}$$

where $A$ is the frontal area (that is, $A = \pi D^2/4$) and $u_\infty$ is the free-stream velocity. We note that $F/A$ is the drag force per unit frontal area of the sphere. The average drag coefficient $c_D$ plotted as a function of the Reynolds number for flow across single sphere and also other various geometries are studied in fluid mechanics books [given by Schlichting].

## 7.6.2 Average Heat Transfer Coefficients

A sufficiently general correlation for the average heat transfer coefficient $h_m$ for flow across a single sphere is given by [Whitaker, 1972]

$$\text{Nu}_m = 2 + (0.4\text{Re}^{0.5} + 0.06\text{Re}^{2/3})\text{Pr}^{0.4} \left(\frac{\mu_\infty}{\mu_w}\right)^{0.25} \tag{7-46}$$

which is valid over the ranges

$$3.5 < \text{Re} < 8 \times 10^4$$
$$0.7 < \text{Pr} < 380$$
$$1 < \frac{\mu_\infty}{\mu_w} < 3.2$$

with the physical properties evaluated at the free-stream temperature, except for $\mu_w$, which is evaluated at the wall temperature. For gases the viscosity correction is neglected, but the physical properties are evaluated at the film temperature. Here the Reynolds number is defined as

$$\text{Re} = \frac{u_\infty D}{\nu}$$

where $D$ is the diameter of the sphere and $u_\infty$ is the free-stream velocity. For ready reference, the expression given by Eq. (7-46) is plotted in Fig. 7.10 as a function of the Reynolds number Re for several different values of the Prandtl number.

**EXAMPLE 7-15**  Water at $T_\infty = 20°C$ flows with a free-stream velocity of $u_\infty = 1$ m/s over a 2.5-cm-diameter sphere whose surface is maintained at a uniform temperature of $T_w = 140°C$. Determine the average heat transfer coefficient.

**SOLUTION**  The physical properties of water at the free-stream temperature $T_\infty = 20°C$ are as follows

$$\begin{aligned} k &= 0.597 \text{ W}/(\text{m} \cdot °\text{C}) \quad \text{Pr} = 7.02 \\ \nu &= 1.006 \times 10^{-6} \text{ m}^2/s \\ \mu_\infty &= 1.006 \times 10^{-3} \text{ kg}/(\text{m} \cdot s) \end{aligned}$$

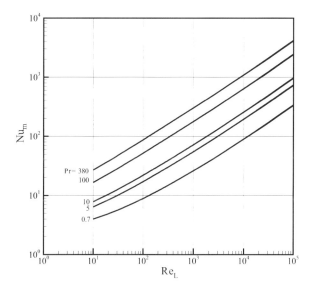

**FIG. 7.10.** Average Nusselt number (Eq. 7-46) as a function of Reynolds number for flow across a single sphere.

and the viscosity of water at $T_w = 140°C$ is

$$\mu_w = 0.198 \times 10^{-3} \text{ kg}/(\text{m} \cdot s)$$

The Reynolds number becomes

$$\begin{aligned}
\text{Re} &= \frac{u_\infty D}{\nu} = \frac{1 \times 0.025}{1.006 \times 10^{-6}} \\
&= 24,850
\end{aligned}$$

We use Eq. (7-46) to determine $\text{Nu}_m$:

$$\begin{aligned}
\text{Nu}_m &= 2 + (0.4\text{Re}^{0.5} + 0.06\text{Re}^{2/3})\text{Pr}^{0.4}\left(\frac{\mu_\infty}{\mu_w}\right)^{0.25} \\
&= 375.1
\end{aligned}$$

$$\begin{aligned}
h_m &= \frac{k}{D}\text{Nu}_m = \frac{0.597}{0.025}(375.1) \\
&= 8958 \text{ W}/(\text{m}^2 \cdot °\text{C})
\end{aligned}$$

**EXAMPLE 7-16** Calculate the heat loss from the sphere of Example 7-15 to the air.

**SOLUTION** The heat loss becomes

$$\begin{aligned}
Q &= h_m(\pi D^2)(T_w - T_\infty) \\
&= 8958(\pi \times 0.025^2)(140 - 20) = 2111 \text{ W}
\end{aligned}$$

## 7.7. NANOFLUID FLOWS OVER A FLAT PLATE

The nanofluid technology has been studied and developed by many research groups. Some have tried to develop mathematical models that empirically relate the Nusselt number (and hence the heat transfer coefficient) to nanofluid flow parameters, but a sophisticated theory is still lacking. Despite the positive results from existing research, further research is required to develop accurate empirical mathematic models for general fluid flow parameters.

The enhanced thermal conductivity discussed in Chapter 1 does account for a significant part of the enhanced heat transfer coefficient, however it does not explain the entire increase. The unusually high increase in nanofluid heat transfer coefficient is due to several physical mechanisms. The *Brownian motion* of the nanoparticles is responsible for transferring energy from the hotter regions of the fluid to cooler ones. Since Brownian motion increases with temperature, its effect also explains the rise in the heat transfer coefficient with a rise in temperature. The movement of the particles in a mixture of two or more types of particles in the direction of decreasing temperature is another physical mechanism which is called the *thermophoresis*. The heat transfer coefficient increases due to reduction of the viscosity within the boundary layer. The *diffusiophoresis*, or the migration of particles from a higher concentration region to a lower concentration region, is another explanatory mechanism that needs to be accounted for. Nanoparticles also enhance the turbulence resulting in an increase in the heat transfer coefficient.

The models approach nanofluid systems in one of two ways. The first approach considers the dispersed phase to be fine enough and distributed uniformly enough to approximate the entire system as a single-phase fluid. This approach is not well-equipped to handle the effect of the physical phenomena described , and results in numerical predictions that are not in good agreement with experimental data. The second approach considers nanofluids to be two-phase systems affected, to varying extents, by gravity, Brownian motion, sedimentation, and other phenomena.

Effects of particle volume concentration, particle material, particle size, particle shape, base fluid material and temperature on heat transfer enhancement are investigated for flow over flat plates. Although the heat transfer data were partially inconclusive or conflicting, the heat transfer enhancement is observed. We can use the selected existing correlation equations for the Nusselt number. The simplest correlation calculations are based on the enhancement in the heat transfer using the newly developed effective thermophysical properties for that specific flow. The main idea is that the nanofluids are assumed to behave more like single-phase fluids than like conventional solid-liquid mixtures. Therefore, the convective heat transfer correlations available in the literature for single-phase flows are used provided that the the nanofluid effective thermophysical properties calculated at the reference temperature are used.

### 7.7.1 Nanofluid Flows over a Flat Plate

Prakash and Giannelis (2004) studied the thermal conductivity of alumina nanofluids by using temperature and concentration dependent viscosity. According to Prakash and Giannelis, the increase of thermal conductivity in nanofluids depends on temperature variations, viscosity, and the Brownian effect. For this reason, they modified the Brownian motion model developed by Prasher, Bhattacharya and Phelan (2005), for laminar flow over flat plates and suggested a new model called the Nanolayer Brownian motion model. This improved model adds nanolayer structure to the previously mentioned Brownian motion model, and is formulated as:

$$k_{nf} = \left(\frac{1+3\theta}{1-\theta}\right)\left(1 + ARe^m Pr^{0.33}\phi\right)k_f \qquad \text{(7-47a)}$$

where

$$\theta = \beta_{\ell f}\frac{(1+\gamma)^3 - (\beta_{p\ell}/\beta_{f\ell})}{(1+\gamma)^3 + 2\beta_{\ell f}/\beta_{p\ell}} \qquad \text{(7-47b)}$$

and $\gamma$ is the ratio of nanolayer thickness to the original particle radius. The three different $\beta s$ stand for thermal conductivities of nanofluids, nanolayers, and nanoparticles, respectively. $k_{nf}$ refer to the effective thermal conductivity of nanofluids including the convective effects, and $k_f$ represents thermal conductivity of base fluids. **A** and **m** parameters depend on the nature of the nanoparticles and fluids, and originate from experimental studies. Finally, $\phi$ is the volume concentration of the nanoparticles. According to this model, theoretical studies show that an increase in thermal conductivity depends on the Re number, and, as mentioned in previous studies, cylindrical shaped particles give better results for thermal conductivity increase. In this study, the particle size was less than $100nm$, and it was concluded that thermal conductivity is related to particle size, concentration of nanoparticles, temperature, viscosity, and Brownian motion. In the literature, generally, $m$ is between 2 to 2.5 (depends on the $\phi$) and $A$ is assumed to be $40,000$.

For the ratio of nanolayer thickness and the definition of different $\beta s$ we refer to Xie, Fujii and Zhang (2005) According to Xie et al, ratio of nanolayer thickness is defined in the following format

$$\gamma = \frac{\delta}{r_p}$$

where $\delta$ is the nanolayer thickness and $r_p$ is the particle radius. The $\beta s$ are given as

$$\beta_{\ell f} = \frac{k_1 - k_f}{k_1 + 2k_f}$$

$$\beta_{p\ell} = \frac{k_p - k_1}{k_p + 2k_1}$$

$$\beta_{f\ell} = \frac{k_f - k_1}{k_f + 2k_1}$$

where subscript $p$ and $f$ stands for nanoparticle and base fluid respectively and $k_1$ is the average thermal conductivity of nanolayer given below

$$k_1 = \frac{k_f M^2}{(M - \gamma)ln(1 + M) + \gamma M}$$

where we define

$$M = \epsilon_p(1 + \gamma) - 1$$
$$\epsilon_p = \frac{k_p}{k_f}$$

Here $\epsilon$ is the reduced thermal conductivity of the nanoparticles.

Although effective properties are suggested to be used with the existing Nusselt number correlation equations for the base flow over flat plates, and several correlation equations for the Nusselt number for a specific nanofluid flows are developed and currently developing.

$$\boxed{\rho_{nf} = (1 - \varphi)\rho_f + \varphi\rho_p} \tag{7-48}$$

$$\boxed{\mu_{nf} = \frac{1}{(1 - \varphi)^{2.5}}\mu_f} \tag{7-49}$$

**EXAMPLE 7-17**  An $Al_2O_3$/ water nanofluid flows over a horizontal plate. The length of the plate is 1 $m$ along the flow direction. Calculate the density, the thermal conductivity and the heat transfer coefficient for a given particle with volume concentration of $\varphi = 2\%$. Assume $\delta = 2\ nm$, $r_p = 19\ nm$, $Re = 0.015$, $Pr = 5.49$. Use the Prakash and Giannelis correlations to calculate the thermal conductivity with $A = 40,000$ and $m = 2.25$. The density and thermal conductivity of water are 992.2 $kg/m^3$ and 0.6 $W/m°C$, and the density and thermal conductivity of alumina are $3,900\ kg/m^3$ and 35.5 $W/m°C$, respectively.

**SOLUTION**  The properties for $Al_2O_3$/ water nanofluid need to be calculated. Density can be calculated using the classical formulas derived for a two-phase mixture as a function of particle volume concentration

$$\rho_p = 3.9\,\text{g/cm}^3 = 3900\ \text{kg/m}^3$$
$$\rho_f = 992.2\ \text{kg/m}^3$$
$$\rho_{nf} = (1 - \varphi)\rho_f + \varphi\rho_p$$
$$\rho_{nf} = (1 - 0.02)992.2 + (0.02)(3900) \approx 1050\ \text{kg/m}^3$$

where subscripts nf, f and p stand for nanofluid, base fluid and nanoparticle, respectively. The ratio of nanolayer thickness is

$$\gamma = \frac{\delta}{r_p} = \frac{2}{19}$$

Knowing the thermal conductivities of the nanoparticle $k_p$ and the water (base fluid) $k_f$, the reduced thermal conductivity of nanoparticle $\epsilon_p$ and $M$ parameter are calculated as

$$\epsilon_p = \frac{k_p}{k_f} = \frac{35.5}{0.6} = 59.2$$

$$M = \epsilon_p(1+\gamma) - 1 = 59.2\left(1 + \frac{2}{19}\right) - 1 = 64.4$$

In order to calculate $\beta s$, parameter $k_1$ is calculated first

$$
\begin{aligned}
k_1 &= \frac{k_f M^2}{(M-\gamma)ln(1+M) + \gamma M} \\
&= \frac{(0.6)(64.4)^2}{\left(64.4 - \frac{2}{19}\right)ln(1+64.4) + \left(\frac{2}{19}\cdot 64.4\right)} \\
&= 9.03
\end{aligned}
$$

Then the three different $\beta s$ are

$$
\begin{aligned}
\beta_{\ell f} &= \frac{k_1 - k_f}{k_1 + 2k_f} = \frac{9.03 - 0.6}{9.03 + 2(0.6)} = 0.82 \\
\beta_{p\ell} &= \frac{k_p - k_1}{k_p + 2k_1} = \frac{35.5 - 9.03}{35.5 + 2(9.03)} = 0.49 \\
\beta_{f\ell} &= \frac{k_f - k_1}{k_f + 2k_1} = \frac{0.6 - 9.03}{0.6 + 2(9.03)} = -0.45
\end{aligned}
$$

If we substitude these numbers into Eqs. (7.47), thermal conductivity of nanofluid is calculated as

$$\theta = 0.82\left[\left(1 + \frac{2}{19}\right)^3 - \left(\frac{0.49}{-0.45}\right)\right] \bigg/ \left[\left(1 + \frac{2}{19}\right)^3 + 2\left(\frac{0.82}{0.49}\right)\right] = 0.425$$

$$k_{nf} = \left(\frac{1 + 3(0.425)}{1 - 0.425}\right)\left(1 + 40000(0.015)^{2.25}(5.49)^{0.33}(0.02)\right)(0.6) = 2.64$$

Similarly the heat transfer coefficient from the Nu number correlation equation is calculated by using Eq. (7.26-a and b)

$$Nu_{nf} = 0.664 Re_{nf}^{1/2} Pr_{nf}^{1/3} = 0.664(0.015)^{1/2}(5.49)^{1/3} = 0.143$$

$$h = \frac{k}{L} Nu = \frac{2.64}{1}(0.143) = 0.3775 \text{ W}/(\text{m}^2 \,{}^\circ\text{C}).$$

## 7.8. MASS TRANSFER

In several engineering applications such as in transpiration cooling or in high-temperature gas-cooled nuclear reactors, mass transfer takes place through a fluid stream that is in laminar or turbulent flow. When the concentration of mass in the fluid stream is very small, the mass transfer to and from the fluid stream is governed by the mass conservation. The similarity between the heat flux

$$q/(\rho c) = -\alpha \, \partial T / \partial x$$

and the mass flux

$$n_A \Big|_{\text{wall}} = -D^* \frac{\partial c_A}{\partial r} \Big|_{\text{wall}}$$

is well established. The mathematical formulation of the mass transfer problem for low concentrations to and from fluid streams is analogous to heat transfer problems to and from fluid streams. In mass transfer, the mass concentration $c_A$ replaces the temperature $T$ and the mass diffusivity $D^*$ replaces the heat diffusivity $\alpha$. The similarity between heat and mass transfer is valid both for the laminar and the turbulent flows. Therefore, *when the concentration of mass in the fluid stream is very small*, various expressions given in this book for heat transfer from laminar and turbulent flows become applicable to mass transfer.

A *mass transfer coefficient* $k_m$ for the transfer of a species $A$ between the fluid stream and the wall surface is defined, in analogy with the heat transfer coefficient, as

$$n_A = k_m(c_{Am} - c_{Aw}) \tag{7-50}$$

where
$$
\begin{aligned}
c_{Am} &= \text{mean concentration } A \text{ in bulk fluid, kg} \cdot \text{mol}/\text{m}^3 \\
c_{Aw} &= \text{concentration } A \text{ at immediate vicinity of wall surface, kg} \cdot \text{mol}/\text{m}^3 \\
n_A &= \text{mass flux of } A \text{ to the wall, kg} \cdot \text{mol}/(\text{m}^2 \cdot \text{s}) \\
k_m &= \text{mass transfer coefficient for } A, \text{ m/s}
\end{aligned}
$$

The forced convection heat transfer for boundary-layer flow problems, the *Nusselt number* is defined as

$$\text{Nu}_x = \frac{hx}{k} \tag{7-51}.$$

For the mass transfer in boundary-layer flow problems the *Sherwood number* Sh is defined as

$$\text{Sh}_x = \frac{k_m x}{D^*} \qquad (7\text{-}52)$$

where

$D^*$ = mass diffusivity
$x$ = distance along plate

In forced-convection heat transfer, the Nusselt number for heat transfer in incompressible flows is a function of Reynolds and Prandtl numbers, given by

$$\text{Nu} = f(\text{Re}, \text{Pr}) \qquad (7\text{-}53)$$

Similarily for mass transfer from an incompressible flow the Sherwood number is a function of Reynolds and Schmidt numbers, that is,

$$\text{Sh} = f(\text{Re}, \text{Sc}) \qquad (7\text{-}54\text{a})$$

where the Schmidt number is defined as

$$\text{Sc} = \frac{v}{D^*} \qquad (7\text{-}54\text{b}).$$

We summarize that the foregoing similarity between heat and mass transfer processes is valid if the concentration of the species in the fluid stream is small, and the mass transfer coefficient $k_m$ is obtained from the analogous heat transfer coefficient $h_m$ by replacing the Nusselt number by the Sherwood number and the Prandtl number by the Schmidt number.

## 7.8.1 Mass Transfer in Boundary Layer Flow over a Flat Plate

In the previous section we presented the heat transfer correlations for laminar and turbulent boundary-layer flow over a flat plate mass transfer correlations by changing the Nusselt number to the Sherwood number and the Prandtl number to the Schmidt number. For mass transfer from laminar boundary-layer flow over a flat plate, the Pohlhausen equation (7-24a) can be written as a mass transfer correlation equation in the form

$$\text{Sh}_x = 0.332\,\text{Sc}^{1/3}\,\text{Re}_x^{1/2} \qquad \text{for } \text{Re}_x < 5 \times 10^5 \qquad (7\text{-}55\text{a})$$

or this expression can be rearranged as

$$\frac{k_m}{u_\infty}\text{Sc}^{2/3} = 0.332\,\text{Re}_x^{-1/2} \qquad \text{for } \text{Re}_x < 5 \times 10^5 \qquad (7\text{-}55\text{b})$$

where

$$k_m = \text{local mass transfer coefficient at } x$$

$$\text{Sh}_x = \frac{k_m x}{D^*} = \text{local Sherwood number}$$

$$\text{Sc} = \frac{v}{D^*} = \text{Schmidt number}$$

The average value of the mass transfer coefficient over the distance $0 \le x \le L$ is determined as

$$\bar{k}_m = 2[k_m]_{x=L}. \tag{7-56}$$

In mass transfer from turbulent boundary-layer flow over a flat plate, mass transfer correlation from the heat transfer for turbulent flow over flow equations can also be written as

$$\frac{k_m}{u_\infty} \text{Sc}^{2/3} = 0.0296 \, \text{Re}_x^{-0.2} \qquad \text{for } 5 \times 10^5 < \text{Re}_x < 10^7 \tag{7-57}$$

with the following change of variables,

$$\text{St}_x = \frac{\text{Nu}_x}{\text{Re}_x \, \text{Pr}} \rightarrow \frac{\text{Sh}_x}{\text{Re}_x \, \text{Sc}} = \frac{k_m x}{D^*} \frac{v}{u_\infty x} \frac{D^*}{v} = \frac{k_m}{u_\infty}$$

where $k_m$ is the local mass transfer coefficient.

When heat transfer and mass transfer take place simultaneously, the ratio of the heat transfer coefficient $h_x$ to the mass transfer coefficient $k_m$ can be of interest. Such a relation can be obtained for laminar flow and for turbulent flow. We note that for both cases it leads to

$$\frac{h_x}{k_m} = \rho c_p \left( \frac{\text{Sc}}{\text{Pr}} \right)^{2/3} = \rho c_p \, \text{Le}^{2/3} \tag{7-58}$$

where the *Lewis number* Le is defined as

$$\text{Le} = \frac{\text{Sc}}{\text{Pr}} = \frac{\alpha}{D^*} \tag{7-59}$$

The same relation is also applicable for the ratio of the average values of the heat and mass transfer coefficients, namely,

$$\frac{h_m}{k_m} = \rho c_p \, \text{Le}^{2/3} = \rho c_p \left( \frac{\alpha}{D^*} \right)^{2/3}. \tag{7-60}$$

**EXAMPLE 7-18** Air at atmospheric pressure and $T_\infty = 30°\text{C}$ flows over a wet-bulb thermometer. The wet-bulb reading of a thermometer, is $T_w = 20°\text{C}$. The air-water diffusivity is given as $D^* = 0.26 \times 10^{-4}$ m/s. (a) Calculate the concentration of water vapor $c_\infty$ in the free stream. The saturation concentration at $T_\infty = 30°\text{C}$ is given as $c_{\text{sat}} = 0.0304$ kg/m$^3$. (b) Determine the relative humidity of the airstream.

**SOLUTION** A wet-bulb thermometer means that a thermometer which is wrapped in a damp cloth. We assume that the steady-state conditions are established so that no net heat exchange takes place at the thermometer. Therefore, heat transferred from the airstream to the wet cloth must be balanced to evaporate the water. Therefore, the energy balance is

$$\begin{pmatrix} \text{Rate of heat} \\ \text{transfer from} \\ \text{air to wet} \\ \text{damp cloth} \end{pmatrix} = \begin{pmatrix} \text{Heat removed} \\ \text{by evaporation} \\ \text{of water from} \\ \text{damp cloth} \end{pmatrix}$$

$$Ah_m(T_\infty - T_w) = Ak_m(c_w - c_\infty)h_{fg}$$

or

$$\frac{h_m}{k_m}(T_\infty - T_w) = (c_w - c_\infty)h_{fg}$$

The ratio $h_m/k_m$ is obtained from Eq. (7-60):

$$\rho c_p \left(\frac{\alpha}{D^*}\right)^{2/3}(T_\infty - T_w) = (c_w - c_\infty)h_{fg} \qquad (i)$$

The properties are evaluated at the film temperature $T_f = (30 + 20)/2 = 25°C = 298K$. We find

Air:  $\rho$  = 1.1774 kg/m$^3$
  $c_p$  = 1.0057 kJ/(kg · °C)
  $\alpha$  = 0.2216 × 10$^{-4}$ m$^2$/s

Water:  $h_{fg}$  = 2407 kJ/kg
  $M_w$  = 18, molecular weight of water
  $T_w$  = 293 $K$, wet-bulb temperature
  $P_w$  = 2.339 $kN/m^2$, from saturated steam tables at $T_w$ = 20°C
  $\mathcal{R}$  = 8314 N · m/(kg · mol · K), universal gas constant

The saturation concentration of water vapor $c_w$ at $T_w = 20°C$ measured by the wet-bulb thermometers is determined from

$$c_w = \frac{P_w M_w}{\mathcal{R}T_w}$$

$$c_w = \frac{(2339)(18)}{(8314)(293)} = 0.01728 \text{ kg/m}^3$$

These quantities are now introduced into Eq. (i):

$$(1.1774)(1005.7)(0.2216/0.26)^{2/3}(30 - 20) = (0.01728 - c_\infty)(2442 \times 10^3)$$

Then the concentration of water vapor in the free stream is determined as

$$c_\infty = 0.01292 \text{ kg/m}^3$$

with

$$c_{\text{sat}} = 0.0304 \text{ kg/m}^3$$

The relative humidity, RH which is the ratio of the concentration $c_\infty$ of water vapor in the free stream to the saturation concentration becomes,

$$\text{RH} = \frac{c_\infty}{c_{\text{sat}}} = \frac{0.01292}{0.0304} = 42.5\%$$

## 7.9. NOTE

The differential equation (7-22$g$) is of the form

$$x\frac{dy}{dx} + Ay = B$$

where $A$ and $B$ are constants. A particular solution $y_P$ of this equation is given by

$$y_P = \frac{B}{A}$$

and the homogeneous solution $y_H$ is

$$y_H = x^{-A}$$

Then the complete solution becomes

$$y = Cx^{-A} + \frac{B}{A}$$

where the integration constant $C$ is determined from the boundary condition for the problem.

## PROBLEMS

*Basic Concepts*

**7-1** Air at atmospheric pressure and at 400 K flows over a flat plate with a velocity of 5 m/s. The transition from laminar to turbulent flow is assumed to take place at a Reynolds number of $5 \times 10^5$; determine the distance from the leading edge of the plate at which transition occurs.

**7-2** Air at atmospheric pressure and at 350 K flows over a flat plate with a velocity of 5 m/s. The average drag coefficient $c_m$ over a distance of 2 mfrom the leading edge is 0.0019. Calculate the drag force acting per 1-m width of the plate over the distance of 2 mfrom the leading edge.

**7-3** Hydrogen at atmospheric pressure and at 350 K flows over a flat plate with a velocity of 5 m/s. The transition from laminar to turbulent flow is assumed to take place at a Reynolds number of $5 \times 10^5$; determine the distance from the leading edge of the plate at which the transition occurs.

**7-4** Hydrogen at atmospheric pressure and at 350 K flows over a flat plate with a velocity of 5 m/$s$. The average drag coefficient $c_m$ over a distance of 2 mfrom the leading edge is 0.005. Calculate the drag force acting per 1-m width of the plate over a distance of 3 mfrom the leading edge.

**7-5** Air at $1/20$ $atm$ and at 345 K has $\rho = 0.0508$ kg/m³, $c_p = 1.009$ kJ/(kg $\cdot °$C), $k = 0.03$ W/(m·℃), and $\mu = 2.052 \times 10^{-5}$ kg/(m $\cdot$ $s$). Calculate the Prandtl number.

**7-6** Mercury at 205℃ has $\rho = 13,168$ kg/m³, $c_p = 0.1356$ kJ/(kg $\cdot °$ C), $k = 12.63$ W/(m·℃), and $\mu = 1.005 \times 10^{-3}$ kg/(m $\cdot s$). Calculate the Prandtl number.

*Laminar Flow over a Flat Plate*

**7-7** Air at atmospheric pressure and at 350 K flows over a flat plate with a velocity of 5 m/$s$. Calculate the average drag coefficient and the drag force acting per 1-m width of the plate over a distance of 2 mfrom the leading edge.

**7-8** Atmospheric air at 27℃ flows along a flat plate with a velocity of $U_\infty = 8$ m/$s$. The critical Reynolds number for transition from laminar to turbulent flow is $\mathrm{Re}_c = 5 \times 10^5$. ($a$) Determine the distance from the leading edge of the plate at which the transition occurs; ($b$) determine the local drag coefficient at the location where the transition occurs; and ($c$) determine the average drag coefficient over the distance where the flow is laminar.

**7-9** Hydrogen at atmospheric pressure and at 80℃ flows over a flat plate with a velocity 2 m/$s$. Determine ($a$) the local drag coefficient at a distance of 2 mfrom the leading edge, and ($b$) the average drag coefficient over a distance of 2 mfrom the leading edge.

**7-10** Engine oil at 80℃ flows over a flat plate with a velocity of 1 m/$s$. Determine ($a$) the local drag coefficient at a distance of 2 mfrom the leading edge, and ($b$) the average drag coefficient and the drag force acting per 1-m width of the plate over the distance of 2 mfrom the leading edge.

**7-11** Ethylene at 80℃ flows over a flat plate with a velocity of 0.2 m/$s$. Determine ($a$) the local drag coefficient at a distance of 2 mfrom the leading edge, and ($b$) the average drag coefficient and the drag force acting per 1-m width of the plate over the distance of 2 mfrom the leading edge.

**7-12** Air at 2 $atm$ pressure and at 350 K flows over a flat plate with a velocity of 1.5 m/$s$. Determine the drag force acting per 1-m width of the plate over a distance of 0.3 mfrom the leading edge.

**7-13** Air at 2 $atm$ pressure and at 350 K flows over a flat plate with a velocity of 2 m/s. Determine the drag force acting per 1-m width of the plate over a distance of 0.5 mfrom the leading edge.

**7-14** Air at 0.5 $atm$ pressure and at 350 K flows over a flat plate with a velocity of 2 m/s. Determine the drag force acting per 1-m width of the plate over a distance of 0.5 mfrom the leading edge.

**7-15** Determine the drag force exerted on a 2-m-long flat plate per meter width by the flow of the following fluids at atmospheric pressure and at 350 K with a velocity of 5 m/s: ($a$) air, ($b$) hydrogen, and ($c$) helium.

**7-16** A fluid of 80°C flows with a free-stream velocity of 0.8 m/s along a 5-m-long flat plate. Compute the average drag coefficient and the drag force acting per 1-m width of the plate over a distance of 0.5 mfrom the leading edge for the following fluids: ($a$) air and ($b$) $CO_2$.

**7-17** A fluid at 80°C flows with a free-stream velocity of 0.5 m/s along a 5-m-long flat plate. Compute the average drag coefficient and the drag force acting per 1-m width of the plate over a distance of 0.3 mfrom the leading edge for the following fluids: ($a$) water and ($b$) ethylene glycol.

**7-18** Air at atmospheric pressure and at 40°C flows with a velocity of 5 m/s over a 2-m-long flat plate whose surface is kept at a uniform temperature of 120°C. Determine the average heat transfer coefficient over the 2-m length of the plate.

**7-19** Engine oil at 40°C flows with a velocity of $u_\infty = 1$ m/s, over a 2-m-long flat plate whose surface is maintained at a uniform temperature of 80°C. Determine the average heat transfer coefficient over the 2-m length of the plate.

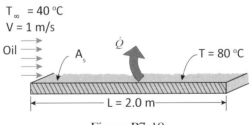

Figure P7-19

**7-20** Air at atmospheric pressure and at 40°C flows with a velocity of 5 m/s over a 2-m-long flat plate whose surface is kept at a uniform temperature of 120°C. Determine the rate of heat transfer between the plate and the air per meter width of the plate.

**7-21** Air at atmospheric pressure and at 54°C flows with a velocity of 10 m/s over a 1-m-long flat plate maintained at 200°C. Calculate the average drag and heat transfer coefficients over the 1-m length of the plate. Determine the rate of heat transfer between the plate and the air per meter width of the plate.

**7-22** Mercury at 65°C flows with a velocity of 0.1 m/s over a flat plate maintained at 120°C. Assuming that the transition from laminar to turbulent flow takes place at $Re_c = 5 \times 10^5$, determine the average heat transfer coefficient over the length of the plate where the flow is laminar.

**7-23** Atmospheric air at 24°C flows with a velocity of 4 m/s along a 2-m-long flat plate maintained at a uniform temperature of 130°C.

(a) Determine the average heat transfer coefficient over the entire length of the plate.

(b) Determine the heat transfer rate from that plate to the air per meter width of the plate.

**7-24** Consider the flow of air, hydrogen, and helium at atmospheric pressure and at 77°C with a velocity of 4 m/s along a 2-m-long flat plate. Determine the value of the local heat transfer coefficient at a distance of 1 mfrom the leading edge of the plate.

**7-25** Determine the value of the local heat transfer coefficient $h_x$ at a distance of 1 mfrom the leading edge of a flat plate for the flow of air at 77°C with a velocity of 4 m/s at pressures of 0.5, 1.0, and 2 atmospheres.

**7-26** Ethylene glycol at 70°C flows over a 0.5-m-long flat plate at 90°C with a velocity of 2 m/s. Calculate the average heat transfer coefficient over the entire length of the plate.

**7-27** Helium at atmospheric pressure and at 20°C flows with a velocity of 10 m/s over a $L = 2$ mlong flat plate maintained at a uniform temperature of 140°C. Calculate the rate of heat loss from the plate per meter width of the plate.

**7-28** Atmospheric air at 20°C flows with a velocity of 2 m/s over the 3 m × 3 msurface of a wall that absorbs solar energy flux at a rate of 500 $W/m^2$ and dissipates heat by convection into the air stream. Assuming negligible heat loss at the back surface of the wall, determine the average temperature of the wall under equilibrium conditions.

**7-29** Atmospheric air at 27°C flows with a velocity of 4 m/s over a 0.5 m×0.5 mflat plate which is uniformly heated with an electric heater at a rate of 2000 $W/m^2$. Calculate the average temperature of the plate.

*Turbulent Flow over a Flat Plate*

**7-30** Air at atmospheric pressure and at 24°C flows with a velocity of $U_\infty = 10$ m/s along a $L = 4$ mlong flat plate which is maintained at a uniform temperature of

130°C. Assuming $Re_c = 2 \times 10^5$, calculate (a) the local heat transfer coefficient at the locations $x = 2, 3$, and 4 mfrom the leading edge of the plate; (b) the average heat transfer coefficient over the length $L = 4$ m; and (c) the heat transfer rate from the plate to the air per meter width of the plate.

**7-31** Ethylene glycol at 40°C flows with a free-stream velocity of 8 m/s along a 3-m-long flat plate maintained at a uniform temperature of 100°C. Calculate the average heat transfer coefficient over the entire length of the plate. Assume transition occurs at $Re_c = 2 \times 10^5$.

**7-32** Helium at atmospheric pressure and at 300 K flows with a velocity of 30 m/s over a 5-m-long and 1-m-wide plate which is maintained at a uniform temperature of 600 K. Calculate the average heat transfer coefficient and the total heat transfer rate. Assume that transition occurs at $Re_c = 2 \times 10^5$.

**7-33** Ethylene glycol at 300 K flows with a velocity of 15 m/s over a 5-m-long and 1m-wide plate which is maintained at a uniform temperature of 330 K. Calculate the average heat transfer coefficient and the total heat transfer rate. Assume that transition occurs at $Re_c = 2 \times 10^5$.

**7-34** Air at 24°C flows along a 4-m-long flat plate with a velocity of 5 m/s. The plate is maintained at 130°C. Calculate the average heat transfer coefficient over the entire length of the plate and the heat transfer rate per meter width of the plate.

**7-35** For the plate in Problem 7-34, calculate the average heat transfer coefficient over the entire length of the plate and the heat transfer rate per meter width of the plate if the air velocity is increased to 10 m/s.

*Flow across a Single Circular Cylinder*

**7-36** Atmospheric air at 27°C with a velocity of 20 m/s flows across a single tube of outside diameter $D = 2.5$ cm. The surface of the cylinder is maintained at a uniform temperature of 127°C. Determine the average heat transfer coefficient and the heat transfer rate from the tube to the air per meter length of the tube.

**7-37** Determine the heat transfer rate from the tube to the air per meter length of the tube if the pressure of the air in Problem 7-36 is increased to 2 *atm*.

**7-38** Engine oil at 20°C flows with a velocity of 1 m/s across a 2.5-cm-outside diameter (OD) tube which is maintained at a uniform temperature of 100°C. Determine the average heat transfer coefficient and the heat transfer rate between the tube surface and the oil per meter length of the tube.

**7-39** Water at 20°C with a free-stream velocity of 1.5 m/s flows across a single circular tube with an outside diameter of 2.5 cm. The tube surface is maintained at a uniform temperature of 80°C. Calculate the average heat transfer coefficient and the heat transfer rate per meter length of the tube.

**7-40** Atmospheric air at $T_\infty = 300$ K and free-stream velocity of $U_\infty = 30$ m/s flows across a single cylinder with an outside diameter $D = 2.5$ cm. The cylinder surface is at a uniform temperature of $T_w = 400$ K. Calculate the mean heat transfer coefficient $h_m$ and the heat transfer rate per meter length of the cylinder.

*Flow across a Single Noncircular Cylinder*

**7-41** Atmospheric air at 300 K with a free-stream velocity of 30 m/s flows across a square duct 2 cm by 2 cm with its cross section oriented such that one of its lateral surfaces is perpendicular to the direction of flow. The duct's surface is kept at a uniform temperature of 400 K. Calculate the average heat transfer coefficient and the heat transfer rate per meter length of the duct.

**7-42** Engine oil at 20°C flows with a velocity of 10 m/s normal to a 5-cm plate which is maintained at a uniform temperature of 100°C. Determine the average heat transfer coefficient and the heat transfer rate between the plate surface and the oil per meter length of the plate.

**7-43** Water at 20°C with a free-stream velocity 1.5 m/s flows across a 2.5 cm by 2.5 cm duct which is maintained at a uniform temperature of 80°C and oriented such that one of its lateral surfaces is perpendicular to the direction of flow. Calculate the average heat transfer coefficient and the heat transfer rate per meter length of the tube.

*Flow across a Single Sphere*

**7-44** Water at 80°C flows with a mass velocity of 50 kg/(m² · s) over a 5-cm-diameter sphere whose surface is maintained at a uniform temperature of 140°C. Determine the average heat transfer coefficient and the heat transfer rate from the sphere to the water.

**7-45** Ethylene glycol at 40°C flows with a velocity of 2 m/s across a 2.5-cm-diameter sphere. The surface of the sphere is maintained at a uniform temperature of 80°C. Compute the average heat transfer coefficient and the rate of heat transfer from the sphere to the fluid.

**7-46** A fluid at 40°C flows with a velocity of 2 m/s across a 2.5-cm-diameter sphere. The surface of the sphere is maintained at a uniform temperature of 100°C. Compute the average heat transfer coefficient for the following fluids: (*a*) $CO_2$ at 1 *atm*, and (*b*) water.

**7-47** Atmospheric air at 20°C flows with a free-stream velocity of 0.5 m/s over a 2-m diameter spherical tank which is maintained at 80°C. Compute the average heat transfer coefficient and the heat transfer rate from the sphere to the air.

**7-48** Water at 20°C flows with a free-stream velocity of 1 m/s over a 2.5-cm-diameter sphere whose surface is maintained at a uniform temperature of 80°C. Determine the average heat transfer coefficient and the rate of heat loss from the sphere to the air.

*Nanofluid Flow over Flat Plate*

**7-49** $Al_2O_3/$ water nanofluid flows over a horizontal plate. The length of the plate is 1 $m$ along the flow direction. Assume $\delta = 2\,nm$, $r_p = 19\,nm$, $Re = 0.015$, $Pr = 5.49$. Use the Prakash and Giannelis correlations to calculate the thermal conductivity with $A = 40,000$ and $m = 2.25$. The density and thermal conductivity of water are 992.2 $kg/m^3$ and 0.6 $W/m°C$, and the density and thermal conductivity of alumina are $3,900\ kg/m^3$ and 35.5 $W/m°C$, respectively. Calculate the density, the thermal conductivity and the heat transfer coefficient for a given particle volume concentration changing from $\phi = 1\%$ to $\phi = 2\%$.

*Mass Transfer in Boundary Layer Flow over a Flat Plate*

**7-50** Air at atmospheric pressure and $T_\infty = 40°C$ flows over a wet-bulb thermometer. The wet-bulb reading of a thermometer, is $T_w = 20°C$. The air-water diffusivity is given as $D^* = 0.26 \times 10^{-4}$ m/s. (a) Calculate the concentration of water vapor $c_\infty$ in the free stream. The saturation concentration at $T_\infty = 40°C$ is given as $c_{sat} = 0.0512$ kg/m³. (b) Determine the relative humidity of the airstream.

# CHAPTER 8

# *Internal Forced Convection Heat Flow*

This chapter is devoted to heat transfer and pressure drop in forced convection inside ducts under both laminar and turbulent flow conditions, with emphasis on the understanding of the physical mechanism and the use of various correlations for predicting heat flow and pressure drop. Turbulent pipe flow is widely used in various industrial applications, and the available correlations of the heat transfer coefficient and the friction factor are mostly of an empirical or semiempirical nature. We present such correlations with particular emphasis on their ranges of validity.

Laminar pipe flow is encountered generally in compact heat exchangers, cryogenic coolant systems, the heating or cooling of heavy fluids such as oils, and many other applications. Numerous analytic expressions are available for predicting the friction factor and heat transfer coefficient in laminar tube flow. We present some of these results and discuss their range of validity.

Heat transfer correlations developed for ordinary fluids break down when they are applied to liquid metals, because the Prandtl number for liquid metals is very low. Therefore, heat transfer to liquid metals has been the subject of numerous investigations, but reliable correlations are still rather limited. We discuss some of the available correlations of heat transfer for the flow of liquid metals in tubes.

## 8.1. BASIC CONCEPTS

The basic concepts, discussed in the previous chapter, on the development of velocity and thermal boundary layers for flow along a flat plate also apply to flow inside ducts at the entrance regions, but some additional features need to be presented.

### 8.1.1 Hydrodynamic Entry Region

To illustrate the concept of the hydrodynamic entry region and its physical significance in heat transfer and pressure drop problems, we consider the flow entering a circular tube, shown in Fig. 8.1. The fluid has a uniform velocity $u_0$ at the tube inlet. As the fluid enters the tube, a velocity boundary layer starts to develop along the wall surface. The velocity of the fluid particles at the wall surface becomes zero, and that in the vicinity of the wall is retarded; as a result, the velocity in the central portion of the tube increases to satisfy the requirement of the continuity of flow. The thickness of the velocity boundary layer $\delta(z)$ continuously grows along the tube surface until it fills the entire tube. The region from the tube inlet to a little beyond the hypothetical location where the boundary layer reaches the tube center is called the *hydrodynamic entry region*. In this region the shape of the velocity profile changes in both the axial and radial directions. The region beyond

**FIG. 8.1.** Concept of hydrodynamic entry region.

the hydrodynamic entry length is called the *hydrodynamically developed region*, because in this region the velocity profile is invariant with distance along the tube.

If the boundary layer remains laminar until it fills the tube, fully developed laminar flow with a parabolic velocity profile prevails in the hydrodynamically developed region. However, if the boundary layer changes to turbulent before its thickness reaches the tube center, fully developed turbulent flow is experienced in the hydrodynamically developed region. When the flow is turbulent, the velocity profile is flatter than the parabolic velocity profile of laminar flow.

For flow inside a circular tube, the Reynolds number, defined as

$$\text{Re} \equiv \frac{u_m D}{\nu} \tag{8-1}$$

is used as a criterion for change from laminar to turbulent flow. In this definition, $u_m$ is the mean flow velocity, $D$ is the tube inside diameter, and $\nu$ is the kinematic viscosity of the fluid. For flow inside a circular tube, the turbulent flow is usually observed for

$$\text{Re} = \frac{u_m D}{\nu} > 2300 \tag{8-2}$$

However, this critical value is strongly dependent on the surface roughness, the inlet conditions, and the fluctuations in the flow. In general, the transition from laminar to turbulent flow occurs in the range 2000 <Re< 4000.

### 8.1.2 Thermal Entry Region

When a fluid enters a tube whose wall is maintained at a uniform temperature different from that of the fluid temperature or is subjected to heating at a uniform rate, heat transfer takes place between the fluid and the tube surface. The resulting temperature distribution in flow inside the tube is such that, starting from the tube inlet, a thermal boundary layer similar to the one for flow over a flat plate can be assumed to develop and grow with the distance along the tube, but it is different from that for flow over a flat plate.

Consider a laminar flow inside a circular tube subjected to uniform heat flux at the wall. Let $r$ and $z$ be the radial and axial coordinates, respectively. A dimensionless temperature $\theta(r,z)$ is defined as

$$\theta(r,z) = \frac{T(r,z) - T_w(z)}{T_m(z) - T_w(z)} \tag{8-3}$$

where

$$
\begin{aligned}
T_w(z) &= \text{tube wall temperature} \\
T_m(z) &= \text{bulk mean fluid temperature over cross-sectional area of tube at } z \\
T(r,z) &= \text{local fluid temperature}
\end{aligned}
$$

Clearly, $\theta(r,z)$ is zero at the tube wall surface and attains some finite value at the tube center. Then, one envisions the development of a thermal boundary layer along the wall surface. The thickness of the thermal boundary layer $\delta_t(z)$ continuously grows along the tube surface until it fills the entire tube. The region from the tube inlet to the hypothetical location where the thermal boundary-layer thickness reaches the tube center is called the *thermal entry region*. In this region, the shape of the dimensionless temperature profile $\theta(r,z)$ changes in both the axial and radial directions.

The region beyond the thermal entry region is called the *thermally developed region*, because in this region the dimensionless temperature profile remains invariant with the distance along the tube; that is,

$$\theta(r) = \frac{T(r,z) - T_w(z)}{T_m(z) - T_w(z)} \tag{8-4}$$

It is difficult to explain qualitatively why $\theta(r)$ should be independent of the $z$ variable while the temperatures on the right-hand side of Eq. (8-4) depend on both $r$ and $z$. However, it can be shown mathematically that for either constant temperature or constant heat flux at the wall, the dimensionless temperature $\theta(r)$ depends only on $r$ for sufficiently large values of $z$.

### 8.1.3 Fully Developed Region

Consider a fluid at a uniform temperature $T_0$ and a uniform velocity $u_0$ entering a tube whose wall is maintained at a constant temperature $T_w$ (i.e., $T_0 \neq T_w$) or subjected to heating at a constant rate. As discussed previously, starting from the inlet, the thermal and velocity boundary layers start to continuously grow along the tube surface until each fills the entire tube. The relative thickness of the velocity and thermal boundary layers during the growth depends on the magnitude of the Prandtl number for the fluid, that is, $\delta > \delta_t$ for Pr$> 1$, $\delta = \delta_t$, for Pr$= 1$, and $\delta < \delta_t$, for Pr$< 1$. Figure 8.2 schematically illustrates, for the case Pr$> 1$, the hypothetical locations $L_h$ and $L_t$ where $\delta$ and $\delta_t$ reach the tube center. The distances $L_h$ and $L_t$, are called the *hydrodynamic entrance length* and the *thermal entrance length*, respectively. In the region beyond $L_h$, the velocity profile does not vary with the axial position along the tube. Similarly, in the region beyond $L_t$. the

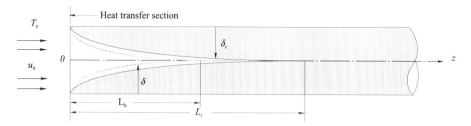

**FIG. 8.2.** Concept of hydrodynamic and thermal entrance lengths and the fully developed region.

dimensionless temperature profile $\theta(r)$ defined by Eq. (8-4) does not vary with the axial position. Then the region beyond $L_h$ or $L_t$ (whichever is greater), where both the velocity and temperature profiles do not vary in the axial direction, is called the *fully developed region* (i.e., the hydrodynamically and thermally developed region).

### 8.1.4 Bulk Mean Fluid Temperature

When a fluid flowing inside a duct is subjected to heating or cooling as a result of heat transfer between the fluid and the tube wall, the temperature of the fluid varies in both the radial and axial directions. The average temperature of the fluid over the duct cross section at any axial location $z$ is of practical interest. Such an averaging cannot be performed by taking a simple arithmetic average of the temperature over the cross section. The averaging must be based on the thermal energy transported with the bulk motion of the fluid as it passes through the cross section. If $u$ is the axial velocity, the quantity

$$\rho c_p u T$$

represents energy flux per unit of cross-sectional area of the duct. With this consideration, the *mean fluid temperature* $T_m(z)$ for flow inside a circular tube of inside radius $R$ is given by

$$T_m(z) = \frac{\int_0^R \rho c_p u(r) T(r, z)(2\pi r)dr}{\int_0^R \rho c_p u(r)(2\pi r)dr} \tag{8-5a}$$

For a constant-property fluid, the $\rho c_p$ term cancels out, and Eq. (8-5$a$) reduces to

$$T_m(z) = \frac{\int_0^R u(r) T(r, z)(2\pi r)dr}{\int_0^R u(r)(2\pi r)dr} = \frac{\int_0^R u(r) T(r, z)(2\pi r)dr}{u_m \pi R^2} \tag{8-5b}$$

In the case of flow between two parallel plates, the appropriate area term should be used in the integration.

### 8.1.5 Heat Transfer Coefficient

In engineering applications involving fluid flow inside a duct, the concept of *heat transfer coefficient* is frequently used in determining heat transfer between the fluid and the wall surface. Here we present the basic definition of the heat transfer coefficient.

Consider a fluid flowing inside a circular tube of inside radius $R$. Let $T(r, z)$ be the temperature distribution in the fluid, where $r$ and $z$ are the radial and axial coordinates, respectively. Since the fluid particles next to the tube wall are stationary, heat transfer between the fluid and the wall surface is by conduction. Then the heat flux from the fluid to the wall surface is determined from

$$q(z) = -k \left. \frac{\partial T(r, z)}{\partial r} \right|_{r=R} \tag{8-6}$$

where $k$ is the thermal conductivity of fluid.

In engineering applications, using this expression to determine the heat transfer between the fluid and the tube wall is not practical because it requires the evaluation of the derivative of temperature at the wall. To avoid this difficulty, a local heat transfer coefficient $h(z)$ is defined as

$$q(z) = h(z)[T_m(z) - T_w(z)] \tag{8-7}$$

where

$$
\begin{aligned}
T_m(z) \;=\; & \text{bulk mean fluid temperature over the tube cross-sectional area} \\
& \text{at location } z \text{ , defined previously} \\
T_w(z) \;=\; & \text{tube wall temperature at } z
\end{aligned}
$$

Equating Eqs. (8-6) and (8-7), we obtain

$$h(z) = -\frac{k}{T_m(z) - T_w(z)} \left. \frac{\partial T(r, z)}{\partial r} \right|_{r=R} \tag{8-8}$$

Clearly, if the temperature distribution in the flow is known, the heat transfer coefficient $h(z)$ is determined from the definition given by Eq. (8-8).

Equation (8-8) can be expressed in terms of the dimensionless temperature $\theta$ defined by Eq. (8-3) as

$$h(z) = -k \left. \frac{\partial \theta(r, z)}{\partial r} \right|_{r=R} \tag{8-9}$$

An examination of Eq. (8-9) reveals that if $\theta(r, z)$ varies in the axial direction, the heat transfer coefficient $h(z)$ also varies with the position along the tube.

In the region sufficiently far away from the tube inlet, the velocity and the dimensionless temperature profiles do not vary with the axial position. Hence in the fully developed region the dimensionless temperature $\theta(r)$ is independent of $z$, and Eq. (8-9) reduces to

$$h = -k \left. \frac{\partial \theta(r)}{\partial r} \right|_{r=R} \tag{8-10}$$

where $\theta(r)$ is defined by Eq. (8-4). This result implies that in the thermally developed region the heat transfer coefficient does not vary with the distance along the tube; and it is valid for heat transfer under conditions of constant wall heat flux or constant wall temperature.

## 8.1.6 Logarithmic Mean Temperature Difference

Consider the flow of a fluid inside a duct whose walls are maintained at a uniform temperature $T_w$. Let the fluid enter the tube at a temperature $T_1$ and leave it at a temperature $T_2$. Figure 8.3 illustrates the axial variation of the bulk mean temperature $T_m(z)$ along

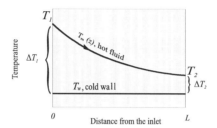

**FIG. 8.3.** Nomenclature for the definition of the Logarithmic Mean Temperature Difference.

the tube for the case of a hot wall. In the determination of the total heat transfer rate between the fluid and the wall, an average temperature difference $\Delta T$ between the wall and the fluid is needed. Let $\Delta T_1$ and $\Delta T_2$ be the inlet and outlet temperature differences between the fluid and the wall at the inlet and outlet, respectively, as illustrated in Fig. 8.3. The *logarithmic mean temperature difference* (LMTD) between the wall and the fluid temperatures over the entire length $L$ of the tube is defined as

$$\Delta T_{\ln} = \frac{\Delta T_1 - \Delta T_2}{\ln(\Delta T_1/\Delta T_2)} \tag{8-11}$$

whereas the arithmetic mean (AM) of $\Delta T_1$ and $\Delta T_2$ is defined as

$$\Delta T_{AM} = \frac{1}{2}(\Delta T_1 + \Delta T_2) \tag{8-12}$$

Note that $\Delta T_{\ln}$ is always less then $\Delta T_{AM}$. If the quantity $\Delta T_1/\Delta T_2$ is not greater than 0.5, then $\Delta T_{\ln}$ can be approximated by the arithmetic mean difference within about 1.4 percent.

## 8.1.7 Friction Factor

In engineering applications the pressure drop $\Delta P$ associated with the flow of fluid inside a duct is a quantity of practical interest, because if the pressure drop is known, the pumping power required to get the fluid pumped through the pipe can be determined.

Consider a fluid flowing with a mean velocity $u_m$ through a circular tube of inside diameter $D$ and length $L$. The pressure drop $\Delta P$ over the length $L$ of the tube is related to the *friction factor* $f$ by the following expression:

$$\Delta P = f \frac{L}{D} \frac{\rho u_m^2}{2} \quad N/m^2 \tag{8-13}$$

In the case of flow through a duct which is not circular, the tube diameter $D$ in the above expression is replaced by the *hydraulic diameter* $D_h$, and we obtain

$$\Delta P = f \frac{L}{D_h} \frac{\rho u_m^2}{2} \tag{8-14a}$$

where the hydraulic diameter $D_h$ is defined as

$$D_h = \frac{4A_c}{P} \tag{8-14b}$$

where $A_c$ is the cross-sectional area for flow and $P$ is the wetted perimeter. Clearly, for a circular tube $D_h = D$.

If $M$ is the flow rate through the pipe in cubic meters per second, the pumping power required to get the fluid through the pipe against the pressure drop $\Delta P$ becomes

$$\boxed{\text{Pumping power} = M\Delta P} \quad N \cdot m/s \text{ or } W \tag{8-15}$$

## 8.1.8 Dimensionless Parameters

The dimensionless parameters, such as the Reynolds, Prandtl, Nusselt, and Stanton numbers, have been used in the study of forced convection over surfaces. They will also be used for forced convection through ducts. Therefore, it is instructive to discuss the physical significance of these parameters in relation to fluid flow and heat transfer.

We consider the Reynolds number based on a characteristic length $L$, rearranged in the form

$$\text{Re} = \frac{u_\infty L}{\nu} = \frac{u_\infty^2/L}{\nu u_\infty/L^2} = \frac{\text{inertia force}}{\text{viscous force}} \tag{8-16a}$$

Then the Reynolds number represents the ratio of inertia force to viscous force. This result implies that viscous forces are dominant for small Reynolds numbers and inertia forces are dominant for large Reynolds numbers. Recall that the Reynolds number was used as the criterion for determining the change from laminar to turbulent flow. As the Reynolds number is increased, the inertia forces become dominant, and small disturbances in the fluid may be amplified to cause the transition from laminar to turbulent flow.

The Prandtl number can be arranged in the form

$$\text{Pr} = \frac{c_p \mu}{k} = \frac{\mu/\rho}{k/(\rho c_p)} = \frac{\nu}{\alpha} = \frac{\text{molecular diffusivity of momentum}}{\text{molecular diffusivity of heat}} \tag{8-16b}$$

Thus it represents the relative importance of momentum and energy transport by the diffusion process. Hence for gases with $\mathrm{Pr} \cong 1$, the transfer of momentum and energy by the diffusion process is comparable. For oils, $\mathrm{Pr} \gg 1$, and hence the momentum diffusion is much greater than the energy diffusion; but for liquid metals, $\mathrm{Pr} < 1$, and the situation is reversed. We recall that in discussing the development of velocity and thermal boundary layers for flow along a flat plate, the relative thickness of velocity and thermal boundary layers depend on the magnitude of the Prandtl number.

The Nusselt number, based on a characteristic length $L$, can be rearranged in the form

$$\mathrm{Nu} = \frac{hL}{k} = \frac{h\Delta T}{k\Delta T/L} \tag{8-16c}$$

where $\Delta T$ is the reference temperature difference between the wall surface and the fluid temperature. Then the Nusselt number may be interpreted as the ratio of heat transfer by convection to that conduction across the fluid layer of thickness $L$. Based on this interpretation, a value of the Nusselt number equal to unity implies that there is no convection and the heat transfer is by pure conduction. A larger value of the Nusselt number implies enhanced heat transfer by convection.

The Stanton number can be rearranged as

$$\mathrm{St} = \frac{h}{\rho c_p u_m} = \frac{h\Delta T}{\rho c_p u_m \Delta T} \tag{8-16d}$$

where $\Delta T$ is a reference temperature difference between the wall surface and the fluid. The numerator represents convection heat flux between the wall and the fluid, and the denominator represents the heat transfer capacity of the fluid flow.

**EXAMPLE 8-1** Engine oil ($\nu = 0.75 \times 10^{-4}$ m$^2$/$s$) flows with a mean velocity of $u_m = 0.3$ m/$s$ inside a circular tube that has an inside diameter $D = 2.5$ cm. Determine whether the flow is laminar or turbulent.

**SOLUTION** We calculate the Reynolds number

$$\mathrm{Re} = \frac{u_m D}{\nu} = \frac{0.3 \times 0.025}{0.75 \times 10^{-4}} = 100$$

Since $\mathrm{Re} < 2300$, the flow is laminar.

**EXAMPLE 8-2** Consider a flow of a fluid in a channel whose walls are maintained at a uniform temperature $T_w = 100°C$. The fluid is heated from $T_1 = 30°C$ to $T_2 = 70°C$ over the length $L$ of the channel. Determine the logarithmic mean temperature difference between the channel wall and the fluid.

**SOLUTION** From Eq. (8-11), the LMTD is calculated as

$$\Delta T_{\mathrm{ln}} = \frac{T_2 - T_1}{\ln[(T_w - T_1)/(T_w - T_2)]} = \frac{70 - 30}{\ln[(100 - 30)/(100 - 70)]} = 47.2 \,°C.$$

**EXAMPLE 8-3**  A fluid flows through a square duct 2 cm by 2 cm. Calculate the hydraulic diameter.

**SOLUTION**  From Eq. (8-14b) the hydraulic diameter of the duct is calculated as

$$D_h = \frac{4A_c}{P} = \frac{4(2 \times 2)}{4 \times 2} = 2 \text{ cm}$$

**EXAMPLE 8-4**  Engine oil is pumped through a tube at a flow rate of $M = 2 \times 10^{-4} \text{ m}^3/s$. The pressure drop across the tube length $L$ is $\Delta P = 1.5 \times 10^4 \text{ N/m}^2$. Calculate the power required for pumping the oil through a tube bundle consisting of 500 such tubes.

**SOLUTION**  The pumping power requirement is determined by Eq. (8-15):

$$\begin{aligned} \text{W} &= \text{M} \cdot \Delta P = (2 \times 10^{-4})(1.5 \times 10^4) \\ &= 3 \text{ N} \cdot m/s \quad (1 \text{ tube}) \\ &= (3 \text{ N} \cdot m/s) \left[ \frac{1}{745.7} (hp \cdot s)/(N \cdot m) \right] \\ &= 0.004 \text{ hp/tube} \end{aligned}$$

Then
$$\text{W(for 500 tubes)} = 0.004 \times 500 = 2 \ hp$$

## 8.2. FULLY DEVELOPED LAMINAR FLOW

We now present expressions for the determination of the friction factor and the heat transfer coefficient for laminar flow in ducts such as a circular tube, a parallel-plate channel, and many others. The use of these relations in the determination of pressure drop and heat transfer associated with the flow is illustrated with examples.

### 8.2.1 Flow Inside a Circular Tube

**FRICTION FACTOR.** Consider an incompressible, constant-property fluid in laminar forced convection inside a circular tube of radius $R$ in the region where flow is hydrodynamically developed. The friction factor for flow inside a circular tube is related to the velocity gradient at the wall by

$$f = -\frac{8\mu}{\rho u_m^2} \frac{du}{dr}\bigg|_{r=R} \tag{8-17}$$

and the fully developed velocity profile for flow inside a circular tube is given by

$$\boxed{\frac{u(r)}{u_m} = 2\left[1 - \left(\frac{r}{R}\right)^2\right]} \tag{8-18a}$$

Then the velocity gradient at the wall surface is determined from this expression:

$$\frac{du(r)}{dr}\bigg|_{r=R} = -\frac{4u_m}{R} = -\frac{8u_m}{D} \qquad (8\text{-}18b)$$

Introducing Eq. (8-18b) into Eq. (8-17), the following expression is obtained for the friction factor $f$ for laminar flow inside a circular tube:

$$\boxed{f = \frac{64\mu}{\rho u_m D} = \frac{64}{\text{Re}}} \qquad (8\text{-}19a)$$

where $D$ is the tube inside diameter and

$$\text{Re} = \frac{\rho u_m D}{\mu} = \frac{u_m D}{\nu} \qquad (8\text{-}19b)$$

is the Reynolds number.

In the literature, the friction factor also has been defined on the basis of hydraulic radius. If $f_r$ denotes the friction factor based on the hydraulic radius, it is related to the friction factor $f$ defined by Eq. (8-19a) by $f = 4f_r$.

**EXAMPLE 8-5**  Compare the mean velocities, friction factors, and pressure drops for fully developed laminar flow at 20°C of Freon [$\mu = 2.65 \times 10^{-4}$ kg/(m · s), $\rho = 1330$ kg/m³], ethylene glycol [$\mu = 2.24 \times 10^{-2}$ kg/(m · s), $\rho = 1117$ kg/m³], and engine oil [$\mu = 0.8$ kg/(m · s), $\rho = 888$ kg/m³] through a 2.5-cm-diameter, 50-m-long tube at a rate of 0.01 kg/s.

**SOLUTION**  The mean velocities of the fluid are

$$\text{Freon: } u_m = \frac{m}{\rho A} = \frac{0.01}{1330 \times (\pi/4 \times 0.025^2)} = 0.0153 \text{ m/s}$$

$$\text{Ethylene glycol: } u_m = \frac{0.01}{1117 \times (\pi/4 \times 0.025^2)} = 0.0182 \text{ m/s}$$

$$\text{Engine oil: } u_m = \frac{0.01}{888 \times (\pi/4 \times 0.025^2)} = 0.0229 \text{ m/s}$$

The Reynolds number for the flows are

$$\text{Freon: Re} = \frac{u_m D}{(\mu/\rho)} = \frac{0.0153 \times 0.025}{2.63 \times 10^{-4}/1330} = 1934$$

$$\text{Ethylene glycol: Re} = \frac{0.0182 \times 0.025}{2.24 \times 10^{-2}/1117} = 22.7$$

$$\text{Engine oil: Re} = \frac{0.0229 \times 0.025}{0.8/888} = 0.635$$

These Reynolds numbers are less than 2300; therefore, the flows are laminar. The friction factors for laminar flows inside a circular tube, according to Eq. (8-19a), become

$$\text{Freon: } f = \frac{64}{\text{Re}} = \frac{64}{1934} = 0.0331$$

$$\text{Ethylene glycol: } f = \frac{64}{22.7} = 2.82$$

$$\text{Engine oil: } f = \frac{64}{0.635} = 100.8$$

The pressure drops across the tube from Eq. (8-14a) are calculated as

$$\text{Freon: } \Delta P = f\frac{L}{D}\frac{\rho u_m^2}{2} = 0.0331\frac{100}{0.025}\frac{(1330)(0.0l53)^2}{2} = 20.6 \text{ N/m}^2$$

$$\text{Ethylene: } \Delta P = 2.82\frac{100}{0.025}\frac{(1ll7)(0.0l82)^2}{2} = 2087 \text{ N/m}^2$$

$$\text{Engine oil: } \Delta P = 100.8\frac{100}{0.025}\frac{(888)(0.0229)^2}{2} = 93,880 \text{ N/m}^2$$

**HEAT TRANSFER COEFFICIENT.** The heat transfer coefficient for flow inside a circular tube in the thermally developed region is related to the dimensionless temperature gradient at the wall by Eq. (8-10) as

$$h = -k \left.\frac{d\theta(r)}{dr}\right|_{r=R} \tag{8-20a}$$

where $\theta(r)$ is defined by Eq. (8-4) as

$$\theta(r) = \frac{T(r,z) - T_w(z)}{T_m(z) - T_w(z)} \tag{8-20b}$$

To determine $h$, the temperature distribution in the flow is needed. We consider below two specific cases: (1) constant heat flux at the wall, and (2) constant temperature at the wall.

**1. Constant heat flux at the wall:** Consider laminar flow inside a circular tube of radius $R$ that is subjected to a uniform heat flux at the wall. In the region sufficiently away from the inlet where the velocity and temperature profiles are fully developed, the dimensionless temperature distribution $\theta(r)$ in the fluid is given by

$$\theta(r) = \frac{24}{11}\left[\frac{3}{4} + \frac{1}{4}\left(\frac{r}{R}\right)^4 - \left(\frac{r}{R}\right)^2\right] \tag{8-21a}$$

and the derivative of this temperature at the wall $r = R$ becomes

$$\left.\frac{d\theta(r)}{dr}\right|_{r=R} = -\frac{48}{11}\frac{1}{2R} = -\frac{48}{11D} \tag{8-21b}$$

Introducing Eq. (8-21b) into Eq. (8-20a), the expression for the heat transfer coefficient $h$ becomes

$$h = \frac{48}{11} \frac{k}{D} \qquad (8\text{-}22a)$$

or

$$\mathrm{Nu} \equiv \frac{hD}{k} = \frac{48}{11} = 4.364 \qquad (8\text{-}22b)$$

where $D$ is the tube's inside diameter and Nu is the Nusselt number.

The result given by Eqs. (8-22a) and (8-22b) represents the heat transfer coefficient for laminar forced convection inside a circular tube in the hydrodynamically and thermally developed region under the constant wall heat flux boundary condition.

**2. Constant wall temperature:** The heat transfer problem described above for the hydrodynamically and thermally developed region also can be solved under a constant wall temperature boundary condition; the resulting expression for the Nusselt number is

$$\mathrm{Nu} \equiv \frac{hD}{k} = 3.66 \qquad (8\text{-}23)$$

which is valid for laminar forced convection inside a circular tube in the hydrodynamically and thermally developed region under the constant wall temperature boundary condition.

In the results given by Eqs. (8-22) and (8-23), the thermal conductivity of the fluid $k$ depends on temperature. When the fluid temperature varies along the tube, $k$ may be evaluated at the *fluid bulk mean temperature* $T_b$, defined as

$$T_b = \frac{1}{2}(T_i + T_o) \qquad (8\text{-}24)$$

where $T_i =$ and $T_o =$ are the bulk fluid temperatures at the inlet and outlet, respectively.

## 8.2.2 Flow Inside Ducts of Various Cross Sections

The Nusselt number and the friction factor for laminar flow in ducts of various cross sections have been determined in the region where velocity and temperature profiles are fully developed. For ducts with a noncircular cross section, the heat transfer coefficient and friction factor, for many cases of practical interest, may be based on the hydraulic diameter $D_h$, defined as

$$D_h = \frac{4A_c}{P} \qquad (8\text{-}25)$$

where $A_c =$ cross-sectional area for flow and $P =$ the wetted perimeter. Then the Nusselt and Reynolds numbers for such cases are defined as

$$\mathrm{Nu} = \frac{hD_h}{k} \qquad (8\text{-}26a)$$

$$\text{Re} = \frac{u_m D_h}{\nu} \qquad (8\text{-}26b)$$

The basis for choosing $D_h$ as in Eq. (8-25) is that for a circular tube $D_h$ becomes the tube diameter $D$, since $A_c = (\pi/4)D^2$ and $P = \pi D$. The hydraulic diameter $D_h$ for parallel plates is twice the distance between the plates.

**TABLE 8.1. Hydrodynamically and thermally developed laminar flow in ducts.**

| Geometry ($L/D_k > 100$) | $\text{Nu}_T$ | $\text{Nu}_H$ | $f\,\text{Re}$ |
|---|---|---|---|
| circle | 3.657 | 4.364 | 64.00 |
| hexagon | 3.34 | 4.002 | 60.22 |
| triangle $60°$, $\frac{2b}{2a} = \frac{\sqrt{3}}{2}$ | 2.47 | 3.111 | 53.33 |
| square, $\frac{2b}{2a} = 1$ | 2.976 | 3.608 | 56.91 |
| rectangle, $\frac{2b}{2a} = \frac{1}{2}$ | 3.391 | 4.123 | 62.20 |
| rectangle, $\frac{2b}{2a} = \frac{1}{4}$ | 3.66 | 5.099 | 74.8 |
| rectangle, $\frac{2b}{2a} = \frac{1}{8}$ | 5.597 | 6.490 | 82.34 |
| parallel plates, $\frac{2b}{2a} = 0$ | 7.541 | 8.235 | 96.00 |
| insulated, $\frac{b}{a} = 0$ | 4.861 | 5.385 | 96.00 |

In Table 8.1 we present the Nusselt number and the friction factor for laminar flow inside ducts of various cross sections. Here the notation $\text{Nu}_T$ and $\text{Nu}_H$ refers to the Nusselt number under constant wall temperature and constant wall heat flux, respectively. The friction factor $f$ is given as a product of $f$ and Re. Both the Nusselt and the Reynolds number are based on the hydraulic diameter $D_h$ as specified by Eqs. (8-25) and (8-26).

**EXAMPLE 8-6** Consider the flow of water with a velocity of $0.0379$ m/s through a tube 2 cm in diameter whose wall is maintained at constant temperature. The flow is hydrodynamically and thermally developed. Calculate the heat transfer coefficient by taking the water properties at $50°C$.

**SOLUTION**  The properties of water at 50℃ are

$$\nu = 0.568 \times 10^{-6} \text{ m}^2/s \quad k = 0.64 \text{ W}/(m \cdot °C)$$

The Reynolds number for the flow is

$$Re = \frac{u_m D}{\nu} = \frac{0.0379 \times 0.02}{0.568 \times 10^{-6}} = 1335$$

Hence the flow is laminar. For the constant wall temperature at the boundary, the Nusselt number for laminar flow inside a circular tube in the hydrodynamically and thermally developed region is given by Eq. (8-23). Therefore the heat transfer coefficient is determined as

$$Nu = \frac{hD}{k} = 3.66$$
$$h = 3.66 \times \frac{0.64}{0.02} = 117.1 \text{ W}/(m^2 \cdot °C)$$

**EXAMPLE 8-7**  The wall of the tube in Example 8-6 is heated by electric resistance, thus maintaining a uniform surface heat flux. Calculate the heat transfer coefficient for this boundary condition.

**SOLUTION**  The Nusselt number for a constant wall heat flux boundary condition for laminar flow inside a circular tube in the hydrodynamically and thermally developed region is given by Eqs. (8-22). Therefore the heat transfer coefficient is determined as

$$h = \frac{48}{11}\frac{k}{D} = \frac{48}{11}\frac{0.64}{0.02} = 139.6 \text{ W}/(m^2 \cdot °C)$$

**EXAMPLE 8-8**  Consider the flow of water with a velocity of 0.0379 m/s through a square duct 2 cm by 2 cm whose walls are maintained at a uniform temperature $T_w = 100℃$. Assume that the flow is hydrodynamically and thermally developed. Determine the duct length required to heat the water from $T_1 = 30℃$ to $T_2 = 70℃$.

**SOLUTION**  The properties of water at the mean bulk temperature $T_b = (30 + 70)/2 = 50℃$ are
$$\rho = 990 \text{ kg/m}^3 \quad \nu = 0.568 \times 10^{-6} \text{ m}^2/s$$
$$k = 0.64 \text{ W}/(m \cdot °C) \quad c_p = 4184.4 \text{ J}(kg \cdot °C)$$

The hydraulic diameter of the duct is

$$D_h = \frac{4A}{P} = \frac{4(2 \times 2)}{4 \times 2} = 2 \text{ cm} = 0.02 \text{ m}$$

The Reynolds number becomes

$$\text{Re} = \frac{u_m D}{\nu} = \frac{0.0379 \times 0.02}{0.568 \times 10^{-6}} = 1335$$

The Nusselt number for a square duct with uniform wall temperature is given in Table 8.1. The heat transfer coefficient is determined as follows:

$$\text{Nu} = 2.976$$

$$h = \text{Nu}\frac{k}{D_h} = 2.976\frac{0.64}{0.02} = 95.23 \text{ W}/(\text{m}^2 \cdot {}^\circ\text{C})$$

The logarithmic mean temperature difference (LMTD) is

$$\text{LMTD} = \frac{T_2 - T_1}{\ln[(T_w - T_1)/(T_w - T_2)]} = 47.2^\circ C$$

Hence

$$Q = hA_s(\text{LMTD})$$

and

$$mc_p(T_2 - T_1) = hA_s(\text{LMTD})$$

where $m$ is the mass flow rate of water and $A_s$ is the surface area of the square duct.

$$m = \rho A u_m$$
$$= (990)(2 \times 2)(0.0379) = 0.015 \text{ kg}/s$$

and

$$(0.015 \text{ kg}/s)\left(4181.4\frac{J}{kg \cdot {}^\circ C}\right)[(70-30)^\circ C] = [95.23 \text{ W}/(\text{m}^2 \cdot {}^\circ\text{C})](A_s \text{ m}^2)(47.2^\circ\text{C})$$

gives

$$A_s = 0.5582 \text{ m}^2 = (4 \times 0.02)L$$

and

$$L \cong 7 \text{ m}$$

## 8.2.3 Hydrodynamic and Thermal Entry Lengths

It is of practical interest to know the hydrodynamic entrance length $L_h$ and the thermal entrance length $L_t$, for flow inside ducts. The hydrodynamic entrance length $L_h$ is defined, somewhat arbitrarily, as the length from the duct inlet required to achieve a maximum velocity of 99 percent of the corresponding fully developed magnitude. The thermal entrance length $L_t$, is defined, somewhat arbitrarily, as the length from the beginning of the heat transfer section required to achieve a local Nusselt number $\text{Nu}_x$ equal to 1.05 times the corresponding fully developed value.

**TABLE 8.2. Hydrodynamic and thermal entrance lengths for laminar flow inside ducts.**

| Geometry | $\dfrac{L_h/D_h}{Re}$ | $\dfrac{L_t/D_h}{Pe}$ Constant wall temperature | $\dfrac{L_t/D_h}{Pe}$ Constant wall heat flux |
|---|---|---|---|
| (circle, $D$) | 0.056 | 0.033 | 0.043 |
| (parallel plates, $2b$) | 0.011 | 0.008 | 0.012 |
| (rectangle $2a \times 2b$) $\dfrac{a}{b}=0.25$ | 0.075 | 0.054 | 0.042 |
| 0.50 | 0.085 | 0.049 | 0.057 |
| 1.0 | 0.09 | 0.041 | 0.066 |

In Table 8.2 we present the hydrodynamic entrance length $L_h$ for laminar flow inside conduits of various cross sections based on the definition discussed previously. Included in this table are the thermal entrance lengths for constant wall temperature and constant wall heat flux boundary conditions for thermally developing, hydrodynamically developed flow. In this table, $D_h$ is the hydraulic diameter, and the Reynolds number is based on the hydraulic diameter.

We note from Table 8.2 that for a given geometry, the hydrodynamic entry length $L_h$ depends on the Reynolds number only, whereas the thermal entry length $L_t$ depends on the Peclet number Pe, which is equal to the product of the Reynolds and Prandtl numbers. Therefore, for liquids that have a Prandtl number of the order of unity, $L_h$ and $L_t$ are of comparable magnitude. For fluids, such as oils, that have a large Prandtl number, $L_t \gg L_h$; and for liquid metals that have a small Prandtl number, $L_t \ll L_h$.

**EXAMPLE 8-9**   Determine the hydrodynamic and thermal entrance lengths in terms of the tube inside diameter $D$ for flow at a mean temperature $T = 60°C$ and Re= 200 inside a circular tube for mercury, air, water, ethylene glycol, and engine oil, under the constant wall heat flux boundary condition.

**SOLUTION**   The hydrodynamic entrance length $L_h$, for laminar flow inside a circular tube, is obtained from Table 8.2 as

$$L_h = 0.056 \mathrm{Re} D$$
$$= (0.056)(200)D \cong 11D$$

Thus, $L_h$ is approximately 11 diameters from the tube inlet for all the fluids considered here.

The thermal entrance length, given heat transfer under the constant wall heat flux boundary condition, is obtained from Table 8.2 as

$$L_t = 0.043\text{Re Pr}D$$
$$= (0.043)(200)\text{Pr}D = 8.6\text{Pr}D$$

Here $L_t$ depends on the Prandtl number, and for the fluids considered in this example it is determined as follows:

| Fluid | Pr | $L_t/d$ |
|---|---|---|
| Mercury | 0.02 | 0.17 |
| Air | 0.7 | 6 |
| Water | 3 | 26 |
| Ethylene glycol | 50 | 430 |
| Engine oil | 1050 | 9030 |

We note that for flow at Re= 200, the thermal entrance length varies from a fraction of the tube diameter for mercury to about 9000 diameters for engine oil , while the hydrodynamic entrance length is about 11 diameters for all the fluids considered here.

## 8.3. DEVELOPING LAMINAR FLOW

The problems of heat transfer for flow inside ducts at the regions near the inlet where the velocity and temperature profiles are developing are of interest in numerous engineering applications. For fluids that have a large Prandtl number, such as oils, the thermal entry lengths are very long, as illustrated in the example in the previous section. Therefore, the heat transfer relations developed previously for the fully developed region are not applicable for the developing region.

In heat transfer problems, the following two different situations need to be taken into consideration:

1. There are situations, as illustrated in Fig. 8.2, in which the heat transfer starts as soon as fluid enters the duct. Then, both the velocity and the thermal boundary layers begin to develop simultaneously, and $L_h$ and $L_t$ are measured from the tube inlet. The region where the velocity and temperature boundary layers grow together is called the *simultaneously developing region*.

2. In some situations, heat transfer to the fluid begins after an isothermal calming section, as illustrated in Fig. 8.4. For such cases, $L_h$ is measured from the duct inlet, because the velocity boundary layer begins to develop as soon as the fluid enters the duct, but $L_t$ is measured from the location where the heat transfer starts, because the thermal boundary layer begins to develop in the heat transfer section. The region $L_t$ is referred to as the *hydrodynamically developed, thermally developing region*.

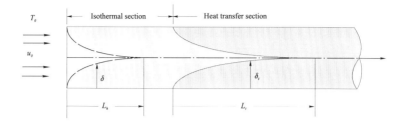

**FIG. 8.4.** Hydrodynamically developed, thermal developing region concept.

In the study of heat transfer coefficients for flow through ducts, a distinction should be made between these two physically different situations. Therefore we examine below the determination of the heat transfer coefficient for these two cases separately.

### 8.3.1 Thermally Developing, Hydrodynamically Developed Laminar Flow

Consider the flow of a fluid inside a duct, as illustrated in Fig. 8.4, in which there is an isothermal section to allow for velocity development before the fluid enters the heat transfer zone. The physical situation is representative of that for fluids that have a large Prandtl number, such as oils, for which the hydrodynamic entrance length is very small in comparison with the thermal entrance length. A classic solution for laminar forced convection inside a circular tube subject to a uniform wall surface temperature with fully developed velocity profile and developing temperature profile was given by Graetz about 100 years ago. A vast amount of literature now exists on the extension of the Graetz problem for boundary conditions other than the uniform surface temperature and geometries other than a circular tube. Figure 8.5 shows the local Nusselt number $\mathrm{Nu}_x$ and the average Nus-

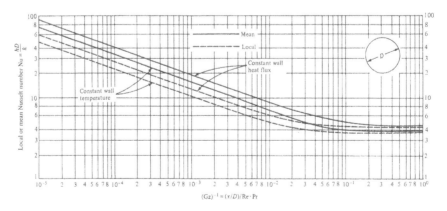

**FIG. 8.5.** Mean and local Nusselt number for thermally developing, hydrodynamically developed laminar flow inside a circular tube.

selt number $\mathrm{Nu}_m$ for laminar flow inside a circular tube plotted against the dimensionless parameter $(x/D)/(\mathrm{Re}\,\mathrm{Pr})$, where $x$ is the axial distance along the conduit measured from the beginning of the heated section. The inverse of this dimensionless parameter is called the Graetz number Gz:

$$(Gz)^{-1} = \frac{x/D}{Re\,Pr} \qquad (8\text{-}27)$$

Here $D$ is the inside diameter of the tube, and the Reynolds and Prandtl numbers are defined as

$$Re = \frac{u_m D}{\nu} \qquad Pr = \frac{\nu}{\alpha} \qquad (8\text{-}28)$$

In Fig. 8.5, the results are given for both the constant wall temperature and constant wall heat flux boundary conditions. The average Nusselt number represents the average value of the local Nusselt number over a distance from the inlet to the location considered. We note from Fig. 8.5 that at distances sufficiently far away from the tube inlet, the asymptotic values of the Nusselt number for the constant wall temperature and the constant wall heat flux are 3.66 and 4.364, respectively. These results are the same as those shown in Table 8.1 for the fully developed region.

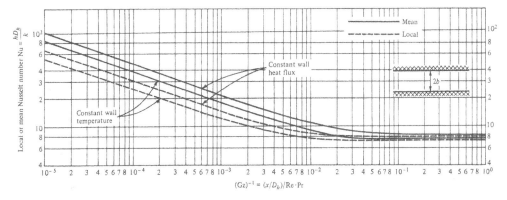

**FIG. 8.6.** Mean and local Nusselt numbers for thermally developing, hydrodynamically developed laminar flow between parallel plates.

Figure 8.6 gives the local and average Nusselt numbers for thermally developing, hydrodynamically developed laminar flow between parallel plates plotted against the dimensionless parameter $(x/D_h)/(Re\,Pr)$, where $D_h$ is the hydraulic diameter and $x$ is the distance along the plate measured from the beginning of the heating section in the direction of flow. The Nusselt numbers are given for both constant wall heat flux and constant wall temperature. The asymptotic values of the Nusselt numbers 8.235 and 7.541 for constant wall heat flux and constant wall temperature, respectively, are the same as those given in Table 8-1 for the hydrodynamically and thermally developed region.

Figure 8.7 shows the mean Nusselt numbers for thermally developing, hydrodynamically developed laminar flow inside a square duct plotted against the dimensionless parameter $(x/D_h)/(Re\,Pr)$. The asymptotic values 3.608 and 2.976 for the constant wall heat flux and constant wall temperature, respectively, are the same as those for $Nu_H$ and $Nu_T$ given in Table 8-1.

303

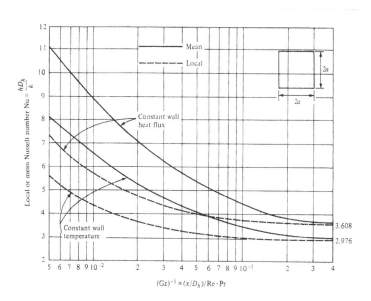

**FIG. 8.7.** Mean and local Nusselt numbers for thermally developing, hydrodynamically developed laminar flow inside a square duct. Based on data given by Chandrupatla and Sastri (1977)

## 8.3.2 Simultaneously Developing Laminar Flow

When heat transfer starts as soon as the fluid enters the duct, as illustrated in Fig. 8.2, the velocity and temperature profiles start developing simultaneously. The analysis of temperature distribution in the flow, and hence of heat transfer between the fluid and the walls, for such situations is more involved because the velocity distribution varies in the axial direction as well as normal to it.

Figure 8.8 shows the mean Nusselt number for simultaneously developing laminar flow inside a circular tube subject to constant wall temperature. The results are given for the Prandtl numbers 0.7, 2, 5 and $\infty$ and are plotted against the dimensionless parameter $(x/D)/(\text{Re Pr})$. The case for Pr= $\infty$ corresponds to the thermally developing but hydrodynamically developed flow, discussed earlier. Clearly, the Nusselt number for simultaneously developing flow is higher than that for hydrodynamically developed flow. It is also apparent from this figure that for fluids with a large Prandtl number, the Nusselt number for simultaneously developing flow is very close to that for thermally developing, hydrodynamically developed flow. The asymptotic Nusselt number for all the cases shown in this figure is equal to the fully developed value 3.66.

Figure 8.9 shows the mean Nusselt number for simultaneously developing flow inside a parallel-plate channel subjected to the same constant temperature at both walls. The results are given for the Prandtl numbers 0.72, 10, and $\infty$ and are plotted against the dimensionless parameter $(x/D_h)/(\text{Re Pr})$. Here, the case for Pr= $\infty$ corresponds to thermally developing, but hydrodynamically developed flow.

304

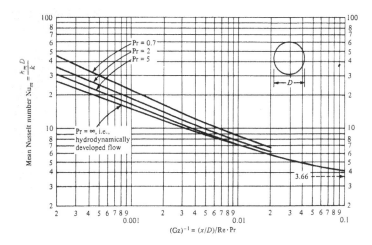

**FIG. 8.8.** Mean Nusselt numbers for simultaneously developing laminar flow inside a circular tube subjected to constant wall temperature. Compiled based on the results from Shah (1975) and Hornbeck (1975).

### 8.3.3 Empirical Correlations

So far we have discussed heat transfer results based on theoretical predictions obtained from the solution of governing equations of motion and energy. In parallel to such studies, empirical relations for predicting the mean Nusselt number for laminar flow in the entrance region of a circular tube also have been developed. One such correlation for the mean Nusselt number for laminar flow in a circular tube at constant wall temperature is given by Hausen as

$$\mathrm{Nu}_m = 3.66 + \frac{0.0668 \mathrm{Gz}}{1 + 0.04(\mathrm{Gz})^{2/3}} \qquad (8\text{-}29)$$

where

$$\mathrm{Nu}_m = \frac{h_m D}{k} \qquad (8\text{-}30\mathrm{a})$$

$$\mathrm{Gz} = \frac{\mathrm{Re\,Pr}}{L/D} \qquad L = \text{distance from the inlet} \qquad (8\text{-}30\mathrm{b})$$

$$\mathrm{Re} = \frac{u_m D}{\nu} \qquad (8\text{-}30\mathrm{c})$$

This relation is recommended for Gz< 100 (see Table 8.3), and all properties are evaluated at the fluid bulk mean temperature. Clearly, as the length $L$ increases, the Nusselt number approaches the asymptotic value 3.66.

A rather simple empirical correlation has been proposed by Sieder and Tate to predict the mean Nusselt number for laminar flow in a circular tube at constant wall temperature:

$$\mathrm{Nu}_m = 1.86(\mathrm{Gz})^{1/3} \left( \frac{\mu_w}{\mu_b} \right)^{0.14} \qquad (8\text{-}31)$$

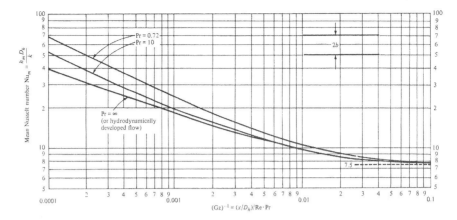

**FIG. 8.9.** Mean Nusselt number for simultaneous developing laminar flow between parallel plates subjected to the same constant temperature the walls.
Compiled based on the results of C.L. Hwang given in Shah (1975).

And it is recommended for

$$0.48 < \text{Pr} < 16{,}700 \qquad (8\text{-}32a)$$

$$0.0044 < \frac{\mu_w}{\mu_b} < 9.75 \qquad (8\text{-}32b)$$

$$(\text{Gz})^{1/3} \left( \frac{\mu_w}{\mu_b} \right)^{0.14} > 2 \qquad (8\text{-}32c)$$

All physical properties are evaluated at the fluid bulk mean temperature, except for $\mu_w$, which is evaluated at the wall temperature. The Graetz number Gz is defined by Eq. (8-30b). The last restriction implies that this equation cannot be used for extremely long tubes, because, as Gz$\to$ 0 with increasing length, the equation has no provision to yield the correct asymptotic value, as is the case for the Hausen equation.

**TABLE 8.3  Simultaneously developing laminar flow inside a circular tube.**

| $\text{Gz}^{-1} = \dfrac{x/D}{\text{Re Pr}}$ | $\text{Nu}_m$ | $\text{Nu}_m \left( \frac{\mu_w}{\mu_b} \right)^{0.14}$ | $\text{Nu}_m$ from Fig. 8.8 | | |
|---|---|---|---|---|---|
| | Eq. (8-29) | Eq. (8-31) | Pr= 0.7 | Pr= 5 | Pr= $\infty$ |
| 0.1 | 4.22 | 4.0 | | | 4.16 |
| 0.02 | 5.82 | 6.85 | 6.8 | 5.8 | 5.8 |
| 0.01 | 7.25 | 8.63 | 8.7 | 7.2 | 7.2 |
| 0.001 | 17.0 | 18.60 | 22.2 | 16.9 | 15.4 |
| 0.001 | 30.0 | 31.80 | 44.1 | 30.3 | 26.7 |

In Table 8.3, we compare the mean Nusselt numbers calculated from Eqs. (8-29) and (8-31) and obtained from Fig. 8.8. The Sieder and Tate equation underestimates $\text{Nu}_m$ for Gz$>$ 10, which is consistent with the restriction of Eq. (8-32c). The results given in

Table 8.3 show that the theoretical prediction of the Nusselt number for simultaneously developing flow given in Fig. 8.8 is reasonably accurate and includes the effects of the Prandtl number.

**EXAMPLE 8-10**  Engine oil at 40°C with a flow rate of 0.3 kg/s enters a 2.5-cm-ID, 40-m-long tube maintained at a uniform temperature of 100°C. The flow is hydro-dynamically developed. Determine (*a*) the mean heat transfer coefficient, and (*b*) the outlet temperature of the oil.

**SOLUTION**  The Reynolds number should be determined to establish whether the flow is laminar or turbulent. The mean fluid temperature inside the tube cannot be calculated yet because the fluid exit temperature is not known. Therefore, we start by evaluating the physical properties of the fluid at an inlet temperature of, say, 40°C. (This assumption will be checked at the end of calculations.) We have

$$\rho = 876 \text{ kg/m}^3 \qquad c_p = 1964 \ J/(kg \cdot °C)$$
$$\nu = 2.4 \times 10^{-4} \text{ m}^2/s \quad h = 0.144 \text{ W}/(\text{m} \cdot °C)$$
$$\text{Pr} = 2870$$

Then

$$u_m = \frac{m}{\rho A} = \frac{0.3}{876(\pi/4)(0.025)^2} = 0.7 \text{ m/s}$$

$$\text{Re} = \frac{u_m D}{\nu} = \frac{0.7(0.025)}{2.4 \times 10^{-4}} = 72.7$$

and the flow is laminar. For fluids with a high Prandtl number (e.g., the oils), the hydrodynamic entrance length is short compared with the thermal entrance length. Therefore, the flow can be regarded as thermally developing and hydrodynamically developed. We calculate the parameter

$$\frac{L/D}{\text{Re Pr}} = \frac{40/0.025}{72.7 \times 2870} = 7.7 \times 10^{-3}$$

From Fig. 8.5, the mean Nusselt number for constant wall temperature is determined as

$$\text{Nu}_m = \frac{h_m D}{k} \cong 7.5$$

$$h_m = 7.5\frac{k}{D} = 7.5 \times \frac{0.144}{0.025}$$
$$= 43.2 \text{ W}/(\text{m}^2 \cdot °C)$$

To calculate the outlet temperature $T_{out}$, we consider an overall energy balance for the length $L$ of the tube, as

Heat supplied to fluid from wall $=$ energy removed by fluid by convection

$$h_m(\pi DL)\Delta T_m = (\dot{m}c_p)(T_{out} - T_{in})$$

where $\Delta T_m$ is the logarithmic mean temperature difference. Introducing $\Delta T_m$, we have

$$h_m(\pi DL)\frac{T_{out} - T_{in}}{\ln[(T_w - T_{in})/(T_w - T_{out})]} = (\dot{m}c_p)(T_{out} - T_{in})$$

or

$$\ln\frac{T_w - T_{in}}{T_w - T_{out}} = \frac{h_m(\pi DL)}{\dot{m}c_p}$$

$$\frac{T_w - T_{out}}{T_w - T_{in}} = \exp\left(-\frac{h_m(\pi DL)}{\dot{m}c_p}\right)$$

$$\frac{100 - T_{out}}{100 - 40} = \exp\left(-\frac{\pi \times 0.025 \times 40 \times 43.2}{0.3 \times 1964}\right) = 0.7943$$

$$T_{out} = 52.34°C$$

The results can be improved by repeating the above calculations for physical properties evaluated at the bulk fluid temperature $(T_{in} + T_{out})/2 = (40 + 52.34)/2 = 46.17°C$.

**EXAMPLE 8-11** Water at an average temperature of 60°C with a flow rate of 0.015 kg/s flows through a 2.5-cm-ID tube which is maintained at a uniform temperature.

($a$) Assuming a fully developed velocity profile, determine the local heat transfer coefficients at locations 1, 2, and 3 m from the inlet.

($b$) Assuming simultaneously developing velocity and temperature, determine the mean heat transfer coefficients over distances of 1, 2, and 3 m from the inlet.

**SOLUTION** Various properties for water at $T_b = 60°C$ are taken as

$$\rho = 985.5 \text{ kg/m}^3 \qquad \mu_b = 4.71 \times 10^{-4} \text{ kg/(m·s)}$$
$$k = 0.651 \text{ W/(m·°C)} \qquad Pr = 3.02$$

Then

$$u_m = \frac{m}{\rho A} = \frac{0.015}{(985.5)(\pi/4)(0.025)^2} = 0.031 \text{ m/s}$$

and the Reynolds number becomes

$$\text{Re} = \frac{\rho u_m D}{\mu} = \frac{(985.5)(0.031)(0.025)}{4.71 \times 10^{-4}} = 1621$$

hence, the flow is laminar.

($a$) For the hydrodynamically developed flow, we obtain the Nusselt number from Fig. 8.5. We have

$$\text{Gz}^{-1} = \frac{x/D}{\text{Re Pr}} = \frac{x/0.025}{1621 \times 3.02} = 8.2 \times 10^{-3} \times x$$

For the given tube lengths the Gz number can be calculated and the local heat transfer coefficient $h(x)$ can be determined from

$$h(x) = \frac{k}{D}\text{Nu}_x = \frac{0.651}{0.025}\text{Nu}_x = 26\text{Nu}_x$$

| $x$, m | $\text{Gz}^{-1}$ | $\text{Nu}_x$ (From Fig. 8.8) | $h(x)$, W/(m$^2 \cdot$°C) |
|---|---|---|---|
| 1 | $8.2 \times 10^{-3}$ | 5.0 | 130 |
| 2 | $1.64 \times 10^{-2}$ | 4.4 | 114 |
| 3 | $2.46 \times 10^{-2}$ | 4.0 | 104 |

($b$) For the simultaneously developing flow, we use Fig. 8.8.

## 8.4. FULLY DEVELOPED TURBULENT FLOW

Turbulent flow is important in engineering applications because it is involved in the vast majority of fluid flow and heat transfer problems encountered in engineering practice. The very simple visual demonstration of the turbulent flow is by injecting a dye in a pipe flow as illustrated in Fi.8.10.

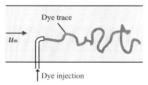

**FIG. 8.10.** Injection of dye in a duct flow to observe the turbulent flow behaviour.

We show how to determine the friction factor and heat transfer in turbulent flow inside conduits.

## 8.4.1 Friction Factor

For fully developed turbulent flow inside smooth pipes, an approximate analytic expression for the friction factor $f$ is given in the form

$$f = (1.82 \log \text{Re} - 1.64)^{-2} \tag{8-33}$$

The hydrodynamic development for turbulent flow occurs for $x/D$ much shorter than that for laminar flow. For example, hydrodynamically developed flow conditions occur for $x/D$ greater than about 10 to 20.

Somewhat simpler approximate expressions for $f$ are also given in the form

$$\boxed{f = 0.316\mathrm{Re}^{-0.25}} \quad \text{for Re} < 2 \times 10^4 \qquad (8\text{-}34\text{a})$$

$$\boxed{f = 0.184\mathrm{Re}^{-0.2}} \quad \text{for } 2 \times 10^4 < \text{Re} < 3 \times 10^5 \qquad (8\text{-}34\text{b})$$

In laminar flow the surface roughness does not affect the friction factor, but in turbulent flow the friction factor is significantly affected by the surface roughness. J. Nikuradse (1933) and made extensive experiments with turbulent flow inside artificially roughened pipes over a wide range of relative roughnesses $\lambda/D$ (i.e., protrusion height to diameter ratio), from about ll to 310. The sand-grain roughness used in these experiments has been adopted as a standard for the effects of roughness. A friction factor correlation has also been developed for turbulent flow inside rough pipes based on experiments performed with rough pipes. The roughness effect can be described by (a) flow area constriction and (b) increase in the wall shear stress.

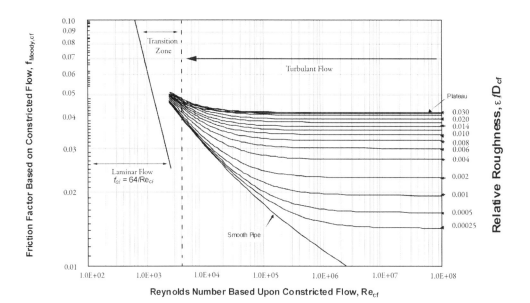

**FIG. 8.11.** Modified Moody chart for friction factor for pressure drop inside circular pipes.
Adapted with permission from Kandlikar. Complied based on Kandlikar, Schmitt, Carrano, Taylor (2005).

Figure 8.11 shows the friction factor chart for fully developed turbulent flow inside smooth and rough pipes including the roughness which is called the Moody chart (Moody, 1944). Here the effects with the use of the constricted flow diameter introduced by S. Kandlikar and his coworkers reported in 2005 for $\epsilon/D > 0.03$. It should be noted that the constricted flow area effect becomes important only in very small pipes, such as in micro channels. Otherwise simply use the friction factor as

$$f_{Darcy,cf} = f$$

and Modified Moody chart applies for both constricted and non-constricted flows.

Included in this figure is the friction factor $f_{Darcy,cf} = 64/Re_{cf}$ for laminar flow inside circular pipes. Here the $Re_{cf}$ is based on the effective flow dimeter of the constricted flow,

$$D_{cf} = D - 2\epsilon.$$

where $D_{cf}$ is the constricted flow diameter and $D$ is the tube base diameter, and $\epsilon$ is the average roughness height.

We note that if the roughness dimensions $\epsilon$ is insignificant compared to the flow diameter, the Modified moody chart will give the same numbers as the original Moddy chart. It is apparent that for the laminar flow the surface roughness has no effect on the friction factor. For the turbulent flow smooth surfaces and for large diameter pipes $f_{Darcy,cf} = f$. For turbulent flow, however, the friction factor is at a minimum for a smooth pipe.

However with smaller channel sizes employed in the microchannels in the range 10 $\mu m$ - 200 $\mu m$ and minichannels the range 200 $\mu m$ - 3 mm, the relative roughness $\epsilon/D$ can be significantly greater than the threshold of 0.05 used in the Moody diagram for a given average roughness $\epsilon$. In those situations one should use the Modified Moody chart with

$$\frac{dP}{dx} = \frac{8m^{*2} f_{Darcy,cf}}{\pi^2 \rho D_{cf}^5}$$

where $dP/dx$ is the pressure gradient in the flow direction, $\rho$ is the density and $m^*$ is the mass flow rate of the fluid.

In general the laminar flow is confined to the region Re< 2000. The transitional turbulence occurs in the region 2000 <Re< 10,000. The fully turbulent flow occurs in the region Re> $10^4$.

## 8.4.2 Heat Transfer Coefficient

The analysis of heat transfer for turbulent flow is much more involved than that for laminar flow. Therefore, a large number of empirical correlations have been developed to determine the heat transfer coefficient.

**DITTUS-BOELTER EQUATION.** A relatively simple expression for the Nusselt number is given by Dittus and Boelter in the form

$$\boxed{\text{Nu} = 0.023 \text{Re}^{0.8}\text{Pr}^n} \tag{8-35}$$

where $n = 0.4$ for heating ($T_w > T_b$) and $n = 0.3$ for cooling ($T_w < T_b$) of the fluid, and

Nu= $hD/k$, Re= $u_m D/\nu$ and Pr= $\nu/\alpha$. Equation (8.35) is applicable for smooth pipes:

$$0.7 \;<\; \mathrm{Pr} < 160$$
$$\mathrm{Re} \;>\; 10{,}000$$
$$\frac{L}{D} \;>\; 60$$

and for small to moderate temperature differences. Fluid properties are evaluated at the bulk mean temperature $T_b$.

**SIEDER AND TATE EQUATION.** For situations involving a large property variation, the Sieder and Tate equation is recommended:

$$\mathrm{Nu} = 0.027 \mathrm{Re}^{0.8} \mathrm{Pr}^{1/3} \left( \frac{\mu_b}{\mu_w} \right)^{0.14} \tag{8-36}$$

This equation is applicable for smooth pipes:

$$0.7 \;<\; \mathrm{Pr} < 16{,}700$$
$$\mathrm{Re} \;>\; 10{,}000$$
$$\frac{L}{D} \;>\; 60$$

All properties are evaluated at the bulk mean temperature $T_b$, except for $\mu_w$, which is evaluated at the wall temperature.

**PETUKHOV EQUATION.** The previous relations are relatively simple, but they give maximum errors of $\pm 25$ percent in the range of $0.67 <\mathrm{Pr}< 100$ and apply to turbulent flow in smooth ducts. A more accurate correlation, which is also applicable for rough ducts, has been developed by Petukhov and coworkers at the Moscow Institute for High Temperature:

$$\mathrm{Nu} = \frac{\mathrm{Re}\,\mathrm{Pr}}{X} \left( \frac{f}{8} \right) \left( \frac{\mu_b}{\mu_w} \right)^n \tag{8-37a}$$

where

$$X = 1.07 + 12.7(\mathrm{Pr}^{2/3} - 1) \left( \frac{f}{8} \right)^{1/2} \tag{8-37b}$$

for liquids

$$n = \begin{cases} 0.11 & \text{heating } (T_w > T_b) \\ 0.25 & \text{cooling } (T_w < T_b) \end{cases}$$

and for gases, although $n = 0$, the property variation will be explained later. Equations

(8-37*a*) and (8-37*b*) are applicable for

$$10^4 \; < \; \text{Re} < 5 \times 10^6$$
$$2 \; < \; \text{Pr} < 140 \quad \text{with 5 to 6 percent error}$$
$$0.5 \; < \; \text{Pr} < 2000 \quad \text{with 10 percent error}$$
$$0.08 \; < \; \frac{\mu_b}{\mu_w} < 40$$

We note that $\mu_w/\mu_b < 1$ when a liquid is heated and $\mu_w/\mu_b > 1$ when the liquid is cooled. All physical properties, except for $\mu_w$, are evaluated at the bulk temperature. The friction factor can be evaluated from Eq. (8-33) for smooth pipes, or obtained from the Modified Moody given in Fig. 8.11 for both smooth and rough tubes.

### 8.4.3 Noncircular Ducts

So far, discussion of the friction factor and heat transfer coefficient for turbulent flow has been restricted to flow inside circular tubes. Numerous engineering applications involve turbulent forced convection inside ducts of noncircular cross section. The friction factor for a circular tube given by the Moody chart (Fig. 8.10) applies to turbulent flow inside noncircular ducts if the tube diameter $D$ is replaced by the hydraulic diameter of the noncircular duct, defined by Eq. (8-25); that is,

$$D_h = \frac{4A_c}{P} \tag{8-38}$$

where $A_c$ is the cross-sectional area for flow and $P$ is the wetted perimeter.

For noncircular ducts, the turbulent flow also occurs for Re> 2300, where the Reynolds number is based on the hydraulic diameter.

With noncircular ducts, the heat transfer coefficient varies around the perimeter and approaches zero near the sharp corners. Therefore, for certain situations, difficulties may arise in applying the circular-tube results to a noncircular duct by using the hydraulic diameter concept.

### 8.4.4 Effects of Surface Roughness and Property Variation

The heat transfer coefficient for turbulent flow in rough-walled duct is higher than that for smooth-walled ducts because roughness disturbs the viscous sublayer. The increased heat transfer due to roughness is achieved at the expense of increased friction to fluid flow. The correlation of heat transfer for turbulent flow in rough-walled ducts is very sparse in the literature. The Petukhov equation (8-37) can be recommended for predicting the heat transfer coefficient in hydrodynamically and thermally developed turbulent flow in rough pipes, because the friction factor $f$ (here we have $f_{Darcy,cf} = f$), can be obtained from the Modified Moody chart (Fig. 8.11) once the relative roughness of the pipe is known.

When heat transfer to or from a fluid flowing inside a duct takes place, the temperature varies over the flow cross section of the duct. For most liquids, although the specific heat and thermal conductivity are rather insensitive to temperature, the viscosity decreases significantly with temperature. For gases, the viscosity and thermal conductivity increase by approximately 0.8 power of the temperature. Therefore, the property variation affects both the heat transfer coefficient and the friction factor.

To compensate for the effects of nonisothermal conditions in the fluid, the Sieder and Tate equation (8-36) and the Petukhov equation (8-37) include a viscosity correction term in the form $(\mu_w/\mu_b)^n$.

For liquids, the variation of viscosity is responsible for the property effects. Therefore, viscosity corrections of the following power-law form are found to be sufficiently good approximations:

$$\frac{\text{Nu}}{\text{Nu}_{\text{iso}}} = \left(\frac{\mu_b}{\mu_w}\right)^n, \qquad \frac{f}{f_{\text{iso}}} = \left(\frac{\mu_b}{\mu_w}\right)^k \tag{8-39}$$

where

$$\mu_b = \text{viscosity evaluated at bulk mean temperature}$$
$$\mu_w = \text{viscosity evaluated at wall temperature}$$
$$\text{Nu}_{\text{iso}}, \text{Nu} = \text{Nusselt number under isothermal and nonisothermal}$$
$$\text{conditions, respectively}$$
$$f_{\text{iso}}, f = \text{friction factor under isothermal and nonisothermal}$$
$$\text{conditions, respectively}$$

In the case of gases, the viscosity, thermal conductivity, and density depend on the absolute temperature. Therefore, temperature corrections of the following form are found to be adequate for most practical applications:

$$\frac{\text{Nu}}{\text{Nu}_{\text{iso}}} = \left(\frac{T_b}{T_w}\right)^n, \qquad \frac{f}{f_{\text{iso}}} = \left(\frac{T_b}{T_w}\right)^k \tag{8-40}$$

where $T_b$ and $T_w$ are the absolute bulk mean and wall temperatures, respectively.

A number of experimental investigations and variable-property analyses to determine the values of the exponents $n$ and $k$ appearing in Eqs. (8-39) and (8-40) have been reported in the literature. In Table 8.4 we present recommended values of these exponents. Thus, by using the corrections given by Eqs. (8-39) and (8-40), we can adjust the Nusselt number and the friction factor for ideal isothermal conditions for the effects of property variations, if no viscosity correction is included in the equation.

TABLE 8.4  The exponents $n$ and $k$ of Eqs. (8-39) and (8-40).

| Type of flow | Fluid | $T_w$ =Constant condition | $n$ | $k$ |
|---|---|---|---|---|
| Laminar | Liquid | Cooling or heating | 0.14 | |
| | Gas | Cooling or heating | 0 | −1 |
| Turbulent | Liquid | Cooling | 0.25 | |
| | Liquid | Heating | 0.11 | |
| | Liquid | Cooling or heating | | −0.25 |
| | Gas | Cooling | 0 | 0.1 |
| | Gas | Heating | 0.5 | 0.1 |

**EXAMPLE 8-12**  Water flows with a mean velocity of $u_m = 2$ m/s inside a circular smooth pipe of inside diameter $D = 5$ cm. The pipe is of commercial steel, and its wall is maintained at a uniform temperature $T_w = 100°C$ by condensing steam on its outer surface. At a location where the fluid is hydrodynamically and thermally developed, the bulk mean temperature of the water is $T_b = 60°C$. Calculate the heat transfer coefficient $h$ by using: $(a)$ The Dittus and Boelter equation, $(b)$ The Sieder and Tate equation and $(c)$ The Petukhov equation.

**SOLUTION**  The physical properties at $T_b = 60°C$ are taken as

$$\mu_b = 4.71 \times 10^{-4} \text{ kg/(m·s)} \quad \mu_w = 2.82 \times 10^{-4} \text{ kg/(m·s)}$$
$$k = 0.651 \text{ W/(m·°C)} \quad \text{Pr} = 3.02 \quad \text{Re} = 2.04 \times 10^5$$

The friction factor for smooth pipe at Re= $2.04 \times 10^5$ is obtained from Fig. 8.10 as $f = 0.0152$. $(a)$ The Dittus and Boelter equation gives

$$\text{Nu} = 0.023(2.04 \times 10^5)^{0.8}(3.02)^{0.4} = 633$$
$$h = 633\frac{0.651}{0.05} = 8242 \text{ W/(m}^2 \cdot °C)$$

$(b)$ The Sider and Tate equation gives

$$\text{Nu} = 0.027(2.04 \times 10^5)^{0.8}(3.02)^{1/3}\left(\frac{4.71}{2.82}\right)^{0.14} = 704$$
$$h = 704\frac{0.651}{0.05} = 9166 \text{ W/(m}^2 \cdot °C)$$

$(c)$ The Petukhov equation gives

$$\text{Nu} = \frac{(2.04 \times 10^5)(3.02)}{X}\left(\frac{0.0152}{8}\right)\left(\frac{4.71}{2.82}\right)^{0.11}$$

where

$$X = 1.07 + 12.7(3.02^{2/3} - 1)\left(\frac{0.0152}{8}\right)^{1/2}$$

Then

$$\begin{aligned} \text{Nu} &= 741.65 \\ h &= 741.65\frac{0.651}{0.05} = 9656 \ \text{W}/(\text{m}^2 \cdot {}^\circ\text{C}) \end{aligned}$$

## 8.5. LIQUID METALS FLOWS

The liquid metals are characterized by their very low Prandtl numbers, which vary from about 0.02 to 0.003. Therefore, the heat transfer correlations in previous sections do not apply to liquid metals: their range of validity does not extend to such low values of the Prandtl number.

Lithium, sodium, potassium, bismuth, and sodium-potassium mixtures are among the common low-melting metals that are suitable for heat transfer purposes as liquid metals. There has been interest in liquid-metal heat transfer in engineering applications because large amounts of heat can be transferred at high temperatures with a relatively low temperature difference between the fluid and the tube wall surface. The high heat transfer rates result from the high thermal conductivity of liquid metals compared with that of ordinary liquids and gases. Therefore, they are particularly attractive as heat transfer media in nuclear reactors and many other high-temperature, high-heat-flux applications. The major difficulty in their use lies in handling them. They are corrosive, and some may cause violent reactions when they come into contact with water or air.

As discussed previously, when Pr≪ 1, as in liquid metals, the thermal boundary layer is much thicker than the velocity boundary layer. This implies that the temperature profile, and hence the heat transfer for liquid metals, is not influenced by the velocity sublayer or viscosity. So in such cases one expects rather weak dependence of heat transfer on the Prandtl number. Thus most empirical correlations of liquid-metal heat transfer have been made by plotting the Nusselt number against the Peclet number, Pe=Re Pr.

We summarize now some empirical and theoretical correlations for heat transfer to liquid metals in fully developed turbulent flow inside a circular tube under the uniform wall heat flux and uniform wall temperature boundary conditions.

### 8.5.1 Uniform Wall Heat Flux

Lubarsky and Kaufman proposed the following empirical relation for calculating the Nusselt number in fully developed turbulent flow of liquid metals in smooth pipes:

$$\boxed{\text{Nu} = 0.625\text{Pe}^{0.4}} \tag{8-41}$$

where

$$\text{Peclet number} \equiv \text{Pe} = \text{Re Pr}$$

for $10^2 <$Pe$< 10^4$, $L/D > 60$, and properties evaluated at the bulk mean fluid temperature.

Skupinski, Tortel, and Vautrey, basing their heat transfer experiments on sodium-potassium mixtures, recommended the following expression for liquid metals in fully developed turbulent flow in smooth pipes:

$$\mathrm{Nu} = 4.82 + 0.0185\mathrm{Pe}^{0.827} \tag{8-42}$$

for $3.6 \times 10^3 <$Re$< 9.05 \times 10^5$, $10^2 <$Pe$< 10^4$, and $L/D > 60$. The physical properties are evaluated at the bulk mean fluid temperature.

Equation (8-41) predicts a lower Nusselt number than Eq. (8-42); therefore it is on the conservative side.

## 8.5.2 Uniform Wall Temperature

Expressions for the Nusselt number for fully developed turbulent flow of liquid metals in smooth pipes subject to uniform wall temperature boundary conditions have also been developed by empirical fits to the results of the theoretical solutions. We present now the results of such solutions.

Azer and Chao:

$$\mathrm{Nu} = 5.0 + 0.05\mathrm{Pe}^{0.77}\mathrm{Pr}^{0.25} \quad \text{for Pr} < 0.1, \ \text{Pe} < 15,000 \tag{8-43}$$

Notter and sleicher:

$$\mathrm{Nu} = 4.8 + 0.0156\mathrm{Pe}^{0.85}\mathrm{Pr}^{0.08} \quad \text{for } 0.004 < \text{Pr} < 0.1, \ \text{Re} < 500,000 \tag{8-44}$$

In calculating Nu, Pe, and Pr in these expressions, the physical properties are evaluated at the bulk mean fluid temperature; the expressions are applicable for $L/D > 60$.

## 8.5.3 Thermal Entry Region

The previous relations for liquid metals in turbulent flow are applicable in the fully developed region. Sleicher, Awad, and Notter examined the heat transfer calculations of Notter and Sleicher in the thermal entry region for both uniform wall heat flux and uniform wall temperature. They noted that the local Nusselt number for the thermal entrance region can be correlated within 20 percent with

$$\mathrm{Nu}_x = \mathrm{Nu}\left(1 + \frac{2}{x/D}\right) \quad \text{for } \frac{x}{D} > 4 \tag{8-45}$$

where

$$\mathrm{Nu} = 6.3 + 0.0167\mathrm{Pe}^{0.85}\mathrm{Pr}^{0.08} \quad \text{for uniform wall heat flux} \tag{8-46}$$

$$\mathrm{Nu} = 4.8 + 0.0156\mathrm{Pe}^{0.85}\mathrm{Pr}^{0.08} \quad \text{for uniform wall temperature} \tag{8-47}$$

and applies in the range $0.004 <$Pr$< 0.1$.

**EXAMPLE 8-13**  Liquid sodium at 180°C with a mass flow rate of 3 kg/s enters a 2.5-cm-ID tube whose wall is maintained at a uniform temperature of 240°C. Calculate the tube length required to heat sodium to 230°C.

**SOLUTION**  The physical properties of sodium at the bulk mean temperature $T_b$,

$$T_b = \frac{180 + 230}{2} = 205°C$$

are taken as

$$\rho = 907.5 \text{ kg/m}^3 \qquad c_p = 1339 \ J/(kg \cdot °C)$$
$$\nu = 0.501 \times 10^{-6} \text{ m}^2/s \quad k = 80.81 \text{ W}/(m \cdot °C) \quad \text{Pr} = 0.0075$$

Then

$$u_m = \frac{m}{\rho A} = \frac{3}{(907.5)(\pi/4)(0.025)^2} = 6.73 \text{ m/s}$$

and

$$\text{Re} = \frac{u_m D}{\nu} = \frac{6.73 \times 0.025}{0.501 \times 10^{-6}} = 3.36 \times 10^5$$
$$\text{Pe} = \text{Re Pr} = (3.36 \times 10^5)(0.0075) = 2520$$

Using Eq. (8-44), we find

$$\text{Nu} = 4.8 + 0.0156\text{Pe}^{0.85}\text{Pr}^{0.08}$$
$$= 4.8 + 0.0156(2520)^{0.85}(0.0075)^{0.08} = 13$$

$$h = \frac{k}{D}\text{Nu} = \frac{80.81}{0.025} \times 13 = 42,021 \text{ W}/(m^2 \cdot °C)$$

The gross energy balance gives

$$mc_p(T_2 - T_1) = h(\pi DL)\frac{T_2 - T_1}{\ln[(T_w - T_1)/(T_w - T_2)]}$$
$$(3)(1339) = \frac{(42,02l)(\pi)(0.025L)}{1.792}$$

gives

$$L = 2.18 \text{ m}$$

We check our assumption:

$$\frac{L}{D} = \frac{2.18}{0.025} = 87 > 60$$

hence the use of Eq. (8-44) is justified.

## 8.6. NANOFLUIDS IN PIPE FLOW

The use of nanofluids for the convective heat transfer enhancement in pipes for laminar and turbulent flows are promising. We already have covered the nanofluids for flow over flat plates in Chapter 7. The pipe flow is one of the most extensively investigated topics in the field of convection in nanofluids. It is shown that nanoparticle suspensions offer better thermal performance than the base liquids at the same Reynolds number, and that heat transfer increases with increasing the nanoparticle volume fraction.

Kim et al., investigated thermodiffusion (Soret effect) and diffusionthermo (Dufour effect) effects in nanofluids. Thermodiffusion stands for mass diffusion that comes from thermal gradients, and diffusionthermo implies that heat transfer comes from concentration gradients. By using a one-fluid approach, characteristic dimensionless properties were obtained. It is beyond the scope of this text to cover those related material, however we will present the relation for the nanofluid thermal conductivity proposed by Kim et al., which is a modified version of the Bruggeman model

$$k_{nf} = \frac{1}{4}\left[\left(3\frac{\phi}{\lambda} - 1\right)\gamma + \left\{3\left(1 - \frac{\phi}{\lambda}\right) - 1\right\} + \sqrt{\Delta}\right]k_f \qquad (8\text{-}48)$$

where

$$\Delta = \left[\left(3\frac{\phi}{\lambda} - 1\right)\gamma + \left\{3\left(1 - \frac{\phi}{\lambda}\right) - 1\right\}\right]^2 + 8\gamma$$

Effective volume $\lambda$ means physically increasing volume quantity by the chaotic motion of nanoparticles such as Brownian motion. In the literature $\lambda$ is described in that format;

$$\lambda = \frac{abc}{(a+t)(b+t)(c+t)} \quad and \quad \gamma = \frac{k_p}{k_f}$$

where $t$ is the nanolayer thickness and $\gamma$ is a thermal conductivity ratio parameter.

The density and viscosity of the nanofluid can be calculated using the classical formulas derived for a two-phase mixture as a function of particle volume concentration as it is presented in Chapter 7.

$$\rho_{nf} = (1 - \phi)\rho_f + \phi\rho_p \qquad (8\text{-}49)$$

$$\mu_{nf} = \frac{1}{(1 - \phi)^{2.5}}\mu_f \qquad (8\text{-}50)$$

**EXAMPLE 8-14**  Consider a fully developed flow of Copper-Water nanofluid. It has a velocity of $0.0379$ m/s and flows through a tube of $2$ cm diameter. The tube wall is maintained at constant temperature. Calculate the density, viscosity, thermal conductivity and heat transfer coefficient by using classical nanofluid correlations and

Modified Bruggeman model. The properties of water and Copper nanoparticles are given in the table below. Assume nanofluid Cu volume concentration to be $\phi = 2\%$. The nanolayer thickness is given as $t = 2\ nm$ with shape factors of spherical nanoparticle parameters of $a = b = c = 19\ nm$.

| | $\rho\ kg/m^3$ | $C_p\ J/kg.K$ | $k\ W/(m.K)$ | $\mu\ kg/(m.s)$ |
|---|---|---|---|---|
| $H_2O$ | 997 | 4180 | 0.607 | $0.891 \times 10^{-3}$ |
| $Cu$ | 8933 | 385 | 401 | |

**SOLUTION**  Density for Copper-Water nanofluid with $\rho_p = 8933\ kg/m^3$, and $\rho_f = 997\ kg/m^3$

$$\begin{aligned} \rho_{nf} &= (1 - \phi)\rho_f + \phi\rho_p \\ &= (1 - 0.02)997 + (0.02)(8933) = 1155.72\ kg/m^3 \end{aligned}$$

where subscripts nf, f and p stand for nanofluid, base fluid and nanoparticle. The viscosity for Cu-water nanofluid is given by Eq. (8.50) as

$$\mu_{nf} = \frac{1}{(1 - \phi)^{2.5}}\mu_f$$

$$\mu_{nf} = \frac{1}{(1 - 0.02)^{2.5}}(0.891 \times 10^{-3}) = 9.372 \times 10^{-4}\ kg/m \cdot s$$

$$Re = \frac{u_m D}{\nu} = \frac{u_m D \rho_{nf}}{\mu_{nf}} = \frac{(0.0379)(0.02)(1155.72)}{9.372 \times 10^{-4}} = 935.$$

Hence the flow is laminar.

The effective volume and thermal conductivity ratio is

$$\gamma = \frac{k_p}{k_f} = \frac{401}{0.607} = 660.6$$

with $a = b = c = 19\ nm$ and $t = 2\ nm$, we calculate the effective volume

$$\lambda = \frac{abc}{(a + t)(b + t)(c + t)} = 0.74$$

where $t$ is the nanolayer thickness.

Next we calculate the effective thermal conductivity using Eq. (8-48)

$$\Delta = \left[\left(3\frac{0.02}{0.74} - 1\right)660.6 + \left\{3\left(1 - \frac{0.02}{0.74}\right) - 1\right\}\right]^2 + 8(660.6) = 371453$$

$$k_{nf} = \frac{1}{4}\left[\left(3\frac{0.02}{0.74} - 1\right)660.6 + \left\{3\left(1 - \frac{0.02}{0.74}\right) - 1\right\} + \sqrt{371453}\right]0.607$$

$$k_{nf} = 0.660\ W/mk$$

It should be noted that adding 0.02 volume concentration of Cu nanoparticles, results in a 9% increase in the fluid thermal conductivity.

For the constant wall temperature at the boundary, similarly, we can use Eq. (8-23) to calculate heat transfer coefficient.

$$Nu = \frac{hD}{k} = 3.66$$

$$h = 3.66\frac{0.660}{0.02} = 120 \text{ W}/(\text{m}^{2\circ}\text{C})$$

## 8.7. FLUID FLOW IN MICROCHANNELS

Small channels have been effective in removing heat through convection from the surface of a microchip. Overheating of these electrical components such as in cell phones, computers, and MP3 players are a concern as the temperatures reach values that threaten the proper functioning and their physical integrity. In another applications, we see the use of microchannels in bioengineering applications. These small scale devices can be used to control the delivery of small amount of medication or to cool a specific part of the body. Lastly we have micro channel use for aerospace applications. Current spacecraft size is on the order of 1000 $kg$. The goal for the future is to reduce this size to the order of 2-5 $kg$. This reduction results in power densities around 100-25 $W/cm^2$ which is an order of magnitude greater than what we have today. Again using forced convection through microchannels is one of the proposed means of cooling. Other uses of microfludics include but are not restricted to fuel cells, microreactors, micropumps and microturbines.

Mini- and microchannels have a higher heat transfer surface area to fluid volume ratio than a conventional channel that enhances convection. The heat transfer coefficient increases as the size of the *hydraulic diameter*, $D$ is reduced in the channel, enabling an excellent cooling apparatus.

Air as a coolant is reliable, safe and easy to maintain, however as components get smaller, the heat transfer requirements increase and air becomes less efficient. If the coolant does not need to be in contact with the electronics, water normally is used due to the fact that it has superior thermal properties. If the coolant comes in contact with electronics, than a dielectric must be used. However, the thermal properties of different dielectrics should be considered.

Microchannels are most commonly used for indirect liquid cooling of microchips in computers and electronics, The laminar flow through (rectangular or other geometries) microchannel equations can be used and are available in the literature. Their use is not any different than the macro channel empirical equations. As much as one increases the heat transfer, the pressure drop due to forcing of a fluid through a small channel may produce design limitations, including the loss of the pumping power and the material mechanical stress limitations.

Forced fluids flowing through these channels can dissipate high surface temperatures. The heat transfer rates may be increased by introducing microjets into the microchannels in order to reach up to 1000 $W/cm^2$ cooling capacity.

We do not have the room to study the micro channel heat transfer in detail, however we will cover some basic concepts as follows. The following is a general channel classifications

| | | |
|---|---|---|
| Conventional Channels | = | $D > 3\,mm$ |
| Minichannels | = | $3\,mm > D > 200\,\mu m$ |
| Transitional Microchannels | = | $200\,\mu m > D > 10\,\mu m$ |
| Transitional Nanochannels | = | $10\,\mu m > D > 0.1\,\mu m$ |
| Molecular Nanochannels | = | $0.1\,\mu m > D$ |

The flow regime through a system is defined using the *Knudsen number, $Kn$* already defined in $Chapter\,1$. In microchannel flows, the parameter $Kn$ is the ratio of the mean free path, $\lambda_{mfp}$, to the hydraulic diameter, $D$ as

$$Kn = \frac{\lambda_{mfp}}{D} \quad \text{for flow inside microchannels} \tag{8-51}$$

The $Kn$ can assist in identifying the flow regime of the system as defined below

| | | |
|---|---|---|
| Continuum Flow | = | $Kn < 10^{-3}$ |
| Molecular Slip Flow | = | $10^{-3} < Kn < 10^{-1}$ |
| Transition Flow | = | $10^{-1} < Kn < 10$ |
| Free Molecular Flow | = | $10 < Kn$ |

The continuum flow assumption will only be valid when $Kn < 10^{-3}$. Gaseous flow in microchannels is considered in continuum when the Knudsen number is less than 0.001. In this regime, the continuum assumption is valid because the molecular mean free path is much smaller compared to the channel size. This assumption is widely used for macroscopic heat transfer problems. Solutions of fluid flow in this regime are obtained using the Navier-Stokes equations. The fluid velocity and temperature in this regime are equivalent to the corresponding wall conditions.

The viscous heating effect is usually neglected at moderate velocity and may only be considered at high velocity. These boundary layer approximations are known to apply. The Nusselt number (Nu) for laminar, fully developed flow is constant and independent of Re, Pr, and the axial location. Under these flow conditions Nu values for a cylindrical channel with uniform wall heat flux and uniform wall temperature are 4.36 and 3.66, respectively. More Nusselt number values for rectangular channels are available in Table 8.1

For flows with *Knudsen number, $Kn$* is between $10^{-3}$ and $10^{-1}$, the continuum model in micro channel studies is still applicable except next to the boundaries. In the region next to the boundaries, the molecules slip along the surface (called velocity slip) and the temperature of the molecules on the surface is not equal to the surface temperature (called temperature slip). The nature of the molecule/surface interaction is taken into account by the surface accommodation coefficients, one for momentum and another for energy exchange.

The commonly used slip boundary conditions are called Maxwellian boundary conditions. In *Knudsen layer*, the Maxwellian velocity slip boundary condition approximates the true gas velocity at the boundary by the velocity that the molecules would have if a linear velocity gradient existed, Fig. 8.12. In other words, the magnitude of the slip is calculated from the velocity gradient evaluated at $y = \delta$. When a gas flows over a surface, the

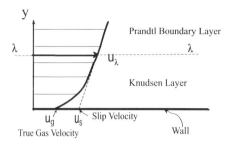

**FIG. 8.12.** Schematic figure showing the wall slip velocity approximation.

molecules leave some of their momentum and create shear stress on the wall. As shown in Fig. 8.13, the specular reflection conserves the tangential momentum of the molecules, and the diffuse reflection results in vanishing tangential momentum. The fraction of the molecules that are diffusely reflected by the wall is defined as the tangential momentum accommodation coefficient, $F_m$. It is also defined as the fraction of the momentum the molecules leave on the surface.

Using the definition of viscosity as

$$\mu = 1/2 \rho u_m \lambda_{mfp} \qquad (8\text{-}52)$$

where $\lambda_{mfp}$ is the molecular mean path. In Fig. 8.13 the Knudsen thickness, $\lambda$ is taken to be equal to $\lambda_{mfp}$. The slip velocity is obtained in the following final form,

$$u_s = \frac{2 - F_m}{F_m} \lambda_{mfp} \frac{du}{dy} \qquad (8\text{-}53)$$

where $\frac{du}{dy}$ is the velocity gradient at the wall. If the surface is smooth and reflects the molecules specularly then $F_m$ will be zero and for diffuse reflection $F_m$ is equal to one. In

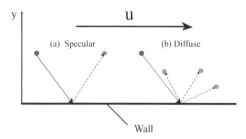

**FIG. 8.13.** Specular and diffuse reflections of gas molecules at the wall.

a rarefied gas flow the fluid temperature at the wall and the wall temperature are different, and this difference is called **the temperature jump**. If we assume the temperature jump to be proportional to the temperature gradient we obtain the first order approximation as,

$$T_s - T_w = \frac{2 - F_T}{F_T} \frac{2\gamma}{(1 + \gamma)} \frac{\lambda_{mfp}}{Pr} \frac{\delta T}{\delta y} \tag{8-54}$$

Here we introduce the definition of the thermal accommodation coefficient, $F_T$ as the ratio of net heat transfer at the wall to the heat that would be transferred to the wall if the reflected molecules were at the wall thermal conditions. If we have a rough surface or if we have a phase change, then $F_T = 1$, $\gamma$ is the specific heat ratio and $Pr$ is the Prandtl number.

## 8.8. FLUID FLOW THROUGH CHANNELS WITH MICRO STRUCTURED WALLS

Small channels at the mini and micro scale can improve cooling to small surfaces due to their high heat transfer surface area to fluid volume ratio. These channels provide a high heat transfer coefficient, however, the increase in performance is accompanied by a high pressure drop. The addition of surface structures at the micro scale can further improve the thermal performance of a small scale heat exchanger because it increases the surface area of the heated region and it creates more mixture within the flow.

Thermal and pressure drop correlations for a rectangular minichannel with micro surface structures in a staggered array for a flow in the laminar regime were developed by Tullius, Tullius and Bayazitoglu (2012). A constant heat flux is applied to the bottom surface of the channel. These correlations are dependent on the height of the fins, $h_f$, the channel clearance or the gap between the height of the channel and the fin, $dh$, the longitudial and transverse spacing of the fins, $S_L$ and $S_T$, the Prandtl number, $Pr$, hydraulic diameter of the fins, $D_f$ and the Reynolds number based on the hydraulic diameter of the fins, $Re$. The hydraulic diameter is obtained by the cross-sectional area of the fin, $A_c$ and the fin perimeter, $P$.

The $Nu$ across the structured surface is defined in Eq. (8-55). The constant is predefined based on the shape of the fins and is given in the table for circular, square, diamond, triangular, ellipsoidal and hexagonal shaped fins.

$$Nu_f = C_{Nu} \left(\frac{S_L}{D_f}\right)^{0.2} \left(\frac{S_T}{D_f}\right)^{0.2} \left(\frac{h_f}{D_f}\right)^{0.25} \left(1 + \frac{dh}{D_f}\right)^{0.4} Re^{0.6} Pr^{0.36} \left(\frac{Pr}{Pr_s}\right)^{0.25} \tag{8-55}$$

| Geometry | Circle | Square | Diamond | Triangle | Ellipse | Hexagon |
|----------|--------|--------|---------|----------|---------|---------|
| $C_{Nu}$ | 0.08 | 0.0937 | 0.036 | 0.0454 | 0.0936 | 0.0752 |

The pressure drop across the channel can be determined using the Darcy friction factor. The correlation between the friction factor and the pressure drop is shown in Eq. (8-56), where $N_y$ is the number of fins in the axial direction. Eq. (8-57) gives the empirical formula for the friction factor. Similar to the $Nu_f$ correlations, the constant $C_f$ is dependent on the shape of the fins.

$$\Delta p = N_y f \frac{\rho u_{max}^2}{2} \qquad (8\text{-}56)$$

$$f = C_f \left(\frac{S_L}{D_f}\right)^{0.2} \left(\frac{S_T}{D_f}\right)^{0.2} \left(\frac{h_f}{D_f}\right)^{0.18} \left(1 + \frac{dh}{D_f}\right)^{0.2} Re^{-0.435} \qquad (8\text{-}57)$$

| Geometry | Circle | Square | Diamond | Triangle | Ellipse | Hexagon |
|---|---|---|---|---|---|---|
| $C_f$ | 2.96 | 5.28 | 1.81 | 2.45 | 3.44 | 4.53 |

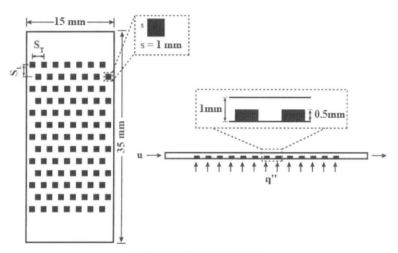

**FIGURE EXAMPLE 8-15**

**EXAMPLE 8-15**   A minichannel $15 \times 1 \times 35$ mm$^3$ (width x height x depth) containing 91 square micro pin fins of $1 \times 0.5 \times 1$ mm$^3$ (width x height x depth) in a staggered array are placed on the bottom surface of the minichannel, as illustrated in the accompanying figure. The longitudional and the transverse spacing of the fins measured are 2 mm and 2 mm. Water with an ambient fluid temperature is initially at room temperature ($25°C$) flows past the heated surface obstructions at a flow rate of 0.5 m/s. What is the heat transfer coefficient on the finned surface?

**SOLUTION**   For the fluid properties at $T = 20°C$, we use Appendix B to find $\nu = 1.006 \times 10^{-6}$ $m^2/s$, $k = 0.597$ W/mK, $Pr = 7.02$, and $\rho = 1000.52$ kg/m$^3$.

First, the number of fins in both the longitudional and transverse direction are determined as

$$N_x = \frac{\text{width of channel}}{S_T} = \frac{15mm}{2} = 7.5$$

Only seven (7) fins fit in the transverse direction. If there are ninety one (91) fins total then there are thirteen (13) rows of fins in the transverse direction. That is $N_y$

$= \frac{N}{N_x} = \frac{91}{7} = 13$. The channel clearance, $dh$ is then determined as the channel height (1 mm) minus the fin height (0.5 mm) which is equal to 0.5 mm. Next we determine the hydraulic diameter, $D_f$

$$D_f = \frac{4A_c}{P} = \frac{(4)(1 \text{ mm}^2)}{4 \text{ mm}} = 1 \text{ mm} = 0.001 \text{ m}$$

where $A_c = 1 \text{ mm} \times 1 \text{ mm} = 1 \text{ mm}^2$ and $P = 4 \times 1\text{mm} = 4 \text{ mm}$

Then the Reynolds number is calculated

$$Re = \frac{uD_f}{\nu} = \frac{(0.5m/s)(0.001m)}{1.006 \times 10^{-6}m^2/s} = 497$$

The constant obtained for the square finned structures is $C_{Nu} = 0.0937$ and the $Nu_f$ is calculated by using Eq. (8-55)

$$Nu_f = 0.0937 \left(\frac{2}{1}\right)^{0.2} \left(\frac{2}{2}\right)^{0.2} \left(\frac{0.5}{1}\right)^{0.25} \left(1 + \frac{0.5}{1}\right)^{0.4}$$
$$\times (497)^{0.6}(7.02)^{0.36} \left(\frac{7.02}{7.02}\right)^{0.25}$$
$$Nu_f = 19.59$$

The heat transfer coefficient, $h$, is determined by using its definition

$$Nu_f = \frac{hD_f}{k}$$
$$h = \frac{Nu_f}{D_f} = \frac{(19.59)(0.597W/mK)}{0.001m}$$
$$h = 11,695.45 \text{ W}/(\text{m}^2\text{K})$$

## 8.9. MASS TRANSFER IN DUCTS

For flow inside ducts for heat transfer problems, the *Nusselt number* is defined as

$$Nu = \frac{hD}{k} \qquad (8-58)$$

For mass transfer problems similarly we define the *Sherwood number* for mass transfer inside ducts as

$$Sh = \frac{k_m D}{D^*} \qquad (8-59)$$

where $D$ is duct hydraulic diameter and $D^*$ is the mass diffusivity.

### 8.9.1 Mass Transfer in Laminar Flow with Fully Developed Velocity and Concentration Distributions inside Ducts

The solution of the mass transfer problem for laminar flow with fully developed velocity and concentration distribution yields analogous results to the heat transfer flows. The Nusselt number in the case of mass transfer is replaced by the Sherwood number. That is,

$$\text{Sh} = \frac{k_m d}{D^*} = 3.66 \quad \text{for uniform wall mass concentration} \tag{8-60}$$

$$= 4.36 \quad \text{for uniform wall mass flux.} \tag{8-61}$$

Because of the analogy, the Sherwood number for mass transfer in laminar flow inside conduits having noncircular cross section can be obtained from those given in Table 8.1 for heat transfer.

### 8.9.2 Mass Transfer in Turbulent Flow inside Pipes

The heat transfer relation for turbulent flow inside a pipe for $T_w < T_b$ was given in Eq. 8.35 as

$$\text{Nu} = 0.023 \text{Re}^{0.8} \, \text{Pr}^{1/3} \quad \text{for } 0.7 < \text{Pr} < 100 \quad \text{Re} > 10,000 \tag{8-62}$$

For mass transfer experiments with liquids flowing in turbulent flow inside soluble tubes so that mass is transferred from the inside surface of the tube to the fluid stream, the surface remains smooth and the mass transfer relation takes a form analogous to

$$\text{Sh} = 0.023 \, \text{Re}^{0.8} \text{Sc}^{1/3} \quad \text{for } 0.6 < \text{Sc} < 2500 \quad 2000 < \text{Re} < 35,000 \tag{8-63}$$

The analogies between heat and momentum transfer can be recast as analogies between mass and momentum transfer. That is, by replacing the Nusselt number by the Sherwood number and the Prandtl number by the Schmidt number, the Reynolds, Prandtl, and von Kármán analogies become analogies between mass and momentum transfer. Then once the friction factor or the drag coefficient is known, the mass transfer coefficient $k_m$ for turbulent flow inside a pipe or along a flat plate can be determined.

**EXAMPLE 8-16** Air at atmospheric pressure and $25°C$ containing small quantities of naphthalene flows with a velocity of $u = 7.6$ m/s inside a pipe with an ID of $D = 2.5 \times 10^{-2}$ m. The mass diffusivity for the air-naphthalene system at 1 atm and $25°C$ is $D^* = 0.0611 \text{ cm}^2/\text{s}$. Determine the mass transfer coefficient for naphthalene transfer from the air stream to the wall surface away from the inlet.

**SOLUTION** The kinematic viscosity of air at $25°C = 298 \, K$ is $v = 1.568 \times 10^{-5} \text{ m}^2/\text{s}$. The Reynolds number for the flow is

$$\text{Re} = \frac{uD}{v} = \frac{(7.6)(2.5 \times 10^{-2})}{1.568 \times 10^{-5}} \simeq 10^4$$

The flow is turbulent, and the mass transfer coefficient can be determined by Eq. (8-63):

$$\mathrm{Sh} = 0.023\, \mathrm{Re}^{0.83}\, \mathrm{Sc}^{1/3}$$

where

$$\mathrm{Sc} = \frac{v}{D_*} = \frac{1.568 \times 10^{-5}}{0.0611 \times 10^{-4}} = 2.57$$

$$\mathrm{Sh} = \frac{k_m D}{D_*} = \frac{k_m (2.5 \times 10^{-2})}{0.0611 \times 10^{-4}}$$

results

$$k_m = 1.89 \times 10^{-2}\ \mathrm{m/s}.$$

## PROBLEMS

*Basic Concepts*

**8-1** Air ($v = 20.76 \times 10^{-6}\ \mathrm{m^2/s}$) flows with a mean velocity of $u_m = 0.5\ \mathrm{m/s}$ inside a circular tube that has an inside diameter $d = 2$ cm. Determine whether the flow is laminar or turbulent.

**8-2** Air flows inside a duct of square cross section with sides of 2 cm. For experimental purposes a Reynolds number of 50,000 is required. Calculate the velocity of the air. Air properties are to be evaluated at $350\ K$.

**8-3** A fluid flows through a duct of rectangular cross section with sides 2 cm x 1.5 cm. Calculate the hydraulic diameter.

**8-4** Engine oil is cooled from 120°C to 80°C while it is flowing with a mean velocity of $0.02\ \mathrm{m/s}$ through a circular tube of inside diameter 2 cm. Calculate the Reynolds number of the flow.

*Fully Developed Laminar Flow*

**8-5** Engine oil is pumped with a mean velocity of $u_m = 0.5\ \mathrm{m/s}$ through a bundle of tubes, each of inside diameter 1.5 cm and length 5 m. The physical properties of the oil are $v = 0.75 \times 10^{-4}\ \mathrm{m^2/s}$ and $\rho = 868\ \mathrm{kg/m^3}$. Calculate the pressure drop across each tube.

**8-6** Determine the friction factor and the pressure drop for fully developed laminar flow of ethylene glycol at 40°C [$\mu = 0.96 \times 10^{-2}\ \mathrm{kg/(m \cdot s)}$, $\rho = 1101\ \mathrm{kg/m^3}$] through a tube with diameter 3 cm and length 10 m. The mass flow rate of ethylene glycol is 0.05 kg/s.

**8-7** Engine oil at 40°C [$\mu = 0.21\ \mathrm{kg/(m \cdot s)}$, $\rho = 875\ \mathrm{kg/m^3}$] flows inside a tube with a mean velocity of $0.5\ \mathrm{m/s}$. The tube is 25 m long and has a 3-cm inside diameter. Determine the pressure drop for the flow.

**8-8** Water at 21°C [$\mu = 9.8 \times 10^{-4}$ kg/(m · s), $\rho = 997.4$ kg/m³] flows inside a 2-cm-diameter, 50-m-long tube at a rate of 0.01 kg/s. Determine the pressure drop for the flow.

**8-9** Mercury at 20°C [$\mu = 1.55 \times 10^{-3}$ kg/(m·s), $\rho = 13,579$ kg/m³] flows inside a 2-cm-diameter, 50-m-long tube at a rate of 0.01 kg/s. Determine the pressure drop for the flow.

**8-10** Freon at 20°C [$\mu = 2.63 \times 10^{-4}$ kg/(m · s), $\rho = 1330$ kg/m³] flows inside a 2-cm-diameter, 50-m-long tube at a rate of 0.005 kg/s. Determine the pressure drop for the flow.

**8-11** Engine oil at 40°C [$\mu = 0.21$ kg/(m · s), $\rho = 875$ kg/m³] with a mean velocity of 0.5 m/s flows through a bundle of 20 tubes, each of 2-cm inside diameter and 10 m long. Calculate the total power required to pump the oil through 20 tubes and overcome the fluid friction.

**8-12** Determine the friction factor for the flow of engine oil at 40°C [$\mu = 0.21$ kg/(m · s), $\rho = 875$ kg/m³] with a mean velocity of 0.5 m/s through a parallel plate channel having a spacing of 2 cm between the plates.

**8-13** Determine the friction factor for the flow of Freon at 20°C [$\mu = 2.63 \times 10^{-4}$ kg/(m· s), $\rho = 1330$ kg/m³] with a mean velocity of 0.01 m/s through a parallel-plate channel having a spacing of 3 cm between the plates.

**8-14** Determine the friction factor for the flow of water at 50°C with a mean velocity of 0.05 m/s through a square duct 2 cm by 2 cm and through an equilateral triangular duct with sides of 2 cm, each having the same length of 20 m.

**8-15** Consider the flow of water at a rate of 0.01 kg/s through an equilateral triangular duct with sides of 2 cm whose walls are kept at a uniform temperature of 100°C. Assume that the flow is hydrodynamically and thermally developed. Determine the duct length required to heat the water from 20°C to 70°C.

**8-16** Engine oil at 50°C with a flow rate of $10^{-3}$ kg/s enters a 1-m-long equilateral triangular duct with sides of 0.5 cm whose walls are maintained at a uniform temperature of 120°C. Assuming hydrodynamically and thermally fully developed flow, determine the outlet temperature of the oil.

**8-17** Oil at 50°C enters a 5-m-long conduit whose cross section can be approximated as two parallel plates with a spacing of 0.5 cm. The flow rate of the oil is 2 kg/(m²·s). The walls are subjected to uniform heating at a rate of 100 $W/m^2$. Assuming hydrodynamically and thermally fully developed flow, determine the average heat transfer coefficient. [Properties of oil may be taken at the anticipated mean temperature of 80°C as $\mu = 0.032$ kg/(m·s), $c_p = 2130$ $W · s/(kg·°C)$, $k = 0.14$ W/(m·°C), $\rho = 850$ $kg/m^3$, and Pr= 487.]

**8-18** Determine the friction factor $f$ for the fully developed laminar flow of engine oil at 60°C with a flow rate of 0.1 kg/s through (a) a circular tube of 1 cm diameter, (b) a square duct 1 cm by 1 cm, and (c) an equilateral-triangular duct with sides of 1 cm and sharp corners. Also determine the pressure drop over the length $L = 10$ m for each of the duct flows.

**8-19** Determine the friction factor $f$ for the fully developed laminar flow of air at 350 $K$ with a velocity of $u_m = 0.5$ m/s inside a square duct 2 cm by 2 cm and a rectangular duct 1 cm by 4 cm. Calculate the pressure drop over the length $L = 10$ m for each of the duct flows.

**8-20** Air at atmospheric pressure, 27°C and with a mean velocity $u_m = 1$ m/s flows inside a 10-m-long conduit whose cross section can be approximated as two parallel plates with a spacing of 8 cm. The bottom wall of the conduit is insulated, and the top wall is kept at a constant temperature of 80°C. Assuming hydrodynamically and thermally fully developed flow, determine the outlet temperature of the air. *Answer*: $T_{out} = 72.5$°C with an assumed value of $T_b = 52$°C.

**8-21** Ethylene glycol at 60°C with a velocity of 0.2 m/s flows through a two-parallel-plate conduit with a spacing of 0.5 cm and length of 10 m. The bottom plate wall is well insulated, and the top plate wall is subjected to uniform heating at a rate of 1000 $W/m^2$. Assuming hydrodynamically and thermally fully developed flow, determine the heat transfer coefficient and the friction coefficient.

**8-22** Determine the hydrodynamic entry lengths for flow at 60°C and at a rate of 0.01 kg/s of water and engine oil through a circular tube with an inside diameter of 2 cm.

**8-23** Determine the thermal entry lengths for laminar flow at 60°C and at a rate of 0.01 kg/s of water and engine oil through a circular tube with an inside diameter of 2 cm subjected to uniform wall temperature.

**8-24** Determine the thermal entry lengths for hydrodynamically developed laminar flow at 60°C at a rate of 0.01 kg/$(m^2 \cdot s)$ of water and engine oil through a parallel-plate channel with a spacing of 1 cm and subjected to uniform wall temperature.

**8-25** Determine the thermal entry length for hydrodynamically developed laminar flow of water at 60°C flowing at 0.01 kg/s through a square duct 1 cm by 1 cm in cross section and subjected to uniform wall temperature.

**8-26** Determine the thermal entry length for hydrodynamically developed laminar flow of glycerin at 20°C flowing at 0.01 kg/s through a square duct 1 cm by 1 cm in cross section and subjected to uniform wall heat flux.

**8-27** Glycerin at 20°C with a flow rate of 0.01 kg/s enters a 1-cm-ID tube which is maintained at a uniform temperature of 80°C. Determine the thermal entry length. Assuming hydrodynamically and thermally fully developed flow, determine the heat transfer coefficient and the tube length required to heat the glycerin to 50°C.

*Developing Laminar Flow*

**8-28** Engine oil at 100℃ with a flow rate of 0.2 kg/s enters a 2-cm-ID, 50-m-long tube maintained at a uniform temperature of 120℃. Assume that the flow is hydrodynamically developed. Determine the mean heat transfer coefficient and the outlet temperature of the oil.

**8-29** Water at 20℃ with a flow rate of 0.01 kg/s enters a 2-cm-ID, 5-m-long tube maintained at a uniform temperature of 100℃ by condensing steam on the outer surface of the tube. Assume that the flow is hydrodynamically developed. Determine the thermal entry length, the average heat transfer coefficient, and the outlet temperature of the water.

**8-30** Water at 20℃ with a flow rate of 0.01 kg/s enters a 2-cm-diameter tube which is maintained at 100℃. Assuming hydrodynamically developed flow, determine the tube length required to heat the water to 70℃.

**8-31** Engine oil at 60℃ with a flow rate of 0.2 kg/s enters a 2-cm-ID tube which is maintained at 120℃. Assuming hydrodynamically developed flow, determine the tube length required to heat the oil to 80℃.

**8-32** Water at an average temperature of 60℃ with a flow rate of 0.01 kg/s flows through a square duct 2 cm by 2 cm in cross section which is maintained at a uniform temperature. Assuming a fully developed velocity profile, determine the average heat transfer coefficients over 1, 2, and 3 m from the inlet. Determine the average heat transfer coefficient for the hydrodynamically and thermally developed region.

**8-33** Water at an average temperature of 50℃ with a flow rate of 0.01 kg/s flows through a tube with a 2-cm ID which is subjected to uniform heat flux. Assuming a fully developed velocity profile, determine the average heat transfer coefficient for the hydrodynamically and thermally developed region.

**8-34** Water at an inlet temperature of 50℃ with a flow rate of 0.01 kg/s flows through a square duct 2 cm by 2 cm in cross section which is maintained at a uniform temperature of 100℃. Assuming hydrodynamically developed flow, determine the length of the duct needed to heat the water to 70℃.

**8-35** Engine oil at 20℃ with a flow rate of 0.1 kg/s enters a 100-m-long square duct 1 cm by 1 cm in cross section whose walls are maintained at a uniform temperature of 80℃. Assuming hydrodynamically developed flow, determine the duct length required to heat the oil to 60℃.

**8-36** Water at 20℃ with a flow rate of 0.02 kg/s enters a square duct 2 cm by 2 cm in cross section whose walls are maintained at a uniform temperature of 80℃. Assuming hydrodynamically developed flow, determine the thermal entry length.

**8-37** Engine oil at 20°C with a flow rate of 0.001 kg/s enters a 3-cm-long duct 1 cm by 1 cm in cross section whose walls are maintained at a uniform temperature of 100°C. Assuming hydrodynamically developed flow, determine the outlet temperature of the oil.

**8-38** Water at a mean temperature of 60°C with a flow rate of 0.01 kg/s flows through a 1-m-long square duct 2 cm by 2 cm in cross section maintained at a uniform temperature. Assuming hydrodynamically developed flow, determine the local heat transfer coefficient at a location 1 m from the inlet.
*Answer*: 123.7 W/(m²·°C).

**8-39** Water at an average temperature of 80°C with a flow rate of 0.01 kg/s flows through a 2-cm-diameter tube which is maintained at a uniform temperature. (*a*) Assuming a fully developed profile, determine the local heat transfer coefficients at locations 1 and 3 m from the inlet. (*b*) Assuming simultaneously developing velocity and temperature, determine the mean heat transfer coefficients over distances of 1 and 3 m from the inlet.

**8-40** Water at an average temperature of 60°C with a flow rate of 0.015 kg/s flows through a 2.5-cm-ID tube which is subjected to uniform wall temperature. (*a*) Assuming a fully developed velocity profile, determine the local heat transfer coefficient at locations 1 and 3 m from the inlet. (*b*) Assuming simultaneously developing velocity and temperature, determine the mean heat transfer coefficients over distances of 1 and 3 m from the inlet.

**8-41** Engine oil at an average temperature of 40°C with a flow rate of 0.3 kg/s enters a 2.5-cm-ID, 40-m-long tube maintained at constant wall temperature. The velocity and temperature profiles are simultaneously developing. Determine the heat transfer coefficient at the exit.

**8-42** Water at 15°C with a flow rate of 0.01 kg/s enters a 2.5-cm-ID, 3-m-long tube maintained at a uniform temperature of $100°C$ by condensing steam on the outer surface of the tube. The velocity and temperature profiles are simultaneously developing. Determine the average outlet temperature of the water.

**8-43** Engine oil at 30°C with a flow rate of 0.2 kg/s enters a 1-cm-ID tube which is maintained at a uniform temperature of 120°C. The velocity and temperature profiles are simultaneously developing. What is the tube length to heat the oil to 40°C?

*Fully Developed Turbulent Flow*

**8-44** Water at a mean temperature of 60°C flows inside a 4-cm-ID tube with a velocity $u = 5$ m/s. The tube wall temperature is 20°C. Determine the heat transfer coefficient for the fully developed turbulent flow.

**8-45** Water at 20℃ with a mass flow rate of 5 kg/s enters a 5-cm-ID, 10-m-long tube whose surface is maintained at a uniform temperature of 60℃. Calculate the outlet temperature of the water.

**8-46** Water at a mean temperature of 60℃ flows inside a 2.5-cm-ID, 10-m-long tube with a velocity of 6 m/s. The tube wall is maintained at a uniform temperature of 100℃ by condensing steam. Determine the heat transfer rate to the water. Assume an inlet temperature of 30℃.

**8-47** A fluid at a mean temperature of 40℃ flows with a velocity of 10 m/s inside a 5-cm-diameter tube. Assuming fully developed turbulent flow and $T_w < 40℃$, determine the average heat transfer coefficient for the flow of (*a*) helium at 1 *atm*, (*b*) air at 1 *atm*, (*c*) water, and (*d*) glycerin.

**8-48** Water at 40℃ with a mass flow rate of 2 kg/s enters a 2.5-cm-ID tube whose wall is maintained at a uniform temperature of 90℃. Calculate the tube length required to heat the water to 60℃.

**8-49** Air at atmospheric pressure and 27℃ enters a 12-m-long, 1.5-cm-ID tube with a mass flow rate of 0.1 kg/s. The tube surface is maintained at a uniform temperature of 80℃. Calculate the average heat transfer coefficient and the rate of heat transfer to the air.
*Answer*: $h = 991.1 \text{ W}/(\text{m}^2 \cdot ℃)$ and $Q = 5.3 \ kW$.

**8-50** Air at 1 *atm* and 27℃ mean temperature flows with a velocity of 10 m/s through a 5-cm-ID, 5-m-long tube. The flow is hydrodynamically developed and thermally developing. Determine the average heat transfer coefficient over the entire length of the tube for air to be heated.

**8-51** Pressurized cooling water at a mean temperature of 200℃ flows with a velocity of 2 m/s between parallel-plate fuel elements in a nuclear reactor. Assuming fully developed turbulent flow and a spacing of 0.25 cm between the plates, determine the average heat transfer coefficient.

**8-52** Cooling water with a velocity of 2 m/s enters a condenser tube at 20℃ and leaves the tube at 40℃. The inside diameter of the tube is $D = 2$ cm. Assuming fully developed turbulent flow, determine the average heat transfer coefficient.

*Liquid Metals in Turbulent Flow*

**8-53** Mercury at 20℃ with a mass flow rate of 5 kg/s enters a 5-cm-ID tube whose surface is maintained at 110℃. Calculate the tube length required to raise the temperature of the mercury to $100℃$.

**8-54** Mercury at an average temperature of 100℃ flows with a velocity of $O.5$ m/s inside a 2.5-cm-diameter tube . The flow is hydrodynamically developed but thermally developing. Determine the entry region heat transfer coefficient under both uniform wall heat flux and uniform wall temperature conditions over the distances $x/D = 20,\ 40$, and 60.

**8-55** Liquid bismuth at 500℃ and with a velocity $u = 1\ m/s$ enters a 1.75-cm-ID tube which is maintained at a uniform temperature of 600℃. Determine the tube length required to raise the temperature of the liquid bismuth to 580℃.

**8-56** Mercury at a temperature of 100℃ and with a velocity of $1\ m/s$ enters a 1.25-cm-ID tube which is maintained at a uniform temperature of 160℃. Determine the tube length required to raise the temperature of the mercury to 150℃.

*Nanofluids in Pipe Flow*

**8-57** Consider a fully developed flow of Silver-Water nanofluid. It has a velocity of 0.041 $m/s$ and flows through a tube 2 $cm$ diameter. The tube wall is maintained at constant temperature. Calculate the density, viscosity, thermal conductivity and heat transfer coefficient by using classical nanofluid correlations and Modified Brugge-man model. The properties of water and Ag nano particles are given in the table below. Assume nanofluid Ag volume concentration to be $\phi = 3\%$. The nanolayer thickness is given as $t = 2\ nm$ with shape factors of spherical nanoparticle parameters of $a = b = c = 19\ nm$.

| | $\rho$, kg/m$^3$ | $C_p$, J/ kgK | $k$, W/ mK | $\mu$, kg/ ms |
|---|---|---|---|---|
| $H_2O$ | 997 | 4180 | 0.607 | $0.891 \times 10^{-3}$ |
| $Ag$ | 10500 | 235 | 429 | |

*Mass Transfer Inside ducts*

**8-58** Air at atmospheric pressure and 25°C containing small quantities of iodine flows with a velocity of $u = 5.18$ m/s inside a smooth pipe with an ID of $D = 3.048 \times 10^{-2}$ m. The mass diffusivity for the air-iodine system at 1 atm and 25°C is $D^* = 0.0834\ \text{cm}^2/\text{s}$ Determine the mass transfer coefficient for iodine transfer from the gas stream to the wall surface away from the entry region.

# CHAPTER 9

# Convection due to Buoyancy Forces (Free Convection)

This chapter is devoted to heat transfer for situations where the fluid motion is created by the buoyancy forces. In the previous chapters we examined heat transfer by forced convection, in which the motion of the fluid was imposed externally by a fan, a blower, or a pump. In some situations convective motion is set up within the fluid without a forced velocity. Consider, for example, a hot plate placed vertically in a body of fluid at rest which is at a uniform temperature lower than that of the plate. Heat transfer will take place first by pure conduction, and a temperature gradient will be established in the fluid. The temperature variation within the fluid will generate a density gradient, which, in a gravitational field, will give rise, in turn, to convective motion as a result of buoyancy forces. The fluid motion set up as a result of the buoyancy force is called free convection, or natural convection.

Fluid motion created by buoyancy forces transferring energy occurs in many engineering applications. Heat transfer from a hot radiator to heat a room, refrigeration coils, transmission lines, electric transformers, electric heating elements, and electronic equipment are typical examples. The seasonal thermal inversion of lakes is also caused by buoyancy-induced free-convection motions.

## 9.1. BASIC CONCEPTS

To demonstrate free convection, we consider a hot wall placed vertically in a large body of cold fluid at rest, as illustrated in Fig. 9.1$a$. The fluid near the wall is hotter than that away from it. The resulting density difference gives rise to a buoyancy force, which causes the hot fluid to rise along the plate and the velocity boundary layer to develop. Note that the velocity profile for free convection is different from that for forced convection over a flat plate. In free convection, the velocity at the wall is zero because of the no-slip condition; it increases with distance from the wall but, after reaching some maximum value, decreases to zero because the fluid at distances sufficiently far from the wall is at rest. An examination of the boundary-layer development along the plate reveals that in the region near the leading edge of the plate, the boundary-layer development is *laminar*. However, after some distance from the leading edge of the plate, transition to a *turbulent boundary layer* begins; eventually, a fully developed *turbulent* boundary layer is established.

Figure 9.1$b$ illustrates the development of the velocity boundary layer for the case of a cold vertical wall in a large body of hot fluid at rest. In this case, as expected, the direction of fluid motion is reversed; namely, the fluid in front of the cold plate moves vertically

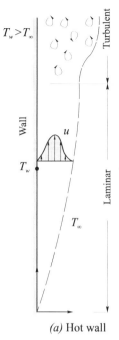

*(a)* Hot wall

**FIG. 9.1a. Development of velocity boundary layer for free convection on a vertical plate for the case of hot wall in a cold fluid.**

down. The velocity profile is similar to that discussed above for the hot plate, but the flow direction is reversed.

The flow velocity in free convection is much smaller than that encountered in forced convection. Therefore, the rate of heat transfer by free convection generally, is much smaller than that by forced convection.

We recall that in forced convection, the Reynolds number was an important dimensionless parameter that affected the flow regime; that is, depending on the magnitude of the Reynolds number, the flow regime could be identified as laminar or turbulent. In the case of free convection, the *Grashof number*, a dimensionless quantity, plays the same role as the Reynolds number in forced convection. Let $X$ be the characteristic dimension of the body which is subjected to free convection, $T_w$ its surface temperature, and $T_\infty$ the temperature of the bulk fluid at rest. Then the Grashof number, Gr, is defined as

$$Gr = \frac{g\beta(T_w - T_\infty)X^3}{\nu^2} \qquad (9\text{-}1)$$

where $g$ is the gravitational acceleration, $\beta$ is the volume coefficient of thermal expansion, and $\nu$ is the kinematic viscosity of the fluid. The characteristic dimension $X$ depends on the geometry of the body. In the case of the vertical plate example considered above, the distance $x$, measured from the leading edge of the plate, is taken as the characteristic length to define the local Grashof number at the location $x$. In the case of free convection from a horizontal tube immersed in a large body of fluid, the outside diameter $D$ of the

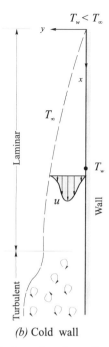

*(b)* Cold wall

**FIG. 9.1b. Development of velocity boundary layer for free convection on a vertical plate for the case of cold wall in a hot fluid.**

tube is taken as the characteristic dimension. The temperature difference is considered to be a positive quantity and hence it is taken as $|T_w - T_\infty|$. The volume expansion coefficient $\beta$ may be determined from physical property tables, such as the one given in the Appendix B. In the case of ideal gases it may be calculated from

$$\beta = \frac{1}{T} \quad \text{for ideal gases} \tag{9-2}$$

where $T$ is the absolute temperature.

We recall that in heat transfer correlations for forced convection, the Nusselt number generally depends on the Reynolds and Prandtl numbers, and the correlation can be expressed formally in the form

$$\text{Nu} = f(\text{Re, Pr}) \quad \text{for forced convection} \tag{9-3a}$$

In the case of free convection, the Nusselt number generally depends on the Grashof and Prandtl numbers, and the heat transfer correlation can be expressed formally in the form

$$\text{Nu} = f(\text{Gr, Pr}) \quad \text{for free convection} \tag{9-3b}$$

The physical situation discussed above on the formation of free convection implies that even in forced convection, the temperature gradients in the fluid may give rise to free convection. Therefore, it is useful to have some criteria for the relative importance of free convection in forced convection. It has been shown that the parameter

$$\frac{Gr}{(Re)^2}$$

is a measure of the relative importance of free convection in relation to forced convection. If $Gr/(Re)^2 \ll 1$, heat flow is considered to be primarily by forced convection, and the heat transfer correlation has the form given by Eq. (9-3$a$). Conversely, for $Gr/(Re)^2 \gg 1$, free convection is dominant, and the heat transfer correlation has the form given by Eq. (9-3$b$).

When $Gr/(Re)^2 \cong 1$, free and forced convection are of the same order of magnitude, and hence both mechanisms must be considered in the heat transfer analysis. The Rayleigh number, Ra, defined as

$$Ra = Gr\ Pr = \frac{g\beta(T_w - T_\infty)X^3}{\nu\alpha} \qquad (9\text{-}4)$$

has also been used instead of the Grashof number to correlate heat transfer in free convection.

For gases, $Pr \cong 1$, and hence the Nusselt number of free convection is a function of the Grashof number only; that is,

$$Nu = f(Gr) \text{ free convection for gases} \qquad (9\text{-}5)$$

The analysis of heat transfer in free convection is a complicated matter except for simple geometries. Therefore, experimental data are needed in order to develop reliable heat transfer correlations. Here we present some of the recommended empirical correlations for determining the free-convection heat transfer coefficient on geometries such as a flat plate, a single long cylinder, and a single sphere as well as for enclosures. The problems of simultaneous free and forced convection are far more complicated, and are not considered here.

## 9.2. FREE CONVECTION ON A FLAT PLATE

Heat transfer by free convection on a flat plate depends not only on the inclination and orientation of the heat transfer surface, but also on whether the heat transfer is taking place under uniform wall surface temperature or uniform wall heat flux conditions. Here we examine these cases and present some recommended heat transfer correlations.

### 9.2.1 Vertical Plate

**1. UNIFORM WALL TEMPERATURE.** McAdams (1959) proposed the following simple correlation for heat transfer by free convection on a vertical wall of height $L$

maintained at a uniform temperature $T_w$ in a fluid at constant temperature $T_\infty$:

$$\boxed{\mathrm{Nu}_m = c(\mathrm{Gr}_L \mathrm{Pr})^n = c(\mathrm{Ra}_L)^n} \tag{9-6}$$

where the Grashof number $\mathrm{Gr}_L$ and the mean Nusselt number $\mathrm{Nu}_m$, based on the plate height $L$, are defined as

$$\mathrm{Nu}_m = \frac{h_m L}{k} \quad \mathrm{Gr}_L = \frac{g\beta(T_w - T_\infty)L^3}{\nu^2} \tag{9-7a,b}$$

and the Rayleigh number $\mathrm{Ra}_L$ becomes

$$\mathrm{Ra}_L = \mathrm{Gr}_L \mathrm{Pr} = \frac{g\beta(T_w - T_\infty)L^3}{\alpha\nu} \tag{9-8}$$

The recommended values of the exponent $n$ and the constant $c$ of Eq. (9-6) are listed in Table 9.1 for both laminar and turbulent flow conditions. The physical properties of the fluid are evaluated at the *film temperature*

$$T_f = \frac{1}{2}(T_w + T_\infty) \tag{9-9}$$

An examination of the values of the exponent $n$ given in Table 9.1 reveals that in turbulent flow the mean heat transfer coefficient $h_m$ is independent of the plate height $L$, since $\mathrm{Gr}_L \sim L^3$ and $h_m \sim (1/L)(\mathrm{Gr}_L)^{1/3}$.

### TABLE 9.1  The constant $c$ and the exponent $n$ of Eq. (9-6)

| Type of flow | Range of $\mathrm{Gr}_L\mathrm{Pr}$ | $c$ | $n$ |
|---|---|---|---|
| Laminar | $10^4$ to $10^9$ | 0.59 | 1/4 |
| Turbulent | $10^9$ to $10^{13}$ | 0.10 | 1/3 |

A more elaborate but more accurate correlation has been proposed by Churchill and Chu for free convection from an isothermal vertical plate:

$$\boxed{\mathrm{Nu}_m = \left\{ 0.825 + \frac{0.387\,\mathrm{Ra}_L^{1/6}}{[1 + (0.492/\mathrm{Pr})^{9/16}]^{8/27}} \right\}^2} \quad \text{for } 10^{-1} < \mathrm{Ra}_L < 10^{12} \tag{9-10}$$

which is applicable for both laminar and turbulent flow conditions. Again, the physical properties of the fluid are evaluated at the *film temperature*, defined by Eq. (9-9). The Rayleigh number $\mathrm{Ra}_L$ and the mean Nusselt number $\mathrm{Nu}_m$ were given previously by Eqs.

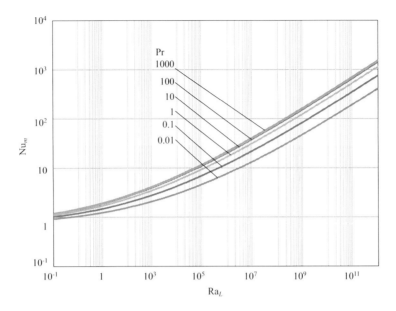

**FIG. 9.2.** Average Nusselt number as a function of Rayleigh number for free convection on an isothermal plate calculated from Eq. (9-10).

(9-7) and (9-8). Figure 9.2 shows the mean Nusselt number $Nu_m$ plotted as a function of the Grashof number $Gr_L$ for several different values of the Prandtl number as calculated from Eq. (9-10).

**EXAMPLE 9-1** A vertical plate 0.3 mhigh and 1 mwide, maintained at a uniform temperature of 124°C, is exposed to quiescent atmospheric air at 30°C. Calculate the average heat transfer coefficient $h_m$ over the entire height of the plate by using the correlations given by both Eqs. (9-6) and (9-10).

**SOLUTION** The physical properties of air at atmospheric pressure and the film temperature $T_f = (124 + 30)/2 = 77°C = 350\ K$ are

$$\nu = 2.076 \times 10^{-5}\ \text{m}^2/s \quad Pr = 0.697$$

$$k = 0.03\ \text{W}/(\text{m}\cdot°\text{C}) \quad \beta = \frac{1}{T_f} = 2.86 \times 10^{-3}\ K^{-1}$$

The Grashof number at $L = 0.3$ m becomes

$$
\begin{aligned}
Gr_{L=0.3} &= \frac{g\beta(T_w - T_\infty)L^3}{\nu^2} \\
&= \frac{(9.81)(2.86 \times 10^{-3})(124 - 30)(0.3)^3}{(2.076 \times 10^{-5})^2} \\
&= 1.651 \times 10^8
\end{aligned}
$$

and

$$\begin{aligned} \mathrm{Ra}_{L=0.3} &= \mathrm{Gr}_{L=0.3}\mathrm{Pr} \\ &= (1.651 \times 10^8)(0.697) \\ &= 1.15 \times 10^8 \end{aligned}$$

Equation (9-6) with $c = 0.59$ and $n = \frac{1}{4}$ from Table 9.1 gives

$$\begin{aligned} \mathrm{Nu}_m &= \frac{h_m L}{k} = 0.59(\mathrm{Ra}_L)^{1/4} \\ &= 0.59(1.15 \times 10^8)^{1/4} \\ &= 61.1 \end{aligned}$$

then the average heat transfer coefficient becomes

$$\begin{aligned} h_m &= \frac{k}{L}\mathrm{Nu}_m \\ &= \frac{0.03}{0.3}61.1 \\ &= 6.11 \ \mathrm{W/(m^2 \cdot {}^\circ C)} \end{aligned}$$

Equation (9-10) gives

$$\begin{aligned} \mathrm{Nu}_m &= \left\{ 0.825 + \frac{0.387\,\mathrm{Ra}_L^{1/6}}{[1 + (0.492/\mathrm{Pr})^{9/16}]^{8/27}} \right\}^2 \\ &= \left\{ 0.825 + \frac{0.387(1.15 \times 10^8)^{1/6}}{[1 + (0.492/0.697)^{9/16}]^{8/27}} \right\}^2 \\ &= 63.51 \end{aligned}$$

and with this Nu the $h_m$ becomes

$$h_m = 6.351$$

**EXAMPLE 9-2** Consider a rectangular plate 0.15 m by 0.3 m , maintained at a uniform temperature $T_w = 80^\circ C$, placed vertically in quiescent atmospheric air at $T_\infty = 24^\circ C$. Compare the heat transfer rates from the plate for the cases when the vertical height is (a) 0.15 m and (b) 0.3 m .

**SOLUTION** The physical properties of air at atmospheric pressure and the film temperature $T_f = (80 + 24)/2 = 52^\circ C = 325$ K are

$$\nu = 1.822 \times 10^{-5} \ \mathrm{m^2/s} \quad \mathrm{Pr} = 0.703$$

$$k = 0.02814 \text{ W}/(\text{m} \cdot {}^\circ\text{C}) \quad \beta = \tfrac{1}{T_f} = 1/325 = 3.077 \times 10^{-3} \text{K}^{-1}$$

(*a*) When the $L = 0.15$ m side is vertical, the Grashof and Rayleigh numbers are

$$
\begin{aligned}
\text{Gr}_{L=0.15} &= \frac{g\beta(T_w - T_\infty)L^3}{\nu^2} \\
&= \frac{(9.81)(3.077 \times 10^{-3})(80 - 24)(0.15)^3}{1.822 \times 10^{-5})^2} \\
&= 1.719 \times 10^7
\end{aligned}
$$

and

$$
\begin{aligned}
\text{Ra}_{L=0.15} &= \text{Gr}_{L=0.15}\text{Pr} \\
&= (1.719 \times 10^7)(0.703) \\
&= 1.21 \times 10^7
\end{aligned}
$$

Using Eq. (9-6) and Table 9.1, we have

$$
\begin{aligned}
\text{Nu}_m &= \frac{h_m L}{k} = 0.59\,\text{Ra}^{1/4} \\
&= (0.59)(1.21 \times 10^7)^{1/4} \\
&= 34.8
\end{aligned}
$$

then

$$
\begin{aligned}
h_m &= \frac{k}{L}\text{Nu}_m \\
&= \frac{0.02814}{0.15}34.8 \\
&= 6.53 \text{ W}/(\text{m}^2 \cdot {}^\circ\text{C})
\end{aligned}
$$

and the heat transfer rate from one surface becomes

$$
\begin{aligned}
Q_{L=0.15} &= Ah_m(T_w - T_\infty) \\
&= (0.15 \times 0.3)(6.53)(80 - 24) \\
&= 16.5 \text{ W}
\end{aligned}
$$

(*b*) When the $L = 0.3$ m side is vertical, the Rayleigh and Nusselt numbers are

$$
\begin{aligned}
\text{Ra}_{L=0.3} &= \text{Ra}_{L=0.15} \times \left(\frac{0.3}{0.15}\right)^3 \\
&= (1.21 \times 10^7)(2)^3 \\
&= 0.968 \times 10^8
\end{aligned}
$$

and

$$
\begin{aligned}
\mathrm{Nu}_m &= 0.59\,\mathrm{Ra}^{1/4} \\
&= (0.59)(0.968 \times 10^8)^{1/4} \\
&= 58.5
\end{aligned}
$$

Then

$$
\begin{aligned}
h_m &= \frac{k}{L}\mathrm{Nu}_m \\
&= \frac{0.02814}{0.3}58.5 \\
&= 5.49\ \mathrm{W/(m^2 \cdot {}^\circ C)}
\end{aligned}
$$

and the heat transfer rate from one surface becomes

$$
\begin{aligned}
Q_{L=0.3} &= Ah_m(T_w - T_\infty) \\
&= (0.3 \times 0.15)(5.49)(80 - 24) \\
&= 13.8\ \mathrm{W}
\end{aligned}
$$

which is lower than in the previous case

## 2. UNIFORM WALL HEAT FLUX.

Free convection on a vertical wall of height $L$ subjected to a uniform heat flux $q_w$ at the wall surface has been studied by several investigators. Based on the experiments with air and water by Vliet and Liu, the following correlations have been proposed for the mean Nusselt number for the laminar and turbulent flow regimes:

$$
\mathrm{Nu}_m = 0.75(\mathrm{Gr}_L^* \mathrm{Pr})^{1/5} \quad \text{for } 10^5 < \mathrm{Gr}_L^* \mathrm{Pr} < 10^{11} \text{ (laminar)} \tag{9-11}
$$

$$
\mathrm{Nu}_m = 0.645(\mathrm{Gr}_L^* \mathrm{Pr})^{0.22} \quad \text{for } 2 \times 10^{13} < \mathrm{Gr}_L^* \mathrm{Pr} < 10^{16} \text{ (turbulent)} \tag{9-12}
$$

where the modified Grashof number $\mathrm{Gr}_L^*$ is defined as

$$
\mathrm{Gr}_L^* = \frac{g\beta q_w L^4}{k\nu^2} \tag{9-13a}
$$

and the average Nusselt number as

$$
\mathrm{Nu}_m = \frac{h_m L}{k} \tag{9-13b}
$$

All physical properties are evaluated at the film temperature as defined by Eq.(9-9). However, in this case, since the wall heat flux is prescribed, the wall surface temperature $T_w$ is *a priori* unknown, and the determination of $T_w$ requires an initial guess and iteration.

## 9.2.2 Horizontal Plate

The average Nusselt number for free convection on a horizontal plate depends, among other parameters, on the orientation of the heat transfer surface that is, whether the hot surface is facing up or down, and conversely, whether the cold surface is facing down or up. We examine free convection on a horizontal plate for both uniform wall temperature and uniform wall heat flux.

**1. UNIFORM WALL TEMPERATURE.** The mean Nusselt number $Nu_m$ for free convection on a horizontal plate maintained at a uniform temperature $T_w$ in a large body of fluid at temperature $T_\infty$ has been correlated by McAdams (1959) by the following simple expression:

$$\boxed{Nu_m = c(Gr\,Pr)^n} \qquad (9\text{-}14a)$$

where

$$Nu_m = \frac{h_m L}{k} \qquad Gr_L \equiv \frac{g\beta(T_w - T_\infty)L^3}{\nu^2} \qquad (9\text{-}14b)$$

**TABLE 9.2  Constant $c$ and exponent $n$ of Eq. (9-14$a$).**
(Free convection on a horizontal plate at uniform temperature.)

| Orientation of plate | Range of $Gr_L Pr$ | $c$ | $n$ | Flow regime |
|---|---|---|---|---|
| Hot surface facing up or cold surface facing down | $10^5$ to $2 \times 10^7$ | 0.54 | 1/4 | Laminar |
| | $2 \times 10^7$ to $3 \times 10^{10}$ | 0.14 | 1/3 | Turbulent |
| Hot surface facing down or cold surface facing up | $3 \times 10^5$ to $3 \times 10^{10}$ | 0.27 | 1/4 | Laminar |

Compiled based on data from McAdams (1959).

The coefficient $c$ and the exponent $n$ are listed in Table 9.2. The physical properties of the fluid are evaluated at the film temperature $T_f$, defined by Eq.(9-9). Note that the values of $c$ and $n$ depend on the orientation of the heat transfer surface as well as on the flow regime. The characteristic length $L$ of the plate is taken as:

**(i):** The length of a side for a square.
**(ii):** The arithmetic mean of the two dimensions for a rectangular square.
**(iii):** $0.9D$ for a circular disc of diameter $D$.

Recent correlations of free convection suggest that improved accuracy may be obtained if the characteristic length $L$ for the plate is defined as

$$L \equiv \frac{A}{P} \qquad (9\text{-}15)$$

where $A$ is the surface area of the plate and $P$ is the perimeter that encompasses the area.

It is apparent from Table 9.2 that for a turbulent flow regime the Nusselt number $\mathrm{Nu}_m$ is independent of the characteristic length.

**EXAMPLE 9-3**  A circular disc heater $0.2$ m  in diameter is exposed to quiescent atmospheric air at $T_\infty = 25°C$. One surface of the disc is insulated, and the other surface is maintained at $T_w = 130°C$. Calculate the amount of heat transferred from the disc when it is ($a$) horizontal with the hot surface facing up, ($b$) horizontal with the hot surface facing down, and ($c$) vertical.

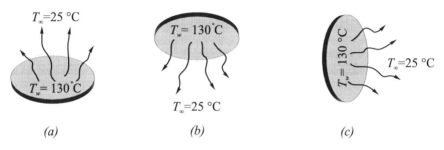

*(a)*            *(b)*            *(c)*

**FIGURE EXAMPLE 9-3.**  A circular disc heater (a) hot surface faces up, (b) hot surface faces down, (c) vertical.

**SOLUTION**  The physical properties of atmospheric air at $T_f = (T_w + T_\infty)/2 = (130 + 25)/2 = 77.5°C = 350.5$ K are taken as

$$\nu = 2.08 \times 10^{-5} \text{ m}^2/s \qquad \mathrm{Pr} = 0.697$$
$$k = 0.03 \text{ W}/(\mathrm{m} \cdot °\mathrm{C}) \qquad \beta = \frac{1}{T_f} = \frac{1}{350.5}$$

The area of the disc is

$$A = \frac{\pi}{4}D^2 = \frac{\pi}{4}(0.2)^2 = 0.0314 \text{ m}^2$$

The characteristic length $L = 0.9D$ for a circular disc of diameter $D$ is suggested by McAdams (1959). Then the Grashof number becomes

$$
\begin{aligned}
\mathrm{Gr} &= \frac{g\beta(T_w - T_\infty)L^3}{\nu^2} \\
&= \frac{(9.81)(1/350.5)(130 - 25)(0.9 \times 0.2)^3}{(2.08 \times 10^{-5})^2} \\
&= 3.96 \times 10^7
\end{aligned}
$$

and

$$\text{Gr Pr} = (3.96 \times 10^7)(0.697) = 2.76 \times 10^7$$

**(a)** For the horizontal disc with the hot surface up, as illustrated in the accompanying figure, the average Nusselt number is determined from Eq. (9- 14a) and Table 9.2. For the turbulent flow condition, we obtain

$$
\begin{aligned}
\text{Nu}_m &= \frac{h_m L}{k} = 0.14(\text{Gr}_L \text{Pr})^{1/3} \\
&= 0.14(2.76 \times 10^7)^{1/3} \\
&= 42.3
\end{aligned}
$$

Then

$$
\begin{aligned}
h_m &= \frac{k}{L}\text{Nu}_m = \frac{0.03}{0.9 \times 0.2}(42.3) \\
&= 7.05 \text{ W}/(\text{m}^2 \cdot {}^\circ\text{C})
\end{aligned}
$$

and

$$
\begin{aligned}
Q &= Ah(T_w - T_\infty) = (0.0314)(7.05)(130 - 25) \\
&= 23.2 \text{ W}
\end{aligned}
$$

**(b)** For the horizontal disc with the hot surface facing down, as illustrated in the accompanying figure, the average Nusselt number is determined from Eq. (9- 14a) and Table 9.2:

$$
\begin{aligned}
\text{Nu}_m &= \frac{h_m L}{k} = 0.27(\text{Gr}_L \text{Pr})^{1/4} \\
&= 0.27(2.76 \times 10^7)^{1/4} \\
&= 19.6
\end{aligned}
$$

Then

$$
\begin{aligned}
h_m &= \frac{k}{L}\text{Nu}_m = \frac{0.03}{0.9 \times 0.2}(19.6) \\
&= 3.27 \text{ W}/(\text{m}^2 \cdot {}^\circ\text{C})
\end{aligned}
$$

and

$$
\begin{aligned}
Q &= Ah(T_w - T_\infty) = (0.0314)(3.27)(130 - 25) \\
&= 10.8 \text{ W}
\end{aligned}
$$

**(c)** For the vertical disc, as illustrated in the accompanying figure, the average

Nusselt number is determined from Eq. (9-6) and Table 9.1:

$$\text{Nu}_m = \frac{h_m L}{k} = 0.59(\text{Gr}_L\text{Pr})^{1/4}$$
$$= 0.59(2.76 \times 10^7)^{1/4}$$
$$= 42.8$$

Then

$$h_m = \frac{k}{L}\text{Nu}_m = \frac{0.03}{0.9 \times 0.2}(42.8)$$
$$= 7.1 \text{ W}/(\text{m}^2 \cdot {}^\circ\text{C})$$

and

$$Q = Ah(T_w - T_\infty) = (0.0314)(7.1)(130 - 25)$$
$$= 23.4 \text{ W}$$

**2. UNIFORM WALL HEAT FLUX.** The average Nusselt number for free convection on a horizontal plate subjected to uniform surface heat flux $q_w$ and exposed to an ambient at constant temperature $T_\infty$ has been studied experimentally by Fujii and Imura, and the following correlations are proposed for the cases in which the heated surface is facing up and facing down.

Horizontal plate with the *heated surface facing upward*:

$$\boxed{\text{Nu}_m = 0.13(\text{Gr}_L\text{Pr})^{1/3}} \quad \text{for } \text{Gr}_L\text{Pr} < 2 \times 10^8 \qquad (9\text{-}16a)$$

$$\boxed{\text{Nu}_m = 0.16(\text{Gr}_L\text{Pr})^{1/3}} \quad \text{for } 5 \times 10^8 < \text{Gr}_L\text{Pr} < 10^{11} \qquad (9\text{-}16b)$$

Horizontal plate with the *heated surface facing downward*:

$$\boxed{\text{Nu}_m = 0.58(\text{Gr}_L\text{Pr})^{1/5}} \quad \text{for } 10^6 < \text{Gr}_L\text{Pr} < 10^{11} \qquad (9\text{-}17)$$

The physical properties are to be evaluated at a mean temperature, defined as

$$T_m = T_w - 0.25(T_w - T_\infty) \qquad (9\text{-}18a)$$

and the thermal expansion coefficient β at $(T_w+T_\infty)/2$. In these expressions, the Grashof number and the mean Nusselt number are defined as follows

$$\text{Gr}_L = \frac{g\beta(T_w - T_\infty)L^3}{\nu^2} \qquad (9\text{-}18b)$$

$$\text{Nu}_m = \frac{h_m L}{k} = \frac{q_w L}{(T_w - T_\infty)k} \qquad (9\text{-}18c)$$

## 9.2.3 Inclined Plates

The heat transfer coefficient for free convection on an inclined plate can be predicted by the vertical plate formulas if the gravitational term $g$ is replaced by $g \cos \theta$, where $\theta$ is the angle the plate makes with the vertical. However, the orientation of the heat transfer surface, whether the surface is facing upward or downward, is also a factor that affects the Nusselt number. In order to make a distinction between the two possible orientations of the surface, we designate the angle $\theta$ that the surface makes with the horizontal as *positive* if the hot surface is facing downward and *negative* if the hot surface is facing upward, as shown in Fig. 9.3.

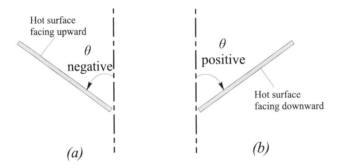

**FIG. 9.3.** The concept of positive and negative inclination angles from the vertical to define the orientation of the hot surface.

Based on the extensive experimental studies by Fujii and Imura, the following correlations are recommended for free convection on an inclined surface subjected to a uniform surface heat flux $q_w$ and exposed to an ambient at a uniform temperature $T_\infty$. The notation for the angle of inclination is as defined in Fig. 9.3.

For an inclined plate with the heated surface facing downward,

$$\boxed{\text{Nu}_m = 0.56(\text{Gr}_L \text{Pr} \cos \theta)^{1/4}} \quad \text{for } +\theta > 88, \quad 10^5 < \text{Gr}_L \text{Pr} < 10^{11} \qquad (9\text{-}19)$$

When the plate is slightly inclined with the horizontal (that is, $88° < \theta < 90°$) and the heated surface is facing downward, Eq. (9-19) is applicable. The power of $\frac{1}{4}$ in Eq. (9-19) implies that the flow is always in the laminar regime.

For an inclined plate with the heated surface facing upward, the heat transfer correlation has been developed as

$$\boxed{\text{Nu}_m = 0.145[(\text{Gr}_L \text{Pr})^{1/3} - (\text{Gr}_c \text{Pr})^{1/3}] + 0.56(\text{Gr}_L \text{Pr} \cos \theta)^{1/4}} \qquad (9\text{-}20)$$

for $\text{Gr}_L \text{Pr} < 10^{11}$, $\text{Gr}_L > \text{Gr}_c$, and $\theta$ lying between $-15°$ and $-75°$. Here, the value of the transition Grashof number $\text{Gr}_c$ depends on the angle of inclination $\theta$, as listed in Table 9.3.

In Eqs. (9-19) and (9-20), all physical properties are evaluated at the mean temperature

$$T_m = T_w - 0.25(T_w - T_\infty)$$

and β is evaluated at $T_\infty + 0.25(T_w - T_\infty)$.

### TABLE 9.3 Transition Grashof number
(See Fig. 9.3 for the definition of θ).

| θ, degrees | $Gr_c$ |
| --- | --- |
| -15 | $5 \times 10^9$ |
| -30 | $10^9$ |
| -60 | $10^8$ |
| -75 | $10^6$ |

Compiled based on data from Fujii and Imura (1972)

**EXAMPLE 9-4**  Consider a 60 cm by 60 cm electrically heated plate with one of its surfaces thermally insulated and the other surface dissipating heat by free convection into atmospheric air at 30°C. The heat flux over the surface of the plate is uniform and results in a mean surface temperature of 50°C. The plate is inclined, making an angle of 50° from the vertical. Determine the heat loss from the plate for the following cases: (a) heated surface facing up; (b) heated surface facing down.

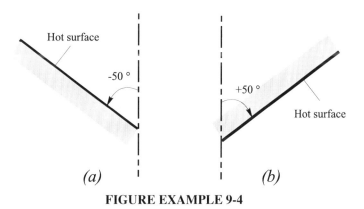

**FIGURE EXAMPLE 9-4**

**SOLUTION**  The physical properties of atmospheric air at a mean temperature $T_m = T_w - 0.25(T_w - T_\infty) = 50 - 0.25(50 - 30) = 45°C = 318\ K$ are taken as

$$\nu = 1.751 \times 10^{-5}\ \text{m}^2/s \quad Pr = 0.704$$
$$k = 0.0276\ \text{W}/(\text{m} \cdot °\text{C}) \quad \beta = \frac{1}{T_\infty + 0.25(T_w - T_\infty)} = \frac{1}{308}\ K^{-1}$$

$$\begin{aligned}
\mathrm{Gr}_L &= \frac{g\beta(T_w - T_\infty)L^3}{\nu^2} = \frac{(9.81)\left(\frac{1}{380}\right)(50-30)(0.6)^3}{(1.751\times10^{-5})^2} \\
&= 4.487\times10^8
\end{aligned}$$

**(a)** For the hot surface facing up, as illustrated in the accompanying figure, $\theta = -50°$, and we have

$$\mathrm{Gr}_c \cong 3.33\times10^8$$

and $\mathrm{Gr}_L > \mathrm{Gr}_c$. Then, from Eq. (9-20) we obtain

$$\begin{aligned}
\mathrm{Nu}_m &= 0.145[(\mathrm{Gr}_L\mathrm{Pr})^{1/3} - (\mathrm{Gr}_c\mathrm{Pr})^{1/3}] + 0.56(\mathrm{Gr}_L\mathrm{Pr}\cos\theta)^{1/4} \\
&= 0.145[(4.487\times10^8\times0.704)^{1/3} - (3.33\times10^8\times0.704)^{1/3}] \\
&\quad + 0.56(3.33\times10^8\times0.704\times\cos(-50°))^{1/4} \\
&= 71.39
\end{aligned}$$

Therefore,

$$\begin{aligned}
h_m &= \frac{k}{L}\mathrm{Nu}_m = \frac{0.0276}{0.6}(71.39) \\
&= 3.284 \ \mathrm{W/(m^2\cdot°C)}
\end{aligned}$$

and

$$\begin{aligned}
Q &= Ah_m(T_w - T_\infty) = (0.6)^2(7.65)(50-30) \\
&= 23.64 \ \mathrm{W}
\end{aligned}$$

**(b)** For the hot surface facing down, as illustrated in the accompanying figure, from Eq. (9-19) we have

$$\begin{aligned}
\mathrm{Nu}_m &= 0.56(\mathrm{Gr}_L\mathrm{Pr}\cos\theta)^{1/4} \\
&= 0.56(3.246\times10^7\times0.704\times\cos50°) \\
&= 34.7
\end{aligned}$$

$$\begin{aligned}
h_m &= \frac{k}{L}\mathrm{Nu}_m = \frac{0.0276}{0.25}(34.7) \\
&= 3.83 \ \mathrm{W/(m^2\cdot°C)}
\end{aligned}$$

and

$$\begin{aligned} Q &= Ah_m(T_w - T_\infty) = (0.6)^2(3.83)(50 - 30) \\ &= 27.58 \text{ W} \end{aligned}$$

## 9.3. FREE CONVECTION ON A LONG CYLINDER

We now examine free convection on a long cylinder in both the vertical and horizontal positions.

### 9.3.1 Vertical Cylinder

The average Nusselt number for free convection on a vertical cylinder is the same as that for a vertical plate if the curvature effects are negligible. Therefore, for an *isothermal vertical cylinder*, the average Nusselt number can be determined from the vertical plate correlation given by Eq. (9-6) or (9-10).

For fluids having a Prandtl number of 0.7 or higher, a vertical cylinder may be treated as a vertical flat plate when

$$\frac{L/D}{(\text{Gr}_D)^{1/4}} < 0.025 \tag{9-21}$$

where $D$ is the diameter of the cylinder and $L$ is the height of the cylinder.

### 9.3.2 Horizontal Cylinder

Morgan (1975) presented a simple correlation for free convection from a *horizontal isothermal cylinder*, covering the range $10^{-10} < \text{Ra}_D < 10^{12}$. It is given in the form

$$\boxed{\text{Nu}_m = \frac{hD}{k} = c\,\text{Ra}_D^n} \tag{9-22}$$

where the constant $c$ and the exponent $n$ are listed in Table 9.4 and $\text{Nu}_m$ and $\text{Ra}_D$ are based on the cylinder diameter $D$:

$$\text{Nu}_m = \frac{h_m D}{k} \tag{9-23a}$$

$$\text{Ra}_D = \text{Gr}_D \text{Pr} = \frac{g\beta(T_w - T_\infty)D^3}{\nu^2}\text{Pr} \tag{9-23b}$$

**TABLE 9.4  Constant $c$ and exponent $n$ of Eq. (9-22).**
(Free convection on a horizontal cylinder.)

| $Ra_D$ | $c$ | $n$ |
|---|---|---|
| $10^{-10} - 10^{-2}$ | 0.675 | 0.058 |
| $10^{-2} - 10^2$ | 1.02 | 0.148 |
| $10^2 - 10^4$ | 0.850 | 0.188 |
| $10^4 - 10^7$ | 0.480 | 0.250 |
| $10^7 - 10^{12}$ | 0.125 | 0.333 |

Compiled based on data from Morgan (1975)

**EXAMPLE 9-5**  A 5-cm-outside-diameter (OD) horizontal tube at a uniform temperature $T_w = 400\ K$ is exposed to quiescent atmospheric air at $T\infty = 300\ K$. Calculate the average heat transfer coefficient $h_m$.

**SOLUTION**  The physical properties of the atmospheric air at $T_f = (T_w + T_\infty)/2 = (300 + 400)/2 = 350\ K$ are taken as

$$\nu = 2.076 \times 10^{-5} m^2/s \quad Pr = 0.697$$
$$k = 0.03\ W/(m \cdot °C) \quad \beta = \tfrac{1}{350}\ K^{-1}$$

and

$$Ra_D = Gr_D Pr = \frac{g\beta(T_w - T_\infty)D^3}{\nu^2}Pr = 5.67 \times 10^5$$

From Eq. (9-22) and Table 9.4 we have

$$Nu_m = 0.48(Ra_D)^{0.25} = 0.48(5.67 \times 10^5)^{0.25}$$
$$= 13.17$$

Thus

$$h_m = \frac{k}{D}Nu_m = \frac{0.03}{0.05}(13.17)$$
$$= 7.9\ W/(m^2 \cdot °C)$$

## 9.4. FREE CONVECTION ON A SPHERE

The average Nusselt number for free convection on a single *isothermal sphere*, for fluids with a Prandtl number close to unity, has been correlated by Yuge with the following expression:

$$Nu_m = \frac{h_m D}{k} = 2 + 0.43 Ra_D^{1/4} \tag{9-24}$$

for $1 < Ra_D < 10^5$ and $Pr \cong 1$.

Amato and Tien, based on experimental data for free convection on a single *isothermal sphere* in water, proposed the following correlation:

$$\boxed{\mathrm{Nu}_m = 2 + 0.50\mathrm{Ra}_D^{1/4}} \tag{9-25}$$

for $3 \times 10^5 < \mathrm{Ra}_D < 8 \times 10^8$ and $10 \leq \mathrm{Nu}_m \leq 90$. Here the Rayleigh number, based on the sphere diameters, is defined as

$$\mathrm{Ra}_D = \mathrm{Gr}_D\mathrm{Pr} = \frac{g\beta D^3(T_w - T_\infty)}{\nu^2}\mathrm{Pr} \tag{9-26}$$

The properties are evaluated at the film temperature $T_f = \frac{1}{2}(T_w + T_\infty)$.

## 9.5. SIMPLIFIED EQUATIONS FOR AIR

**TABLE 9.5  Equations for free convection for air at atmospheric conditions.**

| Geometry | Characteristic dimension $L$ | Type of flow | Range of $\mathrm{Gr}_L\mathrm{Pr}$ | $h_m$ W/(m$^2 \cdot \,^\circ$C) |
|---|---|---|---|---|
| Vertical plates | Height | Laminar | $10^4 - 10^9$ | $h_m = 1.42(\Delta T/L)^{1/4}$ |
| Height cylinders | | Turbulent | $10^9 - 10^{13}$ | $h_m = 1.31\Delta T^{1/3}$ |
| Horizontal | Outside | Laminar | $10^4 - 10^9$ | $h_m = 1.32(\Delta T/D)^{1/4}$ |
| cylinders | diameter | Turbulent | $10^9 - 10^{12}$ | $h_m = 1.24\Delta T^{1/3}$ |
| Horizontal plates | | | | |
| (a) Upper surface | As defined in | Laminar | $10^5 - 2 \times 10^7$ | $h_m = 1.32(\Delta T/L)^{1/4}$ |
| hot or lower | the text | Turbulent | $2 \times 10^7 - 3 \times 10^{10}$ | $h_m = 1.52\Delta T^{1/3}$ |
| surface cold | | | | |
| (b) Lower surface | As defined in | Laminar | $3 \times 10^5 - 3 \times 10^{10}$ | $h_m = 0.59(\Delta T/L)^{1/4}$ |
| hot or upper | the text | | | |
| surface cold | | | | |

Compiled based on data from McAdams (1959).

We present in Table 9.5 simplified expressions for rapid but approximate estimation of the average heat transfer coefficient from isothermal surfaces in air at atmospheric pressure and moderate temperatures. For more accurate results, the previously given, more exact expressions should be used. The correlations given in this table apply to air and to $CO$, $CO_2$, $O_2$, $N_2$, and flue gases for temperatures from 20 to 800°C. The Grashof number is defined as

$$\mathrm{Gr}_L \equiv \frac{g\beta\Delta T L^3}{\nu^2}$$

where $L$ is the characteristic dimension of the body and $\Delta T$ is the temperature difference between the surface and the ambient air, that is, $\Delta T = T_w - T_\infty$.

The correlations given in Table 9.5 for air at atmospheric pressure can be extended to higher or lower pressures by multiplying by the following factors:

$$P^{1/2} \quad \text{for laminar regime}$$
$$P^{2/3} \quad \text{for turbulent regime}$$

where $P$ is the pressure in atmospheres. The expressions given in Table 9.5 are merely approximations; care must be exercised in their use.

**EXAMPLE 9-6** A vertical plate at a uniform temperature of $230°C$ is exposed to atmospheric air at $25°C$. Determine the free-convection heat transfer coefficient, and compare the result with that obtainable from the simplified expressions for free convection to air at atmospheric pressure given in Table 9.5.

**SOLUTION** The physical properties of atmospheric air at $T_f = (T_w + T_\infty)/2 = (230 + 25)/2 = 127.5°C = 450.5\ K$ are taken as

$$\nu = 2.59 \times 10^{-5} m^2/s \quad \text{Pr} = 0.689$$
$$k = 0.0337\ W/(m \cdot °C)$$

The Rayleigh number Ra is

$$
\begin{aligned}
\text{Ra} &= \frac{g\beta(T_w - T_\infty)L^3}{\nu^2}\text{Pr} \\
&= \frac{(9.81)(1/450.5)(230 - 25)(1)^3}{(2.59 \times 10^{-5})} \times 0.689 \\
&= 5.16 \times 10^9
\end{aligned}
$$

therefore the flow is turbulent. From Eq. (9-10) we have

$$
\begin{aligned}
\text{Nu} &= \left\{ 0.825 + \frac{0.387\ \text{Ra}^{1/6}}{[1 + (0.492/\text{Pr})^{9/16}]^{8/26}} \right\}^2 \\
&= 204
\end{aligned}
$$

and

$$
\begin{aligned}
h_m &= \frac{k}{L}\text{Nu}_m = \frac{0.0337}{1}(172.8) \\
&= 5.82\ W/(m^2 \cdot °C)
\end{aligned}
$$

From the simplified expression given in Table 9.5 for air we have

$$h_m = 1.31\Delta T^{1/3} = 1.31(230 - 25)^{1/3}$$
$$= 7.72 \text{ W/(m}^2 \cdot {}^\circ\text{C})$$

**EXAMPLE 9-7**  A block $10 \text{ cm} \times 10 \text{ cm} \times 10 \text{ cm}$ in size, illustrated in the accompanying figure, is suspended in quiescent atmospheric air at $10^\circ$C with one of its surfaces in a horizontal position. All surfaces of the block are maintained at $150^\circ$C. Determine the free-convection heat transfer coefficient for all the surfaces of the block, and compare these results with those obtainable from the simplified expressions given in Table 9.5 for air at atmospheric pressure.

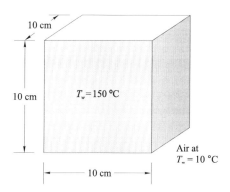

**FIGURE EXAMPLE 9-7**

**SOLUTION**  The physical properties of air at $T_f = (T_w + T_\infty)/2 = (150 + 10)/2 = 80^\circ\text{C} = 353 \ K$ are taken as

$$\nu = 2.107 \times 10^{-5} \text{ m}^2/s \quad \text{Pr} = 0.697$$
$$k = 0.03 \text{ W/(m} \cdot {}^\circ\text{C})$$

The Rayleigh number is

$$\text{Ra} = \frac{g\beta(T_w - T_\infty)L^3}{\nu^2}\text{Pr}$$
$$= \frac{(9.81)(1/353)(150 - 10)(0.1)^3}{2.107 \times 10^{-5}}(0.697)$$
$$= 6.11 \times 10^6$$

*Vertical surfaces of the cube*: The flow is laminar; so from Eq. (9-6) and Table 9.1 we have

$$\text{Nu}_m = 0.59 \text{ Ra}^{1/4} = 29.33$$
$$h_m = \frac{k}{L}\text{Nu}_m = 8.8 \text{ W/(m}^2 \cdot {}^\circ\text{C})$$

and the simplified expression of Table 9.5 for air gives

$$h_m = 1.42 \left(\frac{\Delta T}{L}\right)^{1/4} = 1.42 \left(\frac{150 - 10}{0.1}\right)^{1/4} = 8.69 \text{ W}/(\text{m}^2 \cdot {}^{\circ}\text{C})$$

*Top surface*: The flow is laminar. From Eq. (9-14$a$) and Table 9.2 we have

$$\text{Nu}_m = 0.54 \, \text{Ra}^{1/4} = 26.85$$

$$h_m = \frac{k}{L}\text{Nu}_m = 8.05 \text{ W}/(\text{m}^2 \cdot {}^{\circ}\text{C})$$

and the simplified expression of Table 9.5 for air gives

$$h_m = 1.32 \left(\frac{\Delta T}{L}\right)^{1/4} = 1.32 \left(\frac{150 - 10}{0.1}\right)^{1/4} = 8.07 \text{ W}/(\text{m}^2 \cdot {}^{\circ}\text{C})$$

*Bottom surface*: The flow is laminar. From Eq. (9-14a) and Table 9.2 we have

$$\text{Nu}_m = 0.27 \, \text{Ra}^{1/4} = 13.42$$

$$h_m = \frac{k}{L}\text{Nu}_m = 4.03 \text{ W}/(\text{m}^2 \cdot {}^{\circ}\text{C})$$

and the simplified expression of Table 9.5 for air gives

$$h_m = 0.59 \left(\frac{\Delta T}{L}\right)^{1/4} = 0.59 \left(\frac{150 - 10}{0.1}\right)^{1/4} = 3.61 \text{ W}/(\text{m}^2 \cdot {}^{\circ}\text{C})$$

## 9.6. FREE CONVECTION IN ENCLOSED SPACES

Heat transfer by free convection in enclosed spaces has numerous engineering applications. Typical examples are free convection in wall cavities, between window glazing, in the annulus between concentric cylinders or spheres, and in flat-plate solar collectors.

### 9.6.1 Basic Concepts

The onset of free convection inside enclosed spaces involves an interesting but very complicated flow phenomenon. The subject has been studied experimentally, analytically, and numerically by various investigators, and correlations for predicting the free-convection heat transfer coefficient have been proposed. Before presenting such correlations, however, we shall provide some insight into the physical nature of the problem and give a qualitative discussion of the conditions leading to the onset of free convection in enclosed spaces.

As a classical example, we consider a fluid contained between two large horizontal plates separated by a distance $\delta$, as illustrated in Fig. 9.4. The lower plate is maintained at a uniform temperature $T_h$ which is higher than the temperature $T_c$ of the upper colder

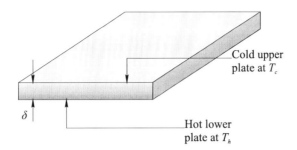

**FIG. 9.4.** A layer of fluid contained between two large horizontal plates.

plate. Then there is a heat flow through the fluid layer in the upward direction, and a temperature profile decreasing upward is established within the fluid. Clearly, the physical situation is such that the denser cold fluid lies above the lighter, warm layers. The fluid remains stationary and the heat transfer takes place by pure conduction so long as the viscous forces are stronger than the buoyancy forces.

Suppose that the temperature difference $T_h - T_c$ between the plate temperatures is increased to a value such that the buoyancy forces overcome the viscous forces. Then the fluid layer can no longer remain stationary, but gives rise to a convective motion under the influence of the buoyancy forces. Theoretical and experimental investigations have verified that, for such a horizontal enclosure, the fluid layer becomes unstable and convection currents are established if $T_h - T_c$ is increased beyond a value corresponding to the *critical Rayleigh number* $\text{Ra}_c$:

$$\text{Ra}_c = \text{Gr Pr} = \frac{g\beta(T_h - T_c)\delta^3}{\nu^2}\text{Pr} = 1708 \qquad (9\text{-}27)$$

Figure 9.5 shows the formation of convective flow patterns giving rise to hexagonal

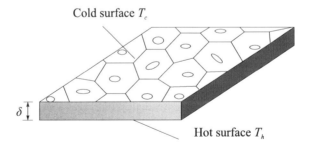

**FIG. 9.5.** The formation of Bernard cells in a horizontal layer of fluid for $\text{Ra}_c > 1708$.

cells called *Bernard cells*. The criterion given by Eq. (9-27) is important in practical applications, because it signifies the transition in the mechanism of heat transfer from pure conduction to convection. Note that heat transfer across the fluid layer is higher with convection than with conduction.

If the lower plate temperature were less than the upper plate temperature, the fluid would always remain stationary, because there would be no buoyancy forces to initiate a convective motion.

These basic concepts concerning the onset of free convection inside horizontal layers can be extended to inclined layers, but the resulting convective flow patterns are more complicated. Consider a fluid contained between two large parallel plates of height $H$ separated by a distance $\delta$ and inclined at an angle $\phi$, as illustrated in Fig. 9.6. The lower

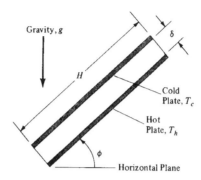

**FIG. 9.6.** **Geometry and coordinates for free convection in an inclined layer.**

plate is maintained at a uniform temperature $T_h$ which is higher than the temperature $T_c$ of the upper, colder plate. This situation gives rise to temperature gradients within the fluid that generate a buoyancy force opposing the stabilizing effects of the viscous forces. Under certain conditions the fluid layer remains virtually stagnant. However, in most practical cases the fluid circulates as a result of the buoyancy produced by the temperature gradients. For this particular situation, the dimensionless parameters that affect the onset of free convection in the fluid include the inclination $\phi$ of the enclosure from the horizontal plane in addition to the Grashof and Rayleigh numbers, defined as

$$\mathrm{Gr}_\delta = \frac{g\beta(T_h - T_c)\delta^3}{\nu^2} \tag{9-28a}$$

$$\mathrm{Ra} = Gr\,Pr = \frac{g\beta(T_h - T_c)\delta^3}{\nu\alpha} \tag{9-28b}$$

as well as the aspect ratio $H/\delta$.

The determination of the criterion for the onset of free convection and the corresponding free-convection heat transfer coefficient is important in engineering applications. We now present some of the correlations for heat transfer in free convection in enclosures.

## 9.6.2 Vertical Layer, $\phi = 90°$

Consider a vertical layer of fluid between two parallel plates of height $H$ separated by a distance $\delta$, as illustrated in Fig. 9.6, but for the case of $\phi = 90°$. The hot and cold plates are maintained at uniform temperatures $T_h$ and $T_c$, respectively. Let $a = H/\delta$ be the aspect ratio. The heat transfer across such a gap by free convection has been experimentally investigated by El Sherbiny, Raithby, and Hollands for air, and the following correlation is proposed for free convection across the air layer:

$$\boxed{\text{Nu}_{90} = [\text{Nu}_1, \text{Nu}_2, \text{Nu}_3]_{\max}} \tag{9-29}$$

which implies that one should select the maximum of the three Nusselt numbers $\text{Nu}_1$, $\text{Nu}_2$, and $\text{Nu}_3$, which are defined as

$$\text{Nu}_1 = 0.0605\, \text{Ra}^{1/3} \tag{9-30a}$$

$$\text{Nu}_2 = \left\{ 1 + \left[ \frac{0.104\, \text{Ra}^{0.293}}{1 + (6310/\text{Ra})^{1.36}} \right]^3 \right\}^{1/3} \tag{9-30b}$$

$$\text{Nu}_3 = 0.242 \left( \frac{\text{Ra}}{a} \right)^{0.272} \tag{9-30c}$$

for

$$\frac{H}{\delta} = 5 \text{ to } 110$$
$$10^2 < \text{Ra} < 2 \times 10^7$$

where

$$a = \frac{H}{\delta} = \text{aspect ratio} \tag{9-31a}$$

and

$$\text{Ra} = \text{Gr}_\delta \text{Pr} = \frac{g\beta(T_h - T_c)\delta^3}{\nu^2} \text{Pr} \tag{9-31b}$$

The Nusselt number can be defined as

$$\text{Nu}_{90} = \frac{q\delta}{k(T_h - T_c)} \tag{9-32}$$

since $q = h(T_h - T_c)$, and all physical properties are evaluated at $(T_h + T_c)/2$. The experimental data for air agree with Eq. (9-29) to within 9 percent. Therefore, knowing the Nusselt number, the heat flux $q$ can be determined.

### 9.6.3 Inclined Layers, $90° < \phi \leq 60°$

Consider an inclined layer of fluid contained between two parallel plates separated by a distance $\delta$, as illustrated in Fig. 9.6. The lower hot plate and the upper cold plate are at temperatures $T_h$ and $T_c$, respectively. For the inclination $\phi = 60°$, the experimental data with air by El Sherbiny, Raithby, and Holland correlated the free-convection heat transfer across the gap by the following expression:

$$\mathrm{Nu}_{60} = [\mathrm{Nu}_1, \ \mathrm{Nu}_2]_{\max} \qquad (9\text{-}33)$$

where one should select the maximum of $\mathrm{Nu}_1$ and $\mathrm{Nu}_2$, defined as

$$\mathrm{Nu}_1 = \left[ 1 + \left( \frac{0.093 \ \mathrm{Ra}^{0.314}}{1 + G} \right)^7 \right]^{1/7} \qquad (9\text{-}34\mathrm{a})$$

$$\mathrm{Nu}_2 = \left( 0.104 + \frac{0.175}{a} \right) \mathrm{Ra}^{0.283} \qquad (9\text{-}34\mathrm{b})$$

$G$ is given by

$$G = \frac{0.5}{[1 + (\mathrm{Ra}/3160)^{20.6}]^{0.1}} \qquad (9\text{-}34\mathrm{c})$$

and the Nusselt number is defined as

$$\mathrm{Nu}_{60} = \frac{q\delta}{k(T_h - T_c)} \qquad (9\text{-}34\mathrm{d})$$

To determine the Nusselt number for inclinations where $60° < \phi < 90°$, a straight-line interpolation between Eqs. (9-29) and (9-33) is proposed; this yields

$$\mathrm{Nu}_\phi = \frac{(90° - \phi°)\mathrm{Nu}_{60°} + (\phi° - 60°)\mathrm{Nu}_{90°}}{30°} \quad \text{for } 60° \leq \phi \leq 90° \qquad (9\text{-}35)$$

The experimental data with air agree with Eq. (9-35) to within 6.5 percent.

## 9.6.4 Inclined Layers, $0° \leq \phi \leq 60°$

Based on the experimental investigations with air, the following correlation is proposed by Hollands, Unny, Raithby, and Konicek for free convection in inclined layers for inclinations $0° \leq \phi \leq 60°$:

$$\mathrm{Nu}_\phi = 1 + 1.44 \left[ 1 - \frac{1708}{\mathrm{Ra}\cos\phi} \right]^* \left[ 1 - \frac{1708(\sin 1.8\phi)^{1.6}}{\mathrm{Ra}\cos\phi} \right]$$
$$+ \left[ \left( \frac{\mathrm{Ra}\cos\phi}{5830} \right)^{1/3} - 1 \right]^* \qquad (9\text{-}36)$$

for high aspect ratio (i.e., $H/\delta \to$ high) and in the range of $0 < \mathrm{Ra} < 10^5$. Here the Nusselt number is defined as

$$\mathrm{Nu}_\phi = \frac{q\delta}{k(T_h - T_c)}$$
$$q = \text{heat flux across layer, W/m}^2$$

and the notation $[\ ]^*$ is used to denote that if the quantity in the bracket is negative, it should be set equal to zero. The experimental data with air agree with Eq. (9-36) to within 5 percent.

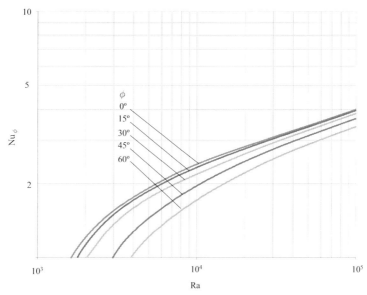

**FIG. 9.7.** A plot of Nusselt number for free convection inside inclined enclosures for $0 \leq \phi \leq 60°$, computed from Eq. (9-36).

Figure 9.7 shows the Nusselt number $Nu_\phi$ computed from Eq. (9-36) plotted against $Ra \cos \phi$ for different inclinations between $\phi = 0°$ and $60°$.

Clearly, Eq. (9-36) includes the horizontal enclosure ($\phi = 0$) as a special case. Thus, by setting $\phi = 0$ in Eq. (9-36), the Nusselt number for free convection inside a horizontal enclosure becomes

$$Nu_{\phi=0} = 1 + 1.44\left[1 - \frac{1708}{Ra}\right]^* + \left[\left(\frac{Ra}{5830}\right)^{1/3} - 1\right]^* \tag{9-37}$$

Note that for Ra< 1708, Eq. (9-37) reduces to

$$Nu_{\phi=0} = 1 \quad \text{for Ra} < 1708$$

which is consistent with the fact that, as we have previously discussed, the free-convection flow between parallel plates sets up at a critical Rayleigh number 1708, and for Ra< 1708 the conduction regime prevails.

**EXAMPLE 9-8** A double-glass window consists of two vertical parallel sheets of glass, each 1.6 m by 1.6 m in size, separated by 1.5 cm of air space at atmospheric pressure. Calculate the free-convection heat transfer coefficient for the air space for a temperature difference of $35°C$. Assume a mean temperature for the air of $27°C$.

**SOLUTION** The physical properties of air at $T_f = 27°C = 300\ K$ are

$$\nu = 1.568 \times 10^{-5}\ \text{m}^2/s \quad Pr = 0.708$$
$$k = 0.02624\ \text{W}/(\text{m} \cdot °\text{C})$$

The Rayleigh number becomes

$$
\begin{aligned}
\text{Ra} &= \frac{g\beta(T_h - T_c)\delta^3}{\nu^2}Pr \\
&= \frac{(9.81)(1/300)(35)(0.015)^3}{(1.568 \times 10^{-5})^2}(0.708) \\
&= 1.112 \times 10^4
\end{aligned}
$$

The aspect ratio is

$$a = \frac{H}{\delta} = \frac{1.6}{0.015} = 106.67$$

We use Eqs. (9-29) and (9-30a) to (9-30c) to calculate the Nusselt number:

$$\text{Nu} = [\text{Nu}_1,\ \text{Nu}_2,\ \text{Nu}_3]_{\text{max}}$$

where Nu is the maximum of the following three Nusselt numbers:

$$
\begin{aligned}
\text{Nu}_1 &= 0.0605\,\text{Ra}^{1/3} = 0.0605(1.112 \times 10^4)^{1/3} \\
&= 1.35 \\
\text{Nu}_2 &= \left\{1 + \left[\frac{0.104\,\text{Ra}^{0.293}}{1 + (6310/\text{Ra})^{1.36}}\right]^3\right\}^{1/3} \\
&= 1.32 \\
\text{Nu}_3 &= 0.242\left(\frac{\text{Ra}}{a}\right)^{0.272} \\
&= 0.86
\end{aligned}
$$

Therefore

$$
\begin{aligned}
\text{Nu} &= \text{Nu}_{\text{max}} = 1.35 \\
h &= \frac{k}{\delta}\text{Nu} = \frac{0.02624}{0.015}1.35 = 2.36\ \text{W}/(\text{m}^2 \cdot °\text{C}) \\
q &= h\Delta T = (2.36)(35) = 82.66\ \text{W}/\text{m}^2
\end{aligned}
$$

**EXAMPLE 9-9** In a horizontal flat-plate solar collector the absorber plate and the glass cover are separated by an air gap at atmospheric pressure. Estimate the heat transfer coefficient for free convection across the air gap for a gap spacing 3.0 cm, assuming that the absorber plate is at 60°C and the glass cover at 30°C.

**SOLUTION** The physical properties of air at $T_f = (T_h + T_c)/2 = (60 + 30)/2 = 45°C = 318\ K$ are

$$\nu = 1.751 \times 10^{-5}\ \text{m}^2/s \quad Pr = 0.704 \quad k = 0.0276\ \text{W}/(\text{m} \cdot °\text{C})$$

The Rayleigh number becomes

$$
\begin{aligned}
\text{Ra} &= \frac{g\beta(T_h - T_c)\delta^3}{\nu^2}\text{Pr} \\
&= \frac{(9.81)(1/318)(60 - 30)(0.03)^3}{(1.751 \times 10^{-5})^2}(0.704) \\
&= 57,356
\end{aligned}
$$

For a horizontal enclosure with $\phi = 0°$, we use Eq. (9-37) to calculate the Nusselt number:

$$\text{Nu} = 1 + 1.44 \left[1 - \frac{1708}{\text{Ra}}\right]^* + \left[\left(\frac{\text{Ra}}{5830}\right)^{1/3} - 1\right]^*$$

where $[\ ]^*$ is used to denote that if the quantity in the bracket is negative, it should be set equal to zero. We have Ra= $57,356$, and so both brackets in Eq. (9-37) are positive; therefore the Nusselt number becomes

$$
\begin{aligned}
\text{Nu} &= 1 + 1.44 \left[1 - \frac{1708}{57,356}\right] + \left[\left(\frac{57,356}{5830}\right)^{1/3} - 1\right] \\
&= 3.54
\end{aligned}
$$

Then,

$$h = \frac{k}{\delta}\text{Nu} = \frac{0.0276}{0.03}(3.54) = 3.26\ \text{W}/(\text{m}^2 \cdot °\text{C})$$

and

$$q = h(T_h - T_c) = 3.26 \times 30 = 97.8\ \text{W}/\text{m}^2$$

## 9.6.5 Horizontal Cylindrical Annulus

Consider a fluid contained in a long, horizontal cylindrical annulus with a gap spacing $\delta = \frac{1}{2}(D_o - D_i)$, where $D_o$ and $D_i$ are, respectively, the diameters of the outer and inner cylinders, as illustrated in Fig. 9.8.

Raithby and Hollands proposed the following correlation for the heat transfer rate $Q$ for the length $H$ of a cylindrical annulus:

$$Q = \frac{2\pi k_{\text{eff}} H}{\ln(D_o/D_i)}(T_i - T_o) \quad W \qquad (9\text{-}38)$$

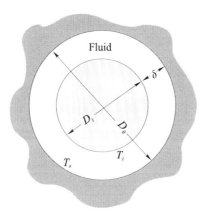

**FIG. 9.8.** Free convection in horizontal cylindrical annulus or spherical annulus.

where

$$\frac{k_{\text{eff}}}{k} = 0.386 \left(\frac{\text{Pr}}{0.861 + \text{Pr}}\right)^{1/4} (\text{Ra}^*_{\text{cyl}})^{1/4}$$

$$(\text{Ra}^*_{\text{cyl}})^{1/4} = \frac{\ln(D_o/D_i)}{\delta^{3/4}(D_i^{-3/5} + D_o^{-3/5})^{5/4}} \text{Ra}_\delta^{1/4}$$

$$H = \text{length of cylindrical annulus}$$

$$\text{Ra}_\delta = \frac{g\beta(T_i - T_o)\delta^3}{\nu^2}\text{Pr}$$

$$\delta = \frac{1}{2}(D_o - D_i)$$

This correlation is applicable over the range $10^2 < \text{Ra}^*_{\text{cyl}} < 10^7$.

## 9.6.6 Spherical Annulus

We now consider a fluid contained between two concentric spheres of inner and outer diameters $D_i$ and $D_o$, respectively, as illustrated in Fig. 9.8. The surfaces are maintained at uniform temperatures $T_i$ and $T_o$. Raithby and Hollands proposed the following correlation for the total heat transfer rate from the spheres:

$$\boxed{Q = k_{\text{eff}}\frac{\pi D_i D_o}{\delta}(T_i - T_o)} \quad W \qquad (9\text{-}39)$$

where

$$\frac{k_{eff}}{k} = 0.74 \left( \frac{\text{Pr}}{0.861 + \text{Pr}} \right)^{1/4} (\text{Ra}^*_{sph})^{1/4}$$

$$(\text{Ra}^*_{sph})^{1/4} = \frac{\delta^{1/4}}{D_o D_i (D_i^{-7/5} + D_o^{-7/5})^{5/4}} \text{Ra}_\delta^{1/4}$$

$$\text{Ra}_\delta = \frac{g\beta(T_i - T_o)\delta^3}{\nu^2}\text{Pr}$$

$$\delta = \frac{1}{2}(D_o - D_i)$$

This correlation is applicable over the range $10^2 < \text{Ra}^*_{sph} < 10^4$.

**EXAMPLE 9-10**  The space between two concentric thin-walled spheres of diameters $D_1 = 10$ cm and $D_2 = 14$ cm contains air at atmospheric pressure. Calculate the heat transfer rate across the spheres by free convection for a temperature difference of $50°$C and a mean air temperature of $27°$C.

**SOLUTION**  The physical properties of air at $300\ K$ are

$$\nu = 1.684 \times 10^{-5}\ \text{m}^2/s \quad \text{Pr} = 0.708$$

$$k = 0.02624\ \text{W}/(\text{m} \cdot °\text{C})$$

The Rayleigh number becomes

$$\begin{aligned}
\text{Ra}_\delta &= \frac{g\beta(T_i - T_o)\delta^3}{\nu^2}\text{Pr} \\
&= \frac{(9.81)(1/300)(50)(0.02)^3}{(1.568 \times 10^{-5})^2}(0.708) \\
&= 37,666
\end{aligned}$$

Equation (9-39) is now used to calculate the total heat transfer rate as follows:

$$\text{Ra}^*_{sph} = \frac{\delta}{(D_o D_i)^4} \frac{\text{Ra}_\delta}{(D_i^{-7/5} + D_o^{-7/5})^5} = 173.4$$

$$k_{eff} = 0.74k \left( \frac{\text{Pr}}{0.861 + \text{Pr}} \right)^{1/4} (\text{Ra}^*_{sph})^{1/4} = 0.0578$$

Then the total heat transfer rate $Q$ becomes

$$Q = k_{\text{eff}}\frac{\pi D_i D_o}{\delta}(Ti - To)$$
$$= 0.0578\frac{\pi(0.1)(0.14)}{0.02}(50)$$
$$= 6.35 \text{ W}$$

## 9.7. PLUMES GENERATED BY FREE CONVECTION

Figure 9.7 illustrated the laminar and turbulent flow regimes of a plume generated by a candle heating of air. The analysis of such flows are beyond the scope of this book and covered in advanced courses.

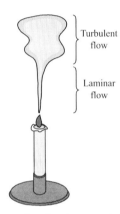

Turbulent flow

Laminar flow

**FIG. 9.11.** Natural convection development in heated air by the candle.

## PROBLEMS

*Free Convection on a Flat Plate*

**9-1** A vertical plate 0.4 m high and 2 m wide, maintained at a uniform temperature of 92°C, is exposed to quiescent atmospheric air at 32°C. Calculate the average heat transfer coefficient he over the entire height of the plate, using the correlations given by both Eqs. (9-6) and (9-10).

**9-2** Calculate the heat transfer rates by free convection from a 0.3-m-high vertical plate maintained at a uniform temperature of 70°C to ambient air at 34°C at 1.0 and 2.0 *atm*.

**9-3** A vertical plate 0.3 m high and 1 m wide, maintained at a uniform temperature of 134°C, is exposed to quiescent atmospheric air at 20°C. Calculate the total heat transfer rate from the plate to the air.

**9-4** Calculate the heat transfer rate from a 0.3-m-high vertical plate at a uniform temperature of $80°C$ to quiescent ambient air at $24°C$ at $3\ atm$ pressure.

**9-5** Calculate the total heat transfer rate by free convection from a vertical plate 0.3 m by 0.3 m with one surface insulated and the other surface maintained at $100°C$ and exposed to atmospheric air at $30°C$.

**9-6** Compare the heat transfer rates by free convection from a 0.3 m by 0.3 m plate with one surface insulated and the other surface maintained at $T_w = 100°C$ and exposed to quiescent atmospheric air at $T_\infty = 30°C$ for the following conditions: (a) the plate is horizontal with the heated surface facing up; (b) the plate is horizontal with the heated surface facing down.

**9-7** Consider a 0.15 m by 0.3 m rectangular plate maintained at a uniform temperature $T_w = 80°C$ placed vertically in quiescent atmospheric air at temperature $T_\infty = 30°C$. Compare the heat transfer rates from the plate when 0.15 m is the vertical height and when 0.3 m is the vertical height.

**9-8** The south-facing wall of the building is 7 m high and 10 m wide. The wall absorbs the incident solar energy at a rate of $600\ W/m^2$. It is assumed that about $200\ W/m^2$ of the absorbed energy is conducted through the wall into the interior of the wall and that the remaining is dissipated by free convection into the surrounding quiescent atmospheric air at $30°C$. Calculate the temperature of the outside surface of the wall.

**9-9** An electrically heated 0.5 m by 0.1 m vertical plate is insulated on one side and dissipates heat from the other surface at a constant rate of $600\ W/m^2$ by free convection into atmospheric air at $30°C$. Determine the surface temperature of the plate.

**9-10** A cube 5 cm $\times$ 5 cm $\times$ 5 cm in size is suspended with one of its surfaces in a horizontal position in quiescent atmospheric air at $20°C$. All surfaces of the cube are maintained at a uniform temperature of $100°C$. Determine the heat loss by free convection from the cube into the atmosphere.
*Answer*: $10.07\ W$.

**9-11** A circular hot plate $D = 25$ cm in diameter with both of its surfaces maintained at a uniform temperature of $100°C$ is suspended in a horizontal position in atmospheric air at $30°C$. Determine the heat transfer rate by free convection from the plate into the atmosphere.

**9-12** A thin electric strip heater 30 cm in width is placed with its width oriented vertically. It dissipates heat by free convection from both its surfaces into atmospheric air at $T_\infty = 20°C$. If the surface of the heater should not exceed $225°C$, determine the length of the strip needed to dissipate $1500\ W$ of energy into the room.

**9-13** A hot iron block at $425°C$ 10 cm $\times$ 15 cm $\times$ 20 cm in size is placed on an asbestos sheet with its 10-cm side oriented vertically. There is negligible heat loss from the surface that is in contact with the asbestos sheet. Calculate the rate of heat loss from its five boundary surfaces by free convection into the surrounding quiescent air at atmospheric pressure and $25°C$.

**9-14** A horizontal square plate heater 0.3 m by 0.3 m is thermally insulated on the bottom side and exposed to quiescent atmospheric air at $T_\infty = 30°C$ on the top side. The plate heater is electrically heated at a rate of $400 \ W/m^2$, and heat dissipates by free convection into the air. Calculate the equilibrium temperature of the plate. [Assume $h = 6 \ \text{W}/(\text{m}^2 \cdot °\text{C})$ as a first approximation.]

**9-15** A circular hot plate $D = 50$ cm in diameter with both surfaces maintained at a uniform temperature of $300°C$ is suspended in a vertical position in water at $20°C$. Determine the heat loss from the hot plate to the water.

**9-16** A circular hot plate $D = 50$ cm in diameter with both surfaces maintained at a uniform temperature of $300°C$ is suspended in a vertical position in atmospheric air at $20 \ C$. Determine the heat loss from the plate to the air.

*Free Convection on a Long Cylinder*

**9-17** A bare 10-cm-diameter horizontal steam pipe is 100 m long and has a surface temperature of $150°C$. Estimate the total heat loss by free convection to atmospheric air at $20°C$.

**9-18** An electric heater of outside diameter $D = 2.5$ cm and length $L = 0.5$ m is immersed horizontally in a large tank of engine oil at $20°C$. If the surface temperature of the heater is $140°C$, determine the rate of heat transfer to the oil.

**9-19** A horizontal electric heater of outside diameter $D = 2.5$ cm and length $L = 0.5$ m dissipates heat by free convection into atmospheric air at $T_\infty = 30°C$. If the surface temperature of the heater is $250°C$, calculate the rate of heat transfer from the heater into the air.

**9-20** A cylindrical electric heater of outside diameter $D = 2.5$ cm and length $L = 2$ m is immersed horizontally in mercury at a temperature of $100°C$. If the surface of the heater is maintained at an average temperature of $300°C$, calculate the rate of heat transfer to the mercury.

**9-21** Calculate the average heat transfer coefficient $h$ from an isothermal horizontal cylinder of diameter $D = 5$ cm at temperature $T_w = 400 \ K$ to quiescent air at atmospheric pressure and at temperature $T_\infty = 300 \ K$.

**9-22** A hot gas at $220°C$ flows through a horizontal pipe of outside diameter $D = 15$ cm. The pipe has an uninsulated portion of length $L = 3$ m that is exposed to atmospheric air at temperature $T_\infty = 30°C$. Assuming that the outside surface of the pipe is at $220°C$, determine the rate of heat loss into the atmosphere.

**9-23** An uninsulated horizontal duct of diameter $D = 20$ cm carrying cold air at $10°C$ is exposed to quiescent atmospheric air at $35°C$. Determine the heat gain by free convection per meter length of the duct.

**9-24** A horizontal pipe of diameter $D = 2$ cm with the outer surface at $225°C$ is exposed to atmospheric air at $25°C$. Calculate the heat transfer rate per meter length of the pipe by free convection.

**9-25** A 1.5-m-long vertical cylinder of diameter $D = 2.5$ cm maintained at a uniform temperature of $140°C$ is exposed to atmospheric air at 15 C. Determine the free-convection heat transfer coefficient.

**9-26** A $D = 5$ cm OD and $L = 40$ cm long tube, maintained at a uniform temperature $T_w = 400$ K, is placed vertically in quiescent air at atmospheric pressure and at temperature $T_\infty = 300$ K. Calculate the average free-convection heat transfer coefficient and the rate of heat loss from the tube to the air.

*Free Convection on a Sphere*

**9-27** Calculate the heat transfer rate by free convection from a 2-cm-diameter sphere whose surface is maintained at $120°C$ to water at $20°C$.

**9-28** Calculate the heat transfer rate by free convection from a 2-cm-diameter sphere whose surface is maintained at $110°C$ to air at $20°C$.

**9-29** Calculate the heat transfer rate by free convection from a 20-cm-diameter sphere whose surface is maintained at $140°C$ to atmospheric air at $1\ atm$ and at $20\ C$.

**9-30** A sphere of diameter $D = 5$ cm whose surface is maintained at a uniform temperature of $120°C$ is submerged in quiescent water at $30°C$. Determine the heat transfer rate by free convection from the sphere to the water.

**9-31** Calculate the heat transfer rate by free convection from a 20-cm-diameter sphere whose surface is maintained at $140°C$ to the surrounding air at $20°C$ and at $1\ atm$.

**9-32** A sphere of diameter $D = 5$ cm, maintained at a uniform temperature of $60°C$, is immersed in water at $20°C$. Calculate the rate of heat loss by free convection.

**9-33** Compare the heat loss by free convection from a spherical body of diameter $D = 0.5$ m, maintained at a uniform temperature $30°C$, to ambient air at $-10°C$ and $3\ atm$.
*Answer*: 185.24 W.

**9-34** A 15-cm-diameter, electrically heated sphere is immersed in a quiescent body of air at $20°C$. Calculate the amount of heat to be supplied by the electric heater in order to keep the surface temperature of the sphere at $100°C$.

*Simplified Equations for Air*

**9-35** A vertical plate 1 m high and 1 m wide at a uniform temperature of $40°C$ is exposed to atmospheric air at $20°C$. Determine the free-convection heat transfer coefficient, and compare the result with that obtainable from the simplified expressions for free convection to air at atmospheric pressure.

**9-36** A vertical plate 0.2 m by 0.2 m in size at a uniform temperature $140°C$ is exposed to atmospheric air at $15°C$ . Calculate the free-convection heat transfer coefficient, and compare the result with that obtainable from the simplified expressions for air at atmospheric pressure.

**9-37** A horizontal plate 0.2 m by 0.2 m in size at a uniform temperature of $140°C$ is exposed to atmospheric air at 15 $C$. Calculate the free-convection heat transfer coefficient for (*a*) the heated surface facing up, and (*b*) the heated surface facing down, and compare the results with those obtainable from the simplified expressions for air at atmospheric pressure.
*Answers*:$2.92 \ W/(m^2·°C)$, $2.95 \ W/(m^2·°C)$.

**9-38** A long horizontal cylinder 5 cm in diameter, maintained at a uniform temperature of $140°C$, is exposed to atmospheric air at $10°C$. Calculate the free-convection heat transfer coefficient, and compare it with that obtainable from the simplified expression for air at atmospheric pressure.

**9-39** Calculate the heat transfer coefficient for free convection from a 2.5-cm-diameter horizontal cylinder maintained at a uniform temperature $325°C$ into atmospheric air at $30°C$. Compare this result with that obtainable from the simplified expression for free convection in air.

**9-40** A horizontal electric heater with an outside diameter of 2.5 cm and length of 0.5 m is exposed to atmospheric air at $15°C$. If the surface of the heater is at $130°C$, determine the heat transfer coefficient for free convection, and compare it with that obtainable from the simplified expression for air at atmospheric pressure.

**9-41** A vertical plate 0.3 m by 0.3 m in size, maintained at a uniform temperature of $70°C$, is exposed to cold atmospheric air at a temperature of $10°C$. Calculate the free-convection heat transfer coefficient, and compare it with that obtainable from the simplified expressions for free convection to air at $4 \ atm$.

*Free Convection in Enclosed Spaces*

**9-42** A double-glass window consists of two vertical parallel sheets of glass, each 1 m by 1 m in size, separated by a 1-cm air space at atmospheric pressure. Calculate the free-convection heat transfer coefficient for the air space for a temperature difference of 30°C. Assume the mean temperature for the air to be 27°C.
*Answer*: 2.62 W/(m²·°C)

**9-43** Two vertical parallel plates, each 1 m × 1 m in size, are separated by a distance of 3 cm filled with atmospheric air. One of the plates is maintained at a uniform temperature of 250°C and the other at 100°C. Calculate the heat transfer rate by free convection between the plates.

**9-44** Two parallel vertical plates, each 2 m high, are separated by a 6-cm air space. One of the plates is maintained at a uniform temperature 130°C and the other at 25°C. Determine the free-convection heat transfer coefficient for free convection between the two plates.

**9-45** Atmospheric air is contained between two large horizontal parallel plates separated by a distance of 5 cm. The lower plate is maintained at 100°C and the upper plate at 30°C. Determine the heat transfer rate between the plates by free convection per square meter of the plate surface.

**9-46** Two parallel horizontal plates are separated by a distance of 2 cm. The lower plate is at a uniform temperature of 220°C, and the upper plate is at 35°C. Determine the heat transfer rate between the plates per square meter of the plate surface.

**9-47** Water is contained between two parallel horizontal plates separated by a distance of 2 cm. The lower plate is at a uniform temperature of 130°C, and the upper plate is at 30°C. Determine the heat transfer rate between the plates per square meter of the plate surface.

**9-48** In a horizontal flat-plate solar collector the absorber plate and the glass cover are separated by an air gap at atmospheric pressure. Estimate the heat transfer coefficient for free convection across the air gap for a gap spacing of 2 cm and 4 cm, assuming that the absorber plate is at 80°C and the glass cover at 30°C.

**9-49** A 50 cm by 50 cm horizontal double window glass is constructed of two glass plates separated by a 2-cm air gap at atmospheric pressure. If the upper and lower glass plates are at temperatures of −15°C and 20°C, respectively, calculate the heat transfer rate across the gap.

**9-50** The annular space between two horizontal thin-walled coaxial cylinders contains air at atmospheric pressure. The inner cylinder has a diameter $D_1 = 8$ cm and is maintained at a uniform temperature $T_1 = 100$°C, while the outer cylinder has a diameter $D_2 = 12$ cm and is maintained at a uniform temperature $T_2 = 50$°C.

Calculate the heat transfer rate by free convection across the air space per meter length of the cylinders.

**9-51** The annular space between two horizontal thin-walled coaxial cylinders contains air at atmospheric pressure. The diameters of the inner and outer cylinders are $D_1 = 8$ cm and $D_2 = 12$ cm, respectively. The temperature difference between the cylinders is $50°C$, and the mean temperature of the air in the annular space is $27°C$. Calculate the heat transfer rate by free convection across the air space per meter length of the cylinders.

**9-52** The annular space between two horizontal thin-walled coaxial cylinders is filled with water. The inner and outer cylinders have diameters $D_1 = 10$ cm and $D_2 = 13$ cm, respectively. Calculate heat transfer by free convection across the water-filled space per meter length of the cylinder for a temperature difference of $50°C$ and a mean temperature of $40°C$ for the water.

**9-53** The annular space between two thin-walled horizontal coaxial cylinders is filled with water. The inner and outer cylinders have diameters $D_1 = 7$ cm and $D_2 = 10$ cm, respectively. Calculate the heat transfer rate across the annulus by free convection when the inside and outside cylinders are maintained at $T_1 = 80°C$ and $T_2 = 40°C$, respectively.

**9-54** The space between two concentric thin-walled spheres contains atmospheric air. The inner and outer spheres have diameters $D_1 = 4$ cm and $D_2 = 6$ cm, respectively, and the temperature difference between the surfaces is $20°C$. Calculate the heat transfer rate across the space by free convection for air at a mean temperature of $27°C$.

**9-55** A spherical storage tank of diameter $D_1 = 2$ m contains a cold liquid at a temperature $T_1 = 10°C$. To reduce heat losses, this storage tank is enclosed inside another spherical shell, and the gap spacing is $3$ cm. The temperature of the outer sphere is $T_2 = 20°C$. Determine the rate of heat loss by free convection across the gap filled with air at atmospheric pressure.

# CHAPTER 10

# *Phase Change Heat Transfer: Condensation and Boiling*

Condensers and boilers are important and widely used types of heat exchangers with unique characteristics of the heat transfer mechanism. If a vapor strikes a surface that is at a temperature below the corresponding saturation temperature, the vapor will immediately condense into the liquid phase. If the condensation takes place continuously over a surface which is kept cooled by some process, and if the condensed liquid is removed from the surface by the force of gravity, then the condensing surface is usually covered with a thin layer of liquid, and the situation is known as *filmwise condensation.*

Under certain conditions, for example, if traces of oil are present during the condensation of steam on a highly polished surface, the film of condensate is broken into droplets, and the situation is known as *dropwise condensation.* The droplets grow, coalesce, and increase in size; eventually they run off the condensing surface under the influence of gravity, sweeping off other droplets in their path. Therefore, with dropwise condensation the condensing surface between the drops is exposed to condensing vapor; as a result, the thermal resistance to heat flow of the condensate layer is much less, and hence the heat transfer rates are several times higher with dropwise condensation than with filmwise condensation.

The presence of condensate acts as a barrier to heat transfer from the vapor to the metal surface, and dropwise condensation offers much less resistance to heat flow on the vapor side than does filmwise condensation. If the vapor contains some noncondensible gas, this gas will collect on the condensing side while condensation takes place, and the noncondensible gas will act as a resistance to heat flow on the condensing side. Therefore, an accurate prediction of the heat transfer coefficient for condensing vapors with and without the presence of noncondensible gas is important in the design of condensers.

When a liquid is in contact with a surface that is maintained at a temperature above the saturation temperature of the liquid, boiling may occur. The phenomenon of heat transfer in boiling is extremely complicated because a large number of variables are involved and because very complex hydrodynamic developments occur during the process. Therefore, considerable work has been directed toward gaining a better understanding of the boiling mechanism.

In this chapter we present some of the recommended correlations for predicting the heat transfer coefficient during condensation and boiling.

## 10.1. LAMINAR FILM CONDENSATION

When the temperature of a vapor is reduced below its saturation temperature, the vapor condenses. In engineering applications, the vapor is condensed by bringing it into contact with a cold surface. The steam condensers for power plants are typical examples of this application. If the liquid wets the surface, the condensation occurs in the form of a smooth film, which flows down the surface under the action of the gravity. The presence of a liquid film over the surface constitutes a thermal resistance to heat flow.

The first fundamental analysis leading to the determination of the heat transfer coefficient during filmwise condensation of pure vapors (i.e., without the presence of non-condensible gas) on a flat plate and a circular tube was given by Nusselt in 1916. Over the years, improvements have been made on Nusselt's theory of film condensation. But except in the case of the condensation of liquid metals, Nusselt's original theory has been successful and still is widely used. Here we present the correlations of the heat transfer coefficient during film condensation of vapors based on Nusselt's theory of condensation.

### 10.1.1 Condensation on Vertical Surfaces

Consider a cold vertical plate at temperature $T_w$ exposed to a large body of saturated vapor at temperature $T_v$ ($> T_w$), as illustrated in Fig. 10.1. Here $x$ is the axial coordinate measured downward along the plate, and $y$ is the coordinate normal to the condensing surface.

Note that the condensate film formed on the surface moves downward under the influence of gravity and that its thickness $\delta(x)$ increases with the distance along the surface. The velocity and temperature profiles are schematically illustrated in Fig. 10.1.

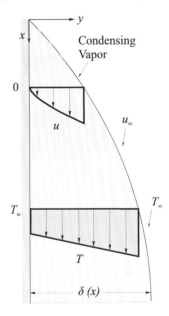

**FIG. 10.1.** Schematic of filmwise condensation on a vertical surface.

This condensation problem was first analyzed by Nusselt under the following assumptions:

1. The plate is maintained at a uniform temperature $T_w$ that is less than the saturation temperature $T_v$ of the vapor.

2. The vapor is stationary or has low velocity, and so it exerts no drag on the motion of the condensate.

3. The downward flow of condensate under the influence of gravity is laminar.

4. The flow velocity associated with the condensate film is low; as a result, the flow acceleration in the condensate layer is negligible.

5. Fluid properties are constant.

6. Heat transfer across the condensate layer is by pure conduction; hence the liquid temperature distribution is linear.

With these considerations, Nusselt developed the following expression for the average value of the heat transfer coefficient $h_m$ for filmwise condensation over a vertical plate of height $L$:

$$h_m = 0.943 \left[ \frac{g\rho_l(\rho_l - \rho_v)h_{fg}k_l^3}{\mu_l(T_v - T_w)L} \right]^{1/4} \quad \text{W}/(\text{m}^2 \cdot {}^\circ\text{C}) \qquad (10\text{-}1a)$$

A comparison of this theoretical result with the results of experiments has shown that the measured heat transfer coefficient is about 20 percent higher than that predicted by the theory. Therefore, McAdams (1954) recommends that Nusselt's theoretical expression, Eq. (10-1$a$), should be multiplied by a factor of 1.2. Then, the recommended equation for the average heat transfer coefficient $h_m$ for filmwise condensation over a vertical plate of height $L$ becomes

$$h_m = 1.13 \left[ \frac{g\rho_l(\rho_l - \rho_v)h_{fg}k_l^3}{\mu_l(T_v - T_w)L} \right]^{1/4} \quad \text{for Re} < 1800 \qquad (10\text{-}1b)$$

where

$$
\begin{aligned}
g &= \text{acceleration due to gravity, } m/s^2 \\
h_{fg} &= \text{latent heat of condensation, J/kg} \\
k_l &= \text{thermal conductivity of liquid, W}/(\text{m} \cdot {}^\circ\text{C}) \\
L &= \text{length of vertical plate, m} \\
\rho_l, \rho_v &= \text{density of liquid and vapor, kg/m}^3 \\
\mu_l &= \text{viscosity of liquid, kg}/(\text{m} \cdot \text{s}) \\
T_v, T_w &= \text{vapor and wall temperature, respectively, }{}^\circ\text{C}
\end{aligned}
$$

and the physical properties, including $h_{fg}$, are evaluated at the film temperature

$$T_f = \frac{1}{2}(T_w + T_v) \tag{10-2}$$

The additional energy needed to cool the condensate film below saturation temperature is accommodated approximately by evaluating $h_{fg}$ at the film temperature instead of at the saturation temperature. The heat transfer coefficient derived above for a vertical plate is also applicable for condensation on the outside or inside surface of a vertical tube, provided that the tube radius is large compared with the thickness of the condensate film.

The *Reynolds number* for condensate flow is defined as

$$\boxed{\mathrm{Re} = \frac{4\dot{m}}{\mu_l P}} \tag{10-3}$$

Here $\dot{m}$ is the total mass flow rate of condensate at the lowest part of the condensing surface (i.e., at $x = L$), in kilograms per second, and $P$ is the wetted perimeter, defined as

$$P = \begin{cases} w & \text{for vertical plate of width } w \\ \pi D & \text{for vertical tube of outside diameter } D \end{cases} \tag{10-4}$$

Experiments have shown that the transition from laminar to turbulent condensate flow takes place at a Reynolds number of about 1800. Therefore, the correlation given by Eq. (10-1b) is valid only for the laminar flow of condensation over the surface. Generally, $\rho_v \ll \rho_l$; hence Eq. (10-1b) reduces to

$$\boxed{h_m = 1.13\left[\frac{g\rho_l^2 h_{fg}k_l^3}{\mu_l(T_v - T_w)L}\right]^{1/4}} \qquad \text{for Re} < 1800 \tag{10-5}$$

which can be rearranged in the form

$$\boxed{h_m\left(\frac{\mu_l^2}{k_l^3\rho_l^2 g}\right)^{1/3} = 1.76\,\mathrm{Re}^{-1/3}} \qquad \text{for Re} < 1800 \tag{10-6}$$

and the physical properties, including $h_{fg}$, are evaluated at the film temperature, defined by Eq. (10-2).

## 10.1.2 Condensation on Inclined Plates

Nusselt's analysis of filmwise condensation for a vertical surface, given above, can readily be extended to condensation on an inclined plane surface making an angle $\phi$ with the horizontal, as illustrated in Fig. 10.2, if the term $g$ is replaced by $g \sin \phi$ in Eq. (10-1b), we find

$$h_m = 1.13 \left[ \frac{g\rho_l(\rho_l - \rho_v)h_{fg}k_l^3}{\mu_l(T_v - T_w)L} \sin\phi \right]^{1/4} \qquad \text{for Re} < 1800 \qquad (10\text{-}7)$$

For $\rho_v \ll \rho_l$, Eq. (10-7) reduces to

$$h_m = 1.13 \left[ \frac{g\rho_l^2 h_{fg}k_l^3}{\mu_l(T_v - T_w)L} \sin\phi \right]^{1/4} \qquad \text{for Re} < 1800 \qquad (10\text{-}8)$$

where $\phi$ is the angle between the plate and the horizontal. The physical properties are evaluated at the film temperature $T_f$, defined by Eq. (10-2).

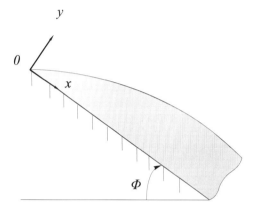

**FIG. 10.2.** Nomenclature for filmwise condensation on an inclined plane surface.

**EXAMPLE 10-1**  Air-free saturated steam at $T_v = 90°C$ and $P = 70.14$ kPa

condenses on the outer surface of a $L = 1.5$ m long, $D = 2.5$ m outside diameter (OD) vertical tube maintained at a uniform temperature $T_w = 70°C$. Assuming filmwise condensation, calculate the average heat transfer coefficient over the entire length of the tube.

**SOLUTION**  The physical properties of water at the film temperature

$T_f = (70 + 90)/2 = 80°C$ are

$$k_l = 0.668 \text{ W}/(\text{m} \cdot °C) \quad \mu_l = 0.355 \times 10^{-3} \text{ kg}/(\text{m} \cdot s)$$

$$\rho_l = 974 \text{ kg}/\text{m}^3 \qquad h_{fg} = 2309 \text{ kJ/kg}$$

$$g = 9.8 \text{ m}^2/s.$$

The average heat transfer coefficient $h_m$ for laminar filmwise condensation on a vertical surface of the tube with $\rho_v \ll \rho_l$, is determined from Eq. (10-5)

$$h_m = 1.13 \left[ \frac{g\rho_l^2 h_{fg} k_l^3}{\mu_l (T_v - T_w) L} \right]^{1/4}$$

$$= 1.13 \left[ \frac{(9.81)(974)^2 (2309 \times 10^3)(0.668)^3}{(0.355 \times 10^{-3})(90 - 70)(1.5)} \right]^{1/4} = 5596 \text{ W}/(\text{m}^2 \cdot {}^\circ\text{C})$$

**EXAMPLE 10-2**   Air-free saturated steam at $T_v = 75^\circ\text{C}$ and $P = 38.58 kPa$ condenses on a 0.5-m-long plate inclined $45^\circ$ from the horizontal and maintained at a uniform temperature of $T_w = 45^\circ\text{C}$. Calculate the average film-condensation heat transfer coefficient $h_m$ over the entire length of the plate.

**SOLUTION**   The physical properties of water at the film temperature $T_f = (75+45)/2 = 60^\circ\text{C}$ are

$$k_l = 0.651 \text{ W}/(\text{m} \cdot {}^\circ\text{C}) \quad \mu_l = 0.471 \times 10^{-3} \text{ kg}/(\text{m} \cdot s)$$
$$\rho_l = 985 \text{ kg}/\text{m}^3 \qquad h_{fg} = 2358.5 \text{ kJ/kg}$$

and $g = 9.8 \text{ m}^2/s$. The average heat transfer coefficient $h_m$ for laminar filmwise condensation on an inclined plate with $\rho_v \ll \rho_l$, is determined from Eq. (10-8):

$$h_m = 1.13 \left[ \frac{g\rho_l^2 h_{fg} k_l^3}{\mu_l (T_v - T_w) L} \sin\phi \right]^{1/4}$$

$$= 1.13 \left[ \frac{(9.81)(985)^2 (2358.5 \times 10^3)(0.651)^3}{(0.471 \times 10^{-3})(75 - 45)(0.5)} \sin 45^\circ \right]^{1/4}$$

$$= 5639 \text{ W}/(\text{m}^2 \cdot {}^\circ\text{C})$$

## 10.1.3 Condensation on a Single Horizontal Tube

The analysis of heat transfer for condensation on the outside surface of a horizontal tube is more complicated than that for a vertical surface. Nusselt's analysis for laminar filmwise condensation on the surface of a horizontal tube gives the average heat transfer coefficient as

$$h_m = 0.725 \left[ \frac{g\rho_l (\rho_l - \rho_v) h_{fg} k_l^3}{\mu_l (T_v - T_w) D} \right]^{1/4} \tag{10-9}$$

where $D$ is the outside diameter of the tube.
   For $\rho_v \ll \rho_l$, Eq. (10-9) reduces to

$$h_m = 0.725 \left[ \frac{g\rho_l^2 h_{fg} k_l^3}{\mu_l (T_v - T_w) D} \right]^{1/4} \tag{10-10}$$

A comparison of Eqs. (10-1a) and (10-10), for filmwise condensation on a vertical tube of length $L$ and a horizontal tube of diameter $D$, yields

$$\frac{h_{m,\text{vert}}}{h_{m,\text{horz}}} = 1.30 \left(\frac{D}{L}\right)^{1/4} \qquad (10\text{-}11)$$

This result implies that for a given $T_v - T_w$, the average heat transfer coefficients for a vertical tube of length $L$ and a horizontal tube of diameter $D$ become equal when $L = 2.87D$. For example, when $L = 100D$, theoretically $h_{m,\text{horz}}$ would be 2.44 times $h_{m,\text{vert}}$. Given this consideration, horizontal tube arrangements are generally preferred to vertical tube arrangements in condenser design.

Condensation on a single horizontal tube hardly changes into turbulent flow. Therefore, Eq. (10-10) is valid for all practical purposes.

**FIG. 10.3.** Film condensation on horizontal tubes arranged in a vertical tier.

## 10.1.4 Condensation on Horizontal Tube Banks

Condenser design generally involves horizontal tubes arranged in vertical tiers as illustrated in Fig. 10.3, in such a way that the condensate from one tube drains onto the tube just below.

If it is assumed that the drainage from one tube flows smoothly onto the tube below, then for a vertical tier of $N$ tubes, each of diameter $D$, the heat transfer coefficient $h$ is obtained by replacing $D$ by $ND$ in Eq. (10-10). We find

$$[h_m]_{N \text{ tubes}} = 0.725 \left[\frac{g\rho_l^2 h_{fg} k_l^3}{\mu_l (T_v - T_w) ND}\right]^{1/4} = \frac{1}{N^{1/4}}[h_m]_{1 \text{ tube}} \qquad \text{for Re} < 1800$$

$$(10\text{-}12)$$

This equation generally yields conservative results, since some turbulence and disturbance of the condensate film are unavoidable during drainage, and this increases the heat transfer coefficient.

Equation (10-12) is valid for laminar filmwise condensation, namely, for Re< 1800. However, for horizontal tubes arranged in a vertical tier, turbulent condensation may be possible at the bottom tubes. The Reynolds number for condensation was defined by Eq. (10-3) as

$$\boxed{\mathrm{Re} = \frac{4\dot{m}}{\mu_l P}} \tag{10-13a}$$

where $\dot{m}$ is the mass flow rate of condensate in Kilograms per second at the lowest part of the tube bank and $P$ is the wetted perimeter. For horizontal tubes, each of length $L$, arranged in vertical tiers, $P$ is given by

$$\boxed{P = 2L} \tag{10-13b}$$

## 10.1.5 Calculation of Reynolds Number

To calculate the Reynolds number for condensate flow, defined previously, we need to know the condensation mass flow rate $\dot{m}$ at the lowest part of the system. Let $A_t$ be the total condensing surface area, $h_m$ the average condensation heat transfer coefficient, $T_v$ the saturation temperature of the condensing vapor, $T_w$ the average temperature of the cold condensing surface, and $h_{fg}$ the latent heat of condensation. Then the total heat transfer rate $Q$ is determined by

$$Q = A_t h_m (T_v - T_w) \tag{10-14a}$$

and the total mass flow rate $\dot{m}$ at the bottom of the condenser becomes

$$\dot{m} = \frac{Q}{h_{fg}} \tag{10-14b}$$

From Eqs. (10-14a) and (10-14b), we have

$$\dot{m} = \frac{A_t h_m (T_v - T_w)}{h_{fg}} \tag{10-14c}$$

Introducing Eq. (10-14c) into the definition of the Reynolds number given by Eq. (10-13a), we obtain

$$\boxed{\mathrm{Re} = \frac{4 A_t h_m (T_v - T_w)}{h_{fg} \mu_l P}} \tag{10-15}$$

Thus, the Reynolds number can be calculated, since the wetted perimeter $P$ was defined previously by Eqs. (10-4) and (10-13$b$); namely,

$$P = \begin{cases} \pi D & \text{for a vertical tube of outside diameter } D \\ w & \text{for a vertical or inclined plate of width } w \\ 2L & \text{for horizontal tubes, each of length } L, \text{arranged} \\ & \text{in vertical tiers} \end{cases} \qquad (10\text{-}16)$$

**EXAMPLE 10-3** Calculate the total mass flow rate of condensation $\dot{m}$, the total heat transfer rate $Q$ over the entire surface, and the Reynolds number Re at the bottom of the surface in Example 10-1.

**SOLUTION** The total mass flow rate of condensate at the bottom of the tube of Example 10-1 is determined from Eq. (10-14$c$):

$$\begin{aligned} \dot{m} &= \frac{(\pi D L)(h_m)(T_v - T_w)}{h_{fg}} \\ &= \frac{(\pi \times 0.025 \times 1.5)(5596)(90 - 70)}{2309 \times 10^3} = 5.71 \times 10^{-3} \text{ kg/s} \end{aligned}$$

where we set $A_t = \pi D L$ for the total condensing surface area. The total heat transfer rate, from Eqs. (10-14$a$) and (10-14$b$), is

$$\begin{aligned} Q &= A_t h_m (T_v - T_w) \\ &= \dot{m} h_{fg} \\ &= 5.71 \times 10^{-3} \times 2309 \times 10^3 \\ &= 13.184 \text{ kW} \end{aligned}$$

The Reynolds number at the bottom of the tube, from Eqs. (10-3) and (10-16), is

$$\text{Re} = \frac{4\dot{m}}{\mu_l P} Q \quad \text{where } P = \pi D$$

Then,

$$\text{Re} = \frac{(4)(5.71 \times 10^3)}{(0.355 \times 10^{-3})(0.025\pi)} = 819.2$$

which is less than 1800. Hence the condensate flow is in the laminar range and the decision made in Example 10-1 to use Eq. (10-5) which is valid for Re$<$ 1800, is justified.

**EXAMPLE 10-4** Calculate the Reynolds number at the bottom of the inclined plate of Example 10-2.

**SOLUTION** First we need to calculate the total mass rate of condensation $\dot{m}$ over the entire surface of the plate. In Example 10-2 the plate width $w$ is not specified, but this is immaterial because the width cancels out in the calculation of the Reynolds number. Therefore we determine $\dot{m}$ from Eq. (10-14c) for a unit width by setting $A_t = 0.5 \times 1$, and obtain

$$
\begin{aligned}
\dot{m} &= \frac{A_t h_m (T_v - T_w)}{h_{fg}} \\
&= \frac{(0.5 \times 1.0)(5639)(75 - 45)}{2358.5 \times 10^3} = 2.582 \times 10^{-2} \text{ kg/s}
\end{aligned}
$$

Then the Reynolds number at the bottom of the inclined plate with the wetted perimeter $P = w = 0.5$ m becomes

$$
\begin{aligned}
\text{Re} &= \frac{4\dot{m}}{\mu_l P} \\
&= \frac{(4)(2.582 \times 10^{-2})}{(0.471 \times 10^{-3})(0.5)} = 438.6
\end{aligned}
$$

which is less than 1800, and the laminar flow assumption in Example 10-2 is valid.

**EXAMPLE 10-5**  Consider $N$ horizontal tubes arranged in a vertical tier. What is the number of tubes that will produce an average condensation heat transfer coefficient for the vertical tier equal to one-half of that for the single horizontal tube at the top?

**SOLUTION**  We assume laminar filmwise condensation and use Eq. (10-12) to calculate $N$ as follows:

$$
\begin{aligned}
[h_m]_{N \text{ tubes}} &= \frac{1}{N^{1/4}} [h_m]_{1 \text{ tube}} \\
\frac{1}{2} [h_m]_{1 \text{ tube}} &= \frac{1}{N^{1/4}} [h_m]_{1 \text{ tube}} \\
\frac{1}{2} &= \frac{1}{N^{1/4}}
\end{aligned}
$$

which gives
$$
N = 16
$$

## 10.2. TURBULENT FILM CONDENSATION

The previous results for film condensation are applicable if the condensate flow is laminar. Kirkbride proposed the following empirical correlation for film condensation on a vertical plate after the start of turbulence:

$$
h_m \left( \frac{\mu_l^2}{k_l^3 \rho_l^2 g} \right)^{1/3} = 0.0077 (\text{Re})^{0.4} \tag{10-17}
$$

valid for Re> 1800; the physical properties of the condensate should be evaluated at $T_f = (T_w + T_v)/2$.

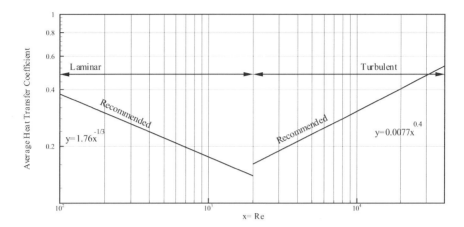

**FIG. 10.4.** Average heat transfer coefficient for filmwise condensation on a vertical surface.

Figure 10.4 shows a plot of Eqs. (10-6) and (10-17) as a function of the Reynolds number for condensate flow in the laminar and turbulent regimes, respectively.

**EXAMPLE 10-6** Air-free steam at $T_v = 100°C$ and atmospheric pressure condenses on a $L = 2$ m long vertical plate. What is the temperature of the plate $T_w$ below which the condensing film at the bottom of the plate will become turbulent?

**SOLUTION** To start the calculations, the physical properties of water at the mean film temperature are needed. As a first guess we take an average film temperature of $60°C$. The properties of water at this temperature were given in Example 10-2, and therefore are not repeated here.

Let $w$ be the width of the plate. The total condensate flow rate at the bottom of the plate at the transition Reynolds number Re= 1800 is determined from Eq. (10-3) by setting $P = w$:

$$\text{Re} = \frac{4\dot{m}}{\mu_l(w)}$$

$$1800 = \frac{4\dot{m}}{(0.471 \times 10^{-3})(w)}$$

which gives

$$\dot{m} = 0.212 \, w \text{ kg/s}$$

The flow at the bottom of the plate will become turbulent at Re= 1800, therefore using Eq. (10-17), the heat transfer coefficient is determined to be

$$h_m = 0.0077 \, \mathrm{Re}^{0.4} k_l \left( \frac{g\rho_l^2}{\mu_l^2} \right)^{1/3}$$

$$= (0.0077)(1800)^{0.4}(0.651) \left[ \frac{(9.81)(985)^2}{(0.471 \times 10^{-3})^2} \right]^{1/3}$$

$$= 3518.4 \ \mathrm{W/(m^2 \cdot {}^\circ C)}$$

The expressions for the total heat transfer rate $Q$ are taken as

$$Q = \dot{m} h_{fg} = A_t h_m (T_v - T_w)$$

and the above values of $\dot{m}$, $h_m$ and $A_t$ are introduced into this equation:

$$(0.212)(w)(2358.5 \times 10^3) = (w \times 2)(3518.4)(100 - T_w)$$

The plate width $w$ cancels out, and the plate temperature $T_w$ is determined to be

$$T_w = 28.9 \,^\circ C$$

To check the accuracy of the initial guess of $60^\circ C$ for the mean condensate temperature, the film temperature $T_f$ is computed:

$$T_f = \frac{28.9 + 100}{2} = 64.5 \,^\circ C$$

The initial guess is sufficiently close to this result; therefore there is no need for iteration.


## Film Condensation inside Horizontal Tubes

The correlations of filmwise condensation given previously are based on the assumption that the vapor is stationary or has a negligible velocity. There are also applications, such as condensers for refrigeration and air conditioning systems, in which vapor condenses inside the tubes, and hence has a significant velocity.

Consider, for example, the filmwise condensation on the inside surface of a long vertical tube. The upward flow of vapor retards the condensate flow and causes the thickening of the condensate layer, which in turn decreases the condensation heat transfer coefficient. Conversely, the downward flow of vapor decreases the thickness of the condensate film, and hence increases the heat transfer coefficient.

The correlation of the effects of vapor velocity for condensation inside tubes is a complicated matter; therefore it is not considered here.

## 10.3. DROPWISE CONDENSATION

Since the original observation of dropwise condensation by Schmidt, Schurig, and Sellschopp, numerous investigations of dropwise condensation have been reported. If traces of oil are present in steam and the condensing surface is highly polished, the condensate film breaks into droplets, giving rise to *so-called dropwise condensation.*

The droplets grow, coalesce, and run off the surface, leaving a greater portion of the condensing surface exposed to incoming steam. Since we never have the entire condensing surface covered with a continous layer of liquid film, the heat transfer coefficient for ideal dropwise condensation of steam is much higher than that for filmwise condensation of steam. The heat transfer coefficients may be 5 to 10 times greater, although the overall heat transfer coefficient between the steam and the coolant in a typical surface condenser may be about 2 to 3 times greater for dropwise than for filmwise condensation. If sustained dropwise condensation can be achieved in practice, the size of condensers can be reduced significantly, with considerable savings in the capital cost. Therefore, considerable research has been done with the objective of producing long-lasting dropwise condensation.

Various types of promoters such as oleic, stearic, and linoleic acids; benzyl mercaptan; and many other chemicals have been used to promote dropwise condensation. The periods for which continuous dropwise conditions are obtainable with different promoters vary between 100 and 300 h with pure steam and are shorter with industrial steam or intermittent operations. Failure occurs because of fouling or oxidation of the surface, because of the gradual removal of the promoter from the surface by the flow of condensate, or because of a combination of these effects.

To prevent failure of dropwise condensation as a result of oxidation, noble-metal coating of the condensing surface has been tried; coatings of gold, silver, rhodium, palladium, and platinum have been used. Although some of these coated surfaces could produce dropwise condensation under laboratory conditions for more than 10,000 h of continuous operation, the cost of coating the condensing surface with noble materials is so high that the economics of such an approach for industrial applications has yet to be proved.

It is unlikely that long-lasting dropwise condensation can be produced under practical conditions by a single treatment with any of the promoters currently available.

Although it may be possible to produce dropwise condensation for up to a year by injecting a small quantity of promoter into the steam at regular intervals, the success of this operation depends on the amount and cost of the promoter and on the extent to which the cumulative effect of the injected promoter can be tolerated in the rest of the plant. Therefore, in the analysis of a heat exchanger involving the condensation of steam, it is recommended that filmwise condensation be assumed for the condensing surface.

## 10.4. CONDENSATION IN THE PRESENCE OF NONCONDENSIBLE GAS

Earlier we considered the heat transfer coefficient for condensing vapors that did not contain any noncondensible gas. If noncondensible gas such as air is present in the vapor, even in very small amounts, the heat transfer coefficient for condensation is greatly reduced. The reason is that when a vapor containing noncondensible gas condenses, the noncondensible gas is left at the surface and the incoming condensible vapor must diffuse through this body of vapor-gas mixture collected in the vicinity of the condensate surface before it reaches the cold surface to condense.

The presence of noncondensible gas adjacent to the condensate surface acts as a thermal resistance to heat transfer. The resistance to this diffusion process causes a drop in the partial pressure of the condensing vapor, which in turn drops the saturation temperature; that is, the temperature of the outside surface of the condensate layer is lower than the saturation temperature of the bulk mixture.

Prediction of the condensation heat transfer coefficient in the presence of noncondensible gas has been the subject of numerous investigations. The results have shown that the heat transfer coefficient is very much dependent on the vapor flow patterns in the vicinity of the condensing surface. For example, high velocities over the condensing surface tend to reduce the accumulation of noncondensible gas and to alleviate the adverse effect of noncondensible gas on the heat transfer. If the noncondensible gas is allowed to accumulate over the condensing surface, a significant reduction in the heat transfer coefficient results.

Depending on the vapor flow patterns in the vicinity of the condensing surface and the amount of noncondensible gas in the bulk mixture, the condensation heat transfer coefficient can be reduced substantially. For examle, 0.5 percent by mass of air in the steam can reduce the filmwise condensation heat transfer coefficient by a factor of 2; or 5 percent by mass of air can easily cut the heat transfer coefficient by a factor of 5. Therefore, in practical applications, to alleviate the adverse effect of noncondensible gas accumulation on heat transfer, provisions are made in the design of a condenser to vent the noncondensible gas accumulating inside the condenser.

## 10.5. POOL BOILING

Pool boiling provides a convenient starting point for discussion of the mechanism of heat transfer in boiling systems. Despite the fact that this subject has been extensively studied and the mechanism of heat transfer is reasonably well understood, it is still not possible to predict theoretically the heat transfer characteristics of this apparently most simple boiling system.

Nukiyama (1934) was the first investigator to establish experimentally the characteristics of pool boiling phenomena. He immersed an electric resistance wire into a body of saturated water and initiated boiling on the surface of the wire by passing current through it. He determined both the heat flux and the temperature from measurements of current and voltage.

Since Nukiyama's original work, numerous investigations of the pool boiling phenomenon have been reported. Figure 10.5 schematically illustrates the characteristics of pool boiling for water at atmospheric pressure. This boiling curve illustrates the variation of the heat transfer coefficient or the heat flux as a function of the temperature difference

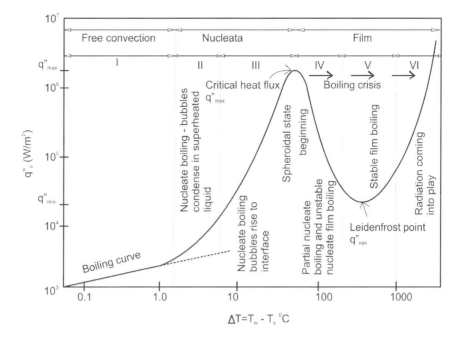

**FIG. 10.5.** Principal boiling regimes in pool of boiling water at atmospheric perssure and saturation temperature $T_s$ from an electrically heated platinum wire. Compiled from Farber, E.A., and R.L. Scorah, (1948).

between the wire and water saturation temperatures.

Scrutiny of this boiling curve reveals that the mechanism of heat transfer can be divided into three distinct regimes: the *free-convection, nucleate boiling*, and *film boiling* regimes. We now examine the heat transfer characteristics of each of these three regimes.

## 10.5.1 Free-Convection Regime

In this regime, the heat transfer from the heater surface to the saturated liquid takes place by *free convection*. The heater surface is only a few degrees above the saturation temperature of the liquid, but the flow produced by free convection in the liquid is sufficient to remove the heat from the surface. The heat transfer correlations, as given in Chap. 9, are in the form

$$\text{Nu} = f(\text{Gr}, \text{Pr}) \tag{10-18}$$

Once the heat transfer coefficient $h$ is obtained, the heat flux for the free convection regime is determined from

$$q = h(T_w - T_{\text{sat}}) \tag{10-19}$$

Various correlations are given in Chap. 9 for determining the free convection heat transfer coefficient $h$ for various geometries, such as vertical, inclined, and horizontal plates; vertical and horizontal cylinders; and many others.

## 10.5.2 Nucleate Boiling Regime

The nucleate boiling regime, in which bubbles are formed on the surface of the heater, can be separated into two distinct regions. In the region designated II, bubbles start to form at the favored sites on the heater surface, but as soon as the bubbles are detached from the surface, they are dissipated in the liquid. In region III, the nucleation sites are numerous and the bubble generation rate is so high that continuous columns of vapor appear. As a result, very high heat fluxes are obtainable in this region.

In practical applications, the nucleate boiling regime is most desirable, because large heat fluxes are obtainable with small temperature differences. In the nucleate boiling regime, the heat flux increases rapidly with increasing temperature difference until the peak heat flux is reached. The location of this peak heat flux is called the burnout point, departure from nucleate boiling (DNB), or critical heat flux (CHF). The reason for calling the peak heat flux the burnout point is apparent from Fig. 10.5. As soon as the peak heat flux is exceeded, an extremely large temperature difference is needed to realize the resulting heat flux. Such a high temperature difference may cause the burning up, or melting away, of the heating element.

Clearly heat transfer in the nucleate boiling regime is affected by the nucleation process, the distribution of active nucleation sites on the surface, and the growth and departure of bubbles. If the number of active nucleation sites increases, the interaction between the bubbles may become important. In addition to these variables, the state of the fluid (i.e., the fluid properties) and the surface condition (i.e., the mechanical and material properties of the surface) are among the factors that affect heat transfer in the nucleate boiling regime.

Numerous experimental investigations have been reported, and various attempts have been made to correlate that portion of the boiling curve characterizing heat transfer in the nucleate boiling regime. The most successful and widely used correlation was developed by Rohsenow. By analyzing the significance of various parameters in relation to forced-convection effects, he proposed the following empirical relation to correlate the heat flux in the entire nucleate boiling regime:

$$\frac{c_{pl}\Delta T}{h_{fg}\text{Pr}_l^n} = C_{sf}\left[\frac{q}{\mu_l h_{fg}}\sqrt{\frac{\sigma^*}{g(\rho_l - \rho_v)}}\right]^{0.33} \qquad (10\text{-}20)$$

In Eq. (10-20) the exponent $n$ and the coefficient $C_{sf}$ are the two provisions for adjusting the correlation for the liquid-surface combination. Table 10.1 lists the experimentally determined values $C_{sf}$ for water boiling on a variety of surfaces which depends on heating surface-fluid combination. The value of $n$ for water should be taken as 1. The other parameters are defined as

$$c_{pl} = \text{specific heat of saturated liquid, J/(kg} \cdot {}^\circ\text{C)}$$

$$h_{fg} = \text{latent heat of vaporization, } J/kg$$

$$g = \text{gravitational acceleration, m/}s^2$$

$$\text{Pr}_l = c_{pl}\mu_l/k_l = \text{Prandtl number of saturated liquid}$$

$$q = \text{boiling heat flux, W/m}^2$$

$$\Delta T = T_w - T_{sat}, \text{ wall and saturation temperature differencetemperature, } {}^\circ\text{C}$$

$$\mu_l = \text{viscosity of saturated liquid, kg/(m} \cdot s)$$

$$\rho_l, \rho_v = \text{density of liquid and saturated vapor, respectively, kg/m}^3$$

$$\sigma^* = \text{surface tension of liquid-vapor interface, N/m}$$

Table 10.2 gives the values of vapor-liquid surface tension for water at different saturation temperatures.

**TABLE 10.1  The coefficient $C_{sf}$ of Eq. (10-20) for water**

| Liquid-surface combination | $C_{sf}$ |
|---|---|
| Copper | 0.0130 |
| Scored copper | 0.0068 |
| Chemically etched stainless steel | 0.0133 |
| Ground and polished stainless steel | 0.0080 |
| Teflon pitted stainless steel | 0.0058 |
| Platinum | 0.0130 |
| Brass | 0.0060 |

Compiled with data from Vahon, Nix and Tanger (1968).

**EXAMPLE 10-7**  During the boiling of saturated water at $T_s = 100{}^\circ\text{C}$ with an electric heating element, a heat flux of $q = 7 \times 10^5$ W/m$^2$ is achieved with a temperature difference of $\Delta T = T_w - T_v = 10.4{}^\circ\text{C}$. What is the value of the constant $C_{sf}$ in Eq. (10-20)?

**SOLUTION**  The physical properties of saturated water and vapor are taken as

$$c_{pl} = 4216 \text{ J/(kg} \cdot {}^\circ\text{C)} \quad h_{fg} = 2257 \times 10^3 \text{ J/kg}$$

$$\rho_l = 960.6 \text{ kg/m}^3 \quad \rho_v = 0.6 \text{ kg/m}^3$$

$$\text{Pr}_l = 1.74 \quad \mu_l = 0.282 \times 10^{-3} \text{ kg/(m} \cdot s)$$

$$\sigma^* = 58.8 \times 10^{-3} \text{ N/m}$$

Eq. (10-20) with $n = 1$ becomes

$$\frac{c_{pl}\Delta T}{h_{fg}\text{Pr}_l} = C_{sf}\left[\frac{q}{\mu_l h_{fg}}\sqrt{\frac{\sigma^*}{g(\rho_l - \rho_v)}}\right]^{0.33}.$$

Substituting the numerical values we have

$$\frac{(4216)(10.4)}{(2257 \times 10^3)(1.74)} =$$

$$C_{sf}\left[\frac{(7 \times 10^5)}{(0.282 \times 10^{-3})(2257 \times 10^3)}\sqrt{\frac{58.8 \times 10^{-3}}{9.81(960.6 - 0.6)}}\right]^{0.333}$$

Then the coefficient $C_{sf}$ becomes

$$C_{sf} = 0.008$$

### TABLE 10.2  Liquid-vapor surface tension σ* for water

| Saturation temperature, °C | Surface tension $\sigma^* \times 10^3$, $N/m$ |
|---|---|
| 0 | 75.6 |
| 15.56 | 73.2 |
| 37.78 | 69.7 |
| 93.34 | 60.1 |
| 100 | 58.8 |
| 160 | 46.1 |
| 226.7 | 31.9 |
| 293.3 | 16.2 |
| 360 | 1.46 |
| 374.11 | 0 |

Compiled with data from Vahon, Nix and Tanger (1968).

**EXAMPLE 10-8**  A brass heating element of surface area $A = 0.04\text{m}^2$, maintained at a uniform temperature $T_w = 112°C$, is immersed in saturated water at atmospheric pressure at temperature $T_s = 100°C$. Calculate the rate of evaporation.

**SOLUTION**  The physical properties of saturated water and vapor at 100°C were given in Example 10-7. Introducing these properties into Eq. (10-20) with $n = 1$ and $\Delta T = T_w - T_s = 112 - 100 = 12°C$, and obtaining the coefficient $C_{sf}$ for water–brass from Table 10.1 as $C_{sf} = 0.006$. Then the heat flux becomes

$$
\begin{aligned}
q &= \left(\frac{c_{pl}\Delta T}{h_{fg}\mathrm{Pr}_l C_{sf}}\right)^3 \mu_l h_{fg}\sqrt{\frac{g(\rho_l - \rho_v)}{\sigma^*}} \\
&= \left[\frac{(4216)(12)}{(2257 \times 10^3)(1.74)(0.006)}\right]^3 (0.282 \times 10^{-3})(2257 \times 10^3) \\
&\quad \times \sqrt{\frac{(9.81)(960.6 - 0.6)}{(58.8 \times 10^{-3})}} \\
&= 2521.23 \ \mathrm{kW/m^2}
\end{aligned}
$$

The total rate of heat transfer is

$$
\begin{aligned}
Q &= \mathrm{area} \times q \\
&= (0.04)(2521.23) \\
&= 100.85 \ \mathrm{kW}
\end{aligned}
$$

The rate of evaporation is

$$
\begin{aligned}
\dot{m} &= \frac{Q}{h_{fg}} \\
&= \frac{100.85 \times 10^3}{2257 \times 10^3} \\
&= 0.0447 \ \mathrm{kg/s} = 160.9 \ \mathrm{kg/h}
\end{aligned}
$$

## 10.5.3 Peak Heat Flux

The correlation given by Eq. (10-20) provides information about the heat flux in nucleate boiling, but it cannot predict the peak heat flux. The determination of peak heat flux in nucleate boiling is of interest because of burnout considerations; that is, if the applied heat flux exceeds the peak heat flux, the transition takes place from the nucleate to the stable film boiling regime, in which, depending on the kind of fluid, boiling may occur at temperature differences well above the melting point of the heating surface. Kutateladze (1951) and Zuber (1958) with developed an expression approximately to determine the peak heat flux.

$$
q\mathrm{max} = C\rho_v^{1/2}h_{fg}[\sigma^* g(\rho_l - \rho_v)]^{1/4} \tag{10-21}
$$

where the value of constant $C$ is 0.131 for horizontal cylinders, spheres and large heated surfaces. For very large surfaces a value of $C=0.149$ is given. Lienhard and coworkers (1973) modified this correlations and introduced a correction factor to determine the peak heat flux

$$
q\mathrm{max} = F(L') \times C\ \rho_v^{1/2}h_{fg}[\sigma^* g(\rho_l - \rho_v)]^{1/4} \tag{10-22}
$$

where

$$\sigma^* \quad = \quad \text{surface tension of liquid-vapor interface, } N/m$$

$$g \quad = \quad \text{gravitational acceleration, } m/s^2$$

$$\rho_l, \ \rho_v \quad = \quad \text{density of liquid and vapor, respectively, kg/m}^3$$

$$h_{fg} \quad = \quad \text{latent heat of vaporization, J/kg}$$

$$q\text{max} \quad = \quad \text{peak heat flux, } W/m^2$$

and $F((L')$ is the correction factor that depends on heat geometry; it is given in Table 10.3. The dimensionless characteristic length ($L'$ of the heater is defined as[4pt]

$$L' = L\sqrt{\frac{g(\rho_l - \rho_v)}{\sigma^*}} \qquad (10\text{-}23)$$

where $L$ is the characteristic dimension of the heater and the other quantities are as defined previously. In Eq. (10-22) the physical properties of the vapor should be evaluated at

$$T_f = \frac{1}{2}(T_w + T_{\text{sat}})$$

The enthalpy of evaporation $h_{fg}$ and the liquid properties should be evaluated at the saturated temperature of the liquid.

**TABLE 10.3  Correction factor $F(L')$ for use in Eq. (10-22)**

| Heater geometry | $F(L')$ | Remarks |
|---|---|---|
| Infinite flat plate facing up | 1.14 | $L' \geq 2.7$; $L$ is the heat width or diameter |
| Horizontal cylinder | $0.89 + 2.27e^{-3.44\sqrt{L'}}$ | $L' \geq 0.15$; $L$ is the cylinder radius |
| Large sphere | 0.84 | $L' \geq 4.26$; $L$ is the sphere radius |
| Small sphere | $\frac{1.734}{(L')^{1/2}}$ | $0.15 \leq L' \leq 4.26$; $L$ is the sphere radius |

(Based on data from Lienhard and Dhir (1973))

**EXAMPLE 10-9**  Water at saturation temperature and atmospheric pressure is boiled in the nucleate boiling regime with a large plate heating element facing up. Calculate the peak heat flux.

**SOLUTION**  The physical properties of saturated water and vapor at $100°C$ were given in Example 10-7. Introducing these properties into Eq. (10-22), with the correction factor $F(L') = 1.14$ obtained from Table 10.3 for a large plate heating element facing up, the peak heat flux $q_{max}$ is determined to be

$$
\begin{aligned}
q_{max} &= F(L') \times 0.131 \rho_v^{1/2} h_{fg} [\sigma^* g(\rho_l - \rho_v)]^{1/4} \\
&= (0.14)(1.131)(0.6)^{1/2}(2257 \times 10^3) \\
&\quad \times [(58.8 \times 10^{-3})(9.81)(960.6 - 0.6)]^{1/4} \\
&= 1.27 \ \mathrm{MW/m^2}
\end{aligned}
$$

## 10.5.4 Film Boiling Regime

The nucleate boiling region ends and the unstable film boiling region begins after the peak heat flux is reached. No correlations are available for the prediction of heat flux in this unstable region until the minimum point in the boiling curve is reached and the stable film boiling region starts. In the stable film boiling regions, V and VI, the heating surface is separated from the liquid by a vapor layer across which heat must be transferred. Since the thermal conductivity of the vapor is low, large temperature differences are needed for heat transfer in this region; therefore, heat transfer in this region is generally avoided when high temperatures are involved. However, stable film boiling has numerous applications in the boiling of cryogenic fluids. A theory for the prediction of the heat transfer coefficient for stable film boiling on the outside of a horizontal cylinder was developed by Bromley. The basic approach in the analysis is similar to Nusselt's theory for filmwise condensation on a horizontal tube. The resulting equation for the average heat transfer coefficient $h_0$ for stable film boiling on the outside of a horizontal cylinder, in the absence of radiation, is given by

$$
h_0 = 0.62 \left[ \frac{k_v^3 \rho_v (\rho_l - \rho_v) g h_{fg}}{\mu_v D_o \Delta T} \left( 1 + \frac{0.4 c_{pv} \Delta T}{h_{fg}} \right) \right]^{1/4} \tag{10-24}
$$

where

$$
\begin{aligned}
h_0 &= \text{average boiling heat transfer coefficient in absence of radiation,} \\
&\quad \mathrm{W/(m \cdot °C)} \\
c_{pv} &= \text{specific heat of saturated vapor, } \mathrm{J/(kg \cdot °C)} \\
D_o &= \text{outside diameter of tube, } m \\
g &= \text{gravitational acceleration, } \mathrm{m/s^2} \\
h_{fg} &= \text{latent heat of vaporization, } J/kg \\
k_v &= \text{thermal conductivity of saturated vapor, } \mathrm{W/(m \cdot °C)} \\
\Delta T &= T_w - T_{sat}, \text{ temperature difference between wall and saturation} \\
&\quad \text{temperatures, } °C
\end{aligned}
$$

In Eq. (10-23), the physical properties of vapor should be evaluated at $T_f = \frac{1}{2}(T_w + T_{sat})$, and the enthalpy of evaporation $h_{fg}$ and the liquid density $\rho_l$ should be evaluated at the saturation temperature $T_{sat}$ of the liquid.

**EXAMPLE 10-10**  Water at saturation temperature and atmospheric pressure is boiled with an electrically heated horizontal platinum wire of diameter $D = 0.2$ cm. Boiling takes place with a temperature difference of $T_w - T_s = 454°C$ in the stable film boiling range. Calculate the film boiling heat transfer coefficient and the heat flux, in the absence of radiation.

**SOLUTION**  The physical properties of vapor are evaluated at $T_f = (T_w + T_s)/2 = (554 + 100)/2 = 327°C = 600\ K$:

$$c_{p,v} = 2026 \text{ J/(kg} \cdot °C) \qquad k_v = 0.0422 \text{ W/(m} \cdot °C)$$

$$\mu_w = 2067 \times 10^{-5} \text{ kg/(m} \cdot \text{s)} \quad \rho_v = 0.365 \text{ kg/m}^3$$

and the liquid density and $h_{fg}$ are evaluated at the saturation temperature $T_s = 100°C$:

$$\rho_l = 960.6 \text{ kg/m}^3 \qquad h_{fg} = 2257 \times 10^3 \text{ J/kg}$$

The heat transfer coefficient $h_0$ for stable film boiling without the radiation effects is computed from Eq. (10-23):

$$
\begin{aligned}
h_0 &= 0.62 \left[ \frac{k_v^3 \rho_v (\rho_l - \rho_v) g h_{fg}}{\mu_v D_o \Delta T} \left( 1 + \frac{0.4 c_{pv} \Delta T}{h_{fg}} \right) \right]^{1/4} \\
&= 0.62 \left[ \frac{(0.0422)^3 (0.365)(960.6 - 0.365)(9.81)(2257 \times 10^3)}{(2.067 \times 10^{-5})(0.002)(454)} \right. \\
&\quad \left. \times \left( 1 + \frac{(0.4)(2026)(454)}{2257 \times 10^3} \right) \right]^{1/4} \\
&= 270.3 \text{ W/(m}^2 \cdot °C)
\end{aligned}
$$

## PROBLEMS

*Laminar Film Condensation*

**10-1.**  Air-free saturated steam at $T_v = 100°C$ condenses on the outer surface of a $L = 2$ m long, $D = 2$ cm OD vertical tube, maintained at a uniform temperature $T_w = 60°C$. Assuming filmwise condensation, calculate the average heat transfer coefficient over the entire length of the tube and the rate of condensate flow at the bottom of the tube.

**10-2.**  Air-free saturated steam at $T_v = 65°C$ condenses on the outer surface of a 1 m by 1 m plate, maintained at a uniform temperature $T_w = 35°C$ by the flow of cooling water on one side. Assuming filmwise condensation, calculate the average heat transfer coefficient over the entire length of the plate and the rate of condensate flow at the bottom of the plate.

**10-3.** Determine the average heat transfer coefficient of Problem 10-1 when the tube is horizontal.

**10-4.** Air-free saturated steam at $T_v = 65°C$ condenses on the surface of a vertical tube with $D = 2$ cm OD which is maintained at a uniform temperature $T_w = 35°C$. Determine the tube length $L$ for a condensate flow rate of $5 \times 10^{-3}$ kg/s per tube.

**10-5.** Air-free saturated steam at $T_v = 50°C$ ($P = 12.35$ kPa) condenses on the outside surface of a $D = 2.5$ cm OD, $L = 2$ m long vertical tube maintained at a uniform temperature of $T_w = 30°C$ by the flow of cooling water through the tube. Assuming filmwise condensation, calculate: (*a*) the average condensation heat transfer coefficient over the entire length of the tube, and (*b*) the rate of condensate flow at the bottom of the tube.
*Answer*: $\dot{m} = 5.7 \times 10^{-3}$ kg/s, $Re = 444 < 1800$.

**10-6.** Calculate the average heat transfer coefficient $h_m$ and the total condensation rate at the tube surface for Problem 10-5 when the tube is in the horizontal position.

**10-7.** Repeat Problem 10-5 for a tube length of $3$ m. Calculate the average heat transfer coefficient $h_m$ and the total condensation rate at the tube surface for the condensation problem when the tube is in the horizontal position.

**10-8.** Saturated, air-free steam at $T_v = 65°C$ ($P = 25.03$ kPa) condenses on the outer surface of a $D = 2.5$ cm OD vertical tube whose surface is maintained at a uniform temperature of $T_w = 35°C$. Determine the tube length needed to condense $30$ kg/h of steam.

**10-9.** Saturated, air-free steam at a temperature $T_v = 80°C$ ($P = 47.39$ kPa)

condenses on the outer surface of a $L = 1.2$ m long, $D = 0.1$ m in diameter vertical tube which is maintained at a uniform temperature of $T_w = 40°C$. Calculate: (*a*) the average heat transfer coefficient hm for filmwise condensation over the entire tube length, (*b*) the total rate of steam condensation at the tube surface, and (*c*) the condensate thickness at the bottom of the tube.

**10-10.** Saturated air-free steam at a temperature $T_v = 80°C$ ($P = 47.39$ kPa) condenses on the outer surface of a $L = 2$ m long, $D = 2.0$ cm OD vertical tube maintained at $T_w = 40°C$. Calculate the average heat transfer coefficient for filmwise condensation over the entire tube length and the total rate of condensation at the surface of the tube.

**10-11.** Saturated air-free steam at a temperature $T_v = 80°C$ ($P = 47.39$ kPa) condenses on the outer surface of a $D = 2.0$ cm OD vertical tube maintained at $T_w = 40°C$. Determine the tube length needed to condense $0.025$ kg/s steam.

**10-12.** Saturated, air-free steam at a temperature $T_v = 50°C$ ($P = 12.35$ kPa) condenses on the outer surface of a $L = 2$ m long, $D = 2.0$ cm OD vertical tube maintained at a uniform temperature of $T_w = 10°C$. Assuming filmwise condensation, calculate the average condensation heat transfer coefficient $h_m$ over the entire length of the tube and the total rate of condensation at the surface of the tube.

**10-13.** Air-free saturated steam at a temperature $T_v = 90°C$ ($P = 70.14$ kPa) condenses on the outer surface of a $D = 2.0$ cm OD vertical tube maintained at a uniform temperature $T_w = 70°C$. Determine the tube length needed to condense 20 kg/h steam.

**10-14.** Saturated Freon-12 vapor at a temperature $T_v = -5°C$ ($P = 0.26$ MPa) condenses on the outer surface of a $L = 1.2$ m long, $D = 1.27$ cm OD vertical tube maintained at a uniform temperature of $T_w = -15°C$. Calculate: ($a$) the average condensation heat transfer coefficient over the entire length of the tube, and ($b$) the total mass rate of condensation at the tube surface. (Take $h_{fg} = 154$ $kJ/kg$ for Freon-12.)

**10-15.** Saturated ammonia vapor at a temperature $T_v = -5°C$ ($P = 0.3528$ MPa) condenses on the outer surface of a $L = 0.75$ m long, $D = 1.27$ cm OD vertical tube maintained at a uniform temperature $T_w = -15°C$. Calculate the average condensation heat transfer coefficient $h_m$ and the total rate of condensation of ammonia over the entire length of the tube. (Take $h_{fg} = 1280$ $kJ/kg$ for ammonia.)

**10-16.** Saturated air-free steam at $T_v = 170°C$ ($P = 0.8$ MPa) condenses on the outer surface of a $D = 2$ cm OD $L = 1.5$ m long vertical tube maintained at a uniform temperature $T_w = 150°C$. Calculate: ($a$) the local film condensation heat transfer coefficient at the bottom of the tube, ($b$) the average condensation heat transfer coefficient over the entire length of the tube, and ($c$) the total condensation rate at the tube surface.

**10-17.** Air-free saturated steam at $T_v = 60°C$ ($P = 19.94$ kPa) condenses on the outer surface of $D = 2.5$ cm OD, $L = 2$ m long 100 horizontal tubes arranged in a 10 by 10 square array. The surface of the tubes is maintained at a uniform temperature $T_w = 40°C$. Calculate the average condensation heat transfer coefficient for the entire tube bundle and the total rate of condensation at the surface of the tubes in the bundle.

**10-18.** A steam condenser consists of 625 $D = 1.25$ cm OD, $L = 3$ m long horizontal tubes arranged in a 25 by 25 square array. Saturated steam at $T_v = 50°C$ ($P = 12.35$ kPa) condenses on the outer surface of the tubes, which are maintained at a uniform temperature $T_w = 30°C$. Calculate the average heat transfer coefficient $h_m$ and the total rate of condensation of steam in the condenser.

**10-19.** Compare the average condensation heat transfer coefficient for filmwise condensation of air-free steam at atmospheric pressure on: ($a$) a single $L = 1$ m long,

$D = 2.5$ cm OD vertical tube and (b) $D = 2.5$ cm OD, $N = 40$ horizontal tubes arranged in a vertical tier.

**10-20.** Saturated air-free steam at a temperature $T_v = 50°C$. ($P = 12.35$ kPa)

condenses on the outer surface of a $D = 2.0$ cm OD horizontal tube maintained at a uniform temperature $T_w = 30°C$. Calculate the tube length required to condense $W = 50$ kg/$h$ steam.

**10-21.** Air-free saturated steam at $T_v = 85°C$ ($P = 57.83$ kPa) condenses on the outer surface of 196 $D = 1.27$ cm OD, horizontal tubes arranged in a 14 by 14 square array. The tube surfaces are maintained at a uniform temperature $T_w = 75°C$. Calculate the length of the matrix needed to condense 0.7 kg/$s$ of steam.

*Turbulent Film Condensation*

**10-22.** Air-free saturated steam at $T_v = 70°C$ ($P = 31.19$ kPa) condenses on the outer surface of a $D = 2.0$ cm OD vertical tube maintained at a uniform temperature $T_w = 50°C$. What length of the tube would produce turbulent film condensation?

**10-23.** Air-free saturated steam at $T_v = 90°C$ ($P = 70.14$ kPa) condenses on the outer surface of a $D = 2.5$ cm OD, $L = 6$ m long vertical tube maintained at a uniform temperature $T_w = 30°C$. Calculate the average heat transfer coefficient over the entire length of the tube and the total rate of condensation of steam at the tube surface.

**10-24.** Air-free saturated steam at $T_v = 50°C$ ($P = 12.35$ kPa) condenses on the outer surface of a $D = 2.0$ cm OD vertical tube maintained at a uniform temperature $T_w = 30°C$. Calculate the tube length $L$ that would produce turbulent film condensation at the bottom of the tube, and calculate the total condensation rate at the tube surface.

*Pool Boiling*

**10-25.** Saturated water at $T_s = 100°C$ is boiled inside a copper pan with a heating surface $A = 5 \times 10^{-2}$ m$^2$ that is maintained at a uniform temperature $T_w = 110°C$. Calculate the surface heat flux and the rate of evaporation.

**10-26.** Saturated water at $T_v = 55°C$ ($P = 15.76$ kPa) is boiled with a copper heating element that has a heating surface $A = 5 \times 10^{-3}$ m$^2$, and maintained at a uniform temperature $T_w = 65°C$. Calculate the rate of evaporation.
*Answer*: $\dot{m} = 6.51 \times 10^{-5} kg/s = 0.235\ kg/hr$

**10-27.** Saturated water at $T_s = 100°C$ is boiled in a $D = 20$ cm diameter Teflon pitted stainless steel pan with a temperature difference of $T_w - T_s = 10°C$. Calculate the rate of evaporation.

**10-28.** Saturated water at $T_s = 100°C$ is boiled with a copper heating element. If the surface heat flux is $q = 300 \ kW/m^2$, calculate the surface temperature of the heating element.

**10-29.** Saturated water at $T_s = 100°C$ is boiled with a copper heating element. If the surface heat flux is $q = 400 \ kW/m^2$, calculate the surface temperature of the heating element.

**10-30.** An electrically heated copper plate with a heating surface $A = 0.2 \ m^2$, maintained at a uniform temperature $T_w = 108°C$, is immersed in a water tank at $T_s = 100°C$ and atmospheric pressure. Calculate the rate of evaporation.

**10-31.** Water at a saturation temperature $T_s = 160°C$ ($P = 0.6178$ MPa) is boiled using an electncally heated copper element with a temperature difference of $T_w - T_s = 10°C$. Calculate the surface heat flwx.

**10-32.** An electrically heated copper kettle with a flat bottom of diameter $D = 25$ cm is to boil water at atmosphenc pressure at a rate of $2.5 \ kg/h$. What is the temperature of the bottom surface of the kettle?

**10-33.** Determine the peak heat flux obtainable with nucleate boiling of saturated water at 1 $atm$ pressure in a gravitational field one-eighth that of the earth. Compare this result with that obtainable at the earth's gravitational field. Assume a large heating element.

**10-34.** An electrically heated, copper spherical heating element of diameter $D = 10$ cm is immersed in water at atmosphenc pressure and saturation temperature. The surface of the element is maintained at a uniform temperature $T_w = 115°C$. Calculate: ($a$) the surface heat flux, ($b$) the rate of evaporation, and ($c$) the peak heat flux.

**10-35.** Water at saturation temperature and atmospheric pressure is boiled with an electrically heated platinum wire of diameter $D_o = 0.2$ cm in the stable film boiling regime with a temperature difference of $T_w - T_s = 654°C$. In the absence of radiation, calculate the film-boiling heat transfer coefficient and the heat flux.

**10-36.** Water at saturation temperature and atmosphenc pressure is boiled with an electncally heated platinum wire of diameter $D_o = 0.6$ cm, in the stable film boiling regime with a temperature difference of $T_w - T_s = 654°C$. In the absence of radiation, calculate the film-boiling heat transfer coefficient and the heat flux.

# CHAPTER 11

# *Basic Radiation Heat Transfer Concepts*

## 11.1. INTRODUCTION

*Thermal radiation* refers to radiation energy that bodies emit because of their own temperature. All bodies at a temperature above absolute zero emit radiation. Radiation heat transfer is important in energy conversion, thermal insulation, space or equipment thermal control. We recall that energy transfer by conduction and convection requires some material carrier, but the transfer of energy by radiation can take place in a vacuum without a material carrier. A typical example of this phenomenon is the transfer of energy from the sun to the earth ; that is, the thermal energy emitted from the sun travels through space and reaches the earth's surface.

If two surfaces having radiation energy exchange separated far from each other, it is called far field radiative heat transfer. When the spacing between the surfaces is at nanoscale it is called near field radiative heat transfer. For this case the energy transfer will be enriched because of the evanescent waves transferring additional energy form one body to the other. The radiation energy calculated with using the far field theory will not be applicable, in fact it will exceed the blackbody limit by several orders of magnitude. In this chapter we will not study nanoscale near field radiative heat transfer.

The actual mechanism of energy transport by radiation is not fully understood, but some theories based on certain concepts have been proposed to explain the propagation process.

One of the concepts, originally proposed by Maxwell, is the treatment of radiation as *electromagnetic waves,* just like radio or sound waves. This concept has been useful in studies on the prediction of the radiation properties of surfaces and materials and studying near field radiative heat transfer.

Another concept, proposed by Max Planck, treats radiation as *photons* or *quanta of energy*. This concept has been employed to predict the magnitude of the radiation energy emitted by a body at a given temperature under idealized conditions for far field radiative heat transfer.

Clearly, both concepts are useful in the study of radiation. We focus our attention on the wave nature of thermal radiation. A body at any given temperature emits thermal radiation at all wavelengths from $\lambda = 0$ to $\lambda = \infty$, but the distribution of the relative magnitude of energy emitted at each wavelength depends on the temperature. At temperatures encountered in most engineering applications, the bulk of the energy emitted by a body lies in the wavelengths, approximately, between $\lambda \simeq 0.1\,\mu m$ and $\lambda \simeq 100\,\mu m$. For this reason, this portion of the wavelength spectrum is generally referred to as the *thermal radiation*. For example, the sun emits thermal radiation at an effective surface temperature of about 5760 K, and the bulk of this energy lies in wavelengths between $\lambda \simeq 0.1\,\mu m$ and

$\lambda \simeq 3\,\mu\text{m}$ ; therefore, this portion of the spectrum is generally known as *solar radiation*. The radiation emitted by the sun at wavelengths between $\lambda = 0.4\,\mu\text{m}$ and $\lambda = 0.7\,\mu\text{m}$ is visible to the eye ; therefore, this portion of the spectrum is called *visible radiation* (i.e., light). Figure 11.1 illustrates such subdivisions on the electromagnetic wave spectrum.

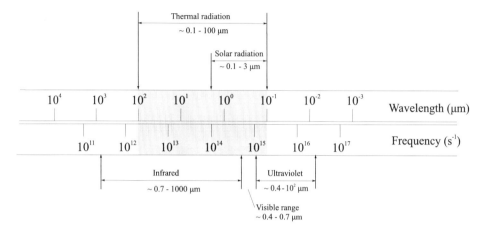

**FIG. 11.1.** Typical spectrum of electromagnetic radiation due to temperature of a body.

Other types of radiation, such as x-rays, gamma rays, microwaves, etc., are well known and are utilized in various branches of science and engineering. X-rays are produced by the bombardment of a metal with high-frequency electrons, and the bulk of the energy is repetitive between $\lambda \simeq 10^{-4}\,\mu\text{m}$ and $\lambda \simeq 10^{-2}\,\mu\text{m}$. Gamma rays are produced by the fission of nuclei or by radioactive disintegration, and the bulk of the energy is concentrated at wavelengths shorter than those of x-rays. Nuclear fission creates three types of particles that can cause harm to organic matter: alpha, beta, and gamma particles. Of these, the first two can be blocked by a shield no thicker than a sheet of paper. The more pervasive particles, gamma particles, occupy wavelengths below 0.01 nm and require significantly more mass to block. The concrete shields erected around every nuclear reactor were built specifically to block gamma radiation. In this book, in general, we are not concerned with such radiation; our interest is mainly in *thermal radiation* as a mechanism of energy transport between objects at different temperatures.

The wave nature of thermal radiation implies that the wavelength $\lambda$ should be associated with the frequency of radiation $\nu$. The relationship between $\lambda$ and $\nu$ is given by

$$\lambda = \frac{c}{\nu} , \tag{11-1}$$

where $c$ is the speed of propagation in the medium. If the medium in which radiation travels is a vacuum, the speed of propagation is equal to the speed of light ; that is,

$$c_0 = 2.9979 \times 10^8 \text{ m/s} . \tag{11-2}$$

In fact, the frequency spectrum in Fig. 11.1 was obtained from this relationship between

$\lambda$ and $\nu$.

It should be noted that the frequency remains constant as radiation propagates through various media, whereas wavelength does not. The ratio of the wavelength in a vacuum to that in another medium defines the refractive index of the medium, $n$.

$$n = \frac{\lambda_0}{\lambda} \tag{11-3}$$

The speed of light also changes from one medium to another, which is dictated by $n$ as follows:

$$c = \frac{c_0}{n} \ . \tag{11-4}$$

For a vacuum $n = 1$, for ordinary gases $n = 1$, for water $n \simeq 1.33$ and for metals, $n$ is very large. Some representative indexes of refraction are given in Table 11.1.

The relationship between the frequency $\nu$, the angular frequency $\omega$, the wavelength $\lambda$, and the wave number $\eta$ are given as

$$\nu = \frac{\omega}{2\pi} = \frac{c}{\lambda} = c\eta \ . \tag{11-5}$$

Here we have the following units

$$\nu = \text{cycles}/s = s^{-1} = \text{Hertz} = \text{Hz}$$

$$\omega = \text{radians}/s = s^{-1}$$

$$\lambda = \mu\text{m} = 10^{-6}\,\text{m}$$

$$\eta = \text{cm}^{-1} \ .$$

The spectral variable wavelength $\lambda$ is used mainly for surface emission and absorption, and wavenumber $\eta$ is used for radiation in gases. The differential relationship between the frequency, the wavelength, and the wave number are:

$$\nu = \frac{c}{\lambda} = \frac{c_0}{n\lambda} = \frac{c_0}{n}\eta \tag{11-6}$$

$$d\nu = -\frac{c_0}{n\lambda^2}\left[1 + \frac{\lambda}{n}\frac{dn}{d\lambda}\right]d\lambda \tag{11-7}$$

$$= \frac{c_0}{n}\left[1 - \frac{\eta}{n}\frac{dn}{d\eta}\right]d\eta \ .$$

For most materials $dn/d\eta \simeq 0$; therefore

$$d\nu = -\frac{c_0}{n\lambda^2}\,d\lambda = -\frac{c_0}{n}\,d\eta \ . \tag{11-8}$$

Each wave or photon carries with it an amount of energy, $\epsilon$ (from quantum mechanics), given as

$$\epsilon = h\nu \tag{11-9}$$

where $\quad \nu \quad = \quad$ frequency ($Hz$)

$\quad\quad h \quad = \quad$ Planck's constant $= 6.626 \times 10^{-34}$ Js.

## 11.2. BLACKBODY RADIATION LAWS

A knowledge of the amount of radiation energy emitted by a body at any given temperature is most important in the study of thermal radiation. A body at any temperature above absolute zero emits thermal radiation at all wavelengths and in all possible directions into space. The concept of a *blackbody* has been introduced as an idealized situation to serve as a reference in determining the emission and absorption of radiation by real bodies.

A blackbody absorbs all incident radiation from all directions at all wavelengths without reflecting, transmitting, or scattering it. The radiation emitted by a blackbody at any temperature $T$ is the maximum possible emission at that temperature. The term *black* should be distinguished from its common usage, where it indicates the blackness of a surface to visual observations.

Non-black surfaces reflect the visible part of the spectrum of electromagnetic waves. The human eye can detect blackness only in the visible range of the spectrum. For example, an object such as ice is bright to the eye but is almost black for long-wave thermal radiation. However, a blackbody is perfectly black to thermal radiation at all wavelengths from $\lambda = 0$ to $\lambda = \infty$.

A black surface also emits a maximum amount of energy. Consider two identical black wall enclosures, insulated to the outside. Both enclosures will be at a single uniform temperature, implying that the black surface absorbs a maximum amount of energy, but also emits maximum energy. Radiation is emitted by a body in all directions. It is of interest to know the amount of radiation emitted by a blackbody streaming into a given direction.

The fundamental quantity that specifies the magnitude of the radiation energy emitted by a blackbody at an absolute temperature $T$, at a wavelength $\lambda$, in any given direction is called the *spectral blackbody radiation intensity* $I_{b\lambda}(T)$. Here the term *spectral* (some books use the term *monochromatic*) is used to denote the wavelength dependence of the radiation intensity, and the subscript $b$ refers to the blackbody.

Max Planck developed the theory of blackbody radiation in which the energy is assumed to be transported in the form of discrete photons. Based on the quantum arguments, Planck has shown that the radiation energy emitted by a blackbody into a vacuum is related to the absolute temperature $T$ of the body and the wavelength (or frequency) of emission. The magnitude of $I_{b\lambda}(T)$ for emission into a vacuum was first determined by Planck as

$$I_{b\lambda}(T) = \frac{2h\,c^2}{\lambda^5 \{\exp[hc/(\lambda kT)] - 1\}} \tag{11-10}$$

where

$h \ (= 6.6256 \times 10^{-34} \ \text{J} \cdot \text{s})$ is the Planck constant,

$k \ (= 1.38054 \times 10^{-23} \ \text{J/K})$ is the Boltzmann constants,

$c \ (= 2.9979 \times 10^{8} \ \text{m/s})$ is the speed of light in a vacuum,

$T$ in Kelvins is the absolute temperature, and

$\lambda$ in µm is the wavelength.

Here $I_{b\lambda}(T)$ represents *the radiation energy emitted by a blackbody at temperature T, streaming through a unit area perpendicular to the direction of propagation, per unit wavelength about the wavelength $\lambda$ per unit solid angle about the propagation of the beam.* Based on this definition, the units of $I_{b\lambda}(T)$ can be written as

$$\frac{\text{RadiationEnergy}}{(\text{Area})(\text{wavelength})(\text{solidangle})(\text{time})} \tag{11-11}$$

where the area is measured perpendicular to the direction of propagation.

If energy is measured in watts, area in square meters, wavelength in micrometers, and the solid angle in *steradian* (sr), then Eq. (11-11) has the dimension

$$\frac{\text{W}}{\text{m}^2 \cdot \text{µm} \cdot \text{sr}}. \tag{11-12}$$

The physical significance of the solid angle is better envisioned by referring to Fig. 11.2. Let $\hat{\Omega}$ be the direction of propagation and $O$ the reference location.

We consider a small area $dA$ at a distance $r$ from $O$ and normal to the direction $\hat{\Omega}$. The solid angle $d\omega$ subtended by $dA$ from $O$ is defined as

$$\boxed{d\omega = \frac{dA}{r^2}}. \tag{11-13}$$

Based on this definition, we can readily infer that the solid angle subtended by a hemisphere from its center is $2\pi$ (that is, $2\pi r^2/r^2$) and by a full sphere from its center is $4\pi$ (that is, $4\pi r^2/r^2$).

In Eq. (11-10), $I_{b\lambda}(T)$ is the blackbody radiation intensity per unit wavelength about the wavelength $\lambda$. However, the radiation is emitted at all wavelengths. To determine the *blackbody radiation intensity $I_b(T)$* emitted by a blackbody at temperature $T$ over all wavelengths, we integrate $I_{b\lambda}(T)$ from $\lambda = 0$ to $\lambda = \infty$:

$$I_b(T) = \int_{\lambda=0}^{\infty} I_{b\lambda}(T)\, d\lambda \qquad \text{W/(m}^2 \cdot \text{sr}). \tag{11-14}$$

## 11.2.1 Blackbody Emissive Power

It is of practical interest to know the amount of radiation energy emitted per unit area of a blackbody at an absolute temperature $T$ in all directions into hemispherical space. To evaluate this quantity, we consider an elemental area $dA$ at temperature $T$, as illustrated in Fig. 11.3a. Let $\hat{n}$ be the normal to this surface, $\theta$ be the polar angle measured from this

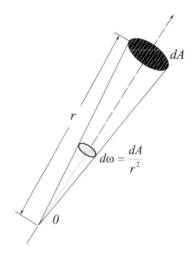

**FIG. 11.2.** Definition of solid angle.

normal, and $\phi$ be the azimuthal angle. The surface emits radiation of spectral intensity $I_{b\lambda}(T)$ in all directions. According to the definition, this intensity, given by Eq. (11-10), is independent of direction. The quantity

$$I_{b\lambda}(T)\,dA\,\cos\theta\,d\omega \qquad (11\text{-}15)$$

represents the spectral radiation energy emitted by the surface element $dA$, streaming through an elemental solid angle $d\omega$ in any given direction $\hat{\Omega}$. In this expression, the term $dA\cos\theta$ is the projection of $dA$ on a plane normal to the direction $\hat{\Omega}$; the use of projected area is necessary because $I_{b\lambda}(T)$, by definition, is based on the area normal to the direction of propagation. Dividing Eq. (11-15) by $dA$, we obtain

$$I_{b\lambda}(T)\,\cos\theta\,d\omega \qquad (11\text{-}16)$$

which represents the spectral blackbody radiation energy emitted by a unit surface area, streaming through a differential solid angle $d\omega$ in any direction $\hat{\Omega}$.

Refer to Fig. 11.3$b$. A differential solid angle $d\omega$ can be related to the polar angle $\theta$ and the azimuthal angle $\phi$ by

$$d\omega = \frac{dA}{r^2} = \frac{(r\,d\theta)(r\,d\phi\,\sin\theta)}{r^2} = \sin\theta\,d\theta\,d\phi \qquad (11\text{-}17)$$

The quantity in Eq. (11-16) becomes

$$I_{b\lambda}(T)\,\cos\theta\,\sin\theta\,d\theta\,d\phi. \qquad (11\text{-}18)$$

The spectral blackbody radiation emitted per unit surface area in all directions into the hemispherical space is obtained by integrating Eq. (11-18) over $0 \leq \phi \leq 2\pi$ and $0 \leq$

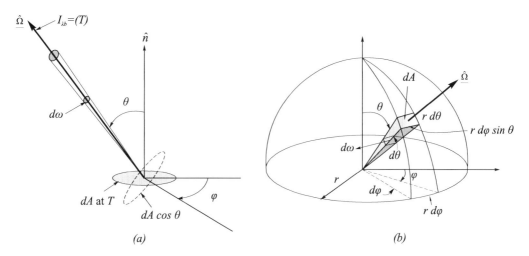

**FIG. 11.3.** Nomenclature for (a) emission of radiation from a surface $dA$, (b) definition of the solid angle $d\omega$ in terms of $(\theta, \phi)$.

$\theta \leq \pi/2$. We obtain

$$
\begin{aligned}
E_{b\lambda}(T) &= I_{b\lambda}(T) \int_{\phi=0}^{2\pi} \int_{\theta=0}^{\pi/2} \cos\theta \, \sin\theta \, d\theta \, d\phi \\
&= 2\pi I_{b\lambda}(T) \int_{\theta=0}^{\pi/2} \cos\theta \, \sin\theta \, d\theta \\
&= 2\pi I_{b\lambda}(T) [\frac{1}{2} \sin^2\theta]_0^{\pi/2}
\end{aligned}
$$

$$
\boxed{E_{b\lambda}(T) = \pi I_{b\lambda}(T)} \qquad \text{W}/(\text{m}^2 \cdot \mu\text{m}). \tag{11-19}
$$

Here $E_{b\lambda}(T)$ is called the *spectral blackbody emissive power*. It represents the radiation energy emitted by a blackbody at an absolute temperature $T$ per unit area per unit time per unit wavelength about $\lambda$ in all directions into the hemispherical space. Thus, it has the units $\text{W}/(\text{m}^2 \cdot \mu\text{m})$. The validity of this formula has also been verified experimentally. Actually it is the spectral blackbody radiation flux given by Max Planck. Therefore

$$
\boxed{E_{b\lambda}(T) = \frac{C_1}{n^2 \lambda^5 \{\exp\left[C_2/(n\lambda T)\right] - 1\}}} \qquad \text{W}/(\text{m}^2 \cdot \mu\text{m}) \tag{11-20}
$$

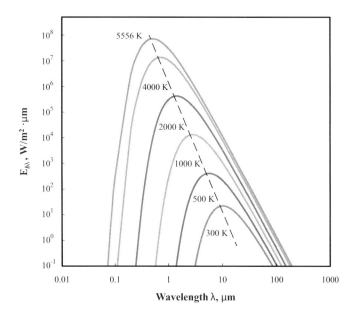

**FIG. 11.4.** Spectral blackbody emissive power at different temperatures.

where
$$C_1 = 2\pi h c_0^2 = 3.743 \times 10^8 \text{ W} \cdot \mu\text{m}^4/\text{m}^2$$

$$C_2 = h c_0 / k = 1.4387 \times 10^4 \ \mu\text{m} \cdot \text{K}$$

$T$ = absolute temperature, K

$\lambda$ = wavelength, $\mu$m

$h$ = Planck's constant = $6.626 \times 10^{-34}$ Js

$k$ = Boltzmann's constant = $1.3806 \times 10^{-23}$ J/K

$c_0$ = speed of light in vacuum

$n$ = refractive index of the medium.

Figure 11.4 shows a plot of the function $E_{b\lambda}(T)$ against the wavelength of radiation for several different values of temperature. An examination of this figure reveals the following features of emission of radiation by a blackbody :

1. The emissive power increases with increasing temperature at all wavelengths.

2. Each curve exhibits a peak.

3. As temperature increases, the peaks tend to shift toward smaller wavelengths.

4. The top curve for $T = 5556\,K$ corresponds approximately to the emission of radiation by a body at the effective surface temperature of the sun $(T_{\text{sun}} = 5762\,K)$.

## 11.2.2 Wien's Displacement Law

In Fig.11.4, the focus of the peaks of the curves is shown by a dashed line. The focus of these peaks is called *Wien's displacement law*. The equation for the blackbody emissive power is normalized as

$$\frac{E_{b\lambda}(T)}{n^3\,T^5} = \frac{C_1}{(n\lambda T)^5\left[e^{C_2/(n\lambda T)} - 1\right]} \tag{11-21}$$

which is the only function of $(n\lambda T)$ . It can, therefore, be plotted as a single line. The maximum of this curve is determined by differentiating it as

$$\frac{d}{d(n\lambda T)}\left(\frac{E_{b\lambda}}{n^3 T^5}\right) = 0 \;, \tag{11-22}$$

which gives the Wien's displacement law

$$\boxed{(n\lambda T)_{\max} = 2897.6\;\mu\text{m}\cdot K} \;. \tag{11-23}$$

For example, for the solar radiation emitted at an effective temperature $T = 5762\,K$ of the sun's surface, the application of Wien's law gives the wavelength at which the peak occurs as

$$\lambda_{\max} \simeq 0.5\;\mu\text{m} \;, \tag{11-24}$$

which lies in the visible range of the spectrum.

For small wavelengths, or for low temperatures,

$$e^{C_2/n\lambda T} - 1 \simeq e^{C_2/n\lambda T} \;. \tag{11-25}$$

Then,

$$\frac{E_{b\lambda}}{n^3\,T^5} \simeq \frac{C_1}{(n\lambda T)^5}\cdot e^{-C_2/(n\lambda T)} \quad \text{for} \quad \frac{C_2}{n\lambda T} \gg 1 \tag{11-26}$$

which is given by Wien before Planck for the blackbody emissive power distribution. Wien's distribution is very accurate for most of the spectrum; mainly, $n\lambda T < 3000\mu\text{m}\cdot K$. Therefore, to simplify, this analysis is often used.

For large wavelengths, or for high temperatures,

$$\frac{C_2}{n\lambda T} = x \;, \tag{11-27}$$

which is a small number; thus,

$$e^x \simeq 1 + x \quad \text{and} \quad e^x - 1 \simeq x \;. \tag{11-28}$$

Therefore,

$$\frac{E_{b\lambda}}{n^3\,T^5} \simeq \frac{C_1}{(n\lambda T)^5} \cdot \frac{1}{\frac{C_2}{n\lambda T}} = \frac{C_1}{C_2} \cdot \frac{1}{(n\lambda T)^4} \ , \qquad (11\text{-}29)$$

which is called the *Rayleigh - Jeans limit*. The blackbody emissive power spectrum approximations are schematically illustrated in the attached figure.

### 11.2.3 Stefan - Boltzmann Law

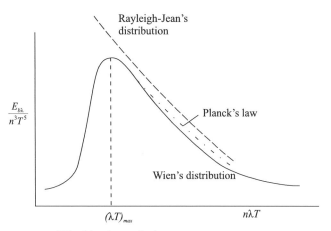

Blackbody emissive power spectrum.

The radiation energy emitted by a blackbody at an absolute temperature $T$ over all wavelengths from $\lambda = 0$ to $\lambda = \infty$ is a quantity of practical interest. It is determined by integrating the spectral blackbody emissive power $E_{b\lambda}(T)$ from $\lambda = 0$ to $\lambda = \infty$:

$$
\begin{aligned}
E_b(T) &= \int_{\lambda=0}^{\infty} E_{b\lambda}(T)\,d\lambda \quad \mathrm{W/m^2} \qquad (11\text{-}30)\\
&= C_1\,n^2\,T^4 \int_0^{\infty} \frac{d\,(n\lambda T)}{(n\lambda T)^5\left[e^{C_2/n\lambda T}-1\right]}\\
&= \frac{C_1}{C_2}\,n^2\,T^4 \int_0^{\infty} \frac{x^3}{e^x-1}\,dx \ .
\end{aligned}
$$

This integration can be performed by recalling that with

$$\frac{1}{e^x-1} = \sum_{m=1}^{\infty} e^{-mx} \qquad (11\text{-}31)$$

$$E_b(T) = \frac{C_1}{C_2^4}\,n^2\,T^4 \int_0^{\infty} \sum_{m=1}^{\infty} x^3\,e^{-mx}\,dx \qquad (11\text{-}32)$$

and using the relation for integration by parts

$$E_b(T) = \frac{C_1}{C_2^4} n^2 T^4 \sum_{m=1}^{\infty} \frac{6}{m^4} \ . \tag{11-33}$$

Recalling again

$$\sum_{m=1}^{\infty} \frac{1}{m^4} = \frac{\pi^4}{90} \tag{11-34}$$

results in

$$E_b(T) = \frac{\pi^4}{15} \frac{C_1}{C_2^4} n^2 T^4 \tag{11-35}$$

with $\sigma = \dfrac{\pi^4}{15} \dfrac{C_1}{C_2^4}$ , we have

$$\boxed{E_b(T) = n^2 \sigma T^4} \quad \text{W}/\text{m}^2. \tag{11-36}$$

This relation is known as the *Stefan-Boltzmann law*. Here $E_b(T)$ is called the *blackbody emissive power*, $T$ is the absolute temperature in $K$, and $\sigma$ is the *Stefan-Boltzmann constant*.

$$\boxed{\sigma = 5.67 \times 10^{-8} \, \text{W}/(\text{m}^2 \cdot K^4).} \tag{11-37}$$

This equation shows that the radiation flux is proportional to the fourth power of the absolute temperature of the body. Therefore, at elevated temperatures radiation is an important mechanism of heat transfer ; it can be more dominant than conduction or convection.

## 11.2.4 Blackbody Radiation Function

The radiation flux emitted by a blackbody at any given temperature $T$ over all wavelengths from $\lambda = 0$ to $\lambda = \infty$ is given by the Stefan-Boltzmann law. The fraction of this total energy that is emitted over any given finite-wavelength band is also a quantity of interest in some applications.

The radiation energy emitted by a blackbody per unit area over a wavelength band from $\lambda = 0$ to $\lambda$ is determined by

$$E_{b,0-\lambda}(T) = \int_0^{\lambda} E_{b\lambda}(T) \, d\lambda \ . \tag{11-38}$$

By dividing this quantity by the total energy emission from $\lambda = 0$ to $\lambda = \infty$, we obtain

$$f_{0\lambda}(T) \;=\; \frac{\int_0^\lambda E_{b\lambda}(T)\,d\lambda}{\int_0^\infty E_{b\lambda}(T)\,d\lambda} \;=\; \frac{\int_0^\lambda E_{b\lambda}(T)\,d\lambda}{\sigma T^4} \;. \tag{11-39}$$

Here, $f_{0\lambda}(T)$ is called the *blackbody radiation function*. It represents the emission of radiation by a blackbody over the wavelength band from $\lambda = 0$ to $\lambda$ as a fraction of the total emission.

In Table 11.1, $f_{0\lambda}(T)$ is listed as a function of $\lambda T$. Here, $\lambda$ is in micrometers and $T$ is in Kelvins. The radiation energy emitted by a blackbody at temperature $T$ over a finite-wavelength band from $\lambda = \lambda_1$ to $\lambda = \lambda_2$ as a fraction of the total emission from $\lambda = 0$ to $\lambda = \lambda$ can be determined in the following manner. We obtain from Table 11.1 the fractional functions $f_{0-\lambda_1}(T)$ and $f_{0-\lambda_2}(T)$, corresponding to $\lambda_1 T$ and $\lambda_2 T$, respectively. Then their difference gives

$$f_{\lambda_1 - \lambda_2}(T) \;=\; f_{0-\lambda_2}(T) - f_{0-\lambda_1}(T) \tag{11-40}$$

where $f_{\lambda_1 - \lambda_2}(T)$ represents the energy contained over the finite-wavelength band between $\lambda_1$ and $\lambda_2$ as a fraction of the total energy emission.

**EXAMPLE 11-1**   At a wavelength of $4\ \mu m$, what is the temperature of the blackbody that will give an emissive power equal to $10^3\ W/(m^2 \cdot \mu m)$ into the vacuum?

**SOLUTION**   Given $\lambda = 4\ \mu m$, $n = 1$, and $E_{b\lambda}(T) = 10^3\ W/(m^2 \cdot \mu m)$, and using Max Planck's the spectral blackbody emissive power expression, we solve for the temperature $T$ as follows:

$$10^3 \;=\; \frac{3.743 \times 10^8}{4^5\,\{\exp\left[1.4387 \times 10^4/(4T)\right] - 1\}}$$

$$\frac{1.4387 \times 10^4}{4T} = \ln\,366.53$$

results

$$T \;=\; 609\ K \;.$$

**EXAMPLE 11-2**   Consider a blackbody emitting radiation at $1500\ K$. Determine the wavelength at which the blackbody spectral emissive power $E_{b\lambda}$ is maximum.

**SOLUTION**   Given $T = 1500\ K$ from Wien's displacement law, we have

$$(\lambda T)_{\max} \;=\; 2897.6\ \mu m \cdot K$$

or

$$\lambda \;=\; \frac{2897.6}{1500} \;=\; 1.93\ \mu m \;.$$

**TABLE 11.1**. Blackbody Radiation Functions

| $n\lambda T$ μm·K | $f_{0\lambda}$ | $n\lambda T$ μm·K | $f_{0\lambda}$ |
|---|---|---|---|
| 555.6 | 0.00000 | 5,777.8 | 0.71806 |
| 666.7 | 0.00000 | 5,888.9 | 0.72813 |
| 777.8 | 0.00000 | 6,000.0 | 0.73777 |
| 888.9 | 0.00007 | 6,111.1 | 0.74700 |
| 1,000.0 | 0.00032 | 6,222.2 | 0.75583 |
| 1,111.1 | 0.00101 | 6,333.3 | 0.76429 |
| 1,222.2 | 0.00252 | 6,444.4 | 0.77238 |
| 1,333.3 | 0.00531 | 6,555.6 | 0.78014 |
| 1,444.4 | 0.00983 | 6,666.7 | 0.78757 |
| 1,555.6 | 0.01643 | 6,777.8 | 0.79469 |
| 1,666.7 | 0.02537 | 6,888.9 | 0.80152 |
| 1,777.8 | 0.03677 | 7,000.0 | 0.80806 |
| 1,888.9 | 0.05059 | 7,111.1 | 0.81433 |
| 2,000.0 | 0.06672 | 7,222.2 | 0.82035 |
| 2,111.1 | 0.08496 | 7,333.3 | 0.82612 |
| 2,222.2 | 0.10503 | 7,444.4 | 0.83166 |
| 2,333.3 | 0.12665 | 7,555.6 | 0.83698 |
| 2,444.4 | 0.14953 | 7,666.7 | 0.84209 |
| 2,555.6 | 0.17337 | 7,777.8 | 0.84699 |
| 2,666.7 | 0.19789 | 7,888.9 | 0.85171 |
| 2,777.8 | 0.22285 | 8,000.0 | 0.85624 |
| 2,888.9 | 0.24803 | 8,111.1 | 0.86059 |
| 3,000.0 | 0.27322 | 8,222.2 | 0.86477 |
| 3,111.1 | 0.29825 | 8,333.3 | 0.86880 |
| 3,222.2 | 0.32300 | 8,888.9 | 0.88677 |
| 3,333.3 | 0.34734 | 9,444.4 | 0.90168 |
| 3,444.4 | 0.37118 | 10,000.0 | 0.91414 |
| 3,555.6 | 0.39445 | 10,555.6 | 0.92462 |
| 3,666.7 | 0.41705 | 11,111.1 | 0.93349 |
| 3,777.8 | 0.43905 | 11,666.7 | 0.94104 |
| 3,888.9 | 0.46031 | 12,222.2 | 0.94751 |
| 4,000.0 | 0.48085 | 12,777.8 | 0.95307 |
| 4,111.1 | 0.50066 | 13,333.3 | 0.95788 |
| 4,222.2 | 0.51974 | 13,888.9 | 0.96207 |
| 4,333.3 | 0.53809 | 14,444.4 | 0.96572 |
| 4,444.4 | 0.55573 | 15,000.0 | 0.96892 |
| 4,555.6 | 0.57267 | 15,555.6 | 0.97174 |
| 4,666.7 | 0.58891 | 16,111.1 | 0.97423 |
| 4,777.8 | 0.60449 | 16,666.7 | 0.97644 |
| 4,888.9 | 0.61941 | 22,222.2 | 0.98915 |
| 5,000.0 | 0.63371 | 27,777.8 | 0.99414 |
| 5,111.1 | 0.64740 | 33,333.3 | 0.99649 |
| 5,222.2 | 0.66051 | 38,888.9 | 0.99773 |
| 5,333.3 | 0.67305 | 44,444.4 | 0.99845 |
| 5,444.4 | 0.68506 | 50,000.0 | 0.99889 |
| 5,555.6 | 0.69655 | 55,555.6 | 0.99918 |
| 5,666.7 | 0.70754 | $\infty$ | 1.00000 |

**EXAMPLE 11-3**  There is a hole of radius $0.2\,\mathrm{cm}$ in a large spherical enclosure whose inner surface is maintained at $800\,K$. Determine the rate of emission of radiative energy through this opening.

**SOLUTION**  Given $T = 800\,K$, the blackbody emissive power can be calculated from the Stefan - Boltzmann law :

$$
\begin{aligned}
E_b(T) &= \sigma T^4 \\
&= (5.67 \times 10^{-8})\,(800)^4 \\
&= 23,224.3 \ \mathrm{W/m^2}.
\end{aligned}
$$

The hole area is $A = \pi(0.002)^2\,m^2$. Therefore, the rate of emission of radiation energy $Q$ through the hole becomes

$$
\begin{aligned}
Q &= A E_b(T) \\
&= \pi(0.002)^2\,(23,224.3) \\
&= 0.29 \ W.
\end{aligned}
$$

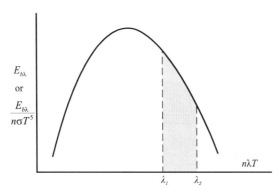

**FIGURE EXAMPLE 11-4**

**EXAMPLE 11-4**  A tungsten filament is heated to $2500\,K$. What fraction of this energy is in the visible range?

**SOLUTION**  The visible range of the spectrum is $\lambda_1 = 0.4\,\mu m$ to $\lambda_2 = 0.7\,\mu m$. Given $T = 2500\,K$ from Table 11.1 for $\lambda_1 T = 0.4\,(2500) = 1000\,\mu m \cdot K$, we obtain

$$
f_{0-\lambda_1} = 0.00032
$$

and for $\lambda_2 T = 0.7(2500) = 1750\,\mu m \cdot K$, we obtain

$$
f_{0-\lambda_2} = 0.03392 \ .
$$

Then

$$
f_{0-\lambda_2} - f_{0-\lambda_1} = 0.03392 - 0.00032 = 0.0336 \ .
$$

Therefore, 3.36 percent of the energy is in the visible range. The area under the blackbody emissive power curve for this region is shown schematically in the attached figure.

## 11.3. RADIATION ENERGY FROM REAL SURFACES

The radiation energy leaving a real surface per unit area per unit time in all directions into the hemispherical space above it is a quantity of practical interest. It is called the *radiation flux* from a surface. An expression defining this quantity in terms of the radiation intensity can be developed by a procedure similar to the derivation of blackbody emissive power.

Radiation intensity from a real surface depends on direction, whereas the blackbody radiation intensity is independent of direction. The intensity may also vary with the position along the surface, but for simplicity of notation let's omit the space variable. The spectral radiation intensity emitted by a real surface at temperature $T$ of wavelength $\lambda$ is always less than that emitted by a blackbody at the same temperature and wavelength. To distinguish these two cases, we use the symbol

$$I_\lambda(\theta, \phi) \qquad \mathrm{W}/(\mathrm{m}^2 \cdot \mu\mathrm{m} \cdot \mathrm{sr}) \qquad (11\text{-}41)$$

for the *spectral radiation from a real surface*.

The radiation is emitted from a surface at all wavelengths. The integration of $I_\lambda(\theta, \phi)$ from $\lambda = 0$ to $\lambda = \infty$ gives

$$I(\theta, \phi) = \int_{\lambda=0}^{\infty} I_\lambda(\theta, \phi) \, d\lambda. \qquad (11\text{-}42)$$

Here $I(\theta, \phi)$ is called the *radiation intensity*.

We refer to the nomenclature in Fig. 11.3. Let $I_\lambda(\theta, \phi)$ be the spectral radiation intensity leaving the surface element in any given direction $\hat{\Omega}$. The spectral radiation energy leaving a unit surface area, streaming through a differential solid angle $d\omega = \sin\theta \, d\theta \, d\phi$ in any direction, is written in analogy to Eq. (11-18) as

$$I_\lambda(\theta, \phi) \cos\theta \sin\theta \, d\theta \, d\phi \qquad (11\text{-}43)$$

The spectral radiation energy leaving a unit surface area in all directions into the hemispherical space is obtained by integrating Eq. (11-43) over the angles $0 \leq \phi \leq 2\pi$ and $0 \leq \theta \leq \pi/2$:

$$q_\lambda = \int_{\phi=0}^{2\pi} \int_{\theta=0}^{\pi/2} I_\lambda(\theta, \phi) \cos\theta \sin\theta \, d\theta \, d\phi. \qquad (11\text{-}44)$$

Here $q_\lambda$ is called the *spectral radiation flux* from a surface, and it has the dimensions of $\mathrm{W}/(\mathrm{m}^2 \cdot \mu\mathrm{m})$.

The integration of Eq. (11-44) from $\lambda = 0$ to $\lambda = \infty$ gives

$$q = \int_{\lambda=0}^{\infty} q_\lambda \, d\lambda \quad \text{W/m}^2 \tag{11-45}$$

where $q$ is called the *(total) radiation flux* from a surface.

### 11.3.1 Radiation Intensity Independent of Direction

When the spectral radiation intensity $I_\lambda(\theta, \phi) \equiv I_\lambda$ is independent of direction, Eq. (11-44) is integrated, to yield

$$q_\lambda = \pi I_\lambda \quad \text{W/(m}^2 \cdot \mu\text{m)} \tag{11-46}$$

where $q_\lambda$ is the spectral radiation flux.

The integration of Eq. (11-46) from $\lambda = 0$ to $\lambda = \infty$ yields

$$q = \pi \int_{\lambda=0}^{\infty} I_\lambda \, d\lambda \quad \text{W/m}^2 \tag{11-47}$$

Thus, given the spectral distribution of the radiation leaving the surface, the radiation flux $q$ from the surface can be calculated from Eq. (11-47).

### 11.4. RADIATION INCIDENT ON A SURFACE

In the preceeding discussions, we focused our attention on the determination of the radiation energy emitted from a blackbody and that from a real surface. In engineering applications, radiation flux incident on a surface is also of interest.

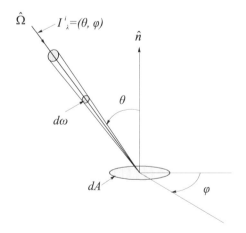

**FIG. 11.5.** Nomenclature for radiation flux incident on a surface.

We refer to the nomenclature shown in Fig. 11.5 for the discussion of radiation flux incident on a surface. Let $I_\lambda^i(\theta, \phi)$ be the spectral radiation intensity incident on a surface element $dA$ in any given direction $\hat{\Omega}$. Here we use the superscript $i$ to distinguish $I_\lambda^i(\theta, \phi)$ from the spectral radiation intensity $I_\lambda(\theta, \phi)$ leaving the surface. Then

$$I_\lambda^i(\theta, \phi) \cos \theta \, d\omega$$

or

$$I_\lambda^i(\theta, \phi) \cos \theta \sin \theta \, d\theta \, d\phi \tag{11-48}$$

represents the radiation energy incident per unit area of the surface from an irradiation through a differential solid angle $d\omega = \sin \theta \, d\theta \, d\phi$ in a given direction $\hat{\Omega}$. The $\cos \theta$ term appearing in Eq. (11-48) results from the fact that the irradiation energy on the surface is based on the actual area, whereas $I_\lambda^i(\theta, \phi)$ is based on the area normal to the direction of propagation.

The spectral radiation flux incident per unit area of the surface due to irradiation from all directions in the hemispherical space above it is determined by integrating Eq. (11-48) over the angles $0 \leq \phi \leq 2\pi$ and $0 \leq \theta \leq \pi/2$. We obtain

$$q_\lambda^i = \int_{\phi=0}^{2\pi} \int_{\theta=0}^{\pi/2} I_\lambda^i(\theta, \phi) \cos \theta \sin \theta \, d\theta \, d\phi \tag{11-49}$$

Here $q_\lambda^i$ is called the *spectral incident radiation flux* on a surface, and it has the dimensions of $W/m^2$.

The integration of Eq. (11-49) from $\lambda = 0$ to $\lambda = \infty$ gives

$$q^i = \int_{\lambda=0}^{\infty} q_\lambda^i \, d\lambda \quad W/m^2 \tag{11-50}$$

where $q^i$ is called the *incident radiation flux*.

## 11.4.1 Radiation Intensity Independent of Direction

When the incident spectral radiation $I_\lambda^i(\theta, \phi) \equiv I_\lambda^i$ is independent of direction, Eq. (11-49) is integrated, to yield

$$q_\lambda^i = \pi I_\lambda^i \quad W/(m^2 \cdot \mu m) \tag{11-51}$$

where $q_\lambda^i$ is the incident spectral radiation flux.

The integration of Eq. (11-51) from $\lambda = 0$ to $\lambda = \infty$ yields

$$q^i = \pi \int_{\lambda=0}^{\infty} I_\lambda^i \, d\lambda \quad W/m^2 \tag{11-52}$$

Given the spectral distribution of the incident radiation, radiation flux $q^i$ incident on a surface can be calculated.

## 11.5. RADIATION PROPERTIES OF SURFACES

Radiation emitted by a body because of its temperature, in general, originates in the interior of the body. In the case of materials such as metals, wood, stone, etc., which are opaque to thermal radiation, the emission is confined to within an extremely short distance from the surface. Similarly, radiation incident on an opaque body is absorbed within a very short distance from the surface. Therefore, for opaque materials the interaction of radiation with matter is treated as a surface phenomenon, because radiation is absorbed or emitted within an extremely short distance from the surface.

In the case of solar radiation incident on a window glass or a body of water, radiation is not immediately absorbed at the surface, but penetrates into the depths of the material. Therefore, water and glass are semi-transparent to solar radiation, which is considered to originate at an effective temperature $T = 5762\,K$ at the sun's surface. On the other hand, thermal radiation incident on a window glass or water from a source at low temperatures ($400\,K$ or less) is absorbed within an extremely short distance from the surface. These examples illustrate that the characteristics of a body for absorption and emission of radiation depend not only on the type of material but also on the temperature (or wavelength) of the source at which the radiation is generated.

Since most engineering materials are opaque to thermal radiation, the interaction of radiation with the matter in engineering applications is generally treated as a surface phenomenon. Given this concentration we examine below the radiation characteristics of surfaces.

### 11.5.1 Emissivity

Radiation emitted by a real body at a temperature $T$ is always less than that of the blackbody. Therefore, the blackbody emission is chosen as a reference. The *emissivity* $\epsilon$ of a surface is defined as the ratio of the energy emitted by a real surface to that emitted by a blackbody at the same temperature ; it has a value between zero and unity. Clearly, there are numerous possibilities for making such a comparison : for example, the comparison can be made at a given wavelength, over all wavelengths, for the energy emitted in a specified direction, or for the energy emitted into the hemispherical space.

Most emissivity data reported in the literature are in the form of *total hemispherical emissivity* averaged over all wavelengths. By definition, the total hemispherical emissivity is the ratio of the total radiation flux $q(T)$ emitted by a real surface at temperature $T$ over all wavelengths into the hemispherical space, to that which would have been emitted by a blackbody, $E_b(T)$, at the same temperature $T$. Then, the *total hemispherical emissivity* $\epsilon(T)$ is defined as

$$\epsilon(T) = \frac{q(T)}{E_b(T)} \ . \tag{11-53}$$

Given the emissivity of a real surface, the radiation energy $q(T)$ emitted by the surface

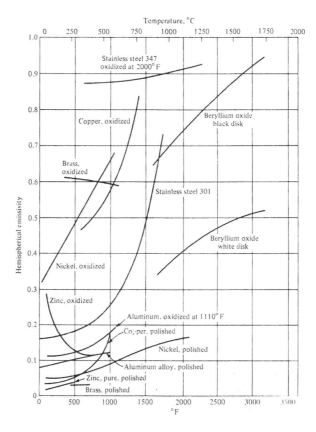

**FIG. 11.6.** Effects of temperature and oxidation of hemispherical emissivity of metals. Compiled based on data from Gubareff, Janssen and Torborg, (1960).

per unit area at temperature $T$ is determined by

$$q(T) = \epsilon(T)\, E_b(T) = \epsilon(T)\, \sigma T^4 \quad \text{W/m}^2 . \qquad (11\text{-}54)$$

The hemispherical emissivity of typical engineering materials is listed in Appendix C. Figure 11.6 illustrates the effects of temperature and oxidation on emissivity. Clearly, oxidation increases the emissivity. We can also speak of the *spectral hemispherical emissivity* $\epsilon_\lambda$ if the emissivity is considered at a specific wavelength $\lambda$.

The spectral hemispherical emissivity $\epsilon_\lambda$ is determined by laboratory tests performed at different wavelengths. Figure 11.7 shows the variation of $\epsilon_\lambda$ with wavelength for typical engineering materials. For example, for window glass there is a sharp change in spectral emissivity at wavelengths of about $3\ \mu\text{m}$.

Spectral information on $\epsilon_\lambda$, such as that shown in Fig.11.7, can be used to calculate the average value of emissivity $\epsilon$ over all wavelength from the following expression:

$$\epsilon = \frac{\int_0^\infty \epsilon_\lambda\, E_{b\lambda}(T)\, d\lambda}{\int_0^\infty E_{b\lambda}(T)\, d\lambda} = \frac{\int_0^\infty \epsilon_\lambda\, E_{b\lambda}(T)\, d\lambda}{\sigma T^4} . \qquad (11\text{-}55)$$

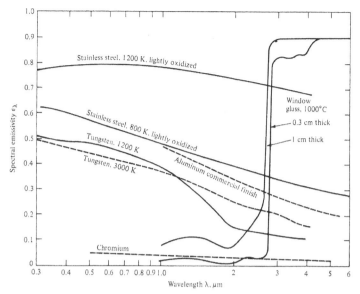

**FIG. 11.7.** Spectral emissivity of materials.

Note that, in this averaging process, the spectral blackbody emissive power $E_{b\lambda}(T)$ is used as the weight factor, because the energy emission is governed by the magnitude of $E_{b\lambda}(T)$.

Generally, it is quite laborious to perform the integration when experimental data are to be used for $\epsilon_\lambda$. To alleviate this difficulty, the integration can be transformed into a summation involving several wavelength bands, over each of which $\epsilon_\lambda$ can be regarded as uniform and taken out of the integral sign. Then the resulting integrals are re-cast as the blackbody radiation functions, which are readily available from Table 11.1.

To illustrate this matter, we consider the entire wavelength spectrum to be divided into three wavelength bands (drawing a figure showing this distribution is suggested, since it may look different than Fig. 11.7.) :

$$\text{From } 0 \text{ to } \lambda_1: \quad \epsilon_\lambda = \epsilon_1 = \text{constant}$$

$$\text{From } \lambda_1 \text{ to } \lambda_2: \quad \epsilon_\lambda = \epsilon_2 = \text{constant}$$

$$\text{From } \lambda_2 \text{ to } \infty: \quad \epsilon_\lambda = \epsilon_3 = \text{constant}.$$

Then the integral in the above emissivity equation is separated into three parts, and the definition of the blackbody radiation function is utilized.

$$\epsilon = \epsilon_1 \frac{\int_0^{\lambda_1} E_{b\lambda}(T)\, d\lambda}{\sigma T^4} + \epsilon_2 \frac{\int_{\lambda_1}^{\lambda_2} E_{b\lambda}(T)\, d\lambda}{\sigma T^4} + \epsilon_3 \frac{\int_{\lambda_2}^{\infty} E_{b\lambda}(T)\, d\lambda}{\sigma T^4} \quad (11\text{-}56)$$

$$\epsilon = \epsilon_1\, f_{0-\lambda_1}(T) + \epsilon_2\, [f_{0-\lambda_2}(T) - f_{0-\lambda_1}(T)] + \epsilon_3\, [1 - f_{0-\lambda_2}] \quad (11\text{-}57)$$

Clearly, by knowing $\epsilon_1$, $\epsilon_2$, and $\epsilon_3$, the evaluation of emissivity $\epsilon$ by using Table 11.1 becomes a relatively easy matter.

We also define the *spectral directional emissivity* $\epsilon'_\lambda$ :

$$\epsilon'_\lambda(\theta, \phi) = \frac{\Delta q_\lambda}{\Delta E_{b\lambda}} = \frac{I_\lambda(\theta, \phi) \cos\theta \, \Delta\omega}{I_{b\lambda} \cos\theta \, \Delta\omega} \quad . \tag{11-58}$$

Therefore,

$$\Delta q_\lambda = \epsilon'_\lambda I_{b\lambda} \cos\theta \, \Delta\omega \quad . \tag{11-59}$$

If the emissivity is a measure perpendicular to the surface, it is called the *normal emissivity*. See Appendix Table C-1 for some measured values. Integrating over the hemispherical surface gives

$$q_\lambda = \int_{\phi=0}^{2\pi} \int_{\theta=0}^{\pi/2} \epsilon'_\lambda I_{b\lambda} \cos\theta \, d\omega = I_{b\lambda} \int_{\cap} \epsilon'_\lambda \cos\theta \, d\omega \quad . \tag{11-60}$$

where $d\omega = \sin\theta \, d\theta \, d\phi$

Now, we revisit the definition of the spectral hemispherical emissivity $\epsilon_\lambda$

$$\begin{aligned}
\epsilon_\lambda &= \frac{q_\lambda}{E_{b\lambda}} \\
&= \frac{I_{b\lambda} \int_{\cap} \epsilon'_\lambda \cos\theta \, d\omega}{\pi I_{b\lambda}} \\
&= \frac{1}{\pi} \int_{\cap} \epsilon'_\lambda \cos\theta \, d\omega \quad ,
\end{aligned} \tag{11-61}$$

where $E_{b\lambda} = \pi I_{b\lambda}$, and $I_{b\lambda}$ is the spectral blackbody radiation intensity.

Similarly, we define the total directional emissivity $\epsilon'$ as

$$\epsilon' = \frac{\Delta q}{\Delta E_b} = \frac{\int_{\lambda=0}^{\infty} I_\lambda(\theta, \phi) \cos\theta \, \Delta\omega \, d\lambda}{I_b \cos\theta \, \Delta\omega} \quad . \tag{11-62}$$

Revisiting the definition of the total hemispherical emissivity $\epsilon$ , we have

$$\epsilon = \frac{1}{\pi} \int_{\cap} \epsilon' \cos\theta \, d\omega \quad . \tag{11-63}$$

## 11.5.2 Absorptivity

A blackbody absorbs all radiation incident upon it, whereas a real surface absorbs only part of it. The *hemispherical absorptivity* $\alpha$ of a real surface is defined as the fraction of the radiation energy incident upon the surface from all directions over the hemispherical space and over all wavelengths that is absorbed by the surface. We can also speak of *spectral hemispherical absorptivity* $\alpha_\lambda$ if the absorptivity refers to radiation incident at a specific wavelength $\lambda$ .

$$\alpha = \frac{q_{\text{absorbed}}}{q_{\text{incident}}} = \frac{q_a}{q^i} = \frac{\int_{\lambda=0}^{\infty} q_{\lambda,a} \, d\lambda}{\int_0^{\infty} q^i \, d\lambda} = \frac{\int_{\lambda=0}^{\infty} \int_{\cap} \alpha'_\lambda I_\lambda^i \cos\theta \, d\omega \, d\lambda}{\int_{\lambda=0}^{\infty} \int_{\cap} I_\lambda^i \cos\theta \, d\omega \, d\lambda} \tag{11-64}$$

where $\alpha'_\lambda$ is the spectral directional absorptivity given by

$$\alpha'_\lambda = \frac{\Delta q_{\lambda,a}}{\Delta q^i_\lambda} = \frac{\Delta q_{\lambda,a}}{I^i_\lambda(\theta, \phi) \cos \theta \, \Delta \omega} \; . \tag{11-65}$$

and $I^i_\lambda$ is the spectral intensity of the incident radiation. If $I^i_\lambda = I_{b_\lambda}(Te)$, where $Te$ is the environmental temperature, then $q^i = \pi I_{b_\lambda}$.

$$\alpha(T, Te) = \frac{1}{\pi} \int_\cap \alpha'_\lambda(T) \cos \theta \, d\omega \, df(\lambda Te) \tag{11-66}$$

Relatively little data is available in the literature on the effect of source temperature on absorptivity of surfaces, except for the case of solar radiation.

### 11.5.3 Graybody Approximation

The radiation properties of a surface, such as absorptivity and emissivity, in general, depend on the wavelength of radiation. However, in radiation calculations, it is not practical to consider heat transfer at each wavelength. To alleviate such difficulties, it is common to assume a uniform emissivity $\epsilon$ over the entire wavelength spectrum. This is called the *graybody approximation*; it is frequently used in engineering applications.

### 11.5.4 Kirchhoff's Law

Under certain conditions, the absorptivity and emissivity of a body are related to each other by Kirchhoff's law. According to this law, the spectral emissivity $\epsilon_\lambda(T)$ for the emission of radiation by a body at temperature $T$ is equal to the spectral absorptivity $\alpha_\lambda(T)$ of the body for radiation originating from a blackbody source at the same temperature $T$. Hence, by Kirchhoff's law we write

$$\epsilon_\lambda(T) = \alpha_\lambda(T) \; . \tag{11-67}$$

Care must be exercised in generalizing this result to the average values of emissivity and absorptivity over the entire wavelength spectrum. That is, Kirchhoff's law is always valid, but the equality

$$\epsilon(T) = \alpha(T) \; , \tag{11-68}$$

is applicable only where the radiation properties of the body are independent of the wavelength (i.e., a graybody) or when the incident and the emitted radiation have the same spectral distribution.

### 11.5.5 Reflectivity

When radiation is incident on a real surface, a fraction of it is reflected by the surface. If the surface is perfectly smooth, the incident and reflected rays are symmetric with respect to the normal at the point of incidence, as illustrated in Fig.11.8 (a). This mirror like

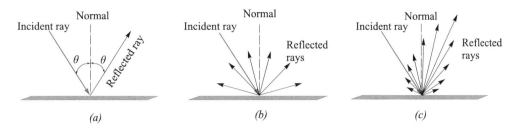

**FIG. 11.8.** Reflection from surfaces. (a) Specular reflection, (b) diffuse reflection, (c) irregular reflection.

reflection is called *specular reflection*. If the surface has some roughness, the incident radiation is scattered in all directions. An idealized reflection law assumes that in such a situation the intensity of the reflected radiation is constant for all angles of reflection and independent of the direction of the incident radiation. Such a reflection is called *diffuse reflection*. Figure 11.8b illustrates diffuse reflection from a surface. Reflection from real surfaces encountered in engineering applications is neither perfectly diffuse nor perfectly specular, but exhibits characteristics that are a combination of the diffuse and specular behavior, as sketched in Fig. 11.8c. However, the concept is useful for studying the effects of the two limiting cases on radiation transfer. The reflectivity of a surface is defined as the fraction of the incident radiation reflected by the surface.

The *hemispherical reflectivity* $\rho$ of a surface is defined as the fraction of the radiation energy incident on a surface from all directions in the hemispherical space and over all wavelengths that is reflected back into the hemispherical space. For an *opaque surface*, the hemispherical reflectivity $\rho$ and the hemispherical absorptivity $\alpha$ are related by

$$\alpha = 1 - \rho \ . \tag{11-69}$$

The *spectral hemispherical reflectivity* $\rho_\lambda$ is the reflection at a specific wavelength $\lambda$. For an opaque surface, the spectral hemispherical reflectivity $\rho_\lambda$ and the spectral hemispherical absorptivity $\alpha_\lambda$ are related by

$$\alpha_\lambda = 1 - \rho_\lambda \ . \tag{11-70}$$

Here,

$$
\begin{aligned}
\rho &= \frac{q_{\text{reflected}}}{q_{\text{incident}}} \\[6pt]
&= \frac{q_r}{q^i} \\[6pt]
&= \frac{\int_{\lambda=0}^{\infty} q_{\lambda,r} \, d\lambda}{\int_{\lambda=0}^{\infty} q^i \, d\lambda} \\[6pt]
&= \frac{\int_{\lambda=0}^{\infty} \int_{\cap} \rho_\lambda' \, I_\lambda^i \, \cos\theta \, d\omega \, d\lambda}{\int_{\lambda=0}^{\infty} \int_{\cap} I_\lambda^i \, \cos\theta \, d\omega \, d\lambda} \ ,
\end{aligned}
\tag{11-71}
$$

where $\rho'_\lambda$ is the spectral directional reflectivity given by

$$\rho'_\lambda = \frac{\Delta q_{\lambda,r}}{\Delta q_\lambda^-} = \frac{\Delta q_{\lambda,r}}{I_\lambda^i(\theta, \phi) \cos\theta \, \Delta\omega} \quad . \tag{11-72}$$

In the above description of reflectivities, we have no provision for identifying the directional distribution of the reflected energy. To describe the directional distribution of the reflected energy, a new reflectivity is defined that is a function of both the incident direction $(\theta, \phi)$ and the reflected direction $(\theta_r, \phi_r)$.

## 11.5.6 Bi-Directional Reflectivity

The total bi-directional reflectivity is defined as

$$\rho''(\theta, \phi, \theta_r, \phi_r) = \frac{\pi I_r(\theta_r, \phi_r)}{\Delta q^i} \tag{11-73}$$

$$= \frac{\pi I_r}{I^i(\theta, \phi) \cos\theta \, \Delta\omega}$$

$$= \frac{\pi \int_{\lambda=0}^{\infty} I_{r,\lambda} \, d\lambda}{\int_{\lambda=0}^{\infty} I^i(\theta, \phi) \cos\theta \, \Delta\omega \, d\lambda}$$

$$= \frac{q_{\text{hypothetically reflected}}}{q_{\text{incident}}} \quad .$$

$q_{\text{hypothetically reflected}}$ is defined as the energy that would be reflected if the reflected intensity distribution were diffused with the same magnitude in every direction. Therefore, $\rho''$ can be greater than one. The spectral bi-directional reflectivity $\rho''_\lambda$ is also defined at a certain wavelength.

The magnitude of the hypothetical reflected intensity is

$$I_r = \frac{1}{\pi} \rho'' \Delta q^i \quad .$$

Now, we revisit the definition of the total directional reflectivity $\rho'$, with the intensity

$$\rho' = \frac{\int_\cap \frac{1}{\pi} \rho'' \Delta q^i \cos\theta_r \, d\omega}{\Delta q^i}$$

$$= \frac{1}{\pi} \int_\cap \rho'' \cos\theta_r \, d\omega_r \quad .$$

Similarly, we also obtain

$$\rho'_\lambda = \frac{1}{\pi} \int_\cap \rho''_\lambda \cos\theta_r \, d\omega_r \quad .$$

For a *Diffuse Reflector* : $\rho' = \rho''$ and $\rho' = \rho''$.
                     $_\lambda$    $_\lambda$

For a *Specular Reflector* : $\rho''$ and $\rho''$ are zero for all angles of reflection except the
                                    $_\lambda$
specular angle, $\theta_r$ and $\phi_r$.

For a *Real Surface* : $\rho = \rho_{specular} + \rho_{diffuse}$.

## 11.5.7 Transmissivity

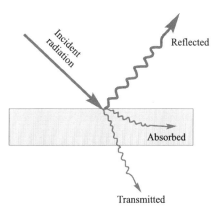

**FIG. 11.9.** Reflection, absorption, and transmission of incident radiation by a semi-transparent material.

If the body is *semi-transparent* to radiation, as glass is to solar radiation, part of the incident radiation is reflected by the surface, part is absorbed by the medium, and the remainder is transmitted, as schematically shown in Fig. 11.9.

The sum of absorptivity and reflectivity is then less than unity, and the difference is called the *transmissivity* of the body. With this consideration, we write

$$\alpha_\lambda + \rho_\lambda + \tau_\lambda = 1 \qquad (11\text{-}74)$$

$$\alpha + \rho + \tau = 1 \qquad (11\text{-}75)$$

where we define $\tau_\lambda$ as the *spectral transmissivity or monocromatic transmissivity* and $\tau$ as the *transmissivity*. Glass and many other crystals, unless very thick, are transparent at certain wavelengths. For a spectrally transparent surface, the spectral surface reflectivity is zero and the equation reduces to

$$\alpha_\lambda + \tau_\lambda = 1 \qquad (11\text{-}76)$$

Similarly for a gray surface the total surface reflectivity is zero and the equation reduces to

$$\alpha + \tau = 1 \qquad (11\text{-}77)$$

**EXAMPLE 11-5** The spectral emissivity of an opaque surface at $1000\ K$ is given by

$$\epsilon_1 = 0.1 \qquad \text{for } \lambda_0 = 0 \text{ to } \lambda_1 = 0.5 \text{ } \mu m$$

$$\epsilon_2 = 0.5 \qquad \text{for } \lambda_1 = 0.5 \text{ to } \lambda_2 = 6 \text{ } \mu m$$

$$\epsilon_3 = 0.7 \qquad \text{for } \lambda_2 = 6 \text{ to } \lambda_3 = 15 \text{ } \mu m$$

$$\epsilon_4 = 0.8 \qquad \text{for } \lambda_3 > 15 \text{ } \mu m \ .$$

Determine the average emissivity over the entire range of wavelengths and the radiation flux emitted by the material at $1000 \text{ } K$.

**SOLUTION** The spectral distribution of emissivity is given in stepwise variations. Therefore, we break the integral into parts:

$$
\begin{aligned}
\epsilon \ &= \ \frac{\int_0^\infty \epsilon_\lambda E_{b\lambda}(T) \, d\lambda}{E_b(T)} \\
&= \ \epsilon_1 \frac{\int_0^{\lambda_1} E_{b\lambda}(T) \, d\lambda}{E_b(T)} + \epsilon_2 \frac{\int_{\lambda_1}^{\lambda_2} E_{b\lambda}(T) \, d\lambda}{E_b(T)} + \epsilon_3 \frac{\int_{\lambda_2}^{\lambda_3} E_{b\lambda}(T) \, d\lambda}{E_b(T)} \\
&+ \ \epsilon_4 \frac{\int_{\lambda_3}^\infty E_{b\lambda}(T) \, d\lambda}{E_b(T)} \\
&= \ \epsilon_1 \, f_{0-\lambda_1} + \epsilon_2 \left( f_{0-\lambda_2} - f_{0-\lambda_1} \right) + \epsilon_3 \left( f_{0-\lambda_3} - f_{0-\lambda_2} \right) + \epsilon_4 \left( f_{0-\infty} - f_{0-\lambda_3} \right)
\end{aligned}
$$

where $f_{0-\lambda}$ is given in Table 11.1. We have

$$\lambda_1 = 0.5 \qquad \lambda_1 T = 0.5(1000) = 500 \text{ } \mu m \cdot K \qquad f_{0-\lambda_1} \simeq 0$$

$$\lambda_2 = 6 \qquad \lambda_2 T = 6(1000) = 6000 \text{ } \mu m \cdot K \qquad f_{0-\lambda_2} = 0.73777$$

$$\lambda_3 = 15 \qquad \lambda_3 T = 15(1000) = 15,000 \text{ } \mu m \cdot K \qquad f_{0-\lambda_3} = 0.96892 \ .$$

Then,

$$
\begin{aligned}
\epsilon \ &= \ 0.1 \, (0) + 0.5 \, (0.73777 - 0) + 0.7 \, (0.96892 - 0.73777) + 0.8 \, (1 - 0.96892) \\
&= \ 0.5556 \ .
\end{aligned}
$$

Knowing the average emissivity $\epsilon(T)$, the radiation energy $q(T)$ emitted by the surface per unit area at a temperature $T = 1000 \text{ } K$ is determined as follows:

$$
\begin{aligned}
q(T) \ &= \ \epsilon(T) \, \sigma T^4 \\
&= \ 0.5556 \, (5.67 \times 10^{-8}) \, (1000)^4 \\
&= \ 31,502.5 \text{ W/m}^2 \ .
\end{aligned}
$$

## 11.6. DIFFUSE SURFACE RADIATION HEAT TRANSFER

In the study of radiation heat exchange among surfaces that are separated by a non-participating medium such as a vacuum or air, the orientation and size of the surfaces relative to each other are factors that strongly affect the radiation exchange. To formalize the effects of orientation in the analysis of radiation heat exchange among the surfaces, the concept of *view factor* has been adopted. The terms *shape factor, angle factor*, and *configuration factor* also have been used in the literature.

A distinction should be made between a diffuse view factor and a specular view factor. The former refers to the situation in which the surfaces are diffuse reflectors and diffuse emitters, whereas the latter refers to the situation in which the surfaces are diffuse emitters and specular reflectors. In this book we use the term view factor for the surfaces which are *diffuse emitters* and *diffuse reflectors*. When we have a surface which is a *specular reflector*, we refer to the term *specular view factor*.

The physical significance of the view factor between two surfaces is that it represents the fraction of the radiative energy leaving one surface that strikes the other surface directly. Therefore, the determination of the view factor between two surfaces is merely a geometrical problem.

The reader is referred to the website prepared by Professor John R. Howell at *http://www.me.utex ell* for the catalog of view (configuration) factors.

## 11.6.1 View Factor between Two Elementary Surfaces

The determination of the view factor between two elementary surfaces is a very straightforward matter, and the results are useful in generalizing and determining the view factor between two arbitrary finite surfaces.

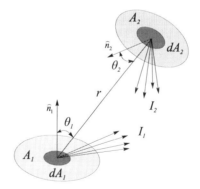

**FIG. 11.10.** Coordinates for the definition of view factor.

Consider two elemental surfaces $dA_1$ and $dA_2$, as illustrated in Fig. 11.10. Let $r$ be the distance between these two surfaces, $\theta_1$ the polar angle between the normal $\hat{n}_1$ to the surface $dA_1$ and the line joining $dA_1$ to $dA_2$, and $\theta_2$ the polar angle between the normal $\hat{n}_2$ to the surface element $dA_2$ and the line $r$.

The right hand side of these equations include the solid angles $d\omega_{12}$ and $d\omega_{21}$. An observer at $dA_1$ sees the surface element $dA_2$ with the solid angle $d\omega_{12}$, and another observer at $dA_2$ sees the surface element $dA_1$ with the solid angle $d\omega_{21}$.

$$d\omega_{12} = \frac{\cos\theta_2\, dA_2}{r^2} \qquad (11\text{-}78)$$

$$d\omega_{21} = \frac{\cos\theta_1\, dA_1}{r^2}. \qquad (11\text{-}79)$$

Let $I_1$ be the intensity of radiation leaving the surface element $dA_1$ diffusely (independent of direction) in all directions, and $I_2$ be the intensity of radiation leaving the surface element $dA_2$ diffusely in all directions. The rate of radiant energy $Q_1$ leaving $dA_1$ over the hemispherical surface is

$$Q_1 = dA_1 \int_{\cap} I_1 \cos\theta_1\, d\omega_1 \qquad (11\text{-}80)$$

where $d\omega_1 = \sin\theta_1\, d\theta_1\, d\phi$. Here, $I_1$ being independent of direction is a constant, and integration gives

$$Q_1 = dA_1 \,\pi I_1 \ . \qquad (11\text{-}81)$$

The rate of radiant energy, $dQ_1$, leaving $dA_1$ over the solid angle $d\omega_{12}$ is

$$dQ_1 = dA_1 \int_{d\omega_{12}} I_1 \cos\theta_1\, d\omega \ . \qquad (11\text{-}82)$$

In addition to $I_1$ being a constant, here we will take $\cos\theta_1$ as approximately constant over the small solid angle $d\omega_{12}$, then

$$dQ_1 = dA_1 I_1 \cos\theta_1\, d\omega_{12} \ . \qquad (11\text{-}83)$$

The *elemental view factor* $dF_{dA_1-dA_2}$, by definition, is the ratio of the radiative energy leaving $dA_1$ that strikes $dA_2$ directly to the radiative energy leaving $dA_1$ in all directions into the hemispherical space. It is given by

$$\boxed{dF_{dA_1-dA_2} = \frac{dQ_1}{Q_1} = \frac{\cos\theta_1\,\cos\theta_2\, dA_2}{\pi r^2}} \ . \qquad (11\text{-}84)$$

Similarly, we define $Q_2$ as the rate of radiant energy leaving $dA_2$ over the hemispherical surface, and $dQ_2$ over the solid angle $d\omega_{21}$ as

$$Q_2 = dA_2\,\pi I_2 \qquad (11\text{-}85)$$

$$dQ_2 = dA_2 I_2 \cos\theta_2\, d\omega_2 \ . \qquad (11\text{-}86)$$

The elemental view factor $dF_{dA_2-dA_1}$ from $dA_2$ to $dA_1$ is now immediately obtained.

$$\boxed{dF_{dA_2-dA_1} = \frac{dQ_2}{Q_2} = \frac{\cos\theta_1\,\cos\theta_2\, dA_1}{\pi r^2}} \qquad (11\text{-}87)$$

The *reciprocity relation* between the view factors $dF_{dA_1-dA_2}$ and $dF_{dA_2-dA_1}$ follows as :

$$\boxed{dA_1 \, dF_{dA_1-dA_2} = dA_2 \, dF_{dA_2-dA_1}} \qquad (11\text{-}88)$$

This relation implies that, for two elemental surfaces $dA_1$ and $dA_2$, if one of the view factors is known, the other can be readily computed by the reciprocity relation.

## 11.7.  VIEW FACTOR BETWEEN TWO FINITE SURFACES

Although developing formal expressions for the view factor between two finite surfaces from the definition of elemental view factors given above is a relatively easy matter, computing the resulting expressions is very difficult except for very simple geometrical arrangements. To illustrate this, we consider the view factor $F_{A_1-A_2}$ from a finite surface $A_1$ to another finite surface $A_2$, as shown in Fig. 11.10. By integrating the elemental view factor $dF_{dA_1-dA_2}$ over the area $A_2$, we obtain the following formal expression for $F_{dA_1-A_2}$

$$F_{dA_1-A_2} = \int_{A_2} \frac{\cos\theta_1 \, \cos\theta_2}{\pi r^2} \, dA_2 \qquad (11\text{-}89\text{a})$$

and integrating again over the area $A_1$ and dividing the resultant expression by $A_1$ we have

$$\boxed{F_{A_1-A_2} = \frac{1}{A_1} \int_{A_1} \int_{A_2} \frac{\cos\theta_1 \, \cos\theta_2}{\pi r^2} \, dA_2 \, dA_1} \qquad (11\text{-}89\text{b})$$

Similarly, the view factor $F_{dA_2-A_1}$ from area $dA_2$ to $A_1$ is obtained as

$$F_{dA_2-A_1} = \int_{A_2} \frac{\cos\theta_1 \, \cos\theta_2}{\pi r^2} \, dA_1 \qquad (11\text{-}90\text{a})$$

and integrating again over the area $A_2$ and dividing the resultant expression by $A_2$ we have

$$\boxed{F_{A_2-A_1} = \frac{1}{A_2} \int_{A_2} \int_{A_1} \frac{\cos\theta_1 \, \cos\theta_2}{\pi r^2} \, dA_1 \, dA_2} \qquad (11\text{-}90\text{b})$$

Then the reciprocity relations between the view factors $F_{dA_1-A_2}$ and $F_{dA_2-A_1}$, $F_{A_1-A_2}$ and $F_{A_2-A_1}$ are obtained as

$$\boxed{\begin{aligned} dA_1 \, F_{dA_1-A_2} &= A_2 \, dF_{A_2-dA_1} \\ A_1 \, F_{A_1-dA_2} &= dA_2 \, F_{dA_2-A_1} \\ A_1 \, F_{A_1-A_2} &= A_2 \, F_{A_2-A_1} \end{aligned}} \qquad (11\text{-}91)$$

The view factor $F_{A_1-A_2}$ represents the fraction of the radiation energy leaving surface $A_1$ diffusely that strikes surface $A_2$ directly. In order to get an insight for the meaning of the view factor $F_{A_1-A_2}$, let's consider the following example. The most common reactor in the Fukushima Number One plant in Japan boasted an electrical power output of $Q_e = 784 MWe$. The thermal power output is found as follows:

$$
\begin{aligned}
Q_r &= \frac{Q_e}{e} \\
&= \frac{784\ MWe}{0.344} \\
&= 2279.1\ MW = 2.28 \times 10^9\ \text{J/s.}
\end{aligned}
$$

With the knowledge that 3.5 percent of the thermal power output is gamma radiation propagating out from the plant is

$$
\begin{aligned}
Q &= Q_r \times 0.035 \\
&= 2279.1\ MW\ 0.035 \\
&= 7.977 \times 10^7\ \text{J/s}
\end{aligned}
$$

of the output energy. The energy per unit area decreases as mankind stays away from the source. Taking the average human surface area $A_2 = 1.73\text{m}^2$. With the normal incident angles $\cos\theta_1 = \cos\theta_2 = \cos 0°$, the view factor which leads us the fraction of energy incident on a man kind is calculated as

$$
\begin{aligned}
F_{A_1-A_2} &= \frac{\cos\theta_1\ \cos\theta_2\ dA_2}{\pi r^2} \\
&= \frac{(\cos 0°)\,(\cos 0°)\,A_2}{\pi r^2} \\
&= \frac{1.378 \times 10^{-4}}{\pi r^2}.
\end{aligned}
$$

This expression concludes that mankind at a distance $r$ is exposed to

$$
\begin{aligned}
Q_{man} &= 7.977 \times 10^7 \times \frac{1.378 \times 10^{-4}}{\pi r^2} \\
&= \frac{11 \times 10^3}{\pi r^2}\ J/s.
\end{aligned}
$$

Therefore living within 500 km of an unshielded nuclear reactor may result in minor radiation sickness, while living within 100 km can kill an individual outright if not treated.

## 11.8. PROPERTIES OF VIEW FACTORS

The evaluation of the double surface integrals that appear in the resulting formal expressions is extremely difficult. We consider an *enclosure* consisting of $N$ zones, each of surface area $A_i$ $(i = 1, 2, \ldots, N)$, as illustrated in Fig. 11.11. It is assumed that each

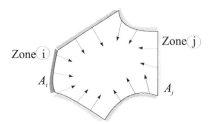

**FIG. 11.11.** An N-zone enclosure.

zone is isothermal, a diffuse emitter, and a diffuse reflector. The surface of each zone may be plane, convex or concave. The view factors between surfaces $A_i$ and $A_j$ of the enclosure obey the following reciprocity relation:

$$A_i \, F_{A_i - A_j} = A_j \, F_{A_j - A_i} \, . \qquad (11\text{-}92)$$

The view factors from one surface, say $A_i$, of the enclosure to all surfaces of the enclosure, including itself, when summed, should be equal to unity by the definition of the view factor. This is called the *summation relation* among the view factors for an enclosure, and it is written as

$$\sum_{k=1}^{N} F_{A_i - A_k} = 1 \qquad (11\text{-}93)$$

where $N$ is the number of zones in the enclosure. In this summation the term $F_{A_i - A_i}$ is the view factor from the surface $A_i$ to itself; it represents the fraction of radiative energy leaving the surface $A_i$ that strikes itself directly. Clearly, $F_{A_i - A_i}$ vanishes if $A_i$ is flat or convex, and it is nonzero if $A_i$ is concave; this is stated as

$$\begin{aligned} F_{A_i - A_i} &= 0 & \text{if } A_i \text{ plane or convex} \\ F_{A_i - A_i} &\neq 0 & \text{if } A_i \text{ concave} \end{aligned} \, .$$

**EXAMPLE 11-6**  Two small surfaces $dA_1 = 5 \, \text{cm}^2$ and $dA_2 = 10 \, \text{cm}^2$ are separated by $r = 100 \, \text{cm}$ and oriented as illustrated in the accompanying figure. Calculate the view factors between the surfaces.

**SOLUTION**  Both surfaces can be approximated as differential surfaces because $dA_i/r^2 \ll 1$.

$$\begin{aligned} dF_{dA_1 - dA_2} &= \frac{\cos\theta_1 \, \cos\theta_2 \, dA_2}{\pi r^2} \\ &= \frac{(\cos 60°) \, (\cos 30°) \, (10)}{\pi (100)^2} = 1.378 \times 10^{-4} \end{aligned}$$

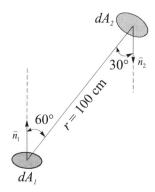

**FIGURE EXAMPLE 11-6**

By the reciprocity relation, we write

$$dF_{dA_2-dA_1} = \frac{dA_1}{dA_2} dF_{dA_1-dA_2}$$

$$= \frac{5}{10}\left(1.378 \times 10^{-4}\right) = 6.89 \times 10^{-5} .$$

**EXAMPLE 11-7**  The view factor $F_{1-3}$ between the base and the top surface of the cylinder shown in the accompanying figure can be obtained from the charts. Develop a relation for the view factors $F_{1-2}$ and $F_{2-1}$ between the base and the lateral cylindrical surface in terms of $F_{1-3}$.

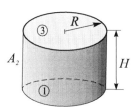

**FIGURE EXAMPLE 11-7**

**SOLUTION**  From the summation rule,

$$F_{1-1} + F_{1-2} + F_{1-3} = 1 .$$

Since $F_{1-1} = 0$, we have

$$F_{1-2} = 1 - F_{1-3} .$$

From the reciprocity relation, Eqn. (11-87),

$$A_1\, F_{1-2} = A_2\, F_{2-1} .$$

Therefore,

$$F_{2-1} = \frac{A_1}{A_2} F_{1-2} = \frac{R}{2H} F_{1-2} \ .$$

## 11.9. VIEW-FACTOR DETERMINATION

### 11.9.1 Evaluation of View Factors

Radiation view factors can be determined by :

1. Analytical or numerical integration, either by area integration or by contour integration;

2. Statistical determination, i.e. by using the Monte Carlo Method;

3. Some special cases, i.e. by using view factor algebra, the cross-string method, the inside sphere method, or the unit sphere method.

Many of the early catalogs and references that presented common configuration factors were out of print or difficult to obtain, and particular factors were scattered throughout the technical literature dealing with basic thermal radiative transfer and the engineering design of lighting systems. Many of the most useful published factors are gathered into a single source at "http://www.me.utexas.edu/ howell/tablecon.html" by Howell.

### 11.9.2 Area Integration

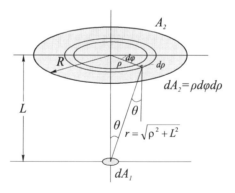

**FIG. 11.12.** Area integration

The terms in the integrand are written in terms of a fixed coordinate system. Here one such area integration will be given for the view factor between a differential area $dA_1$ and a parallel circular disc $A_2$ which are at a distance $L$, as shown in Fig. 11.12. The view factor $F_{dA_1-A_2}$ is

$$F_{dA_1-A_2} = \int_{A_2} \frac{\cos \theta_1 \cos \theta_2}{\pi r^2} \ dA_2 \ . \tag{11-94}$$

From the geometry, the elemental area $dA_2$ is expressed in the $\rho$ and $\phi$ coordinates as

$$dA_2 = \rho\, d\phi\, d\rho \; , \tag{11-95}$$

where $\phi$ is the azimuthal angle. The distance $r$ between the elemental surfaces $dA_1$ and $dA_2$ is given by

$$r^2 = \rho^2 + L^2 \tag{11-96}$$

with

$$\cos\theta_1 = \cos\theta_2 = \cos\theta = \frac{L}{r} = \frac{L}{(\rho^2 + L^2)^{1/2}} \; . \tag{11-97}$$

Substituting the above expressions for $dA_2$, $r$, and $\theta$ into the above definition of view factor and integrating, we obtain the view factor

$$
\begin{aligned}
F_{dA_1 - A_2} &= \frac{1}{\pi} \int_{\rho=0}^{R} \int_{\phi=0}^{2\pi} \frac{L^2}{(\rho^2 + L^2)^2}\, \rho\, d\rho\, d\phi \tag{11-98}\\
&= 2 \int_{\rho=0}^{R} \frac{L^2}{(\rho^2 + L^2)^2}\, \rho\, d\rho = \frac{R^2}{R^2 + L^2} \; .
\end{aligned}
$$

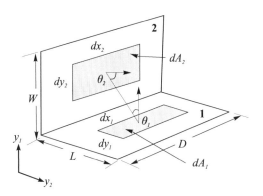

**FIG. 11.13.** Area integration.

Another example is shown in Fig. 11.13 which consists of two adjacent plane walls at right angles to each other. By referring to the geometry, the distance between a line connecting a differential element $dA_1$ on $A_1$ to another element $dA_2$ on $A_2$ we obtain,

$$r = \sqrt{y_2^2 + (y_1^2 + (x_1 - x_2)^2)} \tag{11-99}$$

and the angles $\theta_1$ and $\theta_2$ are given by

$$\cos\theta_1 = \frac{y_1}{r} \; , \qquad \cos\theta_2 = \frac{y_2}{r} \; , \tag{11-100}$$

with $dA_1 = dx_1\, dy_1$ and $dA_2 = dx_2\, dy_2$ . Substituting the above expressions for $r$,

$\theta_1$, and $\theta_2$ into the definition of view factor,

$$F_{12} = \frac{1}{DL} \int_0^L \int_0^D \int_0^W \int_0^D \frac{y_2\, y_1\, dx_1\, dx_2\, dy_1\, dy_2}{\pi \left[ y_2^2 + y_1^2 + (x_1 - x_2) \right]^2} \ . \tag{11-101}$$

## 11.9.3 Contour Integration

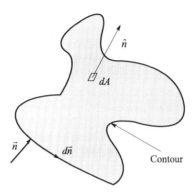

**FIG. 11.14.** Contour integration.

According to Stokes' theorem, a surface integration may be converted to an equivalent contour integral as

$$\oint_C \vec{f} \cdot d\vec{r} = \int_A (\vec{\nabla} \times \vec{f}) \cdot \hat{n}\, dA \ , \tag{11-102}$$

where $f$ is a vector function defined everywhere on the surface $A$, including its boundary $C$, $\hat{n}$ is the unit surface normal vector, $\vec{r}$ is the boundary position vector, and $d\vec{r}$ is the vector describing the boundary contour, as shown in Fig. 11.14. The view factor from differential area $dA_1$ to a finite area $A_2$

$$F_{dA_1 - A_2} = \int_{A_2} \frac{\cos \theta_1 \cos \theta_2}{\pi r^2}\, dA_2 \tag{11-103}$$

can be written in vector form as

$$F_{dA_1 - A_2} = \frac{1}{2\pi} \int_{C_2} \frac{(\vec{r}_{12} \times \vec{n}_1) \cdot \vec{ds}_2}{r^2} \tag{11-104}$$

with

$$\vec{f} = \frac{1}{2\pi} \frac{\vec{r}_{12} \times \vec{n}_1}{r^2} \tag{11-105}$$

where $\vec{r}_{12}$ is the vector pointing from $dA_1$ to a point on the contour of $A_2$ designated by $C_2$ and $dr_2$ and points along the contour of $A_2$.

**EXERCISE :** Prove that these are identical.

**Hint** :  Use the vector identity

$$\vec{\nabla} \times (\phi \vec{a}) \; = \; \phi \, \vec{\nabla} \times \vec{a} - \vec{a} \times \vec{\nabla} \phi \; . \tag{11-106}$$

In a Cartesian coordinate system with

$$d\vec{r}_2 \; = \; dx_2 \, i + dy_2 \, j + dz_2 \, h \tag{11-107}$$

$$F_{dA_1-A_2} \; = \; \frac{\ell_1}{2\pi} \int_{c_2} \frac{(z_2 - z_1) \, dy_2 - (y_2 - y_1) \, dz_2}{r^2} \tag{11-108}$$

$$+ \; \frac{m_1}{2\pi} \int_{c_2} \frac{(x_2 - x_1) \, dz_2 - (y_2 - y_1) \, dx_2}{r^2}$$

$$+ \; \frac{n_1}{2\pi} \int_{c_2} \frac{(y_2 - y_1) \, dx_2 - (x_2 - x_1) \, dy_2}{r^2}$$

where  $\ell_1$ ,  $m_1$  and  $n_1$  are direction cosines of the normal unit vector  $\hat{n}$ .

$$\hat{n} \; = \; \ell \, \hat{i} + m \hat{j} + n \hat{k} \tag{11-109}$$

Recall :

$$\cos \theta_i \; = \; \left. \frac{\hat{n}_i \cdot \vec{r}_{ij}}{r} \right| \, , \qquad |\vec{r}_{ij}| \; = \; r$$

$$\cos \theta_j \; = \; \left. \frac{\hat{n}_j \cdot \vec{r}_{ij}}{r} \right| \; r = \; |\vec{r}_{12}| \; = \; (x_2 - x_1)^2 + (y_2 - y_1)^2 + (z_2 - z_1)^2 \; . \tag{11-110}$$

$$\vec{r}_j - \vec{r}_i \; = \; \vec{r}_{ij} \tag{11-111}$$

## 11.9.4 Graphical Form of the View Factors

The computation of the elemental view factors poses no problem, but the calculation of the view factor between two finite surfaces is very difficult. Considerable effort has been devoted in the literature to the computation of view factors between surfaces, and the results are well documented. In Figs. 11.15 to 11.18 we present in graphical form some of the view factors for simple configurations.

## 11.9.5 View Factor Algebra

The standard view-factor charts are available for only a limited number of simple configurations. However, it may be possible to split up the configuration of a complicated geometric arrangement into a number of simple configurations in such a manner that the view factors can be determined from the standard view-factor charts. Then it may be possible to determine the view factor for the original, complicated configuration by the

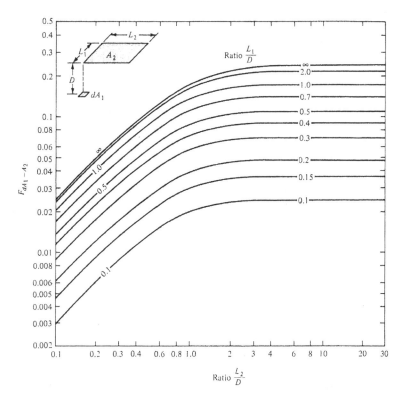

**FIG. 11.15.** View factor $F_{dA_1-A_2}$ from an element surface $dA_1$ to a rectangular surface $A_2$. From Mackey, Wright, Clark, and Gray, (1943).

algebraic sum of the view factors for the separate, simpler configurations. Such an approach is known as *view-factor algebra*. It provides a powerful method for determining the view factors for many complicated configurations.

No standard set of rules can be stated for this method, but appropriate use of the reciprocity relations and the summation rules is the key to the success of this technique.

To illustrate how the summation rule and the reciprocity relation can be applied, we consider the view factor from an area $A_1$ to an area $A_2$, which is divided into two areas, $A_3$ and $A_4$:

$$A_2 = A_3 + A_4 \ . \tag{11-112}$$

Figure 11.19 shows the surfaces and their subdivision. Then the view factor from $A_1$ to $A_2$ can be written as

$$F_{1-2} = F_{1-3} + F_{1-4} \tag{11-113}$$

which is consistent with the definition of the view factor. That is, the fraction of the total energy leaving $A_1$ that strikes $A_3$ and $A_4$ is equal to the fraction that strikes $A_2$.

Additional relationships among these view factors can be obtained. For example, sup-

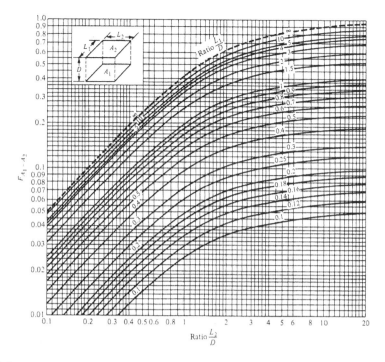

**FIG. 11.16.** View factor $F_{A_1-A_2}$ from a rectangular surface $A_1$ to a rectangular surface $A_2$ which are adjacent and in perpendicular planes. From Mackey, Wright, Clark, and Gray, (1943).

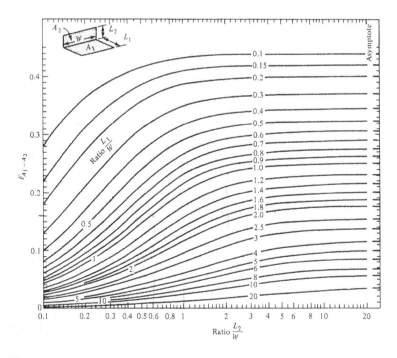

**FIG. 11.17.** View factor $F_{A_1-A_2}$ from an rectangular surface $A_1$ to a rectangular surface $A_2$ which are parallel to and directly opposite each other. From Mackey, Wright, Clark, and Gray, (1943).

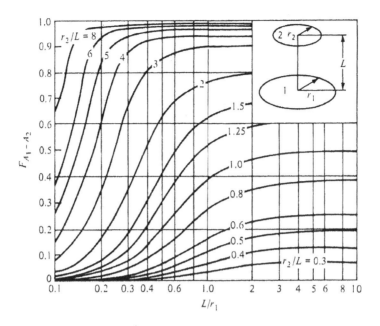

**FIG. 11.18.** View factor $F_{A_1-A_2}$ between two coaxial parallel disks. (From C.O. Mackey, L.T. Wright, R.E. Clark, and N.R. Gray, 1943)

pose both sides of the above equation are multiplied by $A_1$:

$$A_1 F_{1-2} = A_1 F_{1-3} + A_1 F_{1-4} .$$ (11-114)

Then the reciprocity relation is applied to each term:

$$A_2 F_{2-1} = A_3 F_{3-1} + A_4 F_{4-1}$$ (11-115)

or

$$F_{2-1} = \frac{A_3 F_{3-1} + A_4 F_{4-1}}{A_2} = \frac{A_3 F_{3-1} + A_4 F_{4-1}}{A_3 + A_4} .$$ (11-116)

Suppose the area $A_2$ is divided into more parts:

$$A_2 = A_3 + A_4 + \cdots + A_N .$$ (11-117)

Then,

$$F_{2-1} = \frac{A_3 F_{3-1} + A_4 F_{4-1} + \cdots + A_N F_{N-1}}{A_3 + A_4 + \cdots + A_N} .$$ (11-118)

Similarly, other relations among the view factors can be obtained.

**EXAMPLE 11-8**  Determine the view factor $F_{1-2}$ between an elemental surface $dA_1$

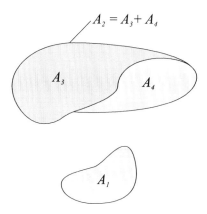

**FIG. 11.19.** View factor algebra.

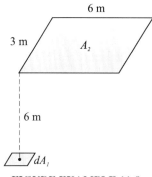

**FIGURE EXAMPLE 11-8**

and the finite rectangular surface $A_2$ for the geometric arrangements shown in the accompanying figure.

**SOLUTION**  Given $L_1 = 3\,m$, $L_2 = 6\,m$, and $D = 6\,m$, we have

$$\frac{L_1}{D} = \frac{3}{6} = 0.5$$

$$\frac{L_2}{D} = \frac{6}{6} = 1 \ .$$

Then we read the view factor $F_{dA_1-A_2}$ from Fig. 11.15 as

$$F_{1-2} = 0.09 \ .$$

**EXAMPLE 11-9**  Determine the view factors $F_{4-2}$ and $F_{3-2}$ between two rectangular surfaces for the geometric arrangement shown in the accompanying figure.

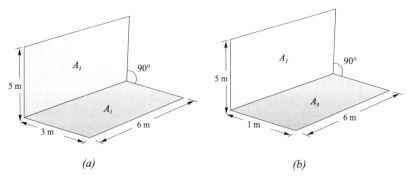

*(a)*                                           *(b)*

**FIGURE EXAMPLE 11-9**

**SOLUTION**   **(a)** Given $L_1 = 3\,m$, $L_2 = 5\,m$, and $W = 5\,m$, we have

$$\frac{L_1}{W} = \frac{3}{6} = 0.5$$

$$\frac{L_2}{W} = \frac{5}{6} = 0.833 \ .$$

Then we read the view factor $F_{A_1 - A_2}$ from Fig. 11.17 as

$$F_{4-2} = 0.285 \ .$$

**(b)** Given $L_1 = 1\,m$, $L_2 = 5\,m$, and $W = 6\,m$, we have

$$\frac{L_1}{W} = \frac{1}{6} = 0.167$$

$$\frac{L_2}{W} = \frac{5}{6} = 0.833 \ .$$

Then we read the view factor $F_{A_1 - A_2}$ from Fig. 11.17 as

$$F_{3-2} = 0.4 \ .$$

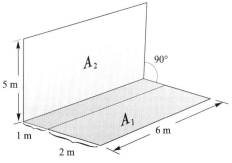

**FIGURE EXAMPLE 11-10**

**EXAMPLE 11-10** Determine the view factor $F_{1-2}$ between two rectangular surfaces $A_1$ and $A_2$ for the geometric arrangement shown in the accompanying figure (Fig. Ex. 11-10).

**SOLUTION** We split up this arrangement into the parts similar to those considered in Example 11-9. Then the view factors for the split-up arrangements are available in Fig. 11.12. From the laws of view-factor algebra applied to this configuration, we write

$$A_4 F_{4-2} = A_1 F_{1-2} + A_3 F_{3-2}$$

$$(3 \times 6)(0.285) = (2 \times 6) F_{1-2} + (1 \times 6)(0.4) .$$

Therefore,

$$F_{1-2} = 0.2275 .$$

### 11.9.6 Crossed-String Method

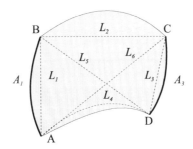

**FIG. 11.20.** Determination of view factor between the surfaces $A_1$ and $A_3$ of a long enclosure.

Consider an enclosure, as shown in Fig. 11.20, consisting of four surfaces that are very long in the direction perpendicular to the plane of the figure (two-dimensional). The surfaces can be flat, convex, or concave. Suppose we wish to find the view factor $F_{1-3}$ between surfaces $A_1$ and $A_3$. We assume that imaginary strings, shown by dashed lines, are tightly stretched among the four corners $A$, $B$, $C$, and $D$ of the enclosure. Let $L_i\,(i = 1, 2, 3, 4, 5, 6)$ denote the lengths of the strings joining the corners, as illustrated in the figure. Hottel has shown that the view factor $F_{1-3}$ can be expressed as

$$\boxed{L_1 F_{1-3} = \frac{(L_5 + L_6) - (L_2 + L_4)}{2}} . \qquad (11\text{-}119)$$

Here we note that the term $L_5 + L_6$ is the sum of the lengths of the *cross strings*, and $L_2 + L_4$ the sum of the lengths of the uncrossed strings. This equation is useful for determining the view factor between the surfaces of a long enclosure, such as a groove, which can be characterized in two-dimensional geometric form as shown in the figure.

**EXAMPLE 11-11** An infinitely long semi-cylindrical surface $A_1$ of radius $b$ and an infinitely long plate $A_3$ of half-width $c$ are located a distance $d$ apart, as illustrated in the accompanying figure. Determine the view factor $F_{1-3}$ between surfaces $A_1$ and $A_3$.

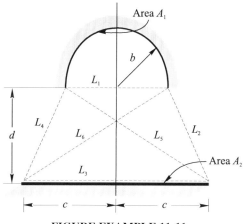

**FIGURE EXAMPLE 11-11**

**SOLUTION**   The dashed lines in the figure are the imaginary strings. The view factor $F_{1-3}$ between surfaces $A_1$ and $A_3$ is given by Eq. (11-~~120~~). Because of the symmetry, we have $L_5 = L_6$ and $L_2 = L_4$ ;   therefore   $119$

$$F_{1-3} = \frac{L_6 - L_4}{L_1}$$

and from the geometry we have

$$L_6 = [(c + b)^2 + d^2]^{1/2}$$
$$L_4 = [(c - b)^2 + d^2]^{1/2}$$
$$L_1 = 2b .$$

Substituting the expressions for $L_6$, $L_4$, and $L_1$ into the above expression, the view factor $F_{1-3}$ is determined as

$$F_{1-3} = \frac{[(c + b)^2 + d^2]^{1/2} - [(c - b)^2 + d^2]^{1/2}}{2b} .$$

### 11.9.7 Inside Sphere Method

The inside sphere method is used with view factor algebra. Consider two surfaces, $A_1$ and $A_2$ which are parts of a sphere as illustrated in Fig. 11.21.

From the geometry we have

$$\theta_1 = \theta_2 = \theta \quad \text{and} \quad S = 2R \cos \theta . \tag{11-120}$$

Therefore,

$$F_{d1-2} = \int_{A_2} \frac{\cos\theta_1 \cos\theta_2}{\pi S^2} \, dA_2 \qquad (11\text{-}121)$$

$$= \int_{A_2} \frac{\cos^2\theta}{\pi (2R\cos\theta)^2} \, dA_2$$

$$= \frac{1}{4\pi R^2} \int_{A_2} dA_2$$

$$= \frac{A_2}{4\pi R^2}$$

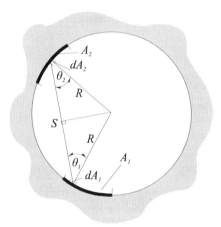

**FIG. 11.21.** Inside Sphere Method

where $4\pi R^2 = A_S$ , the surface area of the sphere. Therefore,

$$F_{d1-2} = \frac{A_2}{A_S} \ . \qquad (11\text{-}122)$$

We see that $F_{d1-2}$ does not depend on the position of $dA_1$ . In fact, within this geometry, the view factor depends on the size of the receiving surface — not on the location of either one. Therefore,

$$F_{1-2} = F_{d1-2} = \frac{A_2}{A_S} \ . \qquad (11\text{-}123)$$

## 11.10. RADIATION EXCHANGE IN AN ENCLOSURE

The analysis of radiation exchange among the surfaces of an enclosure is complicated by the fact that when the surfaces are not black, radiation leaving a surface may be reflected

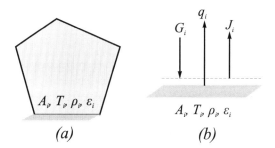

**FIG. 11.22.** (a) An enclosure filled with a non-participating medium; (b) an energy balance per unit area of zone $i$.

back and forth among the surfaces several times, with partial absorption occurring at each reflection. Therefore, a proper analysis of the problem must include the effects of these multiple reflections. To simplify the analysis, we assume that a given enclosure can be divided into several zones, as illustrated in Fig. 11.22, in such a manner that the following conditions are assumed to hold for each of the zones $i = 1, 2, \ldots, N$:

1. Radiative properties (i.e., reflectivity, emissivity, and absorptivity) are uniform and independent of direction and frequency.

2. The surfaces are diffuse emitters and diffuse reflectors.

3. The radiative heat flux leaving the surface is uniform over the surface of each zone.

4. The irradiation is uniform over the surface of each zone.

5. Surfaces are opaque (that is, $\alpha + \rho = 1$).

6. Either a uniform temperature or a uniform heat flux is prescribed over the surface of each zone.

7. The enclosure is filled with a non-participating medium. Assumptions 3 and 4 are generally not correct, but the analysis becomes very complicated without them.

8. No external irradiation to the surfaces.

The objective of the analysis of radiation heat exchange in an enclosure is the *determination of net radiation heat flux* at the zones for which the temperature is prescribed. Conversely, the temperature can be determined at the zones for which the net heat flux is prescribed.

## 11.10.1 Radiosity Concept

We focus our attention on any one of the zones of the enclosure, say zone $i$. By Assumption 3, the radiation energy leaving the surface is assumed to be uniform. We introduce the concept of *radiosity* $J_i$ at zone $i$ to represent the radiation energy leaving this surface per unit area – per unit time, as viewed by an observer immediately above the surface of zone $i$. Figure 11.22 illustrates this hypothetical location symbolically by the dashed line. From physical considerations, we conclude that the radiosity $J_i$ is composed of two components:

$$J_i = \begin{pmatrix} \text{radiation} \\ \text{emitted by} \\ \text{surface } A_i \\ \text{per unit area} \end{pmatrix} + \begin{pmatrix} \text{radiation} \\ \text{reflected by} \\ \text{surface } A_i \\ \text{per unit area} \end{pmatrix} \; \text{W/m}^2 . \qquad (11\text{-}124)$$

Each of these two components is now evaluated.

$$\begin{pmatrix} \text{Radiation emitted} \\ \text{by surface } A_i \text{ per} \\ \text{unit area} \end{pmatrix} = \epsilon_i E_{bi} , \qquad (11\text{-}125)$$

where $\epsilon_i$ is the emissivity and $E_{bi} = \sigma T_i^4$ is the blackbody emissive power at temperature $T_i$ of the zone $A_i$.

$$\begin{pmatrix} \text{Radiation reflected} \\ \text{by surface } A_i \text{ per} \\ \text{unit area} \end{pmatrix} = \rho_i G_i = (1 - \epsilon_i) G_i , \qquad (11\text{-}126)$$

where $G_i$ is the *irradiation* or the radiation flux incident on the surface of zone $i$, in watts per square meter, which is considered uniform over the zone by Assumption 4. In addition, we assumed an opaque surface and set $\rho_i = 1 - \epsilon_i$. By combining the foregoing equations, we obtain the following expression for the radiosity:

$$J_i = \epsilon_i E_{bi} + (1 - \epsilon_i) G_i \quad \text{W/m}^2 , \qquad (11\text{-}127)$$

and solving for $G_i$, we have

$$G_i = \frac{J_i - \epsilon_i E_{bi}}{1 - \epsilon_i} \quad \text{W/m}^2 . \qquad (11\text{-}128)$$

This expression is needed in the relations that are now developed.

## 11.11. NETWORK METHOD FOR RADIATION EXCHANGE IN AN ENCLOSURE

In this section we study the network method for radiation exchange in an enclosure with diffuse surfaces. The problems involving spectacular surfaces are not covered. Before presenting the electric network method, we introduce the concepts leading to the definition of various radiation resistances in the path of the heat flow.

## 11.11.1 Radiation Resistance at a Surface

When a surface is not black, and hence has an emissivity $\epsilon < 1$, the radiation heat transfer at the surface can be presented in a form that represents the *radiation resistance* at the surface as described below.

Let $q_i$ be the net radiation heat flux, in watts per square meter, leaving the surface at zone $i$. By referring to the illustration in Fig. 11.22b, we conclude that $q_i$ is equal to the difference between $J_i$ and $G_i$, and write

$$q_i = J_i - G_i \quad \text{W/m}^2 \ . \tag{11-129}$$

We substitute for $G_i$ to eliminate it:

$$\boxed{q_i = \frac{\epsilon_i}{1 - \epsilon_i}\,(E_{bi} - J_i)} \quad \text{W/m}^2 \ . \tag{11-130}$$

The total net radiation heat flow $Q_i$ leaving surface $A_i$ becomes

$$Q_i = A_i\,q_i = A_i\,\frac{\epsilon_i}{1 - \epsilon_i}\,(E_{bi} - J_i) \tag{11-131}$$

which is rearranged as

$$\boxed{Q_i = \frac{E_{bi} - J_i}{R_i}} \quad \text{W} \tag{11-132}$$

where

$$\boxed{R_i = \frac{1 - \epsilon_i}{A_i\,\epsilon_i}} \ . \tag{11-133}$$

Analogous to Ohm's law, where $R_i$ represents the surface resistance to radiation, and analogous to the concept of *thermal resistance* (or the skin resistance), which we discussed in connection with convective heat transfer over a surface. That is, the total heat transfer rate is equal to the potential difference across the surface divided by the thermal resistance to heat flow over the surface.

When the surface is *black*, we have $\epsilon_i = 1$, which implies that $R_i = 0$. Then, we have

$$\boxed{J_i = E_{bi} = \sigma T_i^4} \quad \text{for } \epsilon_i = 1 \text{ or black surface.} \tag{11-134}$$

Thus, for a black surface, the radiosity is equal to the blackbody emissive power of the surface. Figure 11.23 illustrates the concept of surface thermal resistance to radiation between the potentials $E_{bi}$ and $J_i$. When the net radiation heat flow $Q_i$ at the surface $A_i$ vanishes, the zone $A_i$ is called a *reradiating* or *adiabatic zone*. For such a case, we set $Q_i$ equal to zero and obtain

$$E_{bi} = J_i \ . \tag{11-135}$$

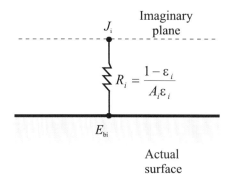

**FIG. 11.23.** Surface resistance to radiation.

This result implies that at a reradiating or adiabatic zone, the radiosity $J_i$ is equal to $E_{bi} = \sigma T_i^4$, and that the emissivity $\epsilon_i$ does not enter the analysis.

### 11.11.2 Radiation Resistance across Two Surfaces

The radiation resistance concept can also be developed for radiation exchange across two surfaces. Figure 11.24 illustrates two surfaces $A_i$ and $A_j$ having emissivities $\epsilon_i$ and $\epsilon_j$, and maintained at uniform but different temperatures $T_i$ and $T_j$, respectively. Let $Q_{i-j}$ denote the net radiation heat transfer from zone $i$ to zone $j$. Then the energy balance for radiation heat exchange between the two zones can be stated as

$$Q_{i-j} = \left( \begin{array}{l} \text{radiation energy} \\ \text{leaving } A_i \text{ that} \\ \text{strikes } A_j \end{array} \right) - \left( \begin{array}{l} \text{radiation energy} \\ \text{leaving } A_j \text{ that} \\ \text{strikes } A_i \end{array} \right) . \qquad (11\text{-}136)$$

To evaluate the two terms on the right-hand side of this equation, we consider $J_i$ and $J_j$, the *radiosities* at the surfaces of zone $i$ and zone $j$, respectively, and the view factors $F_{i-j}$ and $F_{j-i}$ between the two zones. Then, the mathematical expressions for each term on the right-hand side are written as

$$Q_{i-j} = J_i A_i F_{i-j} - J_j A_j F_{j-i} . \qquad (11\text{-}137)$$

We utilize the reciprocity relation $A_i F_{i-j} = A_j F_{j-i}$ between the view factors and rewrite this equation as

$$Q_{i-j} = J_i A_i F_{i-j} - J_j A_i F_{i-j} = A_i F_{i-j}(J_i - J_j) . \qquad (11\text{-}138)$$

Re-arranging it in the form

$$Q_{i-j} = \frac{J_i - J_j}{R_{i-j}} \qquad (11\text{-}139)$$

where

$$R_{i-j} = \frac{1}{A_i F_{i-j}} \quad .$$

(11-140)

Analogous to Ohm's law, $R_{i-j} = 1/A_i F_{i-j}$ represents the *radiation resistance* to heat flow across the fictitious potentials $J_i$ and $J_j$, which are considered to exist just above the surfaces $A_i$ and $A_j$, respectively.

### 11.11.3 Radiation Network for Two Surfaces

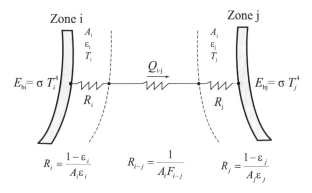

**FIG. 11.24.** Various resistances to radiation in the path of heat flow between surfaces $A_i$ and $A_j$.

Having established the necessary framework by defining various thermal resistances to radiation in the path of heat flow, we are now in a position to construct an analogous *electrical network* for radiation exchange between two surfaces.

Figure 11.24 illustrates various resistances to radiation in the path of heat flow $Q_{i-j}$ by radiation from zone $i$ to the zone $j$. The surface resistances to radiation for surfaces $A_i$ and $A_j$ are given, respectively, by

$$R_i = \frac{1 - \epsilon_i}{A_i \, \epsilon_i} \quad \text{and} \quad R_j = \frac{1 - \epsilon_j}{A_j \, \epsilon_j} \quad ,$$

(11-141)

and the resistance across the fictitious surfaces is given by

$$R_{i-j} = \frac{1}{A_i F_{i-j}} \quad .$$

(11-142)

Then the total heat flow $Q_{i-j}$ from zone $i$ to zone $j$ across the potential difference $E_{bi} - E_{bj}$ is determined by Ohm's law as

$$Q_{i-j} = \frac{E_{bi} - E_{bj}}{R_i + R_{i-j} + R_j} = \frac{\sigma \, (T_i^4 - T_j^4)}{R_i + R_{i-j} + R_j} \quad .$$

(11-143)

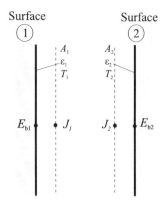

**FIG. 11.25.** Radiation transfer between two large, opaque parallel plates.

## 11.11.4 Radiation Transfer between Two Parallel Plates

Consider an enclosure consisting of two large, parallel, opaque plates, as illustrated in Fig. 11.25. Surfaces 1 and 2 are kept at uniform temperatures $T_1$ and $T_2$, and have emissivities $\epsilon_1$ and $\epsilon_2$, respectively. The configuration shown in this figure is a special case of that considered in Fig. 11.24. Therefore, we write the total heat flow $Q_{1-2}$ as

$$Q_{1-2} = \frac{\sigma\,(T_1^4 - T_2^4)}{R_1 + R_{1-2} + R_2}\ , \tag{11-144}$$

where

$$R_1 = \frac{1 - \epsilon_1}{A\epsilon_1} \qquad R_{1-2} = \frac{1}{AF_{1-2}} \qquad R_2 = \frac{1 - \epsilon_2}{A\epsilon_2}\ . \tag{11-145}$$

For two large parallel plates, $F_{1-2} = 1$, we will have

$$q_{1-2} \equiv \frac{Q_{1-2}}{A} = \frac{\sigma\,(T_1^4 - T_2^4)}{1/\epsilon_1 + 1/\epsilon_2 - 1}\quad \text{W/m}^2\ . \tag{11-146}$$

## 11.11.5 Radiation Exchange in Three or More Zone Enclosures

The radiation network approach described above can readily be generalized to determine radiation exchange among the surfaces of a three or more zone enclosure. That is, the radiation resistance at surface $A_i$ is given by

$$R_i = \frac{1 - \epsilon_i}{A_i\,\epsilon_i} \tag{11-147}$$

and the radiation resistance across the fictitious surfaces above $A_i$ and $A_j$ is given by

$$R_{i-j} = \frac{1}{A_i\,F_{i-j}} = \frac{1}{A_j\,F_{j-i}}\ . \tag{11-148}$$

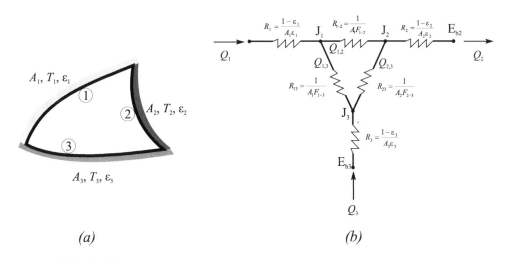

**FIG. 11.26.** (a) A three-zone enclosure; (b) the corresponding radiation network.

To illustrate the application, we consider a three-zone enclosure, as shown in Fig. 11.26. Zones 1, 2, and 3 have surface areas $A_1$, $A_2$, and $A_3$, emissivities $\epsilon_1$, $\epsilon_2$, and $\epsilon_3$, and temperatures $T_1$, $T_2$, and $T_3$, respectively. Figure 11.26b shows the corresponding radiation network. To solve this problem, the algebraic sum of the currents at the nodes $J_1$, $J_2$ and $J_3$ is set equal to zero. This leads to three algebraic equations for the determination of three unknown radiosities, $J_1$, $J_2$ and $J_3$. Knowing the radiosities, the heat flow rates $Q_1$, $Q_2$, and $Q_3$ at each zone are determined by the application of Ohm's law as

$$Q_1 = \frac{\sigma T_1^4 - J_1}{R_1} \quad \text{where} \quad R_1 = \frac{1 - \epsilon_1}{A_1 \epsilon_1} \tag{11-149}$$

$$Q_2 = \frac{\sigma T_2^4 - J_2}{R_2} \quad \text{where} \quad R_2 = \frac{1 - \epsilon_2}{A_2 \epsilon_2} \tag{11-150}$$

and

$$Q_3 = \frac{\sigma T_3^4 - J_3}{R_3} \quad \text{where} \quad R_3 = \frac{1 - \epsilon_3}{A_3 \epsilon_3} . \tag{11-151}$$

**EXAMPLE 11-12**  Consider an enclosure consisting of two parallel, opaque large plates, as illustrated in Fig. 11.25. Calculate the net radiation flux $q_{1-2}$ leaving Plate 1 for $T_1 = 1000\,K$, $T_2 = 500\,K$, $\epsilon_1 = 0.6$, and $\epsilon_2 = 0.8$.

**SOLUTION**  The net radiation flux $q_{1-2}$ in this two-zone enclosure is

$$q_{1-2} = \frac{\sigma(T_1^4 - T_2^4)}{1/\epsilon_1 + 1/\epsilon_2 - 1} \quad \text{W/m}^2 .$$

Therefore, for the specified problem, $q_{1-2}$ becomes

$$q_{1-2} = \frac{(5.67 \times 10^{-8})(1000^4 - 500^4)}{1/0.6 + 1/0.8 - 1} = 27,733.7 \text{ W/m}^2 \ .$$

**EXAMPLE 11-13** Two black rectangular surfaces $A_1$ and $A_2$, arranged as shown in the accompanying figure, are located in a large room whose walls are black and kept at $300\ K$. Determine the net radiative-heat exchange between these two surfaces when $A_1$ is kept at $1000\ K$ and $A_2$ at $500\ K$. Neglect the radiation from the room.

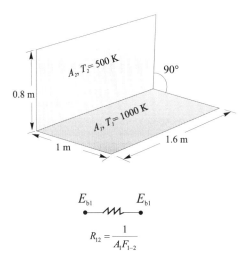

**FIGURE EXAMPLE 11-13**

**SOLUTION** Given: $L_1 = 1\,m$, $L_2 = 0.8\ m$, and $W = 1.6\,m$. The view factor $F_{1-2}$ is obtained from Fig. 11.16 as

$$\frac{L_1}{W} = \frac{1}{1.6} = 0.625$$

$$\frac{L_2}{W} = \frac{0.8}{1.6} = 0.5$$

$$F_{1-2} = 0.2 \ .$$

The corresponding radiation network is illustrated in the accompanying figure. The heat transfer rate becomes

$$Q = \frac{E_{b1} - E_{b2}}{R_{1-2}} = \frac{E_{b1} - E_{b2}}{1/(A_1\,F_{1-2})}$$

$$= A_1\,F_{1-2}\,\sigma\,(T_1^4 - T_2^4)$$

where

$$E_{b1} = \sigma T_1^4 \quad \text{and} \quad E_{b2} = \sigma T_2^4 .$$

Introducing the numerical values, we have

$$Q = (1.0 \times 1.6)\,(0.2)\,(5.67 \times 10^{-8})\,(1000^4 - 500^4)$$

$$= 17 \text{ kW} .$$

**EXAMPLE 11-14**   A cubical room $3\,m$ by $3\,m$ by $3\,m$ is heated through the ceiling by maintaining it at a uniform temperature $T_1 = 343\,K$ while the walls and the floor are at $283\,K$. Assuming that all surfaces have an emissivity of $0.8$, determine the rate of heat loss from the ceiling by radiation.

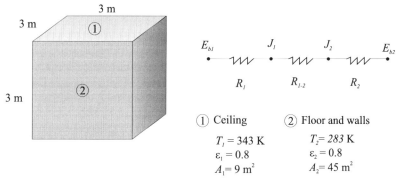

**FIGURE EXAMPLE 11-14**

**SOLUTION**   The problem is illustrated in the accompanying figure, which shows the various given values. The floor and walls are considered to be a single surface. The problem is like a two-zone enclosure, and the equivalent network is illustrated in the accompanying figure. Various potentials and resistances are

$$E_{b1} = \sigma T_1^4$$
$$= (5.67 \times 10^{-8})\,(343)^4 = 784.8 \text{ W/m}^2$$

$$E_{b2} = \sigma T_2^4$$
$$= (5.67 \times 10^{-8})\,(283)^4 = 363.7 \text{ W/m}^2$$

$$R_1 = \frac{1 - \epsilon_1}{A_1\,\epsilon_1} = \frac{1 - 0.8}{(9)\,(0.8)} = 0.02778$$

$$R_2 = \frac{1 - \epsilon_2}{A_2\,\epsilon_2} = \frac{1 - 0.8}{(45)\,(0.8)} = 0.00556$$

$$R_{1-2} = \frac{1}{A_1\,F_{1-2}} = \frac{1}{(9)\,(1)} = 0.11111 .$$

The radiation heat exchange is determined as

$$Q_{1-2} = \frac{E_{b1} - E_{b2}}{R_1 + R_{1-2} + R_2}$$

$$= \frac{784.8 - 363.7}{0.02778 + 0.11111 + 0.00556} = 2915.3 \text{ W} .$$

**EXAMPLE 11-15** A cubical room $3\,m$ by $3\,m$ by $3\,m$ is heated through the floor by maintaining it at a uniform temperature of $310\,K$. Since the side walls are well insulated, the heat loss through them can be considered negligible. The heat loss takes place through the ceiling, which is maintained at $280\,K$. All surfaces have an emissivity $\epsilon = 0.85$. Determine the rate of heat loss by radiation through the ceiling.

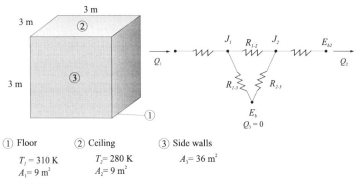

① Floor    ② Ceiling    ③ Side walls

$T_1 = 310$ K    $T_2 = 280$ K    $A_3 = 36 \text{ m}^2$

$A_1 = 9 \text{ m}^2$    $A_2 = 9 \text{ m}^2$

**FIGURE EXAMPLE 11-15**

**SOLUTION** The problem is illustrated in the accompanying figure, which shows various values. The view factors $F_{1-2}$ and $F_{1-3}$ are determined from Figs. 11.16 and 11.17 as

$$F_{1-2} = 0.2 \qquad F_{1-3} = 0.8 .$$

The equivalent network is illustrated in the accompanying figure.

Various potentials and resistances are

$$E_{b1} = \sigma T_1^4 = (5.67 \times 10^{-8}) (310)^4 = 523.64 \text{ W/m}^2$$

$$E_{b2} = \sigma T_2^4 = (5.67 \times 10^{-8}) (280)^4 = 348.51 \text{ W/m}^2$$

$$R_{1-2} = \frac{1}{A_1 F_{1-2}} = \frac{1}{(9)(0.2)} = \frac{1}{1.8}$$

$$R_{2-3} = R_{1-3} = \frac{1}{A_1 F_{1-3}} = \frac{1}{(9)(0.8)} = \frac{1}{7.2}$$

$$R_1 = R_2 = \frac{1 - \epsilon_1}{A_1 \epsilon_1} = \frac{1 - 0.85}{(9)(0.85)} = \frac{1}{51} .$$

The equivalent resistance between $E_{b1}$ and $E_{b2}$ is

$$
\begin{aligned}
R_{\text{equivalent}} &= R_1 + \frac{1}{1/R_{1-2} + 1/(R_{1-3} + R_{2-3})} + R_2 \\
&= \frac{1}{51} + \frac{1}{1.8 + 1/[(1/7.2) + (1/7.2)]} + \frac{1}{51} \\
&= 0.2244 \ .
\end{aligned}
$$

The radiation heat exchange between the floor and the ceiling is determined as

$$
\begin{aligned}
Q_{1-2} &= \frac{E_{b1} - E_{b2}}{R_{\text{equivalent}}} \\
&= \frac{523.64 - 348.51}{0.2244} \\
&= 780.43 \text{ W} \ .
\end{aligned}
$$

## 11.12. RADIATION SHIELDS

The radiation heat transfer between two surfaces can be reduced significantly if a radiation shield made of a low-emissivity material is placed between them. This fact has been utilized extensively in reducing heat gain from the surrounding atmosphere to a cryogenic tank filled with cryogenic fluid at very low temperature. The role of the radiation shield is to increase the thermal resistance to radiation in the path of heat flow, and hence reduce the heat transfer rate.

To illustrate this matter, we first consider radiation heat transfer between two large, opaque parallel plates. Let $T_1$ and $T_2$ be the temperatures and $\epsilon_1$ and $\epsilon_2$ the emissivities of the surfaces. Then the heat transfer rate $Q_0$ across an area $A$ through the plates is determined as

$$
\boxed{Q_0 = \frac{A\sigma\,(T_1^4 - T_2^4)}{1/\epsilon_1 + 1/\epsilon_2 - 1}} \text{ W} \ . \tag{11-152}
$$

We now consider a radiation shield placed between the plates. Let $\epsilon_{3,1}$ and $\epsilon_{3,2}$ be the emissivities of the shield at the surfaces facing plates 1 and 2, respectively. The radiation network for the assembly with one shield can be constructed for the radiation resistances at the surface and across the surfaces, respectively. Figure 11.27 shows the resulting radiation network. By utilizing this network and noting that $F_{1,3} = F_{3,2} = 1$ for large parallel plates, the heat transfer rate $Q_1$ across the system with one shield becomes

$$
Q_1 = \frac{A\sigma\,(T_1^4 - T_2^4)}{1/\epsilon_1 + (1 - \epsilon_{3,1})/\epsilon_{3,1} + (1 - \epsilon_{3,2})/\epsilon_{3,2} + 1/\epsilon_2} \tag{11-153}
$$

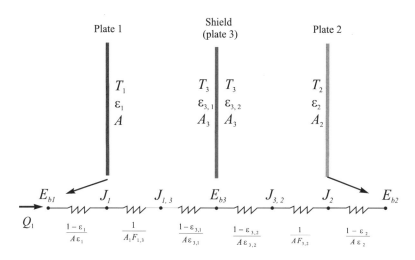

**FIG. 11.27.** Plate-shield assembly and the corresponding radiation network.

which is re-arranged as

$$Q_1 = \frac{A\sigma(T_1^4 - T_2^4)}{(1/\epsilon_1 + 1/\epsilon_2 - 1) + (1/\epsilon_{3,1} + 1/\epsilon_{3,2} - 1)} \quad \text{W} . \qquad (11\text{-}154)$$

A comparison of Eqn. (11-152) with Eqn. (11-154) shows that the effect of the radiation shield is to increase the thermal resistance of the system.

If the emissivities of all surfaces are equal, we have

$$Q_1 = \frac{A\sigma(T_1^4 - T_2^4)}{2(2/\epsilon - 1)} \quad \text{W} . \qquad (11\text{-}155)$$

For a parallel-plate system containing $N$ shields between two surfaces with the emissivities of all surfaces equal, then

$$Q_N = \frac{A\sigma(T_1^4 - T_2^4)}{(N+1)(2/\epsilon - 1)} \quad \text{W} . \qquad (11\text{-}156)$$

The ratio of the heat transfer rates for parallel-plate systems with $N$ shields and with no shield, when all emissivities are equal, is determined from Eqn. (11-156) as

$$\frac{Q_N}{Q_0} = \frac{1}{N+1} . \qquad (11\text{-}157)$$

**EXAMPLE 11-16**  Consider two large parallel plates, one at $T_1 K$ with emissivity $\epsilon_1 = 0.8$ and the other at $T_2 K$ with emissivity $\epsilon_2 = 0.4$. An aluminum radiation shield with emissivity $\epsilon_3 = 0.05$ is placed between the plates. Calculate the percentage reduction in the heat transfer rate resulting from the radiation shield.

**SOLUTION**  The heat transfer rate without the radiation shield is determined as

$$Q_0 = \frac{A\sigma(T_1^4 - T_2^4)}{1/\epsilon_1 + 1/\epsilon_2 - 1}$$

$$= \frac{A\sigma(T_1^4 - T_2^4)}{1/0.8 + 1/0.4 - 1} = 0.36\, A\sigma(T_1^4 - T_2^4) \ .$$

The heat transfer rate with the radiation shield is determined as

$$Q_1 = \frac{A\sigma(T_1^4 - T_2^4)}{(1/\epsilon_1 + 1/\epsilon_2 - 1) + (1/\epsilon_{3,1} + 1/\epsilon_{3,2} - 1)}$$

$$= \frac{A\sigma(T_1^4 - T_2^4)}{(1/0.8 + 1/0.4 - 1) + (1/0.05 + 1/0.05 - 1)}$$

$$= 0.024\, A\sigma(T_1^4 - T_2^4) \ .$$

The reduction in the heat transfer rate resulting from the shield is

$$\frac{Q_0 - Q_1}{Q_0} = \frac{0.36 - 0.024}{0.36} = 0.934 \ .$$

Therefore, the radiation shield reduces the rate of heat loss by 93.4 percent.

Radiation emitted in the interior of a hot body can pass through the medium (if it is not opaque) and leave the body through its outer surfaces. In numerous applications, engineers must concern themselves with the absorption and emission of radiation within the body. The furnaces of the steam boilers, diesel engines, nuclear explosions, plasma generators, for nuclear fusion, propulsion of rockets and ablation are all technological problems that need the solution of the radiative exchange within the medium. Up to now we confined our discussions to radiation exchange among surfaces when the medium separating them was transparent. Radiation propagating through such media remains unchanged. A beam of radiation traveling through a participating medium is attenuated as a result of absorption and augmented as a result of emission of radiation owing to its temperature. These energy transport is governed by the Radiative Transfer Equation (RTE) and its development is outside the scope of this book.

## PROBLEMS

*Blackbody Radiation Laws*

**11-1.** At a wavelength of 0.7 μm, what is the temperature of the blackbody that will give an emissive power equal to $10^2\,\mathrm{W}/(\mathrm{m}^2 \cdot \mu\mathrm{m})$?

**11-2.** Calculate the spectral blackbody emissive power $E_{b\lambda}(T)$ at $\lambda = 2, 3$, and 5 μm for a surface at 1000 K.

**11-3.** Determine the wavelength at which the blackbody spectral emissive power $E_{b\lambda}$ is maximum for a blackbody at 1600 K.

**11-4.** Calculate the wavelength at which the emission of radiation by a blackbody at the following temperatures is maximum:
   *(a)* The effective surface temperature of the Sun, 5762 K.

   *(b)* A tungsten filament at 2300 K

   *(c)* A body at room temperature, 300 K

**11-5.** Consider a blackbody emitting at 1500 K. Calculate the maximum spectral emissive power at this temperature.

**11-6.** Calculate the blackbody emissive power $E_b(T)$ at 1000 K and at 5762 K.

**11-7.** A 1 m×1 m blackbody surface is at 800 K. Determine the rate of emission of radiative energy through this surface.

**11-8.** A blackbody filament is heated to 2300 K. What is the maximum radiative heat flux from the filament?

**11-9.** A large empty box (assumed to be black) has its inner wall at 700 K. If a 1-cm-diameter hole is drilled in the side, how much energy will be emitted from the hole?

**11-10.** A large blackbody enclosure has a small opening area of 1 cm². The radiant energy emitted by the opening is 5.67 W. Determine the temperature of the blackbody enclosure.

**11-11.** The sun radiates as a blackbody at an effective surface temperature of 5762 K. What fraction of the total emitted energy is in the visible range?

**11-12.** The sun radiates as a blackbody at an effective surface temperature of 5762 K. What fraction of the total emitted energy is in the infrared range (i.e., $\lambda = 0.7$ to 1000 μm)?

**11-13.** A tungsten filament (assumed to be black) is heated to 2300 K. What fraction of the total energy is emitted in the wavelength range 0.6 to 1 μm?

**11-14.** A light bulb filament (assumed to be black) is at 3500 K. What percentage of its radiation is in *(a)* the visible range, and *(b)* the infrared range?

**11-15.** A blackbody at 556 K is emitting into air. Calculate *(a)* the wavelength at which the blackbody emissive power is maximum, and *(b)* the energy emitted over the wavelengths $\lambda = 1$ to 8 μm and $\lambda = 8$ to 18 μm.

**11-16.** What is the temperature of a blackbody such that 50 percent of the energy emitted should lie in the wavelength spectrum $\lambda = 0$ to 10 μm?

*Radiation Properties of Surfaces*

**11-17.** The spectral emissivity of an opaque surface at 1500 K is given by

$$\epsilon_1 = 0.1 \quad \text{for } \lambda_0 = 0 \text{ to } \lambda_1 = 0.5 \text{ µm}$$
$$\epsilon_2 = 0.5 \quad \text{for } \lambda_1 = 0.5 \text{ to } \lambda_2 = 6 \text{ µm}$$
$$\epsilon_3 = 0.8 \quad \text{for } \lambda_3 > 6 \text{ µm}$$

Determine the average emissivity over the entire range of wavelengths and the radiative flux emitted by the material at 1500 K.

**11-18.** The spectral emissivity of a filament at 3000 K is given by

$$\epsilon_1 = 0.5 \quad \text{for } \lambda_0 = 0 \text{ to } \lambda_1 = 0.5 \text{ µm}$$
$$\epsilon_2 = 0.1 \quad \text{for } \lambda_1 = 0.5 \text{ µm to } \lambda_2 \to \infty$$

Determine the average emissivity of the filament over the entire range of wavelengths.

**11-19.** The spectral emissivity of an opaque surface at 2000 K is given by

$$\epsilon_1 = 0.2 \quad \text{for } \lambda_0 = 0 \text{ to } \lambda_1 = 0.3 \text{ µm}$$
$$\epsilon_2 = 0.4 \quad \text{for } \lambda_1 = 0.3 \text{ to } \lambda_2 = 3 \text{ µm}$$
$$\epsilon_3 = 0.6 \quad \text{for } \lambda_2 = 3 \text{ to } \lambda_3 = 4 \text{ µm}$$
$$\epsilon_4 = 0.8 \quad \text{for } \lambda_3 = 4 \text{ µm to } \lambda_4 \to \infty$$

Determine the average emissivity over the entire range of wavelengths of the radiative flux emitted by the material at 2000 K.
*Answer*: 0.48.

**11-20.** Spectral emissivity of an opaque surface at 1500 K is given by

$$\epsilon_1 = 0.3 \quad \text{for } \lambda_0 = 0 \text{ to } \lambda_1 = 1.0 \text{ µm}$$
$$\epsilon_2 = 0.8 \quad \text{for } \lambda_1 = 1.0 \text{ to } \lambda_2 \to \infty$$

Determine the average emissivity over the entire range of wavelengths and the emissive power at 1500 K.

*View-Factor Determination*

**11-21.** Two small surfaces $dA_1 = 4 \text{ cm}^2$ and $dA_2 = 6 \text{ cm}^2$ are separated by $r = 50 \text{ cm}$ and oriented as shown in the accompanying figure. Calculate the view factors between the surfaces.

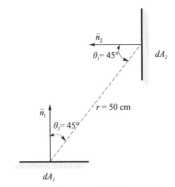

Figure P11-21

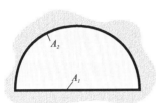

Figure P11-22

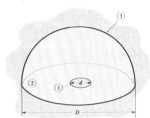

Figure P11-23

**11-22.** Determine the view factors $F_{1-2}$, $F_{2-1}$, between the surfaces of a long semicylindrical duct, shown in the accompanying figure, by view-factor algebra.

*Answers:* $F_{1-2} = 1$, $F_{2-1} = 0.637$, $F_{2-2} = 0.363$

**11-23.** A small circular disk of diameter $d$ is placed centrally at the base of a hemisphere of diameter $D$, as illustrated in diameter $D$, as illustrated in the accompanying figure. Determine the view factors $F_{3-1}$ and $F_{3-2}$ by view-factor algebra.

**11-24.** Consider two concentric spheres. The inner sphere has a radius $R_1 = 5$ cm. Determine the radius $R_2$ of the outer sphere such that $F_{2-1} = 0.6$.

**11-25.** Consider two very long coaxial cylinders. The outer cylinder has a radius $R_2 = 10$ cm. Determine the radius $R_l$ of the inner cylinder such that $F_{2-l} = 0.7$.

**11-26.** Consider two very long coaxial cylinders. The inner cylinder has a radius $R_1 = 5$ cm. Determine the radius $R_2$ of the outer cylinder such that $F_{2-1} = 0.6$.

**11-27.** Consider two very long coaxial cylinders. The inner cylinder has a radius $R_1$ and the outer cylinder has a radius $R_2 = 3R_1$. Determine the view factors $F_{1-2}$, $F_{2-l}$, and $F_{2-2}$, where the subscript 1 refers to the inner cylinder.

**11-28.** Determine the view factor $F_{l-2}$ between two rectangular surfaces $A_1$ and $A_2$ for the geometric arrangement shown in the accompanying figure.

*Answer:* $F_{A1-A2} = 0.16$.

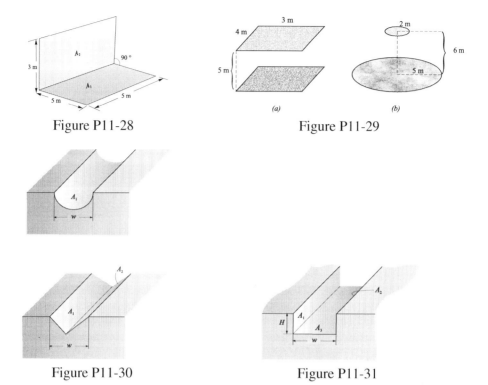

Figure P11-28                    Figure P11-29

Figure P11-30                    Figure P11-31

**11-29.** Determine the view factors between the surfaces shown in the accompanying figure.

**11-30.** For the grooves shown in the accompanying figure (an equilateral triangle and a semicircle), determine the view factor of each groove with respect to the surroundings outside the groove.

**11-31.** For the rectangular groove with $H = 2W$ shown in the accompanying figure, determine the view factor $F_{1-2}$.
*Answer*: $F_{1-2} = 0.618$.

**11-32.** Two aligned, parallel square plates 0.5 m by 0.5 m are separated by 0.7 m, as illustrated in the accompanying figure. Determine the view factor $F_{1-2}$.

**11-33.** Two parallel circular disks of equal diameter 0.6 m separated by 0.5 m have a com-

Figure P11-32                    Figure P11-33

mon central normal, as illustrated in the accompanying figure. Determine the view factor $F_{l-2}$.

**11-34.** Determine the view factors $F_{1-2}$, $F_{2-1}$, and $F_{1-3}$ of the infinitely long surfaces in the accompanying figure.

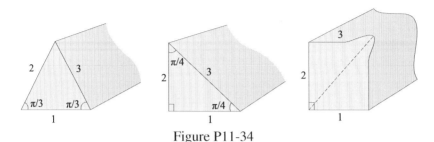

Figure P11-34

**11-35.** Determine the view factor $F_{1-3}$ between surfaces $A_1$ and $A_3$ of Example 11-11 for $b = 3$, $c = 5$, and $d = 10$ cm.

*Network Method for Radiation Exchange in an Enclosure*

**11-36.** Consider an enclosure consisting of two parallel, opaque, large plates that are kept at 500 K and 200 K, respectively, and that have emissivities of 0.8. Calculate the net radiation flux.

**11-37.** Calculate the heat dissipation by radiation through a 0.2-m$^2$ opening of a furnace at 1100 K into an ambient at 300 K. Assume that both the furnace and the ambient are blackbodies.

**11-38.** Consider two parallel, opaque, large plates that are kept at uniform temperatures $T_1$ and $T_2$ and that have emissivities $\epsilon_1 = \epsilon_2 = 0.6$. Calculate the temperature $T_2$ of plate 2 for $T_1 = 800$ K and $q_{1-2} = 1000$ W/m$^2$.

**11-39.** A 15-cm-outside-diameter (OD) and 50-cm-long steam pipe whose surface is at 100° C passes through a room with a wall at 10° C. Assuming the emissivity of the pipe to be 0.9, determine the rate of heat loss from the pipe by radiation.

**11-40.** Two black surfaces $A_1$ and $A_2$, arranged as shown in the accompanying figure, are located in a large room whose walls are black and kept at 250 K. Determine the net radiative heat exchange for the given surface conditions. Neglect the radiation from the room.

**11-41.** A cubical room 2 m by 2 m by 2 m is heated through the floor by maintaining it at a uniform temperature $T_1 = 250$ K, while the walls and the ceiling are at 200 K. Assume that the floor has an emissivity $\epsilon_1 = 0.9$ and the walls and the ceiling have an emissivity $\epsilon_2 = 0.6$. Determine the rate of heat loss from the floor.

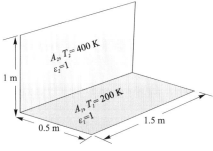

Figure P11-40

**11-42.** A cubical room 2 m by 2 m by 2 m is heated through the floor by maintaining it at a uniform temperature $T_1 = 250$ K. The side walls are well insulated. The heat loss takes place through the ceiling, which is maintained at 200 K. The floor has an emissivity $\epsilon_1 = 0.9$, and the ceiling has an emissivity of 0.6. Determine the rate of heat loss from the floor.

**11-43.** Two square plates, each 2 m by 2 m, are parallel to and directly opposite each other at a distance of 3 m apart. The hot plate is at $T_1 = 1000$ K and has an emissivity $\epsilon_1 = 0.7$. The colder plate is at $T_2 = 400$ K and has an emissivity $\epsilon_2 = 0.6$. The radiation heat exchange takes place between the plates as well as with a large ambient at $T_3 = 300$ K through the opening between the plates. Calculate the net heat transfer rate by radiation at each plate and to the ambient.

*Radiation Shields*

**11-44.** Consider two large parallel plates, one at $T_1 = 1000$K with emissivity $\epsilon_1 = 0.8$ and the other at $T_2 = 500$ K with emissivity $\epsilon_2 = 0.4$. An aluminum radiation shield with an emissivity (on both sides) $\epsilon_3 = 0.05$ is placed between the plates. Sketch the radiation network for the system with and without the radiation shield. Calculate the percentage reduction in the heat transfer rate as a result of the radiation shield.

**11-45.** Two large parallel plates are at temperatures $T_1$ and $T_2$ and have emissivities $\epsilon_1 = 0.9$ and $\epsilon_2 = 0.6$. A radiation shield having an emissivity $E_3$ (on both sides) is placed between the plates. Calculate the emissivity $E_3$ of the shield needed to reduce the radiation loss from the system to one-tenth of that without the shield.

**11-46.** Consider two large parallel plates, one at $T_1 = 1000$ K with emissivity $\epsilon_1 = 0.8$ and the other at $T_2 = 300$ K with emissivity $\epsilon_1 = 0.6$. A radiation shield is placed between them. The shield has an emissivity $\epsilon_{3,1} = 0.1$ on the side facing the hot plate and emissivity $\epsilon_{3,2} = 0.3$ on the side facing the cold plate. Sketch the radiation network. Calculate the reduction in the heat transfer rate between the hot and the cold plates as a result of the radiation shield.

**11-47.** Consider two large parallel plates, one at $T_1 = 800$ K with emissivity $\epsilon_1 = 0.6$

and the other at $T_2 = 300$ K with emissivity $\epsilon_2 = 0.5$. A radiation shield is placed between them. The shield has emissivity $\epsilon_3 = 0.2$ (on both sides). Sketch the radiation network. Calculate the reduction in the heat transfer rate between the plates as a result of the radiation shield, and the final equilibrium temperature of the radiation shield.

**11-48.** Consider two large parallel plates, one at $T_1 = 800$ K with emissivity $\epsilon_1 = 0.9$ and the other at $T_2 = 300$ K with emissivity $\epsilon_2 = 0.5$. A radiation shield with an emissivity $\epsilon_3$ (on both sides) is placed between the plates. Calculate the emissivity of the radiation shield needed to reduce the heat transfer rate to 15 percent of that without the shield.
*Answer*: 0.1543.

# CHAPTER 12

# *Thermal Analysis of Heat Exchangers*

Heat exchangers are devises or systems and they are commonly used for the transfer of heat between a hot and a cold fluid. For example, in car radiators, hot water from the engine is cooled by atmospheric air. In household refrigerators, hot refrigerant from the compressor is cooled by natural convection into the atmosphere by passing it through finned tubes. In space radiators, the waste heat carried by the coolant fluid is dissipated by thermal radiation into the atmosphere-free space. In steam condensers, the latent heat of condensation is removed by the coolant water passing through the condenser tubes. Clearly, different types of heat-exchanging devices are needed for different applications. In this chapter we discuss the classification of heat exchangers, the determination of the overall heat transfer coefficient, the logarithmic mean temperature difference and $\epsilon$-NTU methods for sizing, and heat transfer and estimation in heat exchangers. The problems of optimization and cost estimation are beyond the scope of this work. The basic steps of a design project of a heat exchanger is schematically shown in Fig. 12.1.

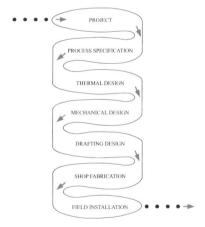

**FIG. 12.1.** Heat exchanger design flow chart.

The thermal engineers are now energy conscious and the design of heat exchangers become very important. There are also situations in which heat exchangers become among the most costly components of the system. Therefore, the design of heat exchangers for new applications is a very complicated matter. The design involves not only heat transfer and pressure drop analysis, but also optimization and cost estimation.

## 12.1. TYPES OF HEAT EXCHANGERS

Heat exchangers are designed in so many sizes, types, configurations, and flow arrangements and used for so many different purposes that some kind of classification, even
though arbitrary, is needed in order to study heat exchangers. Here we briefly discuss the
basic concepts leading to classification. Heat exchangers can be classified according to
*compactness*. The ratio of the heat transfer surface area on one side of the heat exchanger
to the volume can be used as a measure of the compactness of a heat exchanger. A heat
exchanger with a surface area density on any one side greater than about $700 \ m^2/m^3$ is
referred to, quite arbitrarily, as a *compact heat exchanger* regardless of its structural design. For example, automobile radiators with an area density on the order of $1100 \ m^2/m^3$
and the glass ceramic heat exchangers for some vehicular gas-turbine engines that have an
area density on the order of $6600 \ m^2/m^3$ are compact heat exchangers. By this classification, the commonly used plane tubular and shell-and-tube-type heat exchangers, which
have an area density in the range of 70 to $500 \ m^2/m^3$, are not considered compact.

Heat exchangers can be classified according to their *construction* features for example, *tubular, tube-fin, plate, plate-fin, extended surfaces* and *regenerative* exchangers. The
tubular exchangers are widely used; they are manufactured in many sizes, flow arrangements, and types. They can accommodate a wide range of operating pressures and temperatures. Tubular exchangers can be designed for high pressures relative to the environment
and for high-pressure differences between the fluids. Their ease of manufacturing and
relatively low cost have been the principal reason for their widespread use in engineering
applications. A commonly used design, called the *shell-and-tube exchanger*, is shown in
Fig. 12.2. Shell-and-tube heat exchangers consists of round tubes mounted on a cylindrical shell with their axes parallel to that of the shell. Figure 12.3 illustrates the main

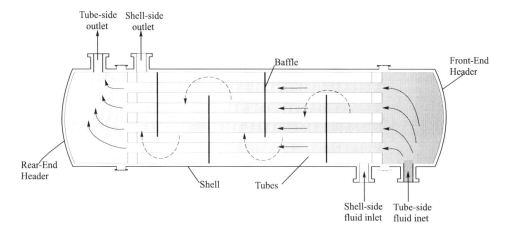

**FIG. 12.2.** A miniature shell-and-tube heat exchanger.

features of a shell-and-tube exchanger that has one fluid flowing inside the tubes and the
other flowing outside the tubes. The principal components of this type of heat exchanger
are the tube bundle, shell, front- and rear-end headers, and baffles. Flow patterns created

**FIG. 12.3.** A shell-and-tube heat exchanger; one shell pass and two tube pass.

by segmental, disc and doughnut, and double segmental baffles are shown in Fig. 12.4. The square pitch, the rotated square, the triangular pitch and the in-line triangular pitch arrangements are illustrated in Figs. 12.5$a, b, c$, and $d$. The flow and tube arrangements

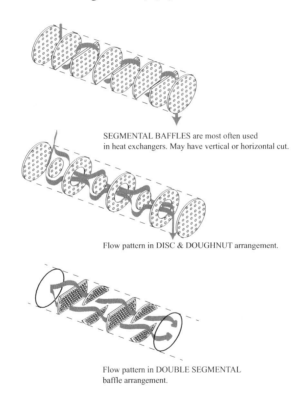

SEGMENTAL BAFFLES are most often used in heat exchangers. May have vertical or horizontal cut.

Flow pattern in DISC & DOUGHNUT arrangement.

Flow pattern in DOUBLE SEGMENTAL baffle arrangement.

**FIG. 12.4.** Flow patterns created by different baffle shapes.

could also vary. A plate-fin heat exchanger and a round tube-fin heat exchanger are shown in Fig. 12.6.

The most common method of classifying heat exchangers is by *flow arrangement*. There are numerous possibilities; we summarize the principal ones.

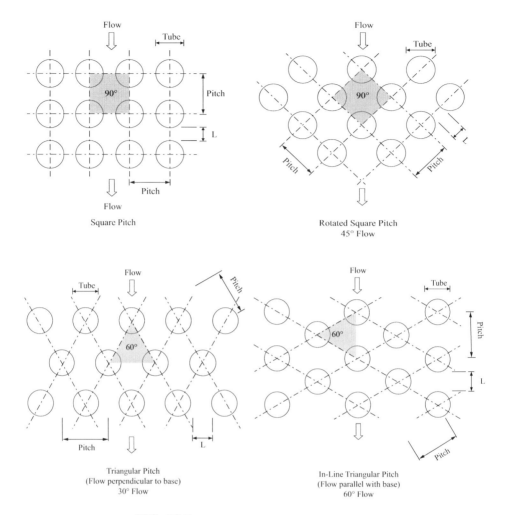

**FIG. 12.5.** A few pitch and flow arrangements.

**Parallel-flow:** The hot and cold fluids enter at the same end of the heat exchanger, flow through in the same direction, and leave together at the other end, as illustrated in Fig. 12.7*a*.

**Counter-flow:** The hot and cold fluids enter at the opposite ends of the heat exchanger and flow through in opposite directions, as illustrated in Fig. 12.7*b*.

**Cross-flow:** In the cross-flow exchanger, the two fluids usually flow at right angles to each other, as illustrated in Fig. 12.7*c*. In a cross-flow arrangement, the flow may be what we call *mixed* or *unmixed*, depending on the design. To illustrate the physical significance of the concept of *mixed* and *unmixed*, we refer to the illustration in Fig. 12.8, which shows an arrangement where both hot and cold fluids flow through individual channels formed by corrugation; therefore, the fluids are not free to move in the transverse direction. In this case each fluid stream is said to be unmixed. In the flow arrangements shown in

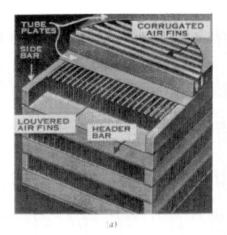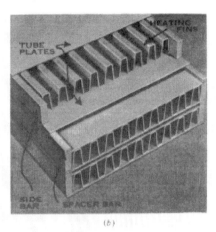

**FIG. 12.6.** A plate-fin and a round tube-fin heat exchanger. (Courtesy of Harrison Division of General Motors Corporation).

Fig. 12.8*b*, the cold fluid flows inside the tubes and is not free to move in the transverse direction. Therefore, the cold fluid is said to be unmixed. However, the hot fluid flows over the tubes and is free to move in the transverse direction. Therefore, the hot fluid stream is said to be mixed. The mixing tends to make the fluid temperature uniform in the transverse direction; therefore, the exit temperature of a mixed steam exhibits negligible variation in the crosswise direction. In a shell-and-tube heat exchanger, the presence of a large number of baffles serves to *mix* the shell- side fluid in the sense discussed above; that is, its temperature tends to be uniform at any cross section.

**Multipass flow:** Multipass flow arrangements are frequently used in heat exchanger design, because multipassing increases the overall effectiveness. A wide variety of multipass flow arrangements are possible. Figure 12.9 illustrates typical arrangements. The tube side front and return head pass partition arrangements are schematically presented in Fig. 12.10.

Heat exchangers can also be classified according to the *heat transfer mechanism*—for example, condensers, boilers, and radiators. Condensers are used in such varied applications as steam power plants, chemical processing plants, and nuclear electric plants for space vehicles. Steam boilers are one of the earliest types of heat exchangers. Radiators for space applications are used in space vehicles to dissipate the waste heat by thermal radiation into the space by taking advantage of the fourth-power relationship between the absolute temperature of the surface and the radiation heat flux.

## 12.2. FLUID TEMPERATURE DISTRIBUTIONS

The temperature of the fluid varies along the path of the heat exchanger for a number of typical single-pass heat transfer matrices as illustrated in Figure 12.11. In each instance,

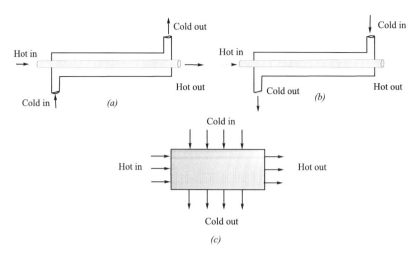

**FIG. 12.7.** (a) Parallel-flow, (b) counter-flow, and (c) cross-flow arrangements.

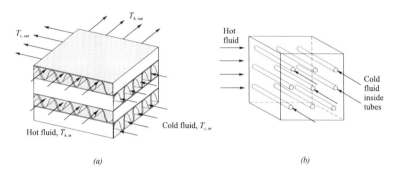

**FIG. 12.8.** Cross-flow arrangements; (a) both fluids unmixed, (b) cold fluid unmixed, hot fluid mixed.

the temperature distribution is plotted as a function of the distance from the cold-fluid inlet end. Figure 12.11a, for example, is characteristic of a pure counter-flow heat exchanger in which the temperature rise in the cold fluid is equal to the temperature drop in the hot fluid; thus the temperature difference $\Delta T$ between the hot and cold fluids is constant throughout. However, in all other cases (Fig. 12.11b to $e$), the temperature difference $\Delta T$ between the hot and cold fluids varies with the position along the path of flow. Figure 12.11b corresponds to a situation in which the hot fluid condenses and heat is transferred to the cold fluid, causing its temperature to rise along the path of flow. In Fig. 12.11c, cold liquid is evaporating and cooling the hot fluid along its path of flow. Figure 12.11d shows a parallel-flow arrangement in which both fluids flow in the same direction, with the cold fluid experiencing a temperature rise and the hot fluid a temperature drop. The outlet temperature of the cold fluid cannot exceed that of the hot fluid. Therefore, the temperature effectiveness of parallel-flow exchangers is limited. Because of this limitation, generally they are not considered for heat recovery. However, since the metal temperature lies approximately midway between the hot and cold fluid temperatures, the wall is almost at a uniform temperature. Figure 12.11e shows a counter-flow arrangement, in which fluids

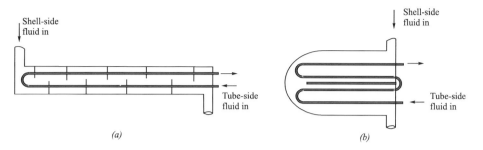

**FIG. 12.9.** Multipass flow arrangements. (a) one shell pass, two tube pass; (b) two shell pass, four tube pass.

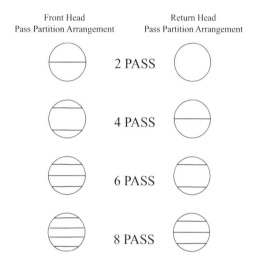

Front Head
Pass Partition Arrangement

Return Head
Pass Partition Arrangement

2 PASS

4 PASS

6 PASS

8 PASS

**FIG. 12.10.** Tube side pass partition arrangements.

flow in opposite directions. The exit temperature of the cold fluid can be higher than that of the hot fluid.

In multipass and cross-flow arrangements, the temperature distributions in the heat exchanger exhibit more complicated patterns. For example, Fig. 12.12 shows the temperature distribution in a one-shell-pass, two-tube-pass heat exchanger.

## 12.3. OVERALL HEAT TRANSFER COEFFICIENT AND THERMAL RESISTANCES

The thermal resistances in the path of heat flow from the hot to the cold fluid in a heat exchanger include: (1) the skin resistances associated with the flow, (2) the scale resistances resulting from the formation of deposits on the walls, and (3) the thermal resistance of the wall material itself. The total thermal resistance to heat flow needs to be determined in order to calculate heat transfer through a heat exchanger. We present an overview of the determination of the *total thermal resistance R* in heat exchangers, then relate this quantity to the commonly used concept of the *overall heat transfer coefficient U*.

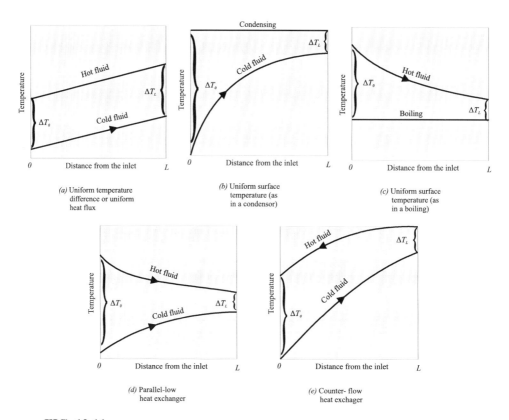

**FIG. 12.11.** Axial fluid temperature distribution in typical single-pass transfer matrices.

We consider a tubular heat exchanger with heat transfer taking place between the fluids flowing inside and outside the tubes. The thermal resistance $R$ to heat flow across the tubes, between the inside and outside flow, is composed of the following resistances:

$$R = \left( \begin{array}{c} \text{thermal} \\ \text{resistance} \\ \text{of inside} \\ \text{flow} \end{array} \right) + \left( \begin{array}{c} \text{thermal} \\ \text{resistance} \\ \text{of tube} \\ \text{material} \end{array} \right) + \left( \begin{array}{c} \text{thermal} \\ \text{resistance} \\ \text{of outside} \\ \text{flow} \end{array} \right) \qquad (12\text{-}1)$$

and the various terms are given by

$$R = \frac{1}{A_i h_i} + \frac{t}{k A_m} + \frac{1}{A_o h_o} \qquad (12\text{-}2)$$

where

$$A_o, \ A_i \ = \ \text{outside and inside surface areas of tube, respectively, } \text{m}^2$$
$$A_m \ = \ \frac{A_o - A_i}{\ln(A_o/A_i)} = \text{logarithmic mean area, } \text{m}^2.$$

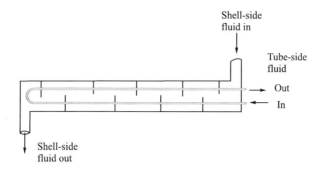

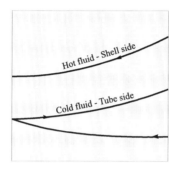

**FIG. 12.12.** Axial temperature distribution in a one shell pass, two tube pass heat exchanger.

$$h_i,\ h_o\ =\ \text{heat transfer coefficients for inside and outside flow,}$$
$$\text{respectively, W}/(\text{m}^2 \cdot {}^\circ\text{C})$$
$$k\ =\ \text{thermal conductivity of tube material, W}/(\text{m} \cdot {}^\circ\text{C})$$
$$R\ =\ \text{total thermal resistance from inside to outside flow, } {}^\circ\text{C/W}$$
$$t\ =\ \text{thickness of tube, } m.$$

The thermal resistance $R$ given by Eq. (12-2) can be expressed as an *overall heat transfer coefficient* based on either the inside or the outside surface of the tube. For example, the overall heat transfer coefficient $U_o$ based on the *outside surface* of the tube is defined as

$$U_o\ =\ \frac{1}{A_o R} = \frac{1}{(A_o/A_i)(1/h_i) + (A_o/A_m)(t/k) + 1/h_o}$$

$$=\ \frac{1}{(D_o/D_i)(1/h_i) + (1/2k)D_o \ln(D_o/D_i) + 1/h_o} \qquad (12\text{-}3)$$

since

$$\frac{A_o}{A_m} = \frac{D_o}{2t} \ln\left(\frac{D_o}{D_i}\right) \qquad D_o - D_i = 2t. \qquad (12\text{-}4)$$

and $D_i$ and $D_o$ are the inside and outside diameters of the tube, respectively.

Similarly, the overall heat transfer coefficient $U_i$ based on the *inside surface* of the tube is defined as

$$U_i = \frac{1}{A_i R} = \frac{1}{1/h_i + (A_i/A_m)(t/k) + (A_i/A_o)(1/h_o)}$$

$$= \frac{1}{1/h_i + (1/2k)D_i \ln(D_o/D_i) + (D_i/D_o)(1/h_o)}. \qquad (12\text{-}5a)$$

When the wall thickness is small and its thermal conductivity is high, the tube resistance can be neglected and Eq. (12-5$a$) reduces to

$$U_i = \frac{1}{1/h_i + 1/h_o}. \qquad (12\text{-}5b)$$

In heat exchanger applications, the heat transfer surface is fouled with accumulated deposits, which introduce additional thermal resistance in the path of heat flow. The effect of fouling is generally introduced in the form of a fouling factor $F$ which has the dimensions $(m^2 \cdot {}^\circ\text{C})/W$.

Based on the experience of manufacturers and users, the Tubular Equipment Manufacturers Association (TEMA) prepared tables of fouling factors as a guide in heat transfer calculations. We present some of their results in Table 12.1. Fouling is a very complicated matter, and representing it by such a simple listing is highly questionable. But in the absence of anything better, this remains the only reference for estimating the effects of fouling in reducing heat transfer.

We now consider heat transfer across a tube which is fouled by deposit formation on both the inside and outside surfaces. The thermal resistance R in the path of heat flow for this case is given by

$$R = \frac{1}{A_i h_i} + \frac{F_i}{A_i} + \frac{t}{k A_m} + \frac{F_o}{A_o} + \frac{1}{A_o h_o} \qquad (12\text{-}6)$$

where $F_i$ and $F_o$ are the fouling factors (i.e., the unit fouling resistances) at the inside and outside surfaces of the tube, respectively, and the other quantities are as defined previously.

In heat exchanger applications, the overall heat transfer coefficient is usually based on the outer tube surface. Then Eq. (12-6) can be represented in terms of the overall heat transfer coefficient based on the outside surface of the tube as

$$U_o = \frac{1}{(D_o/D_i)(1/h_i) + (D_o/D_i)F_i + (D_o/2k)\ln(D_o/D_i) + F_o + 1/h_o} \qquad (12\text{-}7)$$

**TABLE 12.1  Unit fouling resistance (or fouling factor) $F$.**

| | $F,\ m^2 \cdot {}^\circ C/W$ |
|---|---|
| **Water** (52°C or less; velocity 1 m/s or less) | |
| Seawater | 0.000088 |
| Distilled | 0.000088 |
| Engine jacket | 0.00018 |
| Great Lakes | 0.00018 |
| Boiler blowdown | 0.00035 |
| Brackish water | 0.00035 |
| River water | |
|    Minimum | 0.00036 |
|    Mississippi | 0.00053 |
|    Delaware, Schuylkill | 0.00053 |
|    East River & New York Bay | 0.00053 |
|    Chicago Sanitary Canal | 0.00141 |
|    Muddy or Silty | 0.00053 |
| **Industrial Fluids and Gases** | |
| Hydrogen | 0.00176 |
| Engine exhaust | 0.00176 |
| Clean recirculating oil | 0.00018 |
| Vegetable oils | 0.00053 |
| Quenching oils | 0.00070 |
| Fuel oil | 0.00088 |
| Organic vapors | 0.000088 |
| Steam (non-oil-bearing) | 0.000088 |
| Gasoil | 0.00009 |
| Steam, exhaust | 0.00018 |
| Refrigerating vapors | 0.00035 |
| Air | 0.00035 |
| Organic liquids | 0.00018 |
| Refrigerating liquids | 0.00018 |
| Brine (cooling) | 0.00018 |

Compiled from Tubular Exchanger Manufacturers Association.

The values of overall heat transfer coefficients for different types of applications vary widely. Typical ranges of $U_o$ are presented in Table 12.2.

It is apparent that $U_o$ is generally low for fluids that have low thermal conductivity, such as gases or oils.

**TABLE 12.2  Overall heat transfer coefficient values.**

| | |
|---|---|
| Window Glass | 1 to 3 $\text{W}/(\text{m}^2 \cdot {}^\circ\text{C})$ |
| Gas Coolers | 10 to 15 $\text{W}/(\text{m}^2 \cdot {}^\circ\text{C})$ |
| Air Heaters | 10 to 50 $\text{W}/(\text{m}^2 \cdot {}^\circ\text{C})$ |
| Water-to-oil exchangers | 60 to 350 $\text{W}/(\text{m}^2 \cdot {}^\circ\text{C})$ |
| Gas-to-gas exchangers | 60 to 600 $\text{W}/(\text{m}^2 \cdot {}^\circ\text{C})$ |
| Evaporator of refrigerator | 300 to 1,000 $\text{W}/(\text{m}^2 \cdot {}^\circ\text{C})$ |
| Air condensers | 350 to 800 $\text{W}/(\text{m}^2 \cdot {}^\circ\text{C})$ |
| Ammonia condensers | 800 to 1400 $\text{W}/(\text{m}^2 \cdot {}^\circ\text{C})$ |
| Steam condensers | 1500 to 5000 $\text{W}/(\text{m}^2 \cdot {}^\circ\text{C})$ |

**EXAMPLE 12-1**  Determine the overall heat transfer coefficient $U_o$ based on the outer surface of a $D_i = 2.5$ cm, $D_o = 3.34$ cm brass [$k = 110$ W/(m·°C)] tube for the following conditions: The inside and outside heat transfer coefficients are, respectively, $h_i = 1200$ W/(m²·°C) and $h_o = 2000$ W/(m²·°C); the fouling factors for the inside and outside surfaces are $F_i = F_o = 0.00018$ (m²·°C)/W.

**SOLUTION**  Equation (12-7) can be used to determine $U_o$:

$$U_o = \frac{1}{(D_o/D_i)(1/h_i) + (D_o/D_i)F_i + (D_o/2k)\ln(D_o/D_i) + F_o + 1/h_o}$$

Introducing the numerical values, we obtain

$$U_o = 481.3 \text{ W}/(\text{m}^2 \cdot {}^\circ\text{C}$$

with

$$D_o/D_i)(1/h_i) = 3.34/2.5)(1/1200) = 0.00111333$$

$$D_o/D_i)F_i = 3.34/2.5)(0.00018) = 0.00024048$$

**EXAMPLE 12-2**  Hot water at a mean temperature $T_m = 80°\text{C}$ and with a mean velocity $u_m = 0.4$ m/s flows inside a 3.8-cm-ID, 4.8-cm-OD steel tube [$k = 50$ W/(m·°C)]. The flow is considered hydrodynamically and thermally developed. The outside surface is exposed to atmospheric air at $T_\infty = 20°\text{C}$, flowing with a velocity of $u_\infty = 3$ m/s normal to the tube. Calculate the *overall heat transfer coefficient* $U_o$ based on the outer surface of the tube, and the heat loss per meter length of the tube.

**SOLUTION**  The physical properties of water at $T_m = 80°\text{C}$ are

$$\nu = 0.364 \times 10^{-6} \text{ m}^2/s$$

$$k = 0.668 \text{ W}/(\text{m} \cdot {}^\circ\text{C}) \quad \text{Pr} = 2.22$$

The Reynolds number for water flow is

$$\text{Re} = \frac{u_m D}{\nu} = \frac{0.4 \times 0.038}{0.364 \times 10^{-6}} = 41,760$$

We use the Dittus-Boelter equation (Eq 8-35) to determine $h_i$ for water flow:

$$
\begin{aligned}
\text{Nu} &= 0.023\,\text{Re}^{0.8}\text{Pr}^{0.3} \\
&= 0.023(41,760)^{0.8}(2.22)^{0.3} \\
&= 145.3 \\
h_i &= \text{Nu}\frac{k}{D_i} = 145.3\frac{0.668}{0.038} = 2554 \ \text{W}/(\text{m}^2 \cdot {}^\circ\text{C})
\end{aligned}
$$

To evaluate the physical properties of air at the film temperature, the closest approximation for the film temperature is taken as $T_f \cong (80 + 20)/2 = 50^\circ\text{C}$. Then

$$\nu = 18.22 \times 10^{-6} \ m^2/s \quad k = 0.0281 \ \text{W}/(\text{m} \cdot {}^\circ\text{C})$$

$$\text{Pr} = 0.703$$

The Reynolds number for the air flow becomes

$$\text{Re} = \frac{u_\infty D}{\nu} = \frac{(3)(0.048)}{18.22 \times 10^{-6}} = 7990$$

The Nusselt number is determined from Eq. (7-40) with $Pr = 0.72$:

$$
\begin{aligned}
\text{Nu}_m &= 0.3 + \frac{0.62\text{Re}^{1/2}\text{Pr}^{1/3}}{[1 + (0.4/\text{Pr})^{2/3}]^{1/4}}\left[1 + \left(\frac{\text{Re}}{282,000}\right)^{5/8}\right]^{4/5} \\
&= 0.3 + \frac{0.627990^{1/2}0.703^{1/3}}{[1 + (0.4/0.703)^{2/3}]^{1/4}}\left[1 + \left(\frac{7990}{282,000}\right)^{5/8}\right]^{4/5} \\
&= 47.2 \\
h_o &= \text{Nu}\frac{k}{D_o} = 47.23\frac{0.0281}{0.048} = 27.6 \ \text{W}/(\text{m}^2 \cdot {}^\circ\text{C})
\end{aligned}
$$

Neglecting the tube wall resistance to heat flow, the overall heat transfer coefficient becomes

$$
\begin{aligned}
U_o &= \frac{1}{(D_o/D_i)(1/h_i) + (D_o/2k)\ln(D_o/D_i) + 1/h_o} \\
&= \frac{1}{(4.8/3.8)(1/2554) + 0.048/(2 \times 50)\ln(4.8/3.8) + 1/27.6} \\
&= 27.1 \ \text{W}/(\text{m}^2 \cdot {}^\circ\text{C})
\end{aligned}
$$

The heat loss per meter length of the tube is determined as

$$
\begin{aligned}
Q &= A_o U_o \Delta T \\
&= \pi D_o U_o (T_i - T_o) \\
&= (\pi)(0.048)(27.1)(80 - 20) \\
&= 245.6 \ \text{W/m}
\end{aligned}
$$

**EXAMPLE 12-3**  Engine oil at a mean temperature $T_i = 100°C$ flows inside a $D = 3$ cm ID, thin-walled copper tube with a heat transfer coefficient $h_i = 20 \ \text{W/(m}^2 \cdot °C)$. The outer surface of the tube dissipates heat by free convection into atmospheric air at temperature $T_\infty = 20°C$ with a heat transfer coefficient $h_o = 8 \ \text{W/(m}^2 \cdot °C)$. Calculate the overall heat transfer coefficient and the heat loss per meter length of the tube.

**SOLUTION**  We assume that the thermal resistance and the curvature effect of a thin-walled copper tube are negligible. The overall heat transfer coefficient becomes

$$
\begin{aligned}
U &= \frac{1}{1/h_i + 1/h_o} \\
&= \frac{1}{1/20 + 1/8} = 5.71 \ \text{W/(m}^2 \cdot °C)
\end{aligned}
$$

The heat loss per meter length of the tube is

$$
\begin{aligned}
Q &= \pi D U (T_i - T_\infty) \\
&= \pi \times 0.03 \times 5.71 (100 - 20) = 43.1 \ \text{W/m}
\end{aligned}
$$

## 12.4. LOGARITHMIC MEAN TEMPERATURE DIFFERENCE (LMTD) METHOD

In the thermal analysis of heat exchangers, the total heat transfer rate $Q$ through the heat exchanger is a quantity of primary interest. Here we turn our attention to single-pass heat exchangers that have flow arrangements of the type illustrated in Fig. 12.11. It is apparent from this illustration that the temperature difference $\Delta T$ between the hot and cold fluids, in general, is not constant; it varies with distance along the heat exchanger.

In the heat transfer analysis of heat exchangers, it is convenient to establish a mean temperature difference $\Delta T_m$ between the hot and cold fluids such that the total heat transfer rate $Q$ between the fluids can be determined from the following simple expression:

$$
Q = A_t U_m \Delta T_m \tag{12-8}
$$

where $A_t$ is the total heat transfer area and $U_m$ is the average overall heat transfer coefficient based on that area.

An explicit expression for $\Delta T_m$ can be established by considering an energy balance over a differential length along the heat exchanger, then integrating it over the entire path of the flow. It can be shown that this temperature difference is a logarithmic mean of the temperature differences between the hot and cold fluids at both ends of the heat exchanger, and is given by

$$\Delta T_m \equiv \Delta T_{\ln} = \frac{\Delta T_0 - \Delta T_L}{\ln(\Delta T_0 / \Delta T_L)} \tag{12-9}$$

where $\Delta T_{\ln}$ is called the *Logarithmic Mean Temperature Difference* (LMTD), and

$$\Delta T_0, \ \Delta T_L = \left\{ \begin{array}{l} \text{temperature differences between the hot and} \\ \text{cold fluids at the two ends of the heat} \\ \text{exchanger } x = 0 \text{ and } x = L, \text{ respectively} \end{array} \right\}$$

The formula for $\Delta T_{\ln}$ given in Eq. (12-9) is applicable for the single-pass heat transfer matrices illustrated in Fig. 12.11. We note that for the special case of $\Delta T_0 = \Delta T_L$, Eq. (12-9) leads to $\Delta T_{\ln} = 0/0 =$ indeterminate. But by the application of L'Hospital's rule [i.e., by differentiating the numerator and denominator of Eq. (12-9) with respect to $\Delta T_0$], it can be shown that for this particular case $\Delta T_{\ln} = \Delta T_0 = \Delta T_L$.

It is of interest to compare the LMTD of $\Delta T_0$ and $\Delta T_L$ with their arithmetic mean:

$$\Delta T_a = \frac{\Delta T_0 + \Delta T_L}{2}. \tag{12-10}$$

We present in Table 12.3, a comparison of the logarithmic and arithmetic means of the two quantities $\Delta T_0$ and $\Delta T_L$. We note that the arithmetic and logarithmic means are equal for $\Delta T_0 = \Delta T_L$. When $\Delta T_0 \neq \Delta T_L$, the LMTD is always less than the arithmetic mean; if $\Delta T_0$ is not more than 50 percent greater than $\Delta T_L$, the LMTD can be approximated by the arithmetic mean within about 1.04 percent.

### TABLE 12.3 Comparison of logarithmic $\Delta T_{\ln}$ and arithmetic $\Delta T_a$.

| $\frac{\Delta T_0}{\Delta T_L}$ | 1 | 1.2 | 1.5 | 1.7 | 2 |
|---|---|---|---|---|---|
| $\frac{\Delta T_a}{\Delta T_{\ln}}$ | 1 | 1.0028 | 1.0137 | 1.023 | 1.04 |

Thus, the total heat transfer rate between the cold and hot fluids for the single-pass arrangements shown in Fig. 12.11 can be calculated from the following simple expression:

$$Q = A_t U_m \Delta T_{\ln} \tag{12-11}$$

where

$$A_t = \text{total heat transfer area}$$

$U_m$ = average overall heat transfer coefficient between the hot and cold fluids

$\Delta T_{\ln}$ = logarithmic mean temperature difference between the hot and cold fluids, defined by Eq. (12-9)

When $A_t$ and $U_m$ are available and the inlet and outlet temperatures of the hot and cold fluids are given, the total heat transfer rate $Q$ for the heat exchanger can be readily calculated from Eq. (12-11).

**EXAMPLE 12-4** A counter-flow, shell-and-tube-type heat exchanger is to be used to cool water from $T_{h,in} = 22°C$ to $T_{h,out} = 6°C$, using brine entering at $T_{c,in} = -2°C$ and leaving at $T_{c,out} = 3°C$. The overall heat transfer coefficient is estimated to be $U_m = 500 \text{ W}/(\text{m}^2 \cdot °C)$. Calculate the heat transfer surface area for a design heat load of $Q = 10$ kW.

**SOLUTION** The logarithmic mean temperature difference becomes

$$\Delta T_{\ln} = \frac{\Delta T_0 - \Delta T_L}{\ln(\Delta T_0/\Delta T_L)}$$

$$= \frac{19 - 8}{\ln(19/8)} = 12.7\,°C$$

The total heat transfer area is

$$A_t = \frac{Q_t}{U_m \Delta T_{\ln}}$$

$$= \frac{10,000}{(500)(12.7)} = 1.57 \text{ m}^2$$

**EXAMPLE 12-5** Engine oil at $T_i = 40°C$, flowing at a rate of $m = 0.2$ kg/s, enters a $D_i = 2.5$ cm ID copper tube which is maintained at a uniform temperature $T_w = 100°C$ by steam condensing outside. Calculate the tube length required to have the outlet temperature of the oil $T_o = 80°C$.

**SOLUTION** The temperature profiles in the exchanger are shown in the accompanying figure. The physical properties of engine oil are taken at $(40 + 80)/2 = 60°C$ as

$$c_p = 2047 \text{ J}/(\text{kg} \cdot °C) \quad \nu = 0.839 \times 10^{-4} \text{ m}^2/s$$

$$\rho = 864 \text{ kg/m}^3 \quad k = 0.14 \text{ W}/(\text{m} \cdot °C)$$

$$\text{Pr} = 1050$$

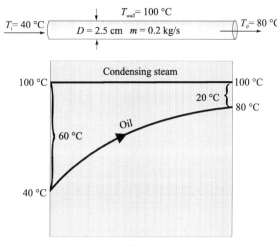

**FIGURE EXAMPLE 12-5**

The Reynolds number for flow inside the tube is

$$
\begin{aligned}
\text{Re} &= \frac{4m}{\pi D(\nu \rho)} \\
&= \frac{(4)(0.2)}{\pi(0.025)(0.839 \times 10^{-4})(864)} = 140.4
\end{aligned}
$$

The flow is laminar. By assuming fully developed flow and a constant tube wall temperature, the Nusselt number for oil flow is given by

$$
Nu = 3.66
$$

and

$$
\begin{aligned}
h_i &= 3.66 \frac{k}{D} \\
&= 3.66 \frac{0.14}{0.025} = 20.5 \ \text{W/(m}^2 \cdot {}^\circ\text{C)}
\end{aligned}
$$

Assuming that the thermal resistance of the copper tube is negligible, the overall heat transfer coefficient becomes

$$
U = h_i = 20.5 \ \text{W/(m}^2 \cdot {}^\circ\text{C)}
$$

The logarithmic mean temperature difference is

$$
\begin{aligned}
\Delta T_{\ln} &= \frac{\Delta T_0 - \Delta T_L}{\ln(\Delta T_0 / \Delta T_L)} \\
&= \frac{60 - 20}{\ln(60/20)} = 36.4^\circ\text{C}
\end{aligned}
$$

The tube length $L$ is determined from the overall energy balance for the tube:

$$mc_p \Delta T_{oil} = U A_s \Delta T_{\ln}$$
$$(0.05)(2047)(80 - 40) = (20.5)(\pi \times 0.025 \times L)(36.4)$$

This gives

$$L = 69.8 \text{ m}$$

## 12.5. CORRECTION FOR THE LMTD

The LMTD defined by Eq. (12-9) is strictly applicable for single-pass, noncross- flow heat exchangers. For cross-flow and multipass arrangements, expressions for the effective temperature difference between the hot and cold fluids can be developed, but the resulting expressions are so complicated that they are not useful for practical purposes. Therefore, for such situations, it is customary to introduce a *correction factor* $F$ so that the simple LMTD can be adjusted to represent the effective temperature difference $\Delta T_{corr}$ for cross-flow and multipass arrangements:

$$\Delta T_{corr} = F(\Delta T_{\ln} \text{ for counter-flow}) \tag{12-12}$$

where $\Delta T_{\ln}$ should be computed on the basis of counter-flow conditions; that is, $\Delta T_0$ and $\Delta T_L$ in the definition of the LMTD given by Eq. (12-9) should be taken as (see Fig. 12.11$e$)

$$\Delta T_0 = T_{h,out} - T_{c,in} \tag{12-13a}$$

$$\Delta T_L = T_{h,in} - T_{c,out} \tag{12-13b}$$

where the subscripts $c$ and $h$ refer, respectively, to the cold and hot fluids. The correction factor $F$ charts are available in the heat exchanger design literature for various heat exchanger configurations. Generally $F$ is less than unity for cross-flow and multipass arrangements; it is unity for a true counter-flow heat exchanger. It represents the degree of departure of the true mean temperature difference from the LMTD for a counter-flow heat exchanger.

## 12.6. EFFECTIVENESS AND NUMBER OF TRANSFER UNITS ($\epsilon$-NTU) METHOD

In the thermal analysis of heat exchangers there are rating and sizing problems. The rating problem is concerned with determining the transfer rate, the fluid outlet temperatures, and the pressure drops for an existing heat exchanger or one that is already sized; hence the heat transfer surface area and the flow passage dimensions are available. The sizing problem is concerned with determining the matrix dimensions needed to meet the specified heat transfer and pressure drop requirements. If we are not concerned with the pressure drop, the rating problem involves determination of the total heat transfer rate for an existing heat exchanger, and the sizing problem involves determination of the total heat transfer surface required to meet a specified heat transfer rate.

Once we know the inlet and outlet temperatures of the hot and cold fluid and the overall heat transfer coefficient are specified, the LMTD method, with or without the correction, can be easily used to solve the rating or sizing problem.

In some situations only the inlet temperatures and the flow rates of the hot and cold fluids are given, and the overall heat transfer coefficient can be estimated. For such cases, the logarithmic mean temperature cannot be determined because the outlet temperatures are not known. Therefore, using the LMTD method for the thermal analysis of heat exchangers, tedious iterations are involved in order to determine the proper value of LMTD which will satisfy the requirement that the heat transferred in the heat exchanger be equal to the heat carried out by the fluid.

In such situations the analysis can be simplified significantly by using the $\epsilon$-NTU, or effectiveness method, developed originally by Kays and London.

In this method, effectiveness $\epsilon$ is defined as

$$\epsilon = \frac{Q}{Q_{max}} = \frac{\text{actual heat transfer rate}}{\substack{\text{maximum possible heat transfer rate} \\ \text{from one stream to another}}} \qquad (12\text{-}14)$$

The maximum possible heat transfer rate $Q_{max}$ is obtained with a counter-flow exchanger if the temperature change of the fluid with the minimum value of $mc_p$ equals the difference in the inlet temperatures of the hot and cold fluids. Here we consider $(mc_p)_{min}$, because the energy given up by one fluid should equal that received by the other fluid. If we consider $(mc_p)_{max}$, then the other fluid should undergo a temperature change greater than the maximum available temperature difference; that is, $\Delta T$ for the other fluid should be greater than $T_{h,in} - T_{c,in}$. This is not possible. Given this consideration, $Q_{max}$ is chosen as

$$Q_{max} = (mc_p)_{min}(T_{h,in} - T_{c,in}) \qquad (12\text{-}15)$$

Then, given $\epsilon$ and $Q_{max}$, the actual heat transfer rate $Q$ is

$$\boxed{Q = \epsilon(mc_p)_{min}(T_{h,in} - T_{c,in})} \qquad (12\text{-}16)$$

Here $(mc_p)_{min}$ is the smaller of $m_h c_{ph}$ and $m_c c_{pc}$ for the hot and cold fluids; $T_{h,in}$ and $T_{c,in}$ are the inlet temperatures of the hot and cold fluids, respectively.

Clearly, if the effectiveness $\epsilon$ of the exchanger is known, Eq. (12-16) provides an explicit expression for the determination of $Q$ through the exchanger.

A considerable amount of effort has been directed toward the development of simple explicit expressions for the effectiveness of various types of heat exchangers. For convenience in such developments, a dimensionless parameter called the *number of (heat) transfer units* (NTU) is defined as

$$\text{NTU} = AU_m/C_{min} \qquad (12\text{-}17)$$

where $C_{min} = (mc_p)_{min}$, that is, the smaller of $m_h c_{ph}$ and $m_c c_{pc}$. The physical significance of NTU can be viewed as follows:

$$\text{NTU} = \frac{AU_m}{C_{min}} = \frac{\text{heat capacity of exchanger, } W/^\circ C}{\text{heat capacity of flow, } W/^\circ C} \qquad (12\text{-}18)$$

For a specified value of $U_m/C_{min}$, the NTU is a measure of the actual heat transfer area $A$, or the "physical size" of the exchanger. The higher the NTU, the larger the physical size.

Analytic expressions for $\epsilon$-NTU relations have been developed for various types of heat exchangers, including parallel-flow, counter-flow, cross- flow, multipass, and many others. The reader should consult Kays and London for extensive documentation of effectiveness charts for various flow arrangements.

### TABLE 12.4 Heat exchanger effectivenesses
$$NTU = UA/C_{min} \text{ and } C = C_{min}/C_{max}$$

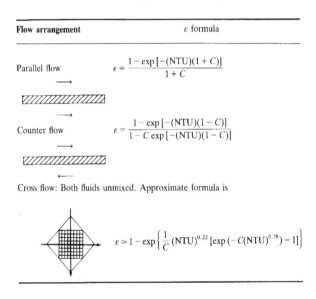

| Flow arrangement | $\epsilon$ formula |
|---|---|
| Parallel flow | $\epsilon = \dfrac{1 - \exp\left[-(\text{NTU})(1 + C)\right]}{1 + C}$ |
| Counter flow | $\epsilon = \dfrac{1 - \exp\left[-(\text{NTU})(1 - C)\right]}{1 - C\exp\left[-(\text{NTU})(1 - C)\right]}$ |

Cross flow: Both fluids unmixed. Approximate formula is

$$\epsilon \simeq 1 - \exp\left\{ \frac{1}{C} (\text{NTU})^{0.22} \left[\exp\left(-C(\text{NTU})^{0.78}\right) - 1\right]\right\}$$

In Figs. 12-13 to 12-17 we present some effectiveness charts for typical flow arrangements. Also, Table 12.3 lists some explicit expressions for the effectiveness. In these figures, the physical significance of $(C_{min}/C_{max}) \to 0$ needs further clarification.

Consider the actual heat transfer rate $Q$ through the heat exchanger, given by

$$Q = m_h c_{ph}(T_{h,in} - T_{h,out}) = m_c c_{pc}(T_{c,out} - T_{c,in}) \qquad (12\text{-}19)$$

Then, from Eqs. (12-16) and (12-19), we write

$$\epsilon = \frac{C_h(T_{h,in} - T_{h,out})}{C_{min}(T_{h,in} - T_{c,in})} \qquad (12\text{-}20)$$

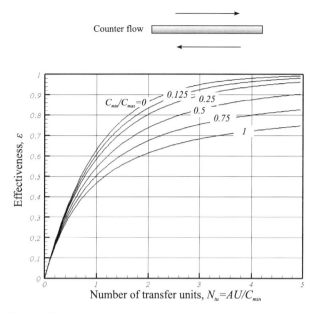

**FIG. 12.13.** Effectiveness for a counter-flow heat exchanger.

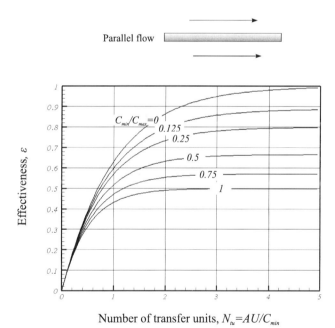

Number of transfer units, $N_{tu}=AU/C_{min}$

**FIG. 12.14.** Effectiveness for a parallel-flow heat exchanger.

or

$$\epsilon = \frac{C_c(T_{c,out} - T_{c,in})}{C_{min}(T_{h,in} - T_{c,in})}$$ 
(12-21)

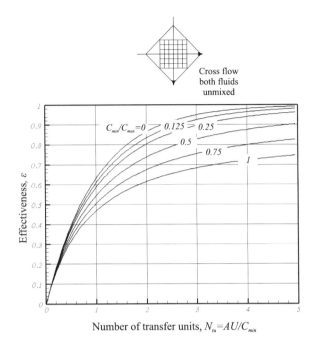

**FIG. 12.15.** Effectiveness for a cross-flow heat exchanger, both fluids unmixed.

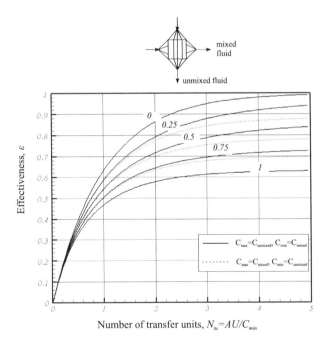

**FIG. 12.16.** Effectiveness for a cross-flow heat exchanger, one fluid is mixed the other is unmixed.

where we define

$$C_h \equiv m_h c_{ph} \qquad C_c \equiv m_c c_{pc} \qquad (12\text{-}22)$$

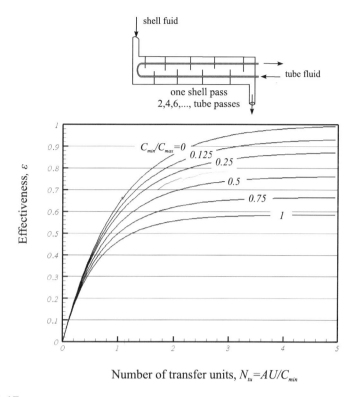

**FIG. 12.17.** Effectiveness for a single shell pass heat exchanger with two tube passes.

and $C_{min} \equiv$ smaller of $C_h$ and $C_c$. In the case of condensers and boilers, the fluid temperature on the boiling or condensing side remains essentially constant. Now, if the effectiveness $\epsilon$ as defined by Eqs. (12-20) and (12-21) should remain finite while $T_{in} - T_{out}$ for the condensing or boiling side is practically zero, $C_c$ or $C_h$ on the phase change side should behave as an infinite specific heat capacity. Such a requirement implies that for a boiler or condenser we must have $C_{max} \to \infty$, and as a result,

$$C = \frac{C_{min}}{C_{max}} \to 0. \qquad (12\text{-}23)$$

Therefore, the case $C \to 0$ *implies a boiler or a condenser.*

An examination of the results presented in Figs. 12-13 to 12-17 reveals that for $\epsilon <$ 40 percent, the capacity ratio $C = C_{min}/C_{max}$ does not have much effect on the effectiveness $\epsilon$.

A counter-flow exchanger has the highest $\epsilon$ for specified values of NTU and $C$ compared with that for other flow arrangements. Therefore, for a given NTU and $C$, a counter-flow arrangement yields maximum heat transfer performance.

Having established the framework for the definition and the determination of the heat exchanger effectiveness $\epsilon$, we are now in a position to make use of the effectiveness concept in solving *rating* and *sizing* problems.

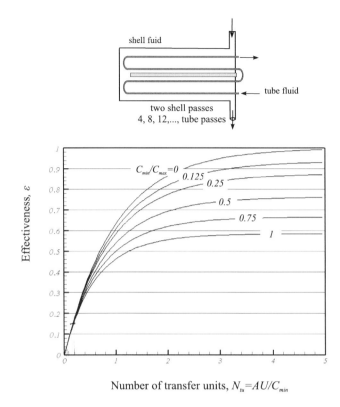

**FIG. 12.18.** Effectiveness for a two shell pass heat exchanger with four, eight, twelve, etc. tube passes.

**RATING PROBLEM.** Suppose the inlet temperatures $T_{c,in}$ and $T_{h,in}$, the flow rates $m_c$ and $m_h$, the physical properties of both fluids, the overall heat transfer coefficient $U_m$, and the total heat transfer area $A$ are all given. The type of exchanger and its flow arrangement are specified. We wish to determine the total heat flow rate $Q$ and the outlet temperatures $T_{h,out}$ and $T_{c,out}$. The calculation is as follows:

1. Calculate $C = C_{min}/C_{max}$ and NTU$= U_m A/C_{min}$ from the specified input data.

2. Knowing NTU and $C$, determine $\epsilon$ from the chart or from the equation for the specific geometry and flow arrangement.

3. Knowing $\epsilon$, compute the total heat transfer rate $Q$ from

$$Q = \epsilon C_{min}(T_{h,in} - T_{c,in})$$

4. Calculate the outlet temperatures from

$$T_{h,out} = T_{h,in} - \frac{Q}{C_h}$$
$$T_{c,out} = T_{c,in} + \frac{Q}{C_c}$$

The preceding discussion of the ε-NTU method clearly illustrates that the rating problem when the outlet temperatures are not given can readily be solved with the ε-NTU method, but a tedious iteration procedure would be required to solve it with the LMTD method, and the convergence might not be easy.

**SIZING PROBLEM.** Suppose the inlet and outlet temperatures, the flow rate, the overall heat transfer coefficient, and the total heat transfer rate are given, and the flow arrangement is specified. The procedure to determine the total heat transfer surface $A$ is as follows:

1. Calculate ε from Eqs. (12-20) and (12-21).

2. Calculate $C = C_{min}/C_{max}$.

3. Knowing ε and $C$, determine NTU from the appropriate ε-NTU chart.

4. Knowing NTU, calculate the heat transfer surface $A$ from Eq. (12-17):

$$A = \frac{(\text{NTU})C_{min}}{U_m}$$

The use of the ε-NTU method is generally preferred for the design of compact heat exchangers for automotive, aircraft, air conditioning, and various industrial applications where the inlet temperatures of the hot and cold fluids are specified and the heat transfer rates are to be determined. In the process, power, and petrochemical industries, both the inlet and outlet temperatures of the hot and cold fluids are specified; hence the LMTD method is generally used.

**EXAMPLE 12-8**   A counter-flow double pipe heat exchanger is to heat water from $10°C$ to $70°C$ at a rate of $1.7$ kg/s. The heating is to be accomplished by geothermal water available at $140°C$ at a mass flow rate of $2.3$ kg/s. The inner tube is thin-walled and has a diameter of $1.4$ cm. The overall heat transfer coefficient of the heat exchanger is $590$ W/m$^2$K, determine the length of the heat exchanger required to achieve the desired heating. (Use the following specific heats, $c_{p,water} = 4.18$ kJ/(kgK), $c_{p,geo} = 4.31$ kJ/(kgK).)

**SOLUTION**   The schematics of this exchanger is in the accompanying Figure Example 12-8.

We will first determine the length by using the LMTD method:

The total heat transfer rate $Q$ is

$$\begin{aligned} Q &= [\dot{m}c_p(T_{out} - T_{in})]_{water} \\ &= (1.7)(4.18 \text{ kJ/(kgK)})(70 - 10) = 426.36 \text{ kW} \end{aligned}$$

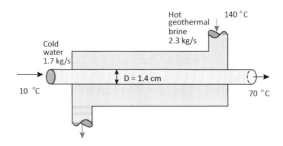

**FIGURE EXAMPLE 12-10**

The total heat transfer rate $Q$ is also expressed as

$$Q = [\dot{m}c_p(T_{in} - T_{out})]_{geothermal}$$

$$T_{out} = T_{in} - \frac{Q}{\dot{m}c_p}$$

$$= 140 - \frac{426.36}{(2.3)(4.31)} = 97\,^{\circ}\text{C}$$

$$\Delta T_1 = T_{h,in} - T_{c,out} = (140 - 70) = 70\,^{\circ}\text{C}$$
$$\Delta T_2 = T_{h,out} - T_{c,in} = (97 - 10) = 87\,^{\circ}\text{C}$$

$$\Delta T_{ln} = \frac{\Delta T_1 - \Delta T_2}{ln(\Delta T_1/\Delta T_2)}$$

$$\Delta T_{ln} = 78.19\,^{\circ}\text{C}$$

$$Q = UA_s\Delta T_{ln}$$

which gives the area $A$ as

$$A_s = \frac{Q}{U\Delta T_{ln}} = \frac{426.36 \times 10^3}{(590)(78.19)} = 9.24\,\text{m}^2$$

$$A_s = \pi DL$$

$$L = \frac{A_s}{\pi D} = \frac{9.24}{\pi(0.014)} = 210.08\,\text{m}$$

Alternatively we can solve the same problem using the $\epsilon$-NTU method:

**488**

$$C_h = \dot{m}_h c_{ph} = (2.3)(4.31) = 9.913 \text{ kW/K}$$
$$C_c = \dot{m}_c c_{pc} = (1.7)(4.18) = 7.106 \text{ kW/K}$$
$$\frac{C_{min}}{C_{max}} = \frac{7.106}{9.913} = 0.717$$
$$Q = \dot{m}c_p\Delta T = (1.7)(4.18)(70 - 10) = 426.36 \text{ kW}$$
$$\epsilon = \frac{Q}{Q_{max}} = \frac{426.36}{C_{min}\Delta T} = \frac{426.36}{(7.106)(140 - 10)} = 0.4615$$

From Fig. 12.13, we obtain

$$\text{NTU} = \frac{AU_m}{C_{min}} = 0.8$$

which gives the area $A$ as

$$A = \frac{(\text{NTU})C_{min}}{U_m}$$
$$= \frac{(0.8)(7106)}{590} = 9.635 \text{ m}^2$$

which gives

$$L = \frac{A}{\pi d} = 219.1 \text{ m}$$

**EXAMPLE 12-9**  A cross-flow heat exchanger with the flow arrangement shown in Fig. 12.15 is to heat water with hot exhaust gas. The exhaust gas $[c_p = 1050 \text{ J/(kg} \cdot {}^\circ\text{C)}]$ enters at $T_{h,in} = 200{}^\circ\text{C}$ and $m_h = 2.5$ kg/s, while the water enters at $T_{c,in} = 30{}^\circ\text{C}$ and $m_c = 1.5$ kg/s. The heat transfer surface is $A = 17.5$ m$^2$ and the overall heat transfer coefficient is $U_m = 150$ W/(m$^2 \cdot {}^\circ$C). Calculate (a) the total heat transfer rate, and (b) the outlet temperatures of the water and exhaust gas.

**SOLUTION**  (a) Since the exit temperatures are not known, the effectiveness method should be used to solve this problem.

$$C_h = m_h c_{ph} = (2.5)(1050) = 2625 \text{ W/}^\circ\text{C}$$
$$C_c = m_c c_{pc} = (1.5)(4180) = 6270 \text{ W/}^\circ\text{C}$$

Therefore $C_{min} = C_h < C_c$, and

$$\frac{C_{min}}{C_{max}} = \frac{2625}{6270} = 0.42$$

$$\text{NTU} = \frac{AU_m}{C_{min}} = \frac{17.5 \times 150}{2625} = 1$$

From Fig. 12.15, we obtain

$$\epsilon = 0.48$$

The total heat transfer rate $Q$ is

$$
\begin{aligned}
Q &= \epsilon Q_{max} = \epsilon C_{min}(T_{h,in} - T_{c,in}) \\
&= (0.48)(2625)(200 - 30) \\
&= 214.2 \text{ kW}
\end{aligned}
$$

(b) The outlet temperature of the exhaust gas is determined as

$$
\begin{aligned}
Q &= m_h c_{ph}(T_{h,in} - T_{h,out}) \\
214,200 &= 2625(200 - T_{h,out})
\end{aligned}
$$

which gives

$$T_{h,out} = 118.4 \,^\circ\text{C}$$

The outlet temperature of the water is

$$
\begin{aligned}
Q &= m_c c_{pc}(T_{c,out} - T_{c,in}) \\
214,200 &= 6270(T_{c,out} - 30)
\end{aligned}
$$

which gives

$$T_{c,out} = 64.2 \,^\circ\text{C}$$

**EXAMPLE 12-10**  A two-shell-pass, four-tube-pass heat exchanger with the flow arrangement shown in Fig. 12.17 is used to cool processed water flowing at a rate $m_h = 5$ kg/s from $t_1 = 75^\circ$C to $t_2 = 25^\circ$C on the tube side, with cold water entering the shell side at $T_1 = 10^\circ$C at a rate $m_c = 6$ kg/s. The overall heat transfer coefficient is $U_m = 750$ W/(m$^2 \cdot ^\circ$C). This heat exchanger is illustrated in the accompanying figure. Calculate (a) the heat transfer surface area, and (b) the outlet temperature of the coolant water.

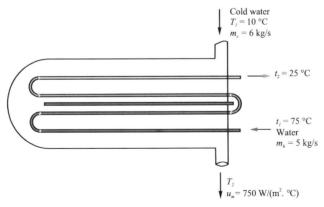

**FIGURE EXAMPLE 12-10**

## SOLUTION

$$\begin{aligned} C_h &= m_h c_{ph} = (5)(4180) = 20,900 \text{ W/}^\circ\text{C} \\ C_c &= m_c c_{pc} = (6)(4180) = 25,080 \text{ W/}^\circ\text{C} \end{aligned}$$

Therefore $C_{min} = C_h < C_c$, and

$$\frac{C_{min}}{C_{max}} = \frac{20,900}{25,080} = 0.83$$

The total heat transfer rate $Q$ is

$$\begin{aligned} Q &= m_h c_{ph}(T_{h,in} - T_{h,out}) \\ &= (5)(4180)(75 - 25) = 1,045,000 \text{ W} \end{aligned}$$

The effectiveness is

$$\begin{aligned} \epsilon &= \frac{Q}{Q_{max}} = \frac{Q}{C_{min}(T_{h,in} - T_{c,in})} \\ &= \frac{1,045,000}{(20,900)(75 - 10)} = 0.77 \end{aligned}$$

From Fig. 12.17, we obtain

$$\text{NTU} = \frac{AU_m}{C_{min}} = 4.5$$

which gives

$$\begin{aligned} A &= \frac{(\text{NTU})C_{min}}{U_m} \\ &= \frac{(4.5)(20,900)}{750} = 125.4 \text{ m}^2 \end{aligned}$$

(b) The exit temperature of the coolant water $T_{c,out}$ is determined from the energy balance:

$$\begin{aligned} Q &= m_c c_{pc}(T_{c,out} - T_{c,in}) \\ &= (6)(4180)(T_{c,out} - 10) \end{aligned}$$

which gives

$$T_{c,out} = 51.7\,^\circ\text{C}$$

*Note:* Once we know the inlet and exit temperatures, this problem can easily be solved by LMTD, which gives a heat transfer area of $A = 113.7 \text{ m}^2$. Since LMTD doesn't involve reading values from a chart, it is more accurate.

## 12.7. A NOTE ON COMPACT HEAT EXCHANGERS

The compact heat exchangers with a surface area density greater than about $700\ m^2/m^3$ are quite arbitrarily referred to as a compact heat exchanger. They are generally used for applications in which gas flows. Hence the heat transfer coefficient of the gases is low, and the smallness of weight and size is important. These heat exchangers are available in a wide variety of configurations of the heat transfer matrix, and their heat transfer and pressure drop characteristics have been studied extensively by Kays and London. Figure

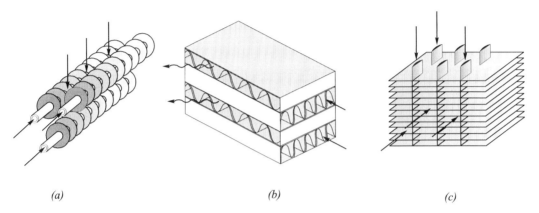

(a)           (b)           (c)

**FIG. 12.18.** Typical heat transfer matrices for compact heat exchangers. (a) Circular finned-tube matrix; (b) plain plate-fin matrix; (c) finned flat-tube matrix.

12.18 shows typical heat transfer matrices for compact heat exchangers. Figure 12.18$a$ shows a circular finned-tube array with fins on individual tubes, Fig. 12.18$b$ shows a plain plate-fin matrix formed by corrugation, and Fig. 12.18$c$ shows a finned flat-tube matrix.

The heat transfer and pressure drop characteristics for compact heat exchangers are determined experimentally from the given charts and they are available in heat exchanger design books.

Thus, once the heat transfer and the friction factor charts for a specified matrix are available and the Reynolds number Re for the flow is given, the heat transfer coefficient $h$ and the friction factor $f$ for flow across the matrix can be evaluated. Then the rating and sizing problems associated with the heat exchanger matrix can be performed using either the LMTD or the effectiveness method of analysis. We now describe the pressure drop analysis for compact heat exchangers.

As the fluid enters a heat exchanger, it experiences pressure losses owing to contraction resulting from an area change and an irreversible free expansion after a sudden contraction. As the fluid passes through the heat exchanger matrix (i.e., the core), it experiences pressure loss because of fluid friction. Also, depending on whether heating or cooling takes place, a pressure change results from flow acceleration or deceleration. Finally, as the fluid leaves the heat exchanger matrix, there are pressure losses associated with the area change and the flow separation. Therefore, in general, the pressure drop associated with flow through a compact heat exchanger matrix consists of three components: the *core friction*, the *core acceleration*, and the *entrance* and *exit losses*. Here we present the pressure drop analysis for finned-tube exchangers only.

## PROBLEMS

*Overall Heat Transfer Coefficient and Thermal Resistances*

**12-1.** Determine the overall heat transfer coefficient $U_o$ based on the outer surface of a $D_i = 2.5$ cm, $D_o = 3.34$ cm steel pipe [$k = 54$ W/(m·°C)] for the following conditions: The inside and outside heat transfer coefficients are, respectively, $h_f = 1200$ W/(m²·°C) and $h_o = 2000$ W/(m²·°C); the fouling factors for the inside and outside surfaces are $F_i = F_o = 0.00018$ (m²·°C)/W.

**12-2.** Determine the overall heat transfer coefficient $U_i$ based on the inside surface of a $D_i = 2.5$ cm, $D_o = 3.34$ cm brass tube [$k = 110$ W/(m·°C)] for the following conditions: The inside and outside heat transfer coefficients are, respectively, $h_i = 1200$ W/(m²·°C) and $h_o = 2000$ W/(m²·°C); the fouling factors for the inside and outside surfaces are $F_i = F_o = 0.00018$ (m²·°C)/W.

**12-3.** Determine the overall heat transfer coefficient $U_o$ based on the outer surface of a $D_i = 2.5$ cm, $D_o = 3.34$ cm brass tube [$k = 110$ W/(m²·°C)] for the following conditions: The inside heat transfer coefficient is $h_i = 1000$ W/(m²·°C) and the fouling factors for the surfaces are $F_i = F_o = 0.00018$ (m²·°C)/W. The outside heat transfer coefficients are (a) $h_o = 1500$ W/(m²·°C), (b) $h_o = 2000$ W/(m²·°C), and (c) $h_o = 2500$ W/(m²·°C).

**12-4.** Water at a mean temperature of $T_m = 80$°C and a mean velocity of $U_m = 3$ m/s flows inside a 2.5-cm-ID thin-walled copper tube. Atmospheric air at $T_\infty = 20$°C and a velocity of $U_\infty = 8$ m/s flows across the tube. Neglecting the tube wall resistance, calculate the overall heat transfer coefficient and the rate of heat loss per meter length of the tube.

**12-5.** Water at $T_i = 25$°C and a velocity of $U_m = 1.5$ m/s enters a long brass condenser tube with $D_i = 1.34$ cm and $D_o = 1.58$ cm [$k = 110$ W/(m·°C)]. The heat transfer coefficient for condensation at the outer surface of the tube is $h_o = 12,000$ W/(m²·°C). Calculate the overall heat transfer coefficient $U_o$ based on the outer surface.

**12-6.** Engine oil at $T_i = 50$°C and a mean velocity of $U_m = 0.25$ m/s enters a $D_i = 2.22$ cm, $t = 0.17$ cm thick brass horizontal tube [$k = 110$ W/(m·°C)]. Heat is dissipated from the outer surface of the tube by free convection into ambient air at $T_\infty = 20$°C. Calculate the overall heat transfer coefficient $U_o$ based on the tube outer surface.

**12-7.** Engine oil at $T_i = 50$°C and a mean velocity of $U_m = 0.25$ m/s enters a steel pipe with $D_i = 1.34$ cm and $D_o = 1.58$ cm [$k = 54$ W/(m·°C)]. Heat is dissipated from the horizontal outer surface of the pipe by free convection into ambient air at

$T_\infty = 20°C$. Calculate the overall heat transfer coefficient $U_o$ based on the tube outer surface.

**12-8.** Engine oil at a mean temperature $T_i = 80°C$ and mean velocity $U = 0.25$ m/s flows inside $D = 1$ cm ID, thin-walled, horizontal copper tubing. The outer surface of the tube dissipates heat by free convection into atmospheric air at a temperature $T_\infty = 25°C$. Calculate (*a*) the temperature of the tube wall, (*b*) the overall heat transfer coefficient, and (*c*) the heat loss per meter length of the tube.

## *Logarithmic Mean Temperature Difference Method*

**12-9.** A counter-flow shell-and-tube heat exchanger is to be used to cool water from $T_{h,in} = 30°C$ to $T_{h,out} = 10°C$, using brine at $T_{c,in} = 1°C$ and $T_{c,out} = 5°C$. The overall heat transfer coefficient is estimated to be $U_m = 500$ W/(m² · °C). Calculate the heat transfer surface area for a design heat load of $Q = 10\ kW$.

**12-10.** Steam condenses at $T_h = 60°C$ on the shell side of a steam condenser while cooling water flows inside the tubes at a rate of $m_c = 3$ kg/s. The inlet and outlet temperatures of the water are $T_{c,in} = 20°C$ and $T_{c,out} = 50°C$, respectively. The overall heat transfer coefficient is $U_m = 2000$ W/(m² · °C). Calculate the surface area required.

**12-11.** A counter-flow shell-and-tube heat exchanger is to be used to heat water from $T_{c,in} = 10°C$ to $T_{c,out} = 70°C$, with oil $[C_p = 2100$ J/(kg · °C)] entering at $T_{h,in} = 120°C$ and leaving at $T_{h,out} = 60°C$ at a rate of $m_h = 5$ kg/s. The overall heat transfer coefficient is $U_m = 300$ W/(m² · °C). Calculate the heat transfer surface required.

**12-12.** A counter-flow heat exchanger is to cool $m_h = 1$ kg/s of water from 65°C to 5°C by using a refrigerant $[C_{pc} = 920$ J/(kg · °C)] entering at $T_{c,in} = -20°C$ and a flow rate of $m_c = 8$ kg/s. The overall heat transfer coefficient is $U_m = 1000$ W/(m² · °C). Calculate the heat transfer area required.

**12-13.** Engine oil at 60°C, flowing at a rate $m = 0.5$ kg/s, enters a $D_i = 3$ cm ID copper tube which is maintained at a uniform temperature $T_w = 100°C$ by condensing steam outside. Calculate the tube length required if the outlet temperature is to be $T_o = 80°C$.

**12-14.** A counter-flow heat exchanger is to be used to heat $m_c = 3$ kg/s of water from $T_{c,in} = 20°C$ to $T_{c,out} = 80°C$, using hot exhaust gas $[c_p = 1000$ J/(kg · °C)] entering at $T_{h,in} = 220°C$ and leaving at $T_{h,out} = 90°C$. The overall heat transfer coefficient is $U_m = 200$ W/(m² · °C). Calculate the heat transfer surface required.

**12-15.** A single-pass, counter-flow, shell-and-tube heat exchanger is used to heat water from $T_{c,in} = 15°C$ to $T_{c,out} = 80°C$ at a rate $m_c = 5$ kg/s, using oil entering the shell side at $T_{h,in} = 140°C$ and leaving at $T_{h,out} = 90°C$. The overall heat transfer coefficient is $U_m = 400$ W/(m$^2 \cdot$ °C). Calculate the heat transfer surface required.

**12-16.** A counter-flow heat exchanger is to be designed to cool $m_h = 0.5$ kg/s of oil $[c_p = 2000$ J/(kg $\cdot$ °C)] from $T_h, in = 60°C$ to $T_{h,out} = 40°C$ with cooling water entering at $T_{c,in} = 20°C$ and leaving $T_{c,out} = 30°C$. The overall heat transfer coefficient is $U_m = 200$ W/(m$^2 \cdot$ °C). Calculate the heat transfer surface required.

**12-17.** The design heat load for an oil cooler is $Q = 500$ $kW$. Calculate the heat transfer surface $A$ required if the inlet and outlet temperature differences are, respectively, $\Delta T_0 = 40°C$ and $\Delta T_L = 15°C$ and the average value of the overall heat transfer coefficient is $U_m = 500$ W/(m$^2 \cdot$ °C).

**12-18.** Engine oil at a mean temperature $T_m = 80°C$ and mean velocity $U = 0.2$ m/s flows inside $D = 1.9$ cm ID, thin-walled horizontal copper tubing. At the outer surface, atmospheric air at $T_\infty = 15°C$ and a velocity of $U_\infty = 5$ m/s flows across the tube. Neglecting the tube wall resistance, calculate the overall heat transfer coefficient and the rate of heat loss to the air per meter length of the tube.

**12-19.** Water at a mean temperature $T_i = 80°C$ and a mean velocity $u = 0.15$ m/s flows inside a $D = 2.5$ cm ID, thin-walled horizontal copper tube. At the outer surface of the tube, heat is dissipated by free convection into atmospheric air at a temperature $T_\infty = 15°C$. Assuming that the tube wall resistance is negligible, calculate the overall heat transfer coefficient and the heat loss per meter length of the tube.

.

*Effectiveness and Number of Transfer Units ($\epsilon$-NTU) Method*

**12-20.** Hot chemical products $[C_{ph} = 2500$ J/(kg $\cdot$ °C)] at $T_{h,in} = 600°C$ and at a flow rate $m_h = 30$ kg/s are used to heat cold chemical products $[c_{pc} = 4200$ J/(kg $\cdot$ °C)] at $T_{c,in} = 100°C$ and $m_c = 30$ kg/s in the parallel-flow arrangement shown in Fig. 12.14. The total heat transfer surface is $A = 50$ m$^2$, and the overall heat transfer coefficient can be taken as $U_m = 1500$ W/(m$^2 \cdot$ °C). Calculate the outlet temperatures of the hot and cold chemical products for $m_h = m_c$.

**12-21.** Hot chemical products $[c_{ph} = 2500$ J/(kg $\cdot$ °C)] at $T_{h,in} = 600°C$ and at a flow rate $m_h = 30$ kg/s are used to heat cold chemical products $[c_{pc} = 4200$ J/(kg $\cdot$ °C)] at $T_{c,in} = 100°C$ and $m_c = 30$ kg/s in the counter-flow arrangement shown in Fig. 12.13. The total heat transfer surface is $A = 50$ cm$^2$, and the overall heat transfer coefficient can be taken as $U_m = 1500$ W/(m$^2 \cdot$ °C). Calculate the outlet temperatures of the cold and hot chemical products for $m_h = m_c$.

**12-22.** A counter-flow heat exchanger with the flow arrangement of Fig. 12.13 is to heat air to $T_{c,out} = 500°C$ with the exhaust gas from a turbine. Air enters the exchanger at $T_{c,in} = 300°C$ and $m_c = 4$ kg/s, while the exhaust gas enters at $T_{h,in} = 650°C$

and $m_h = 4$ kg/s. The overall heat transfer coefficient is $U_m = 80$ W/(m$^2 \cdot$ °C). The specific heat for both air and the exhaust gas can be taken as $c_{ph} = c_{pc} = 1100$ J/(kg $\cdot$ °C). Calculate the heat transfer surface $A$ required and the outlet temperature of the exhaust gas.

**12-23.** A counter-flow heat exchanger with the flow arrangement shown in Fig. 12.13 is to heat cold fluid entering at $T_{c,in} = 30$°C and $m_c c_{pc} = 15{,}000$ W/°C with hot fluid entering at $T_{h,in} = 120$°C and $m_h c_{ph} = 10{,}000$ W/°C. The overall heat transfer coefficient is $U_m = 400$ W/(m$^2 \cdot$ °C), and the total heat transfer surface is $A = 20$ m$^2$. Calculate the total heat transfer rate $Q$ and the outlet temperatures of the hot and cold fluids.

**12-24.** A counter-flow heat exchanger with the flow arrangement shown in Fig. 12.13 is to heat air entering at $T_{c,in} = 400$°C and $m_c = 6$ kg/s with exhaust gas entering at $T_{h,in} = 800$°C and $m_h = 4$ kg/s. The overall heat transfer coefficient is $U_m = 100$ W/(m$^2 \cdot$ °C), and the outlet temperature of the air is $551.5$°C. the specific heat for both air and the exhaust gas may be taken as $c_{ph} = c_{pc} = 1100$ J/(kg $\cdot$ °C). Calculate the heat transfer surface $A$ required and the outlet temperature of the hot exhaust gas.
*Answer:* $T_{h\ out} = 572.8$°C

**12-25.** A counter-flow shell-and-tube heat exchanger with the flow arrangement shown in Fig. 12.13 is used to heat water with hot exhaust gases. The water enters at $T_{c,in} = 25$°C and leaves at $T_{c,out} = 80$°C at a rate $m_c = 2$ kg/s. Exhaust gases $[c_p = 1030$ J/(kg $\cdot$ °C)$]$ enter at $T_{h,in} = 175$°C and leave at $T_{h,out} = 90$°C. The overall heat transfer coefficient is $U_m = 200$ W/(m$^2 \cdot$ °C). Calculate the heat transfer surface area required.

**12-26.** A cross-flow heat exchanger with the flow arrangement shown in Fig. 12.15 is to heat water with hot exhaust gas. The water enters the tubes at $T_{c,in} = 25$°C and $m_c = 1$ kg/s, while the exhaust gas enters the exchanger at $T_{h,in} = 200$°C and $m_h = 2$ kg/s. The total heat transfer surface is $A = 30$ m$^2$, and the overall heat transfer coefficient is $U_m = 120$ W/(m$^2 \cdot$ °C). The specific heat for the exhaust gas may be taken as $c_{ph} = 1100$ J/(kg $\cdot$ °C). Calculate the total heat transfer rate $Q$ and the outlet temperatures $T_{c,out}$ and $T_{h,out}$ of the water and the exhaust gas.

**12-27.** A cross-flow heat exchanger with the flow arrangement shown in Fig. 12.15 has a heat transfer surface $A = 12$ m$^2$ . It will be used to heat air entering at $T_{c,in} = 10$°C and $m_c = 3$ kg/s with hot water entering at $T_{h,in} = 80$°C and $m_h = 0.4$ kg/s. The overall heat transfer coefficient can be taken as $U_m = 300$ W/(m$^2 \cdot$ °C). Calculate the total heat transfer rate $Q$ and the outlet temperatures of the air and water.

**12-28.** A cross-flow heat exchanger with the flow arrangement shown in Fig. 12.15 is used to heat water with an engine oil. Water enters at $T_{c,in} = 30$°C and leaves at $T_{c,out} = 85$°C at a rate $m_c = 1.5$ kg/s, while the engine oil $[c_{ph} = 2300$ J/(kg $\cdot$ °C)$]$

enters at $T_{h,in} = 120°C$ at a flow rate $m_h = 3.5$ kg/s. The heat transfer surface is $A = 30$ m$^2$ . Calculate the overall heat transfer coefficient $U_m$ using the $\epsilon$-NTU method.

12-29. A cross-flow heat exchanger with the flow arrangement shown in Fig. 12.15 is used to heat pressurized water to $T_{c,out} = 90°C$ with a hot exhaust gas. The hot gas $[c_{ph} = 1050$ J/(kg $\cdot$ °C)] enters the exchanger at $T_{h,in} = 300°C$ and a flow rate $m_h = 1$ kg/s, while the pressurized water enters at $T_{c,in} = 30°C$ and a flow rate $m_c = 0.25$ kg/s. The heat transfer surface area is $A = 3$ m$^2$ . Calculate the overall heat transfer coefficient $U_m$, using the $\epsilon$-NTU method.

12-30. A cross-flow heat exchanger with the flow arrangement shown in Fig. 12.15 is to heat water with hot exhaust gas. The exhaust gas $[c_p = 1100$ J/(kg $\cdot$ °C)] enters at $T_{h,in} = 300°C$ and $m_h = 3$ kg/s, while the water enters at $T_{c,in} = 20°C$ and $m_c = 2$ kg/s. The overall heat transfer coefficient is $U_m = 100$ W/(m$^2$ $\cdot$ °C), and the heat transfer surface is $A = 20$ m$^2$ . Calculate $(a)$ the total heat transfer rate and $(b)$ the outlet temperatures of water and exhaust gas.

12-31. A single-shell-pass, two-tube-pass condenser with the flow arrangement shown in Fig. 12.16 is to condense steam at $T = 80°C$ with cooling water entering at $T_{c,in} = 20°C$ and $m_c = 500$ kg/s. The total heat transfer rate is given by $Q = 14,000$ $kW$. The overall heat transfer coefficient is $U_m = 4000$ W/(m$^2$ $\cdot$ °C). Calculate the total heat transfer surface $A$ and the outlet temperature $T_{c,out}$ of the cooling water.

12-32. A one-shell-pass, two-tube-pass heat exchanger with the flow arrangement shown in Fig. 12.16 is to heat water entering at $T_{c,in} = 40°C$ and leaving at $T_{c,out} = 140°C$, with $m_c = 2$ kg/s, with pressurized hot water entering at $T_{h,in} = 300°C$ and $m_h = 2$ kg/s. The overall heat transfer coefficient is $U_m = 1250$ W/(m$^2$ $\cdot$ °C). Calculate the heat transfer surface $A$ required and the outlet temperature of the hot water.

12-33. A single-shell-pass and two-tube-pass heat exchanger with the flow arrangement shown in Fig. 12.16 is used to heat water entering at $t_{c,in} = 15°C$ and $m_c = 2$ kg/s with ethylene glycol $[c_p = 2600$ J/(kg $\cdot$ °C)] entering at $T_{h,in} = 85°C$ and $m_h = 1$ kg/s. The overall heat transfer coefficient is $U_m = 500$ W/(m$^2$ $\cdot$ °C), and the heat transfer surface $A = 10$ m$^2$ . Calculate the rate of heat transfer $Q$ and the outlet temperatures of the water and ethylene glycol.

12-34. A two-shell-pass, four-tube-pass heat exchanger with the flow arrangement shown in Fig. 12.17 is to cool $m_h = 3$ kg/s of oil $[c_{ph} = 2100$ J/(kg $\cdot$ °C)] from $T_{h,in} = 85°C$ to $T_{h,out} = 35°C$ with water $[c_{pc} = 4180$ J/(kg $\cdot$ °C)] entering the exchanger at $T_{c,in} = 14°C$ and $m_c = 2$ kg/s. The overall heat transfer coefficient is $U_m = 400$ W/(m$^2$ $\cdot$ °C). Calculate the total heat transfer surface required.

**12-35.** A two-shell-pass, four-tube-pass heat exchanger with the flow arrangement shown in Fig. 12.17 is to be used to heat $m_c = 1.2$ kg/s water from $T_{c,in} = 20°C$ to $T_{c,out} = 80°C$ by using $m_h = 2.2$ kg/s oil entering at $T_{h,in} = 160°C$. The overall heat transfer coefficient is $U_m = 300$ W/(m$^2 \cdot$ °C), and the specific heat of oil is $c_{ph} = 2100$ J/($kg \cdot$ °C). Determine the heat transfer surface required.

# APPENDICES

# APPENDIX A: CONSTANTS AND CONVERSION FACTORS

## Table A-1 Commonly Used Constants

| | |
|---|---|
| $g_c$ = gravitational acceleration conversion factor | = 32.1739 ft · lb/(lbf · s$^2$) |
| | = 4.1697×10$^8$ ft · lb/(lbf · h$^2$) |
| | = 1 g · cm/(dyn · s$^2$) |
| | = 1 kg · m/(N · s$^2$) |
| | = 1 lb · ft/(pdl · s$^2$) |
| | = 1 slug · ft/(lbf · s$^2$) |
| $J$ = mechanical equivalent of heat | = 778.16 ft · lbf/Btu |
| $\mathcal{R}$ = gas constant | = 1544 ft · lbf/(lb · mol · °R) |
| | = 0.730 ft$^3$ · atm/(lb · mol · °R) |
| | = 0.08205 m$^3$ · atm/(kg · mol · K) |
| | = 8.314 J/(g · mol · K) |
| | = 8.314 N · m/(g · mol · K) |
| | = 8314 N · m/(kg · mol · K) |
| | = 1.987 cal/(g · mol · K) |
| $\sigma$ = Stefan-Boltzmann constant | = 0.1714×10$^{-8}$ Btu/(h · ft$^2$ · °R$^4$) |
| | = 5.6697×10$^{-8}$ W/(m$^2$ · K$^4$) |

# Table A-2 Conversion factors

1. Acceleration
   $1 \text{ ft/s}^2 = 0.3048 \text{ m/s}^2$
   $1 \text{ m/s}^2 = 3.2808 \text{ ft/s}^2$

2. Area
   $1 \text{ in}^2 = 6.4516 \text{ cm}^2$
   $1 \text{ in}^2 = 6.4516 \times 10^{-4} \text{ m}^2$
   $1 \text{ ft}^2 = 929 \text{ cm}^2$
   $1 \text{ ft}^2 = 0.0929 \text{ m}^2$
   $1 \text{ m}^2 = 10.764 \text{ ft}^2$

3. Density
   $1 \text{ lb/in}^3 = 27.680 \text{ g/cm}^3$
   $1 \text{ lb/in}^3 = 27.680 \times 10^3 \text{ kg/m}^3$
   $1 \text{ lb/ft}^3 = 16.019 \text{ kg/m}^3$
   $1 \text{ kg/m}^3 = 0.06243 \text{ lb/ft}^3$
   $1 \text{ slug/ft}^3 = 515.38 \text{ kg/m}^3$
   $1 \text{ lb} \cdot \text{mol/ft}^3 = 16.019 \text{ kg} \cdot \text{mol/m}^3$
   $1 \text{ kg} \cdot \text{mol/m}^3 = 0.06243 \text{ lb} \cdot \text{mol/ft}^3$

4. Diffusivity (heat, mass, momentum)
   $1 \text{ ft}^2/\text{s} = 0.0929 \text{ m}^2/\text{s}$
   $1 \text{ ft}^2/\text{h} = 0.2581 \text{ cm}^2/\text{s}$
   $1 \text{ ft}^2/\text{h} = 0.2581 \times 10^{-4} \text{ m}^2/\text{s}$
   $1 \text{ m}^2/\text{s} = 10.7639 \text{ ft}^2/\text{s}$
   $1 \text{ cm}^2/\text{s} = 3.8745 \text{ ft}^2/\text{h}$

5. Energy, heat, power
   $1 \text{ J} = 1 \text{ W} \cdot \text{s} = 1 \text{ N} \cdot \text{m}$
   $1 \text{ J} = 10^7 \text{ erg}$
   $1 \text{ Btu} = 1055.06 \text{ J}$
   $1 \text{ Btu} = 1055.06 \text{ W} \cdot \text{s}$
   $1 \text{ Btu} = 1055.06 \text{ N} \cdot \text{m}$
   $1 \text{ Btu} = 252 \text{ cal}$
   $1 \text{ Btu} = 0.252 \text{ kcal}$
   $1 \text{ Btu} = 778.169 \text{ ft} \cdot \text{lbf}$
   $1 \text{ Btu/h} = 0.2931 \text{ W}$
   $1 \text{ Btu/h} = 0.2931 \times 10^{-3} \text{ kW}$
   $1 \text{ Btu/h} = 3.93 \times 10^{-4} \text{ hp}$
   $1 \text{ cal} = 4.1868 \text{ J (or W} \cdot \text{s or N} \cdot \text{m)}$
   $1 \text{ cal} = 3.968 \times 10^{-3} \text{ Btu}$
   $1 \text{ kcal} = 3.968 \text{ Btu}$
   $1 \text{ hp} = 550 \text{ ft} \cdot \text{lbf/s}$
   $1 \text{ hp} = 745.7 \text{ W} = 745.7 \text{ N} \cdot \text{m/s}$
   $1 \text{ Wh} = 3.413 \text{ Btu}$
   $1 \text{ kWh} = 3413 \text{ Btu}$

6. Heat capacity, heat per unit mass, specific heat
   $1 \text{ Btu/(h} \cdot {}^\circ\text{F)} = 0.5274 \text{ W/}^\circ\text{C}$
   $1 \text{ W/}^\circ\text{C} = 1.8961 \text{ Btu/(h} \cdot {}^\circ\text{F)}$
   $1 \text{ Btu/lb} = 2325.9 \text{ J/kg}$
   $1 \text{ Btu/lb} = 2.3259 \text{ kJ/kg}$
   $1 \text{ Btu/(lb} \cdot {}^\circ\text{F)} = 4186.69 \text{ J/(kg} \cdot {}^\circ\text{C)}$
   $1 \text{ Btu/(lb} \cdot {}^\circ\text{F)} = 4.18669 \text{ kJ/(kg} \cdot {}^\circ\text{C)}$
   [or $\text{J/(g} \cdot {}^\circ\text{C)}$]
   $1 \text{ Btu/(lb} \cdot {}^\circ\text{F)} = 1 \text{ cal/(g} \cdot {}^\circ\text{C)} = 1 \text{ kcal/(kg} \cdot {}^\circ\text{C)}$

7. Heat flux
   $1 \text{ Btu/(h} \cdot \text{ft}^2) = 3.1537 \text{ W/m}^2$
   $1 \text{ Btu/(h ft}^2) = 3.1537 \times 10^{-3} \text{ kW/m}^2$
   $1 \text{ W/m}^2 = 0.31709 \text{ Btu/(h} \cdot \text{ft}^2)$

8. Heat generation rate
   $1 \text{ Btu/(h} \cdot \text{ft}^3) = 10.35 \text{ W/m}^3$
   $1 \text{ Btu/(h} \cdot \text{ft}^3) = 8.9 \text{ kcal/(h} \cdot \text{m}^3)$
   $1 \text{ W/m}^3 = 0.0966 \text{ Btu/(h} \cdot \text{ft}^3)$

9. Heat transfer coefficient
   $1 \text{ Btu/(h} \cdot \text{ft}^2 \cdot {}^\circ\text{F)} = 5.677 \text{ W/(m}^2 \cdot {}^\circ\text{C)}$
   $1 \text{ Btu/(h} \cdot \text{ft}^2 \cdot {}^\circ\text{F)} = 5.677 \times 10^{-4} \text{ W/(cm}^2 \cdot {}^\circ\text{C)}$
   $1 \text{ W/(m}^2 \cdot {}^\circ\text{C)} = 0.1761 \text{ Btu/(h} \cdot \text{ft}^2 \cdot {}^\circ\text{F)}$
   $1 \text{ Btu/(h} \cdot \text{ft}^2 \cdot {}^\circ\text{F)} = 4.882 \text{ kcal/(h} \cdot \text{m}^2 \cdot {}^\circ\text{C)}$

10. Length
    $1 \text{ A} = 10^{-8} \text{ cm}$
    $1 \text{ A} = 10^{-10} \text{ m}$
    $1 \text{ } \mu\text{m} = 10^{-3} \text{ mm}$
    $1 \text{ } \mu\text{m} = 10^{-4} \text{ cm}$
    $1 \text{ } \mu\text{m} = 10^{-6} \text{ m}$
    $1 \text{ in} = 2.54 \text{ cm}$
    $1 \text{ in} = 2.54 \times 10^{-2} \text{ m}$
    $1 \text{ ft} = 0.3048 \text{ m}$
    $1 \text{ m} = 3.2808 \text{ ft}$
    $1 \text{ mi} = 1609.34 \text{ m}$
    $1 \text{ mi} = 5280 \text{ ft}$
    $1 \text{ light year} = 9.46 \times 10^{15} \text{ m}$

11. Mass
    $1 \text{ oz} = 28.35 \text{ g}$
    $1 \text{ lb} = 16 \text{ oz}$
    $1 \text{ lb} = 453.6 \text{ g}$
    $1 \text{ lb} = 0.4536 \text{ kg}$

1 kg = 2.2046 lb
1 slug = 32.1739 lb
1 t (metric) = 1000 kg
1 t (metric) = 2205 lb
1 ton (short) = 2000 lb
1 ton (long) = 2240 lb

12. Mass flux

$1\ \text{lb} \cdot \text{mol}/(\text{ft}^2 \cdot \text{h})$
$= 1.3563 \times 10^{-3}\ \text{kg} \cdot \text{mol}/(\text{m}^2 \cdot \text{s})$
$1\ \text{kg} \cdot \text{mol}/(\text{m}^2 \cdot \text{s}) = 737.3\ \text{lb} \cdot \text{mol}/(\text{ft}^2 \cdot \text{h})$
$1\ \text{lb}/(\text{ft}^2 \cdot \text{h}) = 1.3563 \times 10^{-3}\ \text{kg}/(\text{m}^2 \cdot \text{s})$
$1\ \text{lb}/(\text{ft}^2 \cdot \text{s}) = 4.882\ \text{kg}/(\text{m}^2 \cdot \text{s})$
$1\ \text{kg}/(\text{m}^2 \cdot \text{s}) = 737.3\ \text{lb}/(\text{ft}^2 \cdot \text{h})$
$1\ \text{kg}/(\text{m}^2 \cdot \text{s}) = 0.2048\ \text{lb}/(\text{ft}^2 \cdot \text{s})$

13. Pressure, force

$1\ \text{N} = 1\ \text{kg} \cdot \text{m}/\text{s}^2$
$1\ \text{N} = 0.22481\ \text{lbf}$
$1\ \text{N} = 7.2333\ \text{pdl}$
$1\ \text{N} = 10^5\ \text{dyn}$
$1\ \text{lbf} = 32.174\ \text{ft} \cdot \text{lb}/\text{s}^2$
$1\ \text{lbf} = 4.4482\ \text{N}$
$1\ \text{lbf} = 4.4482\ \text{kg} \cdot \text{m}/\text{s}^2$
$1\ \text{lbf} = 32.1739\ \text{pdl}$
$1\ \text{lbf}/\text{in}^2 \equiv 1\ \text{psi} = 6894.76\ \text{N}/\text{m}^2$
$1\ \text{lbf}/\text{ft}^2 = 47.880\ \text{N}/\text{m}^2$
$1\ \text{bar} = 10^5\ \text{N}/\text{m}^2 = 10^5\ \text{Pa}$
$1\ \text{atm} = 14.696\ \text{lbf}/\text{in}^2$
$1\ \text{atm} = 2116.2\ \text{lbf}/\text{ft}^2$
$1\ \text{atm} = 1.0132 \times 10^5\ \text{N}/\text{m}^2$
$1\ \text{atm} = 1.0132\ \text{bar}$
$1\ \text{Pa} = 1\ \text{N}/\text{m}^2$

14. Specific heat

$1\ \text{Btu}/(\text{lb} \cdot {}^\circ\text{F}) = 1\text{kcal}/(\text{kg} \cdot {}^\circ\text{C}) = 1\text{cal}/(\text{g} \cdot {}^\circ\text{C})$
$1\ \text{Btu}/(\text{lb} \cdot {}^\circ\text{F}) = 4186.69\ \text{J}/(\text{kg} \cdot {}^\circ\text{C})$
$\text{[or W} \cdot \text{s}/(\text{kg} \cdot {}^\circ\text{C})]$
$1\ \text{Btu}/(\text{lb} \cdot {}^\circ\text{F}) = 4.18669\ \text{J}/(\text{g} \cdot \text{K})$
$\text{[or W} \cdot \text{s}/(\text{g} \cdot {}^\circ\text{C})]$
$1\ \text{J}/(\text{g} \cdot {}^\circ\text{C}) = 0.23885\ \text{Btu}/(\text{lb} \cdot {}^\circ\text{F})$
$\text{[cal}/(\text{g} \cdot {}^\circ\text{C}) \text{ or kcal}/(\text{kg} \cdot {}^\circ\text{C})]$

15. Speed

$1\ \text{ft}/\text{s} = 0.3048\ \text{m}/\text{s}$
$1\ \text{m}/\text{s} = 3.2808\ \text{ft}/\text{s}$
$1\ \text{mi}/\text{h} = 1.4667\ \text{ft}/\text{s}$
$1\ \text{mi}/\text{h} = 0.44704\ \text{m}/\text{s}$

16. Surface tension

$1\ \text{lbf}/\text{ft} = 14.5937\ \text{N}/\text{m}$
$1\ \text{N}/\text{m} = 0.068529\ \text{lbf}/\text{ft}$

17. Temperature

$1\ \text{K} = 1.8\,{}^\circ\text{R}$
$T({}^\circ\text{F}) = 1.8(\text{K} - 273) + 32$
$T(\text{K}) = \frac{1}{1.8}({}^\circ\text{F} - 32) + 273$
$T({}^\circ\text{C}) = \frac{1}{1.8}({}^\circ\text{R} - 492)$
$\Delta T({}^\circ\text{C}) = \Delta T({}^\circ\text{F})/1.8$

18. Thermal conductivity

$1\ \text{Btu}/(\text{h} \cdot \text{ft} \cdot {}^\circ\text{F}) = 1.7303\ \text{W}/(\text{m} \cdot {}^\circ\text{C})$
$1\ \text{Btu}/(\text{h} \cdot \text{t} \cdot {}^\circ\text{F}) = 1.7303 \times 10^{-2}\ \text{W}/(\text{cm} \cdot {}^\circ\text{C})$
$1\ \text{Btu}/(\text{h} \cdot \text{ft} \cdot {}^\circ\text{F}) = 0.4132\ \text{cal}/(\text{s} \cdot \text{m} \cdot {}^\circ\text{C})$
$1\ \text{W}/(\text{m} \cdot {}^\circ\text{C}) = 0.5779\ \text{Btu}/(\text{h} \cdot \text{ft} \cdot {}^\circ\text{F})$
$1\ \text{W}/(\text{cm} \cdot {}^\circ\text{C}) = 57.79\ \text{Btu}/(\text{h} \cdot \text{ft} \cdot {}^\circ\text{F})$

19. Thermal resistance

$1\ \text{h} \cdot {}^\circ\text{F}/\text{Btu} = 1.896\,{}^\circ\text{C}/\text{W}$
$1\,{}^\circ\text{C}/\text{W} = 0.528\ \text{h} \cdot {}^\circ\text{F}/\text{Btu}$

20. Viscosity

$1\ \text{P} = 1\ \text{g}/(\text{cm} \cdot \text{s})$
$1\ \text{p} = 10^2\ \text{cP}$
$1\ \text{P} = 241.9\ \text{lb}/(\text{ft} \cdot \text{h})$
$1\ \text{cP} = 2.419\ \text{lb}/(\text{ft} \cdot \text{h})$
$1\ \text{lb}/(\text{ft} \cdot \text{s}) = 1.4882\ \text{kg}/(\text{m} \cdot \text{s})$
$1\ \text{lb}/(\text{ft} \cdot \text{s}) = 14.882\ \text{P}$
$1\ \text{lb}/(\text{ft} \cdot \text{s}) = 1488.2\ \text{cP}$
$1\ \text{lb}/(\text{ft} \cdot \text{h}) = 0.4134 \times 10^{-3}\ \text{kg}/(\text{m} \cdot \text{s})$
$1\ \text{lb}/(\text{ft} \cdot \text{h}) = 0.4134 \times 10^{-2}\ \text{P}$
$1\ \text{lb}/(\text{ft} \cdot \text{h}) = 0.4134\ \text{cP}$

21. Volume

$1\ \text{in}^3 = 16.387\ \text{cm}^3$
$1\ \text{cm}^3 = 0.06102\ \text{in}^3$
$1\ \text{oz (U.S. fluid)} = 29.573\ \text{cm}^3$
$1\ \text{ft}^3 = 0.0283168\ \text{m}^3$
$1\ \text{ft}^3 = 28.3168\ \text{liters}$
$1\ \text{ft}^3 = 7.4805\ \text{gal (U.S.)}$
$1\ \text{m}^3 = 35.315\ \text{ft}^3$
$1\ \text{gal (U.S.)} = 3.7854\ \text{liters}$
$1\ \text{gal (U.S.)} = 3.7854 \times 10^{-3}\ \text{m}^3$
$1\ \text{gal (U.S.)} = 0.13368\ \text{ft}^3$

## APPENDIX B: SELECTED PHYSICAL PROPERTIES

### Table B-1  Physical properties of selected gases at atmospheric pressure

| $T, K$ | $\rho$, kg/m$^3$ | $c_p$, kJ/(kg · °C) | $\mu$, kg/(m · s) | $v$, m$^2$/s | $k$, W/(m · K) | $\alpha$, m$^2$/s | Pr |
|---|---|---|---|---|---|---|---|
| Air | | | | | | | |
| 100 | 3.6010 | 1.0266 | $0.6924 \times 10^{-5}$ | $1.923 \times 10^{-6}$ | 0.009246 | $0.02501 \times 10^{-4}$ | 0.770 |
| 150 | 2.3675 | 1.0099 | $1.0283 \times 10^{-5}$ | $4.343 \times 10^{-6}$ | 0.013735 | $0.05745 \times 10^{-4}$ | 0.753 |
| 200 | 1.7684 | 1.0061 | $1.3289 \times 10^{-5}$ | $7.490 \times 10^{-6}$ | 0.01809 | $0.10165 \times 10^{-4}$ | 0.739 |
| 250 | 1.4128 | 1.0053 | $1.488 \times 10^{-5}$ | $10.000 \times 10^{-6}$ | 0.02227 | $0.13161 \times 10^{-4}$ | 0.722 |
| 300 | 1.1774 | 1.0057 | $1.983 \times 10^{-5}$ | $16.840 \times 10^{-6}$ | 0.02624 | $0.22160 \times 10^{-4}$ | 0.708 |
| 350 | 0.9980 | 1.0090 | $2.075 \times 10^{-5}$ | $20.760 \times 10^{-6}$ | 0.03003 | $0.2983 \times 10^{-4}$ | 0.697 |
| 400 | 0.8826 | 1.0140 | $2.286 \times 10^{-5}$ | $25.900 \times 10^{-6}$ | 0.03365 | $0.3760 \times 10^{-4}$ | 0.689 |
| 450 | 0.7833 | 1.0207 | $2.484 \times 10^{-5}$ | $31.710 \times 10^{-6}$ | 0.03707 | $0.4222 \times 10^{-4}$ | 0.683 |
| 500 | 0.7048 | 1.0295 | $2.671 \times 10^{-5}$ | $37.900 \times 10^{-6}$ | 0.04038 | $0.5564 \times 10^{-4}$ | 0.680 |
| 550 | 0.6423 | 1.0392 | $2.848 \times 10^{-5}$ | $44.340 \times 10^{-6}$ | 0.04360 | $0.6532 \times 10^{-4}$ | 0.h80 |
| 600 | 0.5879 | 1.0551 | $3.018 \times 10^{-5}$ | $51.340 \times 10^{-6}$ | 0.04659 | $0.7512 \times 10^{-4}$ | 0.680 |
| 650 | 0.5430 | 1.0635 | $3.177 \times 10^{-5}$ | $58.510 \times 10^{-6}$ | 0.04953 | $0.8578 \times 10^{-4}$ | 0.682 |
| 700 | 0.5030 | 1.0752 | $3.332 \times 10^{-5}$ | $66.250 \times 10^{-6}$ | 0.05230 | $0.9672 \times 10^{-4}$ | 0.684 |
| 750 | 0.4709 | 1.0856 | $3.481 \times 10^{-5}$ | $73.910 \times 10^{-6}$ | 0.05509 | $1.0774 \times 10^{-4}$ | 0.686 |
| 800 | 0.4405 | 1.0978 | $3.625 \times 10^{-5}$ | $82.290 \times 10^{-6}$ | 0.05779 | $1.1951 \times 10^{-4}$ | 0.689 |
| 850 | 0.4149 | 1.1095 | $3.765 \times 10^{-5}$ | $90.750 \times 10^{-6}$ | 0.06028 | $1.3097 \times 10^{-4}$ | 0.692 |
| 900 | 0.3925 | 1.1212 | $3.899 \times 10^{-5}$ | $99.300 \times 10^{-6}$ | 0.06279 | $1.4271 \times 10^{-4}$ | 0.696 |
| 950 | 0.3716 | 1.1321 | $4.023 \times 10^{-5}$ | $108.20 \times 10^{-6}$ | 0.06525 | $1.5510 \times 10^{-4}$ | 0.699 |
| 1000 | 0.3524 | 1.1417 | $4.152 \times 10^{-5}$ | $117.8 \times 10^{-6}$ | 0.06752 | $1.6779 \times 10^{-4}$ | 0.702 |
| 1100 | 0.3204 | 1.160 | $4.44 \times 10^{-5}$ | $138.6 \times 10^{-6}$ | 0.07320 | $1.9690 \times 10^{-4}$ | 0.704 |
| 1200 | 0.2947 | 1.179 | $4.69 \times 10^{-5}$ | $159.1 \times 10^{-6}$ | 0.0782 | $2.2510 \times 10^{-4}$ | 0.707 |
| 1300 | 0.2707 | 1.197 | $4.93 \times 10^{-5}$ | $182.1 \times 10^{-6}$ | 0.0837 | $2.5830 \times 10^{-4}$ | 0.705 |
| 1400 | 0.2515 | 1.214 | $5.17 \times 10^{-5}$ | $205.5 \times 10^{-6}$ | 0.0891 | $2.920 \times 10^{-4}$ | 0.705 |
| 1500 | 0.2355 | 1.230 | $5.40 \times 10^{-5}$ | $229.1 \times 10^{-6}$ | 0.0946 | $3.262 \times 10^{-4}$ | 0.705 |
| 1600 | 0.2211 | 1.248 | $5.63 \times 10^{-5}$ | $254.5 \times 10^{-6}$ | 0.100 | $3.609 \times 10^{-4}$ | 0.705 |
| 1700 | 0.2082 | 1.267 | $5.85 \times 10^{-5}$ | $280.5 \times 10^{-6}$ | 0.105 | $3.977 \times 10^{-4}$ | 0.705 |
| 1800 | 0.1970 | 1.287 | $6.07 \times 10^{-5}$ | $308.1 \times 10^{-6}$ | 0.111 | $4.379 \times 10^{-4}$ | 0.704 |
| 1900 | 0.1858 | 1.309 | $6.29 \times 10^{-5}$ | $338.5 \times 10^{-6}$ | 0.117 | $4.811 \times 10^{-4}$ | 0.704 |
| 2000 | 0.1762 | 1.338 | $6.50 \times 10^{-5}$ | $369.0 \times 10^{-6}$ | 0.124 | $5.260 \times 10^{-4}$ | 0.702 |
| 2100 | 0.1682 | 1.372 | $6.72 \times 10^{-5}$ | $399.6 \times 10^{-6}$ | 0.131 | $5.715 \times 10^{-4}$ | 0.700 |
| 2200 | 0.1602 | 1.419 | $6.93 \times 10^{-5}$ | $432.6 \times 10^{-6}$ | 0-139 | $6.120 \times 10^{-4}$ | 0.707 |
| 2300 | 0.1538 | 1.482 | $7.14 \times 10^{-5}$ | $464.0 \times 10^{-6}$ | 0.149 | $6.540 \times 10^{-4}$ | 0.710 |
| 2400 | 0.1458 | 1.574 | $7.35 \times 10^{-5}$ | $504.0 \times 10^{-6}$ | 0.161 | $7.020 \times 10^{-4}$ | 0.718 |
| 2500 | 0.1394 | 1.688 | $7.57 \times 10^{-5}$ | $543.5 \times 10^{-6}$ | 0.175 | $7.441 \times 10^{-4}$ | 0.730 |

# Table B-1 *(continued)*

| $T, K$ | $\rho,$ kg/m$^3$ | $c_p,$ kJ/(kg $\cdot$ °C) | $\mu,$ kg/(m $\cdot$ s) | $v,$ m$^2$/s | $k,$ W/(m $\cdot$ K) | $\alpha,$ m$^2$/s | Pr |
|---|---|---|---|---|---|---|---|
| **Helium** | | | | | | | |
| 33 | 1.4657 | 5.200 | $,50.2 \times 10^{-7}$ | $3.42 \times 10^{-6}$ | 0.0353 | $0.04625 \times 10^{-4}$ | 0.74 |
| 144 | 3.3799 | 5.200 | $125.5 \times 10^{-7}$ | $37.11 \times 10^{-6}$ | 0.0928 | $0.52750 \times 10^{-4}$ | 0.70 |
| 200 | 0.2435 | 5.200 | $156.6 \times 10^{-7}$ | $64.38 \times 10^{-6}$ | 0.1177 | $0.92880 \times 10^{-4}$ | 0.694 |
| 255 | 0.1906 | 5.200 | $181.7 \times 10^{-7}$ | $95.50 \times 10^{-6}$ | 0.1357 | $1.36750 \times 10^{-4}$ | 0.70 |
| 366 | 0.13280 | 5.200 | $230.5 \times 10^{-7}$ | $173.60 \times 10^{-6}$ | 0.1691 | $2.44900 \times 10^{-4}$ | 0.71 |
| 477 | 0.10204 | 5.200 | $275.0 \times 10^{-7}$ | $269.30 \times 10^{-6}$ | 0.197 | $3.71600 \times 10^{-4}$ | 0.72 |
| 589 | 0.08282 | 5.200 | $311.3 \times 10^{-7}$ | $375.80 \times 10^{-6}$ | 0.225 | $5.21500 \times 10^{-4}$ | 0.72 |
| 700 | 0.07032 | 5.200 | $347.5 \times 10^{-7}$ | $494.20 \times 10^{-6}$ | 0.251 | $6.66100 \times 10^{-4}$ | 0.72 |
| 800 | 0.06023 | 5.200 | $381.7 \times 10^{-7}$ | $634.10 \times 10^{-6}$ | 0.275 | $8.77400 \times 10^{-4}$ | 0.72 |
| 900 | 0.05286 | 5.200 | $413.6 \times 10^{-7}$ | $781.30 \times 10^{-6}$ | 0.298 | $10.83400 \times 10^{-4}$ | 0.72 |
| **Carbon dioxide** | | | | | | | |
| 220 | 2.4733 | 0.783 | $11.105 \times 10^{-6}$ | $4.490 \times 10^{-6}$ | 0.010805 | $0.05920 \times 10^{-4}$ | 0.818 |
| 250 | 2.1657 | 0.804 | $12.590 \times 10^{-6}$ | $5.813 \times 10^{-6}$ | 0.012884 | $0.07401 \times 10^{-4}$ | 0.793 |
| 300 | 1.7973 | 0.871 | $14.958 \times 10^{-6}$ | $8.321 \times 10^{-6}$ | 0.016572 | $0.10588 \times 10^{-4}$ | 0.770 |
| 350 | 1.5362 | 0.900 | $17.205 \times 10^{-6}$ | $11.190 \times 10^{-6}$ | 0.02047 | $0.14808 \times 10^{-4}$ | 0.755 |
| 400 | 1.3424 | 0.942 | $19.32 \times 10^{-6}$ | $14.390 \times 10^{-6}$ | 0.02461 | $0.19463 \times 10^{-4}$ | 0.738 |
| 450 | 1.1918 | 0.980 | $21.34 \times 10^{-6}$ | $17.900 \times 10^{-6}$ | 0.02897 | $0.24813 \times 10^{-4}$ | 0.721 |
| 500 | 1.0732 | 1.013 | $23.26 \times 10^{-6}$ | $21.670 \times 10^{-6}$ | 0.03352 | $0.30840 \times 10^{-4}$ | 0.702 |
| 550 | 0.9739 | 1.047 | $25.08 \times 10^{-6}$ | $25.740 \times 10^{-6}$ | 0.03821 | $0.37500 \times 10^{-4}$ | 0.685 |
| 600 | 0.8938 | 1.076 | $26.83 \times 10^{-6}$ | $30.020 \times 10^{-6}$ | 0.04311 | $0.44830 \times 10^{-4}$ | 0.668 |
| **Carbon monoxide** | | | | | | | |
| 220 | 1.55363 | 1.0429 | $13.832 \times 10^{-6}$ | $8.903 \times 10^{-6}$ | 0.01906 | $0.11760 \times 10^{-4}$ | 0.758 |
| 250 | 1.36490 | 1.0425 | $15.40 \times 10^{-6}$ | $11.280 \times 10^{-6}$ | 0.02144 | $0.15063 \times 10^{-4}$ | 0.750 |
| 300 | 1.13876 | 1.0421 | $17.843 \times 10^{-6}$ | $15.670 \times 10^{-6}$ | 0.02525 | $0.21280 \times 10^{-4}$ | 0.737 |
| 350 | 0.97425 | 1.0434 | $20.09 \times 10^{-6}$ | $20.620 \times 10^{-6}$ | 0.02883 | $0.28360 \times 10^{-4}$ | 0.728 |
| 400 | 0.85363 | 1.0484 | $22.19 \times 10^{-6}$ | $25.990 \times 10^{-6}$ | 0.03226 | $0.36050 \times 10^{-4}$ | 0.722 |
| 450 | 0.75848 | 1.0551 | $24.18 \times 10^{-6}$ | $31.880 \times 10^{-6}$ | 0.04360 | $0.44390 \times 10^{-4}$ | 0.718 |
| 500 | 0.68223 | 1.0635 | $26.06 \times 10^{-6}$ | $38.190 \times 10^{-6}$ | 0.03863 | $0.53240 \times 10^{-4}$ | 0.718 |
| 550 | 0.62024 | 1.0756 | $27.89 \times 10^{-6}$ | $44.970 \times 10^{-6}$ | 0.04162 | $0.62400 \times 10^{-4}$ | 0.721 |
| 600 | 0.56850 | 1.0877 | $29.60 \times 10^{-6}$ | $52.060 \times 10^{-6}$ | 0.04446 | $0.71900 \times 10^{-4}$ | 0.724 |
| **Ammonia, NH$_3$** | | | | | | | |
| 220 | 0.9304 | 2.198 | $7.255 \times 10^{-6}$ | $7.8 \times 10^{-6}$ | 0.0171 | $0.2054 \times 10^{-4}$ | 0.93 |
| 273 | 0.7929 | 2.177 | $9.353 \times 10^{-6}$ | $11.8 \times 10^{-6}$ | 0.0220 | $0.1308 \times 10^{-4}$ | 0.90 |
| 323 | 0.6487 | 2.177 | $11.035 \times 10^{-6}$ | $17.0 \times 10^{-6}$ | 0.0270 | $0.1920 \times 10^{-4}$ | 0.88 |
| 373 | 0.5590 | 2.236 | $12.886 \times 10^{-6}$ | $23.0 \times 10^{-6}$ | 0.0327 | $0.2619 \times 10^{-4}$ | 0.87 |
| 423 | 0.4934 | 2.315 | $14.672 \times 10^{-6}$ | $29.7 \times 10^{-6}$ | 0.0391 | $0.3432 \times 10^{-4}$ | 0.87 |
| 473 | 0.4405 | 2.395 | $16.490 \times 10^{-6}$ | $37.4 \times 10^{-6}$ | 0.0467 | $0.4421 \times 10^{-4}$ | 0.84 |
| **Steam (H$_2$O vapor)** | | | | | | | |
| 380 | 0.5863 | 2.060 | $12.71 \times 10^{-6}$ | $21.6 \times 10^{-6}$ | 0.0246 | $0.2036 \times 10^{-4}$ | 1.060 |
| 400 | 0.5542 | 2.014 | $13.44 \times 10^{-6}$ | $24.2 \times 10^{-6}$ | 0.0261 | $0.2338 \times 10^{-4}$ | 1.040 |
| 450 | 0.4902 | 1.980 | $15.25 \times 10^{-6}$ | $31.1 \times 10^{-6}$ | 0.0299 | $0.3070 \times 10^{-4}$ | 1.010 |
| 500 | 0.4405 | 1.985 | $17.04 \times 10^{-6}$ | $38.6 \times 10^{-6}$ | 0.0339 | $0.3870 \times 10^{-4}$ | 0.996 |
| 550 | 0.4005 | 1.997 | $18.84 \times 10^{-6}$ | $47.0 \times 10^{-6}$ | 0.0379 | $0.4750 \times 10^{-4}$ | 0.991 |
| 600 | 0.3652 | 2.026 | $20.67 \times 10^{-6}$ | $56.6 \times 10^{-6}$ | 0.0422 | $0.5730 \times 10^{-4}$ | 0.986 |
| 650 | 0.3380 | 2.056 | $22.47 \times 10^{-6}$ | $77.2 \times 10^{-6}$ | 0.0505 | $0.7720 \times 10^{-4}$ | 1.000 |
| 750 | 0.2931 | 2.119 | $26.04 \times 10^{-6}$ | $88.8 \times 10^{-6}$ | 0.0549 | $0.8830 \times 10^{-4}$ | 1.005 |
| 800 | 0.2739 | 2.152 | $27.86 \times 10^{-6}$ | $102.0 \times 10^{-6}$ | 0.0592 | $1.0010 \times 10^{-4}$ | 1.010 |
| 850 | 0.2579 | 2.186 | $29.69 \times 10^{-6}$ | $115.2 \times 10^{-6}$ | 0.0637 | $1.1300 \times 10^{-4}$ | 1.019 |

# Table B-1 *(continued)*

| $T, K$ | $\rho,$ kg/m$^3$ | $c_p,$ kJ/(kg $\cdot$ °C) | $\mu,$ kg/(m $\cdot$ s) | $v,$ m$^2$/s | $k,$ W/(m $\cdot$ K) | $\alpha,$ m$^2$/s | Pr |
|---|---|---|---|---|---|---|---|
| Hydrogen | | | | | | | |
| 30 | 0.84722 | 10.840 | $1.606 \times 10^{-6}$ | $1.895 \times 10^{-6}$ | 0.0228 | $0.02493 \times 10^{-4}$ | 0.759 |
| 50 | 0.50955 | 10.501 | $2.516 \times 10^{-6}$ | $4.880 \times 10^{-6}$ | 0.0362 | $0.06760 \times 10^{-4}$ | 0.721 |
| 100 | 0.24572 | 11.229 | $4.212 \times 10^{-6}$ | $17.14 \times 10^{-6}$ | 0.0665 | $0.24080 \times 10^{-4}$ | 0.712 |
| 150 | 0.16371 | 12.602 | $5.595 \times 10^{-6}$ | $34.18 \times 10^{-6}$ | 0.0981 | $0.47500 \times 10^{-4}$ | 0.718 |
| 200 | 0.12270 | 13.540 | $6.813 \times 10^{-6}$ | $55.53 \times 10^{-6}$ | 0.1282 | $0.77200 \times 10^{-4}$ | 0.719 |
| 250 | 0.09819 | 14.059 | $7.919 \times 10^{-6}$ | $80.64 \times 10^{-6}$ | 0.1561 | $1.13000 \times 10^{-4}$ | 0.713 |
| 300 | 0.08185 | 14.314 | $8.963 \times 10^{-6}$ | $141.9 \times 10^{-6}$ | 0.206 | $2.03100 \times 10^{-4}$ | 0.697 |
| 400 | 0.06135 | 14.491 | $10.864 \times 10^{-6}$ | $177.1 \times 10^{-6}$ | 0.228 | $2.56800 \times 10^{-4}$ | 0.690 |
| 450 | 0.05462 | 14.499 | $11.779 \times 10^{-6}$ | $215.6 \times 10^{-6}$ | 0.251 | $3.16400 \times 10^{-4}$ | 0.682 |
| 500 | 0.04918 | 14.507 | $12.636 \times 10^{-6}$ | $257.0 \times 10^{-6}$ | 0.272 | $3.81700 \times 10^{-4}$ | 0.675 |
| 550 | 0.04469 | 14.532 | $13.475 \times 10^{-6}$ | $301.6 \times 10^{-6}$ | 0.292 | $4.51600 \times 10^{-4}$ | 0.668 |
| 600 | 0.04085 | 14.537 | $14.285 \times 10^{-6}$ | $349.7 \times 10^{-6}$ | 0.315 | $5.30600 \times 10^{-4}$ | 0.664 |
| 700 | 0.03492 | 14.574 | $5.8900 \times 10^{-6}$ | $455.1 \times 10^{-6}$ | 0.351 | $6.90300 \times 10^{-4}$ | 0.659 |
| 800 | 0.03060 | 14.675 | $17.40 \times 10^{-6}$ | $569 \times 10^{-6}$ | 0.384 | $8.56300 \times 10^{-4}$ | 0.664 |
| 900 | 0.02723 | 14.821 | $18.78 \times 10^{-6}$ | $690 \times 10^{-6}$ | 0.412 | $10.21700 \times 10^{-4}$ | 0.676 |
| 1000 | 0.02451 | 14.968 | $20.16 \times 10^{-6}$ | $822 \times 10^{-6}$ | 0.440 | $11.99700 \times 10^{-4}$ | 0.703 |
| 1200 | 0.02050 | 15.366 | $22.75 \times 10^{-6}$ | $1107 \times 10^{-6}$ | 0.488 | $15.48400 \times 10^{-4}$ | 0.715 |
| 1300 | 0.01890 | 15.575 | $24.08 \times 10^{-6}$ | $1273 \times 10^{-6}$ | 0.512 | $17.39400 \times 10^{-4}$ | 0.733 |
| 1333 | 0.01842 | 15.638 | $24.44 \times 10^{-6}$ | $1328 \times 10^{-6}$ | 0.519 | $18.01300 \times 10^{-4}$ | 0.736 |
| Oxygen | | | | | | | |
| 100 | 3.9918 | 0.9479 | $7.768 \times 10^{-6}$ | $1.946 \times 10^{-6}$ | 0.00903 | $0.023876 \times 10^{-4}$ | 0.815 |
| 150 | 2.6190 | 0.9178 | $11.490 \times 10^{-6}$ | $4.387 \times 10^{-6}$ | 0.01367 | $0.056880 \times 10^{-4}$ | 0.773 |
| 200 | 1.9559 | 0.9131 | $14.850 \times 10^{-6}$ | $7.593 \times 10^{-6}$ | 0.01824 | $0.102140 \times 10^{-4}$ | 0.745 |
| 250 | 1.5618 | 0.9157 | $17.87 \times 10^{-6}$ | $11.45 \times 10^{-6}$ | 0.02259 | $0.157940 \times 10^{-4}$ | 0.725 |
| 300 | 1.3007 | 0.9203 | $20.63 \times 10^{-6}$ | $15.86 \times 10^{-6}$ | 0.02676 | $0.223530 \times 10^{-4}$ | 0.709 |
| 350 | 1.1133 | 0.9291 | $23.16 \times 10^{-6}$ | $20.80 \times 10^{-6}$ | 0.03070 | $0.296800 \times 10^{-4}$ | 0.702 |
| 400 | 0.9755 | 0.9420 | $25.54 \times 10^{-6}$ | $26.18 \times 10^{-6}$ | 0.03461 | $0.376800 \times 10^{-4}$ | 0.695 |
| 450 | 0.8682 | 0.9567 | $27.77 \times 10^{-6}$ | $31.99 \times 10^{-6}$ | 0.03828 | $0.460900 \times 10^{-4}$ | 0.694 |
| 500 | 0.7801 | 0.9722 | $29.91 \times 10^{-6}$ | $38.34 \times 10^{-6}$ | 0.04173 | $0.550200 \times 10^{-4}$ | 0.697 |
| 550 | 0.7096 | 0.9881 | $31.97 \times 10^{-6}$ | $45.05 \times 10^{-6}$ | 0.04517 | $0.644100 \times 10^{-4}$ | 0.700 |
| 600 | 0.6504 | 1.0044 | $33.92 \times 10^{-6}$ | $52.15 \times 10^{-6}$ | 0.04832 | $0.739900 \times 10^{-4}$ | 0.704 |
| Nitrogen | | | | | | | |
| 100 | 3.4808 | 1.0722 | $6.862 \times 10^{-6}$ | $1.971 \times 10^{-6}$ | 0.009450 | $0.025319 \times 10^{-4}$ | 0.786 |
| 200 | 1.7108 | 1.0429 | $12.947 \times 10^{-6}$ | $7.568 \times 10^{-6}$ | 0.01824 | $0.102240 \times 10^{-4}$ | 0.747 |
| 300 | 1.1421 | 1.0408 | $17.84 \times 10^{-6}$ | $15.63 \times 10^{-6}$ | 0.02620 | $0.220440 \times 10^{-4}$ | 0.713 |
| 400 | 0.8538 | 1.0459 | $21.98 \times 10^{-6}$ | $25.74 \times 10^{-6}$ | 0.03335 | $0.373400 \times 10^{-4}$ | 0.691 |
| 500 | 0.6824 | 1.0555 | $25.70 \times 10^{-6}$ | $37.66 \times 10^{-6}$ | 0.03984 | $0.553000 \times 10^{-4}$ | 0.684 |
| 600 | 0.5687 | 1.0756 | $29.11 \times 10^{-6}$ | $51.19 \times 10^{-6}$ | 0.04580 | $0.748600 \times 10^{-4}$ | 0.686 |
| 700 | 0.4934 | 1.0969 | $32.13 \times 10^{-6}$ | $65.13 \times 10^{-6}$ | 0.05123 | $0.946600 \times 10^{-4}$ | 0.691 |
| 800 | 0.4277 | 1.1225 | $34.84 \times 10^{-6}$ | $81.46 \times 10^{-6}$ | 0.05609 | $1.168500 \times 10^{-4}$ | 0.700 |
| 900 | 0.3796 | 1.1464 | $37.49 \times 10^{-6}$ | $91.06 \times 10^{-6}$ | 0.06070 | $1.394600 \times 10^{-4}$ | 0.711 |
| 1000 | 0.3412 | 1.1677 | $40.00 \times 10^{-6}$ | $117.2 \times 10^{-6}$ | 0.06475 | $1.625000 \times 10^{-4}$ | 0.724 |
| 1100 | 0.3108 | 1.1857 | $42.28 \times 10^{-6}$ | $136.0 \times 10^{-6}$ | 0.06850 | $1.859100 \times 10^{-4}$ | 0.736 |
| 1200 | 0.2851 | 1.2037 | $44.50 \times 10^{-6}$ | $156.1 \times 10^{-6}$ | 0.07184 | $2.093200 \times 10^{-4}$ | 0.748 |

Compiled from Eckert and Drake (1972).

# Table B-2 Physical properties of selected saturated liquids

| $T,°C$ | $\rho,$ kg/m$^3$ | $c_p,$ kJ/(kg · °C) | $v,$ m$^2$/s | $k,$ W/(m · K) | $\alpha,$ m$^2$/s | Pr | $\beta, K^{-1}$ |
|---|---|---|---|---|---|---|---|
| Ammonia NH$_3$ | | | | | | | |
| −50 | 703.69 | 4.463 | $0.435 \times 10^{-6}$ | 0.547 | $1.742 \times 10^{-7}$ | 2.60 | |
| −40 | 691.68 | 4.467 | $0.406 \times 10^{-6}$ | 0.547 | $1.775 \times 10^{-7}$ | 2.28 | |
| −30 | 679.34 | 4.476 | $0.387 \times 10^{-6}$ | 0.549 | $1.801 \times 10^{-7}$ | 2.15 | |
| −20 | 666.69 | 4.509 | $0.381 \times 10^{-6}$ | 0.547 | $1.819 \times 10^{-7}$ | 2.09 | |
| −10 | 653.55 | 4.564 | $0.378 \times 10^{-6}$ | 0.543 | $1.825 \times 10^{-7}$ | 2.07 | |
| 0 | 640.10 | 4.635 | $0.373 \times 10^{-6}$ | 0.540 | $1.819 \times 10^{-7}$ | 2.05 | |
| 10 | 626.16 | 4.714 | $0.368 \times 10^{-6}$ | 0.531 | $1.801 \times 10^{-7}$ | 2.04 | |
| 20 | 611.75 | 4.798 | $0.359 \times 10^{-6}$ | 0.521 | $1.775 \times 10^{-7}$ | 2.02 | $2.45 \times 10^{-3}$ |
| 30 | 596.37 | 4.890 | $0.349 \times 10^{-6}$ | 0.507 | $1.742 \times 10^{-7}$ | 2.01 | |
| 40 | 580.99 | 4.999 | $0.340 \times 10^{-6}$ | 0.493 | $1.701 \times 10^{-7}$ | 2.00 | |
| 50 | 564.33 | 5.116 | $0.330 \times 10^{-6}$ | 0.476 | $1.654 \times 10^{-7}$ | 1.99 | |
| Carbon dioxide, CO$_2$ | | | | | | | |
| −50 | 1,156.34 | 1.84 | $0.119 \times 10^{-6}$ | 0.0855 | $0.4021 \times 10^{-7}$ | 2.96 | |
| −40 | 1,117.77 | 1.88 | $0.118 \times 10^{-6}$ | 0.1011 | $0.4810 \times 10^{-7}$ | 2.46 | |
| −30 | 1,076.76 | 1.97 | $0.113 \times 10^{-6}$ | 0.1099 | $0.5133 \times 10^{-7}$ | 2.20 | |
| 0 | 926.99 | 2.47 | $0.108 \times 10^{-6}$ | 0.1045 | $0.4578 \times 10^{-7}$ | 2.38 | |
| 10 | 860.03 | 3.14 | $0.101 \times 10^{-6}$ | 0.0971 | $0.3608 \times 10^{-7}$ | 2.80 | |
| 20 | 772.57 | 5.0 | $0.091 \times 10^{-6}$ | 0.0872 | $0.2219 \times 10^{-7}$ | 4.10 | $14.00 \times 10^{-3}$ |
| 30 | 597.81 | 36.4 | $0.080 \times 10^{-6}$ | 0.0703 | $0.0279 \times 10^{-7}$ | 28.7 | |
| Dichlorodifluoromethane (Freon-12), CCl$_2$F$_2$ | | | | | | | |
| −50 | 1,546.75 | 0.8750 | $0.310 \times 10^{-6}$ | 0.067 | $0.501 \times 10^{-7}$ | 6.2 | $2.63 \times 10^{-3}$ |
| −40 | 1,518.71 | 0.8847 | $0.279 \times 10^{-6}$ | 0.069 | $0.514 \times 10^{-7}$ | 5.4 | |
| −30 | 1,489.56 | 0.8956 | $0.253 \times 10^{-6}$ | 0.069 | $0.526 \times 10^{-7}$ | 4.8 | |
| −20 | 1,460.57 | 0.9073 | $0.235 \times 10^{-6}$ | 0.071 | $0.539 \times 10^{-7}$ | 4-4 | |
| −10 | 1,429.49 | 0.9203 | $0.221 \times 10^{-6}$ | 0.073 | $0.550 \times 10^{-7}$ | 4.0 | |
| 0 | 1397.45 | 0.9345 | $0.214 \times 10^{-6}$ | 0.073 | $0.557 \times 10^{-7}$ | 3.8 | |
| 10 | 1,364.30 | 0.9496 | $0.203 \times 10^{-6}$ | 0.073 | $0.560 \times 10^{-7}$ | 3.6 | |
| 20 | 1,330.18 | 0.9659 | $0.198 \times 10^{-6}$ | 0.073 | $0.560 \times 10^{-7}$ | 3.5 | |
| 30 | 1,295.10 | 0.9835 | $0.194 \times 10^{-6}$ | 0.071 | $0.560 \times 10^{-7}$ | 3.5 | |
| 40 | 1,257.13 | 1.0019 | $0.191 \times 10^{-6}$ | 0.069 | $0.555 \times 10^{-7}$ | 3.5 | |
| 50 | 1,215.96 | 1.0216 | $0.190 \times 10^{-6}$ | 0.067 | $0.545 \times 10^{-7}$ | 3.5 | |
| Engine oil (unused) | | | | | | | |
| 0 | 899.12 | 1.796 | 0.00428 | 0.147 | $0.911 \times 10^{-7}$ | 47,100 | |
| 20 | 888.23 | 1.880 | 0.00090 | 0.145 | $0.872 \times 10^{-7}$ | 10,400 | $0.70 \times 10^{-3}$ |
| 40 | 876.05 | 1.964 | 0.00024 | 0.144 | $0.834 \times 10^{-7}$ | 2,870 | |
| 60 | 864.04 | 2.047 | $0.839 \times 10^{-4}$ | 0.140 | $0.800 \times 10^{-7}$ | 1,050 | |
| 80 | 852.02 | 2.131 | $0.375 \times 10^{-4}$ | 0.138 | $0.769 \times 10^{-7}$ | 490 | |
| 100 | 840.01 | 2.219 | $0.203 \times 10^{-4}$ | 0.137 | $0.738 \times 10^{-7}$ | 276 | |
| 120 | 828.96 | 2.307 | $0.124 \times 10^{-4}$ | 0.135 | $0.710 \times 10^{-7}$ | 175 | |
| 140 | 816.94 | 2.395 | $0.080 \times 10^{-4}$ | 0.133 | $0.686 \times 10^{-7}$ | 116 | |
| 160 | 805.89 | 2.483 | $0.056 \times 10^{-4}$ | 0.132 | $0.663 \times 10^{-7}$ | 84 | |

## Table B-2 *(continued)*

| $T$,°C | $\rho$, kg/m$^3$ | $c_p$, kJ/(kg · °C) | $v$, m$^2$/s | $k$, W/(m · K) | $\alpha$, m$^2$/s | Pr | $\beta$, K$^{-1}$ |
|---|---|---|---|---|---|---|---|
| **Ethylene glycol. $C_2H_4(OH_2)$** | | | | | | | |
| 0 | 1.130.75 | 2.294 | $57.53 \times 10^{-6}$ | 0.242 | $0.934 \times 10^{-7}$ | 615 | |
| 20 | 1,116.65 | 2.382 | $19.18 \times 10^{-6}$ | 0.249 | $0.933 \times 10^{-7}$ | 204 | $0.65 \times 10^{-3}$ |
| 40 | 1,101.43 | 2.474 | $8.69 \times 10^{-6}$ | 0.256 | $0.933 \times 10^{-7}$ | 93 | |
| 60 | 1,087.66 | 2.562 | $4.75 \times 10^{-6}$ | 0.260 | $0.932 \times 10^{-7}$ | 51 | |
| 80 | 1,077.56 | 2.650 | $2.98 \times 10^{-6}$ | 0.261 | $0.921 \times 10^{-7}$ | 32.4 | |
| 100 | 1,058.50 | 2.742 | $2.03 \times 10^{-6}$ | 0.263 | $0.908 \times 10^{-7}$ | 22.4 | |
| **Eutectic calcium chloride solution, 29.9% $CaCl_2$** | | | | | | | |
| −50 | 1,319.76 | 2.608 | $36.35 \times 10^{-6}$ | 0.402 | $1.166 \times 10^{-7}$ | 312 | |
| −40 | 1,314.96 | 2.6356 | $24.97 \times 10^{-6}$ | 0.415 | $1.200 \times 10^{-7}$ | 208 | |
| −30 | 1,310.15 | 2.6611 | $17.18 \times 10^{-6}$ | 0.429 | $1.234 \times 10^{-7}$ | 139 | |
| −20 | 1,305.51 | 2.688 | $11.04 \times 10^{-6}$ | 0.445 | $1.267 \times 10^{-7}$ | 87.1 | |
| −10 | 1,300.70 | 2.713 | $6.96 \times 10^{-6}$ | 0.459 | $1.300 \times 10^{-7}$ | 53.6 | |
| 0 | 1,296.06 | 2.738 | $4.39 \times 10^{-6}$ | 0.472 | $1.332 \times 10^{-7}$ | 33.0 | |
| 10 | 1,291.41 | 2.763 | $3.35 \times 10^{-6}$ | 0.485 | $1.363 \times 10^{-7}$ | 24.6 | |
| 20 | 1,286.61 | 2.788 | $2.72 \times 10^{-6}$ | 0.498 | $1.394 \times 10^{-7}$ | 19.6 | |
| 30 | 1,281.96 | 2.814 | $2.27 \times 10^{-6}$ | 0.511 | $1.419 \times 10^{-7}$ | 16.0 | |
| 40 | 1,277.16 | 2.839 | $1.92 \times 10^{-6}$ | 0.523 | $1.445 \times 10^{-7}$ | 13.3 | |
| 50 | 1,272.51 | 2.868 | $1.65 \times 10^{-6}$ | 0.535 | $1.468 \times 10^{-7}$ | 11.3 | |
| **Glycerin, $C_3H_5(OH)_3$** | | | | | | | |
| 0 | 1,276.03 | 2.261 | 0.00831 | 0.282 | $0.983 \times 10^{-7}$ | $84.7 \times 10^3$ | |
| 10 | 1,270.11 | 2.319 | 0.00300 | 0.284 | $0.965 \times 10^{-7}$ | $31.0 \times 10^3$ | |
| 20 | 1,264.02 | 2.386 | 0.00118 | 0.286 | $0.947 \times 10^{-7}$ | $12.5 \times 10^3$ | $0.50 \times 10^{-3}$ |
| 30 | 1,258.09 | 2.445 | 0.00050 | 0.286 | $0.929 \times 10^{-7}$ | $5.38 \times 10^3$ | |
| 40 | 1,252.01 | 2.512 | 0.00022 | 0.286 | $0.914 \times 10^{-7}$ | $2.45 \times 10^3$ | |
| 50 | 1,244.96 | 2.583 | 0.00015 | 0.287 | $0.893 \times 10^{-7}$ | $1.63 \times 10^3$ | |
| **Mercury, Hg** | | | | | | | |
| 0 | 13,628.22 | 0.1403 | $0.124 \times 10^{-6}$ | 8.20 | $42.99 \times 10^{-7}$ | 0.0288 | |
| 20 | 13,579.04 | 0.1394 | $0.114 \times 10^{-6}$ | 8.69 | $46.06 \times 10^{-7}$ | 0.0249 | $1.82 \times 10^{-4}$ |
| 50 | 13,505.84 | 0.1386 | $0.104 \times 10^{-6}$ | 9.40 | $50.22 \times 10^{-7}$ | 0.0207 | |
| 100 | 13,384.58 | 0.1373 | $0.0928 \times 10^{-6}$ | 10.51 | $57.16 \times 10^{-7}$ | 0.0162 | |
| 150 | 13,264.28 | 0.1365 | $0.0853 \times 10^{-6}$ | 11.49 | $63.54 \times 10^{-7}$ | 0.0134 | |
| 200 | 13,144.94 | 0.1360 | $0.0802 \times 10^{-6}$ | 12.34 | $69.08 \times 10^{-7}$ | 0.0116 | |
| 250 | 13,025.60 | 0.1357 | $0.0765 \times 10^{-6}$ | 13.07 | $74.06 \times 10^{-7}$ | 0.0103 | |
| 315.5 | 12,847 | 0.134 | $0.0673 \times 10^{-6}$ | 14.02 | $8.15 \times 10^{-7}$ | 0.0083 | |
| **Methyl chloride, $CH_3Cl$** | | | | | | | |
| −50 | 1,052.58 | 1.4759 | $0.320 \times 10^{-6}$ | 0.215 | $1.388 \times 10^{-6}$ | 2.31 | |
| −40 | 1,033.35 | 1.4826 | $0.318 \times 10^{-6}$ | 0.209 | $1.368 \times 10^{-6}$ | 2.32 | |
| −30 | 1,016.53 | 1.4922 | $0.314 \times 10^{-6}$ | 0.202 | $1.337 \times 10^{-6}$ | 2.35 | |
| −20 | 999.39 | 1.5043 | $0.309 \times 10^{-6}$ | 0.196 | $1.301 \times 10^{-6}$ | 2.38 | |
| −10 | 981.45 | 1.5194 | $0.306 \times 10^{-6}$ | 0.187 | $1.257 \times 10^{-6}$ | 2.43 | |
| 0 | 962.39 | 1.5378 | $0.302 \times 10^{-6}$ | 0.178 | $1.213 \times 10^{-6}$ | 2.49 | |
| 10 | 942.36 | 1.5600 | $0.297 \times 10^{-6}$ | 0.171 | $1.166 \times 10^{-6}$ | 2.55 | |
| 20 | 923.31 | 1.5860 | $0.293 \times 10^{-6}$ | 0.163 | $1.112 \times 10^{-6}$ | 2.63 | |
| 30 | 903.12 | 1.6161 | $0.288 \times 10^{-6}$ | 0.154 | $1.058 \times 10^{-6}$ | 2.72 | |
| 40 | 883.10 | 1.6504 | $0.281 \times 10^{-6}$ | 0.144 | $0.996 \times 10^{-6}$ | 2.83 | |
| 50 | 861.15 | 1.6890 | $0.274 \times 10^{-6}$ | 0.133 | $0.921 \times 10^{-6}$ | 2.97 | |

## Table B-2 *(continued)*

| $T, °C$ | $\rho,$ kg/m$^3$ | $c_p,$ kJ/(kg · °C) | $v,$ m$^2$/s | $k,$ W/(m · K) | $\alpha,$ m$^2$/s | Pr | $\beta, K^{-1}$ |
|---|---|---|---|---|---|---|---|
| Sulfur dioxide. SO$_2$ | | | | | | | |
| −50 | 1,560.84 | 1.3595 | $0.484 \times 10^{-6}$ | 0.242 | $1.141 \times 10^{-7}$ | 4.24 | |
| −40 | 1,536.81 | 1.3607 | $0.424 \times 10^{-6}$ | 0.235 | $1.130 \times 10^{-7}$ | 3.74 | |
| −30 | 1,520.64 | 1.3616 | $0.371 \times 10^{-6}$ | 0.230 | $1.117 \times 10^{-7}$ | 3.31 | |
| −20 | 1,488.60 | 1.3624 | $0.324 \times 10^{-6}$ | 0.225 | $1.107 \times 10^{-7}$ | 2.93 | |
| −10 | 1,463.61 | 1.3628 | $0.288 \times 10^{-6}$ | 0.218 | $1.097 \times 10^{-7}$ | 2.62 | |
| 0 | 1,438.46 | 1.3636 | $0.257 \times 10^{-6}$ | 0.211 | $1.081 \times 10^{-7}$ | 2.38 | |
| 10 | 1,412.51 | 1.3645 | $0.232 \times 10^{-6}$ | 0.204 | $1.066 \times 10^{-7}$ | 2.18 | |
| 20 | 1,386.40 | 1.3653 | $0.210 \times 10^{-6}$ | 0.199 | $1.050 \times 10^{-7}$ | 2.00 | $1.94 \times 10^{-3}$ |
| 30 | 1,359.33 | 1.3662 | $0.190 \times 10^{-6}$ | 0.192 | $1.035 \times 10^{-7}$ | 1.83 | |
| 40 | 1,329.22 | 1.3674 | $0.173 \times 10^{-6}$ | 0.185 | $1.019 \times 10^{-7}$ | 1.70 | |
| 50 | 1,299.10 | 1.3683 | $0.162 \times 10^{-6}$ | 0.177 | $0.999 \times 10^{-7}$ | 1.61 | |
| Water, H$_2$O | | | | | | | |
| 0 | 1,002.28 | 4.2178 | $1.788 \times 10^{-6}$ | 0.552 | $1.308 \times 10^{-7}$ | 13.6 | |
| 20 | 1,000.52 | 4.1818 | $1.006 \times 10^{-6}$ | 0.597 | $1.430 \times 10^{-7}$ | 7.02 | $0.18 \times 10^{-3}$ |
| 40 | 994.59 | 4.1784 | $0.658 \times 10^{-6}$ | 0.628 | $1.512 \times 10^{-7}$ | 4.34 | |
| 60 | 985.46 | 4.1843 | $0.478 \times 10^{-6}$ | 0.651 | $1.554 \times 10^{-7}$ | 3.02 | |
| 80 | 974.08 | 4.1964 | $0.364 \times 10^{-6}$ | 0.668 | $1.636 \times 10^{-7}$ | 2.22 | |
| 100 | 960.63 | 4.2161 | $0.294 \times 10^{-6}$ | 0.680 | $1.680 \times 10^{-7}$ | 1.74 | |
| 120 | 945.25 | 4.250 | $0.247 \times 10^{-6}$ | 0.685 | $1.708 \times 10^{-7}$ | 1.446 | |
| 140 | 928.27 | 4.283 | $0.214 \times 10^{-6}$ | 0.684 | $1.724 \times 10^{-7}$ | 1.241 | |
| 160 | 909.69 | 4.342 | $0.190 \times 10^{-6}$ | 0.680 | $1.729 \times 10^{-7}$ | 1.099 | |
| 180 | 889.03 | 4.417 | $0.173 \times 10^{-6}$ | 0.675 | $1.724 \times 10^{-7}$ | 1.004 | |
| 200 | 866.76 | 4.505 | $0.160 \times 10^{-6}$ | 0.665 | $1.706 \times 10^{-7}$ | 0.937 | |
| 220 | 842.41 | 4.610 | $0.150 \times 10^{-6}$ | 0.652 | $1.680 \times 10^{-7}$ | 0.891 | |
| 240 | 815.66 | 4.756 | $0.143 \times 10^{-6}$ | 0.635 | $1.639 \times 10^{-7}$ | 0.871 | |
| 260 | 785.87 | 4.949 | $0.137 \times 10^{-6}$ | 0.611 | $1.577 \times 10^{-7}$ | 0.874 | |
| 280.6 | 752.55 | 5.208 | $0.135 \times 10^{-6}$ | 0.580 | $1.481 \times 10^{-7}$ | 0.910 | |
| 300 | 714.26 | 5.728 | $0.135 \times 10^{-6}$ | 0.540 | $1.324 \times 10^{-7}$ | 1.019 | |

Compiled from Eckert and Drake (1972).

# Table B-3 Physical properties of selected liquid metals

| Metal | Melting - Boiling points °C | $T$ °C | $\rho$ kg/m³ | $c_p$ kJ/(kg·°C) | $\mu$ kg/(m·s) | $\nu$ m²/s | $k$ W/(m·°C) | $\alpha$ m²/s | Pr |
|---|---|---|---|---|---|---|---|---|---|
| Bismuth | 271 - 1477 | 315 | 10,011 | 0.144 | $16.2 \times 10^{-4}$ | $0.160 \times 10^{-5}$ | 16.4 | $11.25 \times 10^{-6}$ | 0.0142 |
| | | 538 | 9,734 | 0.155 | $11.0 \times 10^{-4}$ | $0.113 \times 10^{-5}$ | 15.6 | $10.34 \times 10^{-6}$ | 0.0110 |
| | | 760 | 9,467 | 0.165 | $7.9 \times 10^{-4}$ | $0.083 \times 10^{-5}$ | 15.6 | $9.98 \times 10^{-6}$ | 0.0083 |
| Lead | 327 - 1737 | 371 | 10,540 | 0.159 | $2.40 \times 10^{-4}$ | $0.023 \times 10^{-5}$ | 16.1 | $9.61 \times 10^{-6}$ | 0.024 |
| | | 704 | 10,140 | 0.155 | $1.37 \times 10^{-4}$ | $0.014 \times 10^{-5}$ | 14.9 | $9.48 \times 10^{-6}$ | 0.0143 |
| Lithium | 179 - 1317 | 204.4 | 509.2 | 4.365 | $5.416 \times 10^{-4}$ | $1.1098 \times 10^{-5}$ | 46.37 | $20.96 \times 10^{-6}$ | 0.051 |
| | | 315.6 | 498.8 | 4.270 | $4.465 \times 10^{-4}$ | $0.8982 \times 10^{-5}$ | 43.08 | $20.32 \times 10^{-6}$ | 0.0443 |
| | | 426.7 | 489.1 | 4.211 | $3.927 \times 10^{-4}$ | $0.8053 \times 10^{-5}$ | 38.24 | $18.65 \times 10^{-6}$ | 0.0432 |
| | | 537.8 | 476.3 | 4.171 | $3.473 \times 10^{-4}$ | $0.7304 \times 10^{-5}$ | 30.45 | $15.40 \times 10^{-6}$ | 0.0476 |
| Mercury | 38.9 - 357 | -17.8 | 13,707.1 | 0.1415 | $18.334 \times 10^{-4}$ | $0.1342 \times 10^{-5}$ | 9.76 | $5.038 \times 10^{-6}$ | 0.0266 |
| | | 100 | 13,384.5 | 0.1373 | $12.420 \times 10^{-4}$ | $0.0928 \times 10^{-5}$ | 10.51 | $5.716 \times 10^{-6}$ | 0.0162 |
| | | 200 | 13,144.9 | 0.1570 | $10.541 \times 10^{-4}$ | $0.0802 \times 10^{-5}$ | 12.34 | $6.908 \times 10^{-6}$ | 0.0116 |
| Sodium | 97.8 - 883 | 93.3 | 931.6 | 1.384 | $7.131 \times 10^{-4}$ | $0.7689 \times 10^{-5}$ | 84.96 | $56.29 \times 10^{-6}$ | 0.0116 |
| | | 204.4 | 907.5 | 1.339 | $4.521 \times 10^{-4}$ | $0.5010 \times 10^{-5}$ | 80.81 | $66.80 \times 10^{-6}$ | 0.0075 |
| | | 315.6 | 878.5 | 1.304 | $3.294 \times 10^{-4}$ | $0.3766 \times 10^{-5}$ | 75.78 | $66.47 \times 10^{-6}$ | 0.00567 |
| | | 426.7 | 852.8 | 1.277 | $2.522 \times 10^{-4}$ | $0.2968 \times 10^{-5}$ | 69.39 | $64.05 \times 10^{-6}$ | 0.00464 |
| | | 537.8 | 823.8 | 1.264 | $2.315 \times 10^{-4}$ | $0.2821 \times 10^{-5}$ | 64.37 | $62.09 \times 10^{-6}$ | 0.00455 |
| | | 648.9 | 790.0 | 1.261 | $1.964 \times 10^{-4}$ | $0.2496 \times 10^{-5}$ | 60.56 | $61.10 \times 10^{-6}$ | 0.00408 |
| | | 760.0 | 767.5 | 1.270 | $1.716 \times 10^{-4}$ | $0.2245 \times 10^{-5}$ | 56.58 | $58.34 \times 10^{-6}$ | 0.00385 |
| Potassium | 63.9 - 760 | 426.7 | 741.7 | 0.766 | $2.108 \times 10^{-4}$ | $0.2839 \times 10^{-5}$ | 39.45 | $69.74 \times 10^{-6}$ | 0.0041 |
| | | 537.8 | 714.4 | 0.762 | $1.711 \times 10^{-4}$ | $0.2400 \times 10^{-5}$ | 36.51 | $67.39 \times 10^{-6}$ | 0.0036 |
| | | 648.9 | 690.3 | 0.766 | $1.463 \times 10^{-4}$ | $0.2116 \times 10^{-5}$ | 33.74 | $64.10 \times 10^{-6}$ | 0.0033 |
| | | 760.0 | 667.7 | 0.783 | $1.331 \times 10^{-4}$ | $0.1987 \times 10^{-5}$ | 31.15 | $59.86 \times 10^{-6}$ | 0.0033 |
| NaK (56% Na, 44% K) | -11.1 - 784 | 93.3 | 889.8 | 1.130 | $5.622 \times 10^{-4}$ | $0.6347 \times 10^{-5}$ | 25.78 | $27.76 \times 10^{-6}$ | 0.0246 |
| | | 204.4 | 865.6 | 1.089 | $3.803 \times 10^{-4}$ | $0.4414 \times 10^{-5}$ | 26.47 | $28.23 \times 10^{-6}$ | 0.0155 |
| | | 315.6 | 838.3 | 1.068 | $2.935 \times 10^{-4}$ | $0.3515 \times 10^{-5}$ | 27.17 | $30.50 \times 10^{-6}$ | 0.0115 |
| | | 426.7 | 814.2 | 1.051 | $2.150 \times 10^{-4}$ | $0.2652 \times 10^{-5}$ | 27.68 | $32.52 \times 10^{-6}$ | 0.0081 |
| | | 537.8 | 788.4 | 1.047 | $2.026 \times 10^{-4}$ | $0.2581 \times 10^{-5}$ | 27.68 | $33.71 \times 10^{-6}$ | 0.0076 |
| | | 648.9 | 759.5 | 1.051 | $1.695 \times 10^{-4}$ | $0.2240 \times 10^{-5}$ | 27.68 | $34.86 \times 10^{-6}$ | 0.0064 |

Compiled from Eckert and Drake (1972).

# Table B-4 Physical properties of selected solid metals

| Metal | Melting point, °C | Properties at 20°C | | | | Thermal conductivity $k$, W/(m·°C) | | | | | |
|---|---|---|---|---|---|---|---|---|---|---|---|
| | | $\rho$, kg/m³ | $c_p$, kJ/(kg·°C) | $k$, W/(m·°C) | $\alpha$, m²/s | −100°C | 0°C | 100°C | 300°C | 600°C | 1000°C |
| **Aluminum** | | | | | | | | | | | |
| Pure | 660 | 2,707 | 0.896 | 204 | $8.418 \times 10^{-5}$ | 215 | 202 | 206 | 228 | | |
| Beryllium | 1277 | 1,850 | 1.825 | 200 | $5.92 \times 10^{-5}$ | | | | | | |
| Bismuth | 272 | 9,780 | 0.122 | 7.86 | $0.66 \times 10^{-5}$ | | | | | | |
| Cadmium | 321 | 8,650 | 0.231 | 96.8 | $4.84 \times 10^{-5}$ | | | | | | |
| **Copper** | | | | | | | | | | | |
| Pure | 1085 | 8,954 | 0.3831 | 386 | $11.234 \times 10^{-5}$ | 407 | 386 | 379 | 369 | 353 | |
| Aluminum bronze, 95% Cu. 5% Al | | 8,666 | 0.410 | 83 | $2.330 \times 10^{-5}$ | | | | | | |
| Bronze, 75% Cu. 25% Sn | | 8,666 | 0.343 | 26 | $0.859 \times 10^{-5}$ | | | | | | |
| Red brass, 85% Cu. 9% Sn, 6% Zn | | 8,714 | 0.385 | 61 | $1.804 \times 10^{-5}$ | | 59 | 71 | | | |
| Brass, 70% Cu. 30% Zn | | 8,522 | 0.385 | 111 | $3.412 \times 10^{-5}$ | 88 | | 128 | 147 | | |
| Constantan, 60% Cu. 40% Ni | | 8,922 | 0.410 | 22.7 | $0.612 \times 10^{-5}$ | 21 | | 22.2 | | | |
| **Iron** | | | | | | | | | | | |
| Pure | 1537 | 7,897 | 0.452 | 73 | $2.034 \times 10^{-5}$ | 87 | 73 | 67 | 55 | 40 | 35 |
| Wrought iron, 0.5% C | | 7,849 | 0.46 | 59 | $1.626 \times 10^{-5}$ | | 59 | 57 | 48 | 36 | 33 |
| Steel (C max ≈ 1.5%): | | | | | | | | | | | |
| Carbon steel C ≈ 0.5% | | 7,833 | 0.465 | 54 | $1.474 \times 10^{-5}$ | | 55 | 52 | 45 | 35 | 29 |
| 1.0% | | 7,801 | 0.473 | 43 | $1.172 \times 10^{-5}$ | | 43 | 43 | 40 | 33 | 28 |
| 1.5% | | 7,753 | 0.486 | 36 | $0.970 \times 10^{-5}$ | | 36 | 36 | 35 | 31 | 28 |

# Table B-4 Physical properties of selected solid metals (continued)

| Metal | Melting point, °C | Properties at 20°C ρ, kg/m³ | $c_p$, kJ/(kg·°C) | $k$, W/(m·°C) | $\alpha$, m²/s | Thermal conductivity $k$, W/(m·°C) −100°C | 0°C | 100°C | 300°C | 600°C | 1000°C |
|---|---|---|---|---|---|---|---|---|---|---|---|
| Chrome steel | | | | | | | | | | | |
| Cr = 0% | | 7,897 | 0.452 | 73 | $2.026 \times 10^{-5}$ | 87 | 73 | 67 | 55 | 40 | 35 |
| 1% | | 7,865 | 0.46 | 61 | $1.665 \times 10^{-5}$ | | 62 | 55 | 47 | 36 | 33 |
| 5% | | 7,833 | 0.46 | 40 | $1.110 \times 10^{-5}$ | | 40 | 38 | 36 | 29 | 29 |
| 20% | | 7,689 | 0.46 | 22 | $0.635 \times 10^{-5}$ | | 22 | 22 | 22 | 24 | 29 |
| Tungsten steel | | | | | | | | | | | |
| W = 0% | | 7,897 | 0.452 | 73 | $2.026 \times 10^{-5}$ | | | | | | |
| 1% | | 7,913 | 0.448 | 66 | $1.858 \times 10^{-5}$ | | | | | | |
| 5% | | 8,073 | 0.435 | 54 | $1.525 \times 10^{-5}$ | | | | | | |
| 10% | | 8,314 | 0.419 | 48 | $1.391 \times 10^{-5}$ | | | | | | |
| Lead | 328 | 11,373 | 0.130 | 35 | $2.343 \times 10^{-5}$ | 36.9 | 35.1 | 33.4 | 29.8 | | |
| Magnesium, Pure | 650 | 1,746 | 1.013 | 171 | $9.708 \times 10^{-5}$ | 178 | 171 | 168 | 157 | | |
| Molybdenum | 2,621 | 10,220 | 0.251 | 123 | $4.790 \times 10^{-5}$ | 138 | 125 | 118 | 111 | 106 | 99 |
| Nickel | | | | | | | | | | | |
| Pure (99.9%) | 1,455 | 8,906 | 0.4459 | 90 | $2.266 \times 10^{-5}$ | 104 | 93 | 83 | 64 | | |
| Ni-Cr | | | | | | | | | | | |
| 90% Ni, 10% Cr | | 8,666 | 0.444 | 17 | $0.444 \times 10^{-5}$ | | 17.1 | 18.9 | 22.8 | 22.5 | |
| 80% Ni, 20% Cr | | 8,314 | 0.444 | 12.6 | $0.343 \times 10^{-5}$ | | 12.3 | 13.8 | 17.1 | | |
| Platinum | 1,772 | 21,450 | 0.133 | 71.5 | $2.5 \times 10^{-5}$ | | | | | | |
| Silver, Pure | 962 | 10,524 | 0.2340 | 419 | $17.004 \times 10^{-5}$ | 419 | 417 | 415 | | | |
| Tin, pure | 232 | 7,304 | 0.2265 | 64 | $3.884 \times 10^{-5}$ | 74 | 65.9 | 59 | | | |
| Titanium | 1,680 | 4,500 | 0.5 | 22 | $0.9 \times 10^{-5}$ | | | | | | |
| Tungsten | 3,387 | 19,350 | 0.1344 | 163 | $6.271 \times 10^{-5}$ | | 166 | 151 | 133 | 112 | |
| Uranium | 1,133 | 19,070 | 0.116 | 27.6 | $1.25 \times 10^{-5}$ | | | | | | |
| Zinc, pure | 420 | 7,144 | 0.3843 | 112.2 | $4.106 \times 10^{-5}$ | 114 | 112 | 109 | 100 | | |

Compiled from Eckert and Drake (1972).

# Table B-5 Physical properties of insulating materials

| Material | $T$, °C | $k$, W/(m·°C) | $\rho$, kg/m³ | $c_p$, kJ/(kg·°C) | $\alpha$, m²/s |
|---|---|---|---|---|---|
| Asbestos | | | | | |
| Loosely packed | −45 | 0.149 | | | |
| | 0 | 0.154 | 470–570 | 0.816 | $3.3 - 4 \times 10^{-7}$ |
| | 100 | 0.161 | | | |
| Asbestos-cement boards | 20 | 0.74 | | | |
| Sheets | 51 | 0.166 | | | |
| Felt, 40 laminations/in | 38 | 0.057 | | | |
| | 150 | 0.069 | | | |
| | 260 | 0.083 | | | |
| 20 laminations/in | 38 | 0.078 | | | |
| | 150 | 0.095 | | | |
| | 260 | 0.112 | | | |
| Corrugated, 4 plies/in | 38 | 0.087 | | | |
| | 93 | 0.100 | | | |
| | 150 | 0.119 | | | |
| Balsam wool | 32 | 0.04 | 35 | | |
| Board and slab | | | | | |
| Cellular glass | 30 | 0.058 | 145 | 1.000 | |
| Glass fiber, organic bonded | 30 | 0.036 | 105 | 0.795 | |
| Polystyrene, expanded extruded (R-12) | 30 | 0.027 | 55 | 1.210 | |
| Mineral fiberboard; roofing material | 30 | 0.049 | 265 | | |
| Wood, shredded/cemented | 30 | 0.087 | 350 | 1.590 | |
| Cardboard, corrugated | — | 0.064 | | | |
| Celotex | 32 | 0.048 | | | |
| Corkboard | 30 | 0.043 | 160 | | |
| Cork, regranulated | 32 | 0.045 | 45–120 | 1.88 | $2 - 5.3 \times 10^{-7}$ |
| Ground | 32 | 0.043 | 150 | | |
| Diatomaceous earth (Sil-o-cel) | 0 | 0.061 | 320 | | |
| Felt, hair | 30 | 0.036 | 130–200 | | |
| Wool | 30 | 0.052 | 330 | | |
| Fiber, insulating board | 20 | 0.048 | 240 | | |
| Glass wool | 23 | 0.038 | 24 | 0.7 | $22.6 \times 10^{-7}$ |
| Insulex, dry | 32 | 0.064 | | | |
| Kapok | 30 | 0.035 | | | |

# Table B-5 *(continued)*

| Material | $T$, °C | $k$, W/(m · °C) | $\rho$, kg/m³ | $c_p$, kJ/(kg · °C) | $\alpha$, m²/s |
|---|---|---|---|---|---|
| Loose fill | | | | | |
|    Cork, granulated | 30 | 0.045 | 160 | | |
|    Diatomaceous silica, coarse powder | 30 | 0.069 | 350 | | |
|    Diatomaceous silica, fine powder | 30 | 0.091 | 400 | | |
| | 30 | 0.052 | 200 | — | |
| | 30 | 0.061 | 975 | — | |
|    Glass fiber, poured or blown | 30 | 0.043 | 16 | 0.835 | |
|    Vermiculite flakes | 30 | 0.068 | 80 | 0.835 | |
| | | 0.063 | 160 | | |
| Formed / Foamed-in-Place | | | | | |
|    Mineral wool granules with asbestos/ | | | | | |
|      inorganic binders, sprayed | 30 | 0.046 | 190 | | |
|    Polyvinyl acetate cork mastic; | | | | | |
|      sprayed or troweled | 30 | 0.100 | | | |
|    Urethane, two-part mixture; rigid foam | 30 | 0.026 | 70 | 1.045 | |
| Magnesia, 85% | 38 | 0.067 | 270 | | |
| | 93 | 0.071 | | | |
| | 150 | 0.074 | | | |
| | 204 | 0.080 | | | |
| Rock wool, 10 lb/ft³ | 32 | 0.040 | 160 | | |
|    Loosely packed | 150 | 0.067 | 64 | | |
| | 260 | 0.087 | | | |
| Sawdust | 23 | 0.059 | | | |
| Silica aerogel | 32 | 0.024 | 140 | | |
| Wood shavings | 23 | 0.059 | | | |

Compiled from Brown and Marco (1958).

# Table B-6 Physical properties of non-metals

| Material | $T,$ °C | $k,$ W/(m · °C) | $\rho,$ kg/m³ | $c_p,$ kJ/(kg · °C) | $\alpha,$ m²/s |
|---|---|---|---|---|---|
| Asphalt | 20–55 | 0.02–1.26 | | | |
| Brick | | | | | |
|   Building brick, common | 20 | 0.69 | 1600 | 0.84 | $5.2 \times 10^{-7}$ |
|     Face | | 1.32 | 2000 | | |
|   Carborundum brick | 600 | 18.5 | | | |
| | 1400 | 11.1 | | | |
|   Chrome brick | 200 | 2.32 | 3000 | 0.84 | $9.2 \times 10^{-7}$ |
| | 550 | 2.47 | | | $9.8 \times 10^{-7}$ |
| | 900 | 1.99 | | | $7.9 \times 10^{-7}$ |
|   Diatomaceous earth, molded | | | | | |
|     and fired | 200 | 0.24 | | | |
| | 870 | 0.31 | | | |
|   Fireclay brick, burned 1330°C | 500 | 1.04 | 2000 | 0.96 | $5.4 \times 10^{-7}$ |
| | 800 | 1.07 | | | |
| | 1100 | 1.09 | | | |
|     Burned 1450°C | 500 | 1.28 | 2300 | 0.96 | $5.8 \times 10^{-7}$ |
| | 800 | 1.37 | | | |
| | 1100 | 1.40 | | | |
|     Missouri200 | 1.00 | 2600 | 0.96 | 4.0 | |
| | 600 | 1.47 | | | |
| | 1400 | 1.77 | | | |
|     Magnesite | 200 | 3.81 | | 1.13 | |
| | 650 | 2.77 | | | |
| | 1200 | 1.90 | | | |
| Clay | 30 | 1.3 | 1460 | 0.88 | |
| Cement, portland | 23 | 0.29 | 1500 | | |
|   Mortar | 23 | 0.72-1.16 | | | |
| Coal. anthracite | 30 | 0.26 | 1200–1500 | 1.26 | |
|   Powdered | 30 | 0.116 | 737 | 1.30 | |
| Concrete, cinder | 23 | 0.76 | | | |
|   Stone 1-2-4 mix | 20 | 1.37 | 1900–2300 | 0.88 | $8.2 - 6.8 \times 10^{-7}$ |
| Cotton | 20 | 0.06 | 80 | 1.30 | |

## Table B-6 *(continued)*

| Material | $T$, °C | $k$, W/(m · °C) | $\rho$, kg/m³ | $c_p$, kJ/(kg · °C) | $\alpha$, m²/s |
|---|---|---|---|---|---|
| Glass, window | 20 | 0.78 (avg) | 2700 | 0.84 | $3.4 \times 10^{-7}$ |
|   Corosilicate | 30–75 | 1.09 | 2200 | | |
|   Plate (soda lime) | 30 | 1.4 | 2500 | 0.75 | |
|   Pyrex | 30 | 1.4 | 2225 | 0.835 | |
| Paper | 30 | 0.11-0.18 | 930 | 1.340 | |
| Paraffin | 30 | 0.20-0.25 | 900 | 2.890 | |
| Plaster, gypsum | 20 | 0.48 | 1440 | 0.84 | $4.0 \times 10^{-7}$ |
|   Metal lath | 20 | 0.47 | | | |
|   Wood lath | 20 | 0.28 | | | |
| Rubber, vulcanized | | | | | |
|   Soft | 30 | 0.12 | 1100 | 2.010 | |
|   Hard | 30 | 0.13 | 1190 | | |
| Sand | 30 | 0.27 | 1515 | 0.800 | |
| Stone | | | | | |
|   Granite | | 1.73–3.98 | 2640 | 0.82 | $8 - 18 \times 10^{-7}$ |
|   Limestone | 100–300 | 1.26–1.33 | 2500 | 0.90 | $5.6 - 5.9 \times 10^{-7}$ |
|   Marble | | 2.07–2.94 | 2500-2700 | 0.80 | $10 - 13.6 \times 10^{-7}$ |
|   Sandstone | 40 | 1.83 | 2160–2300 | 0.71 | $11.2 - 11.9 \times 10^{-7}$ |
| Teflon | 30 | 0.35 | 2200 | — | |
| Tissue, human skin | 30 | 0.37 | — | — | |
|   Fat layer | 30 | 0.20 | — | — | |
|   Muscle | 30 | 0.41 | — | — | |
| Wood (across the grain) | | | | | |
|   Balsa | 30 | 0.055 | 140 | | |
|   Cypress | 30 | 0.097 | 460 | | |
|   Fir | 23 | 0.11 | 420 | 2.72 | $0.96 \times 10^{-7}$ |
|   Maple or oak | 30 | 0.166 | 540 | 2.4 | $1.28 \times 10^{-7}$ |
|   Yellow pine | 23 | 0.147 | 640 | 2.8 | $0.82 \times 10^{-7}$ |
|   White pine | 30 | 0.112 | 430 | | |

## Table B-7 Abbreviated saturated steam table

| Temperature $T$, °C | Pressure $P$, kPa | Enthalpy of evaporation $h_{fg}$, kJ/kg | Liquid density $\rho_\ell$, kg/m³ | Vapor density $\rho_v$, kg/m³ |
|---|---|---|---|---|
| 0.01 | 0.6113 | 2501.3 | 1000.0 | 0.0049 |
| 5 | 0.8721 | 2489.6 | 1000.0 | 0.0068 |
| 10 | 1.2276 | 2477.7 | 1000.0 | 0.0094 |
| 15 | 1.7051 | 2465.9 | 999.0 | 0.0129 |
| 20 | 2.339 | 2454.1 | 998.0 | 0.0173 |
| 25 | 3.169 | 2442.3 | 997.0 | 0.0231 |
| 30 | 4.246 | 2430.5 | 996.0 | 0.0304 |
| 35 | 5.628 | 2418.6 | 994.0 | 0.0397 |
| 40 | 7.384 | 2406.7 | 992.1 | 0.0512 |
| 45 | 9.593 | 2394.8 | 990.1 | 0.0655 |
| 50 | 12.349 | 2382.7 | 988.1 | 0.0831 |
| 55 | 15.758 | 2370.7 | 985.2 | 0.1045 |
| 60 | 19.940 | 2358.5 | 983.3 | 0.1304 |
| 65 | 25.03 | 2346.2 | 980.4 | 0.1614 |
| 70 | 31.19 | 2333.8 | 977.5 | 0.1983 |
| 75 | 38.58 | 2321.4 | 974.7 | 0.2421 |
| 80 | 47.39 | 2308.8 | 971.8 | 0.2935 |
| 85 | 57.83 | 2296.0 | 968.1 | 0.3536 |
| 90 | 70.14 | 2283.2 | 965.3 | 0.4235 |
| 95 | 84.55 | 2270.2 | 961.5 | 0.5045 |
| 100 | 101.35 | 2257.0 | 957.9 | 0.598 |
| 110 | 143.27 | 2230.2 | 950.6 | 0.826 |
| 120 | 198.53 | 2202.6 | 943.4 | 1.121 |
| 130 | 270.1 | 2174.2 | 934.6 | 1.496 |
| 140 | 361.3 | 2144.7 | 925.9 | 1.965 |

| Temperature $T$, °C | Pressure $P$, MPa | Enthalpy of evaporation $h_{fg}$, kJ/kg | Liquid density $\rho_\ell$, kg/m³ | Vapor density $\rho_v$, kg/m³ |
|---|---|---|---|---|
| 150 | 0.4758 | 2114.3 | 916.6 | 2.549 |
| 160 | 0.6178 | 2082.6 | 907.4 | 3.256 |
| 170 | 0.7917 | 2049.5 | 897.7 | 4.119 |
| 180 | 1.0021 | 2015.0 | 887.3 | 5.153 |
| 190 | 1.2544 | 1978.8 | 876.4 | 6.388 |
| 200 | 1.5538 | 1940.7 | 864.3 | 7.852 |
| 210 | 1.9062 | 1900.7 | 852.5 | 9.578 |
| 220 | 2.318 | 1858.5 | 840.3 | 11.602 |
| 230 | 2.795 | 1813.8 | 827.1 | 13.970 |
| 240 | 3.344 | 1766.5 | 813.7 | 16.734 |
| 250 | 3.973 | 1716.2 | 799.4 | 19.948 |
| 260 | 4.688 | 1662.5 | 783.7 | 23.691 |
| 270 | 5.499 | 1605.2 | 768.1 | 28.058 |
| 280 | 6.412 | 1543.6 | 750.8 | 33.145 |
| 290 | 7.436 | 1477.1 | 732.1 | 39.108 |
| 300 | 8.581 | 1404.9 | 712.3 | 46.147 |
| 310 | 9.856 | 1326.0 | 691.1 | 54.50 |
| 320 | 11.274 | 1238.6 | 667.1 | 64.57 |
| 330 | 12.845 | 1140.6 | 640.6 | 76.95 |
| 340 | 14.586 | 1027.9 | 610.5 | 92.62 |
| 350 | 16.513 | 893.4 | 574.7 | 113.47 |
| 360 | 18.651 | 720.5 | 528.3 | 143.99 |
| 370 | 21.03 | 441.6 | 451.9 | 203.05 |
| 374.14 | 22.09 | 0 | 316.96 | 316.96 |

Compiled from Keenan and Keyes (1969).

## Table B-8 Illustration of physical properties of gases at atmospheric pressure in both Btu and SI units

| °F | °C | $c_p$, $\dfrac{Btu}{lb \cdot °F}$ | $c_p \times 10^{-3}$, $\dfrac{W \cdot s}{kg \cdot °C}$ | $k$, $\dfrac{Btu}{h \cdot ft \cdot °F}$ | $k$, $\dfrac{W}{m \cdot °C}$ | $\mu$, $\dfrac{lb}{ft \cdot h}$ | $\mu \times 10^5$, $\dfrac{kg}{m \cdot s}$ | $\rho$, $\dfrac{lb}{ft^3}$ | $\rho$, $\dfrac{kg}{m^3}$ | $\nu$, $\dfrac{ft^2}{h}$ | $\nu \times 10^4$, $\dfrac{m^2}{s}$ | $\alpha$, $\dfrac{ft^2}{h}$ | $\alpha \times 10^4$, $\dfrac{m^2}{s}$ | $P_r$ |
|---|---|---|---|---|---|---|---|---|---|---|---|---|---|---|
| **Air** | | | | | | | | | | | | | | |
| −200 | −128.9 | 0.2392 | 1.001 | 0.0079 | 0.0137 | 0.0252 | 1.042 | 0.153 | 2.462 | 0.165 | 0.0426 | 0.216 | 0.0557 | 0.760 |
| 0 | −17.8 | 0.2400 | 1.005 | 0.014 | 0.0242 | 0.0415 | 1.716 | 0.0864 | 1.390 | 0.480 | 0.1239 | 0.675 | 0.1742 | 0.711 |
| 200 | 93.3 | 0.2414 | 1.011 | 0.0181 | 0.0313 | 0.0519 | 2.146 | 0.0602 | 0.969 | 0.862 | 0.2225 | 1.245 | 0.3213 | 0.692 |
| 400 | 204.4 | 0.2451 | 1.026 | 0.0224 | 0.0388 | 0.0624 | 2.580 | 0.0462 | 0.743 | 1.351 | 0.3487 | 1.977 | 0.6103 | 0.683 |
| **N₂** | | | | | | | | | | | | | | |
| −200 | −128.9 | 0.252 | 1.055 | 0.0079 | 0.0137 | 0.0237 | 0.980 | 0.148 | 2.381 | 0.160 | 0.0413 | 0.212 | 0.0547 | 0.756 |
| 0 | −17.8 | 0.2484 | 1.040 | 0.0132 | 0.0228 | 0.039 | 1.612 | 0.0835 | 1.344 | 0.467 | 0.1205 | 0.635 | 0.1639 | 0.734 |
| 200 | 93.3 | 0.249 | 1.042 | 0.0173 | 0.0299 | 0.0498 | 2.059 | 0.0582 | 0.936 | 0.856 | 0.2209 | 1.194 | 0.3082 | 0.717 |
| 400 | 204.4 | 0.2515 | 1.053 | 0.021 | 0.0363 | 0.0601 | 2.485 | 0.0448 | 0.721 | 1.342 | 0.3464 | 1.864 | 0.4811 | 0.719 |
| **O₂** | | | | | | | | | | | | | | |
| −200 | −128.9 | 0.2175 | 0.911 | 0.0079 | 0.0137 | 0.0272 | 1.124 | 0.169 | 2.719 | 0.161 | 0.0417 | 0.215 | 0.0555 | 0.749 |
| 0 | −17.8 | 0.2182 | 0.914 | 0.0135 | 0.0234 | 0.044 | 1.819 | 0.096 | 1.545 | 0.458 | 0.1821 | 0.644 | 0.1662 | 0.711 |
| 200 | 93.4 | 0.2223 | 0.931 | 0.018 | 0.0311 | 0.0583 | 2.410 | 0.0665 | 1.070 | 0.877 | 0.2264 | 1.217 | 0.3141 | 0.720 |
| 400 | 204.4 | 0.2305 | 0.965 | 0.0233 | 0.0403 | 0.0712 | 2.943 | 0.0512 | 0.824 | 1.391 | 0.3590 | 1.973 | 0.5092 | 0.704 |
| **NH₃** | | | | | | | | | | | | | | |
| 0 | −17.8 | 0.522 | 2.185 | 0.0117 | 0.0202 | 0.0213 | 0.880 | 0.0441 | 0.710 | 0.483 | 0.1247 | 0.508 | 0.1311 | 0.95 |
| 200 | 93.3 | 0.532 | 2.227 | 0.0192 | 0.0332 | 0.0303 | 1.253 | 0.0307 | 0.494 | 0.999 | 0.2578 | 1.173 | 0.3028 | 0.84 |
| 400 | 204.4 | 0.574 | 2.403 | 0.0280 | 0.0484 | 0.0394 | 1.629 | 0.0236 | 0.380 | 1.669 | 0.4308 | 2.064 | 0.5327 | 0.807 |
| **Freon-11** | | | | | | | | | | | | | | |
| 0 | −17.8 | 0.124 | 0.519 | 0.00412 | 0.00713 | 0.0232 | 0.959 | 0.0398 | 0.640 | 0.583 | 0.1505 | 0.829 | 0.2140 | 0.701 |
| 100 | 37.8 | 0.134 | 0.561 | 0.00519 | 0.00898 | 0.0274 | 1.133 | 0.0322 | 0.518 | 0.851 | 0.2196 | 1.205 | 0.3110 | 0.706 |
| 200 | 93.3 | 0.145 | 0.607 | 0.00627 | 0.01085 | 0.0312 | 1.290 | 0.0278 | 0.447 | 1.122 | 0.2896 | 1.555 | 0.4013 | 0.722 |
| **Steam** | | | | | | | | | | | | | | |
| 212 | 100.0 | 0.451 | 1.888 | 0.0145 | 0.0251 | 0.0313 | 1.294 | 0.0372 | 0.599 | 0.842 | 0.2173 | 0.864 | 0.2230 | 0.96 |
| 300 | 148.9 | 0.456 | 1.909 | 0.0171 | 0.0296 | 0.0360 | 1.488 | 0.0328 | 0.528 | 1.098 | 0.2834 | 1.14 | 0.2942 | 0.95 |
| 400 | 204.4 | 0.462 | 1.934 | 0.0200 | 0.0346 | 0.0407 | 1.683 | 0.0288 | 0.463 | 1.422 | 0.3670 | 1.50 | 0.3872 | 0.94 |

**Table B-9  Illustration of physical properties of metals and nonmetals in both Btu and SI units**

| Material | Temperature, °F | Temperature, °C | $c_p$, Btu/(lb·°F) | $c_p \times 10^{-3}$, W·s/(kg·°C) | $k$, Btu/(h·ft·°F) | $k$, W/(m·°C) | $\rho$, lb/ft³ | $\rho$, kg/m³ | $\alpha$, ft²/h | $\alpha \times 10^6$, m²/s |
|---|---|---|---|---|---|---|---|---|---|---|
| **Metals** | | | | | | | | | | |
| Aluminum | 32 | 0 | 0.208 | 0.871 | 117 | 202.4 | 169 | 2,719 | 3.33 | 85.9 |
| Copper | 32 | 0 | 0.091 | 0.381 | 224 | 387.6 | 558 | 8,978 | 4.42 | 114.1 |
| Gold | 68 | 20 | 0.030 | 0.126 | 169 | 292.4 | 1204 | 19,372 | 4.68 | 120.8 |
| Iron, pure | 32 | 0 | 0.104 | 0.435 | 36 | 62.3 | 491 | 7,900 | 0.70 | 18.1 |
| Cast iron ($c \cong 4\%$) | 68 | 20 | 0.10 | 0.417 | 30 | 51.9 | 454 | 7,304 | 0.66 | 17.0 |
| Lead | 70 | 21.1 | 0.030 | 0.126 | 20 | 34.6 | 705 | 11,343 | 0.95 | 25.5 |
| Mercury | 32 | 0 | 0.033 | 0.138 | 4.83 | 8.36 | 849 | 13,660 | 0.172 | 4.44 |
| Nickel | 32 | 0 | 0.103 | 0.431 | 34.4 | 59.52 | 555 | 8,930 | 0.60 | 15.5 |
| Silver | 32 | 0 | 0.056 | 0.234 | 242 | 418.7 | 655 | 10,539 | 6.60 | 170.4 |
| Steel, mild | 32 | 0 | 0.11 | 0.460 | 26 | 45.0 | 490 | 7,884 | 0.48 | 12.4 |
| Tungsten | 32 | 0 | 0.032 | 0.134 | 92 | 159.2 | 1204 | 19,372 | 2.39 | 61.7 |
| Zinc | 32 | 0 | 0.091 | 0.381 | 65 | 112.5 | 446 | 7,176 | 1.60 | 41.3 |
| **Nonmetals** | | | | | | | | | | |
| Asbestos | 32 | 0 | 0.25 | 1.047 | 0.087 | 0.151 | 36 | 579 | 0.010 | 0.258 |
| Brick, fireclay | 400 | 204.4 | 0.20 | 0.837 | 0.58 | 1.004 | 144 | 2,317 | 0.020 | 0.516 |
| Cork, ground | 100 | 37.8 | 0.48 | 2.010 | 0.024 | 0.042 | 8 | 128.7 | 0.006 | 0.155 |
| Glass, Pyrex | | | 0.20 | 0.837 | 0.68 | 1.177 | 150 | 2,413 | 0.023 | 0.594 |
| Granite | 32 | 0 | 0.19 | 0.796 | 1.6 | 2.768 | 168 | 2,703 | 0.050 | 1.291 |
| Ice | 32 | 0 | 0.49 | 2.051 | 1.28 | 2.215 | 57 | 917 | 0.046 | 1.187 |
| Oak, across grain | 85 | 29.4 | 0.41 | 1.716 | 0.111 | 0.192 | 44 | 708 | 0.0062 | 0.160 |
| Pine, across grain | 85 | 29.4 | 0.42 | 1.758 | 0.092 | 0.159 | 37 | 595 | 0.0059 | 0.152 |
| Quartz sand, dry | 85 | | 0.19 | 0.796 | 0.15 | 0.260 | 103 | 1,657 | 0.008 | 0.206 |
| Rubber, soft | | | 0.45 | 1.884 | 0.10 | 0.173 | 69 | 1,110 | 0.003 | 0.077 |

## APPENDIX C: RADIATION PROPERTIES

# Table C-1 Normal emissivity of surfaces

| Surface | $T$, °C | $\varepsilon_n$ | Surface | $T$, °C | $\varepsilon_n$ |
|---|---|---|---|---|---|
| Metals | | | Metals | | |
| Aluminum | | | Lead (continued) | | |
|   Highly polished, plate | 200–600 | 0.038–0.06 |   Gray, oxidized | 23 | 0.28 |
|   Bright, foil | 21 | 0.04 |   Oxidized at 200°C | 200 | 0.63 |
|   Heavily oxidized | 100–500 | 0.20–0.33 | | | |
| | | | Nickel | | |
| Brass | | |   Electrolytic | 37–260 | 0.04–0.06 |
|   Highly polished | 250–360 | 0.028–0.031 |   Pure, polished | 260 | 0.07 |
|   Dull plate | 50–350 | 0.22 |   Oxidized at 600°C | 260–540 | 0.37–0.48 |
|   Oxidized | 200–500 | 0.60 | | | |
| | | | Platinum | | |
| Chromium, polished | 37–1100 | 0.08–0.40 |   Plate, polished | 260–540 | 0.06–0.10 |
| | | |   Filament | 26–1225 | 0.04–0.19 |
| Copper | | | | | |
|   Polished, electrolytic | 80 | 0.018 | Silver | | |
|   Polished | 37–260 | 0.04–0.05 |   Polished | 37–625 | 0.02–0.03 |
|   Calorized | 37–260 | 0.18 | | | |
|   Black oxidized | 37 | 0.78 | Stainless steel | | |
| | | |   Polished | 23 | 0.17 |
| Gold polished | 37–260 | 0.02 |   Cleaned | 23 | 0.21–0.39 |
| | | | | | |
| Iron | | | Tin | | |
|   Polished | 425–1025 | 0.14–0.38 |   Polished | 37 | 0.05 |
|   Oxidized | 100 | 0.74 | | | |
|   Cast iron, oxidized | | | Tungsten | | |
|     at 600°C | 200–600 | 0.64–0.78 |   Filament | 3300 | 0.39 |
|   Cast plate, smooth | 22 | 0.80 | | | |
|   Cast plate, rough | 22 | 0.82 | Zinc | | |
| | | |   Polished | 225–325 | 0.05–0.06 |
| Lead | | |   Oxidized at 400°C | 400 | 0.11 |
|   Pure, polished | 260 | 0.08 |   Galvanized | 23–27 | 0.23–0.28 |

## Table C-1 *(continued)*

| Surface | $T$, °C | $\varepsilon_n$ | Surface | $T$, °C | $\varepsilon_n$ |
|---|---|---|---|---|---|
| Nonmetals | | | Nonmetals | | |
| Alumina | | | Ice *(continued)* | | |
| (85–99.5% $Al_2O_3$) | | | Rough crystals | 0 | 0.985 |
| effect of mean | | | | | |
| grain size | | | Marble, light gray, polished | 22 | 0.93 |
| 10 μm | 1000–1560 | 0.30–0.18 | | | |
| 50 μm | 1000–1560 | 0.39–0.28 | Mica | 37 | 0.75 |
| 100 μm | 1000–1560 | 0.50–0.40 | | | |
| | | | Paints | | |
| Asbestos | | | Aluminum 10%, | | |
| Paper | 37 | 0.93 | lacquer 22% | 100 | 0.52 |
| Board | 37 | 0.96 | Aluminum 26%, | | |
| | | | lacquer 27% | 100 | 0.30 |
| Brick | | | Other aluminum paints | 100 | 0.27 |
| Magnesite, refractory | 1000 | 0.38 | Lacquer, white | 100 | 0.925 |
| Red, rough | 21 | 0.93 | Lacquer, black matte | 80 | 0.97 |
| Gray, glazed | 1100 | 0.75 | Oil paints, all colors | 100 | 0.92–0.96 |
| Silica | 540 | 0.80 | Oil paints | 20 | 0.89–0.97 |
| Carbon | | | Paper | | |
| Fllament | 1050–1400 | 0.526 | Ordinary | 20–95 | 0.80–0.92 |
| Candle soot | 95–270 | 0.952 | Tar | 20 | 0.93 |
| Lampblack | 20 | 0.93–0.967 | | | |
| | | | Porcelain, glazed | 22 | 0.92 |
| Ceramic | | | | | |
| Earthenware, glazed | 20 | 0.90 | Quartz | | |
| Earthenware, matte | 20 | 0.93 | Glass, 1.98 mm thick | 280 | 0.90 |
| Porcelain | 22 | 0.92 | Glass, 1.98 mm thick | 840 | 0.41 |
| Refractory, black | 93 | 0.94 | Glass, 6.88 mm thick | 280 | 0.93 |
| | | | Glass, 6.88 mm thick | 840 | 0.47 |
| Clay, fired | 70 | 0.91 | | | |
| | | | Rubber | | |
| Concrete, rough | 37 | 0.94 | Hard | 23 | 0.94 |
| | | | Soft, gray | 23 | 0.86 |
| Glass | | | | | |
| Smooth | 22 | 0.94 | Soil | 37 | 0.93–0.96 |
| Pyrex, lead, and soda | 260–530 | 0.95–0.85 | | | |
| | | | Water, deep | 0–100 | 0.96 |
| Ice | | | | | |
| Smooth | 0 | 0.97 | Wood | 20 | 0.80–0.90 |

## Table C-2 Solar absorptivity of surfaces (receiving surface at room temperature)

| Surface | α | Surface | α |
|---|---|---|---|
| Metals | | Nonmetals | |
| Aluminum | | Asphalt | |
|    Polished | 0.10 |    Pavement | 0.85 |
|    Anodized | 0.14 |    Pavement free from dust | 0.93 |
|    Foil | 0.15 | | |
| | | Brick | |
| Brass | |    White glazed | 0.26 |
|    Polished | 0.3–0.5 |    Red | 0.70–0.77 |
| | | | |
| Chromium, electroplated | 0.41 | Concrete | |
| | |    Black | 0.91 |
| Copper | |    Uncolored | 0.65 |
| Highly polished | 0.18 |    Gray colored | 0.0.79 |
| Tarnished by exposure | 0.64 | | |
| | | Granite | 0–45 |
| Gold | 0.21 | | |
| | | Grass | 0.75–0.8 |
| Iron | | | |
|    Matte, oxidized | 0.96 | Gravel | 0.29 |
| | | | |
| Lead roofing, old | 0.77 | Leaves, green | 0.71–0.79 |
| | | | |
| Nickel | | Magnesium oxide (MgO) | 0.15 |
|    Highly polished | 0.15 | | |
|    Polished | 0.36 | Marble | |
|    Oxidized | 0.79 |    White | 0.44 |
| | |    Ground, unpolished | 0–47 |
| Platinum, bright | 0.31 | | |
| | | Paints | |
| Silver | |    Oil, white lead | 0.24–0.26 |
|    Highly polished | 0.07 |    Oil, light cream | 0.30 |
| | |    Aluminum | 0.55 |
| Stainless steel, type 301 | |    Oil, light gray | 0.75 |
|    Polished | 0.37 |    Oil black on galvanized iron | 0.90 |
|    Clean | 0.52 | | |
| | | Paper | |
| Zinc | |    White | 0.28 |
|    Highly polished | 0.34 | | |
|    Polished | 0 55 | Sand | 0.76 |
| | | | |
| | | Slate | |
| | |    Silver gray | 0.79 |
| | |    Dark gray | 0.90 |
| | | | |
| | | Snow, clean | 0.2–0.35 |
| | | | |
| | | Soot, coal | 0.95 |

# APPENDIX D: ERROR FUNCTION

## Table D-1  Error function, erf($\xi$)

$$\text{erf}(\xi) = \frac{2}{\sqrt{\pi}} \int_0^\xi e^{-y^2}\, dy \qquad \text{erf}(\infty) = 1$$

| $\xi$ | erf($\xi$) | $\xi$ | erf($\xi$) | $\xi$ | erf($\xi$) | $\xi$ | erf($\xi$) | $\xi$ | erf($\xi$) | $\xi$ | erf($\xi$) |
|---|---|---|---|---|---|---|---|---|---|---|---|
| | | | (continued) | | | | | | | | |
| 0.00 | 0.00000 | 0.40 | 0.42839 | 0.76 | 0.71754 | 1.16 | 0.89910 | 1.52 | 0.96841 | 1.92 | 0.993380 |
| 0.02 | 0.02256 | 0.42 | 0.44749 | 0.78 | 0.73001 | 1.18 | 0.90484 | 1.54 | 0.97059 | 1.94 | 0.993920 |
| 0.04 | 0.04511 | 0.44 | 0.46622 | 0.80 | 0.74210 | 1.20 | 0.91031 | 1.56 | 0.97263 | 1.96 | 0.994430 |
| 0.06 | 0.06762 | 0.46 | 0.48466 | 0.82 | 0.75381 | 1.22 | 0.91553 | 1.58 | 0.97455 | 1.98 | 0.994890 |
| 0.08 | 0.09008 | 0.48 | 0.50275 | 0.84 | 0.76514 | 1.24 | 0.92050 | 1.60 | 0.97636 | 2.00 | 0.995320 |
| 0.10 | 0.11246 | 0.50 | 0.52050 | 0.86 | 0.77610 | 1.26 | 0.92524 | 1.62 | 0.97804 | 2.10 | 0.997020 |
| 0.12 | 0.13476 | 0.52 | 0.53790 | 0.88 | 0.78669 | 1.28 | 0.92973 | 1.64 | 0.97962 | 2.20 | 0.998130 |
| 0.14 | 0.15695 | 0.54 | 0.55494 | 0.90 | 0.79691 | 1.30 | 0.93401 | 1.66 | 0.98110 | 2.30 | 0.998850 |
| 0.16 | 0.17901 | 0.56 | 0.57162 | 0.92 | 0.80677 | 1.32 | 0.93806 | 1.68 | 0.98249 | 2.40 | 0.999310 |
| 0.18 | 0.20094 | 0.58 | 0.58792 | 0.94 | 0.81627 | 1.34 | 0.94191 | 1.70 | 0.98379 | 2.50 | 0.999590 |
| 0.20 | 0.22270 | 0.60 | 0.60386 | 0.96 | 0.82542 | 1.36 | 0.94556 | 1.72 | 0.98500 | 2.60 | 0.999764 |
| 0.22 | 0.24430 | 0.62 | 0.61941 | 0.98 | 0.83423 | 1.38 | 0.94902 | 1.74 | 0.98613 | 2.70 | 0.999866 |
| 0.24 | 0.26570 | 0.64 | 0.63459 | 1.00 | 0.84270 | 1.40 | 0.95228 | 1.76 | 0.98719 | 2.80 | 0.999925 |
| 0.26 | 0.28690 | 0.66 | 0.64938 | 1.02 | 0.85084 | 1.42 | 0.95538 | 1.78 | 0.98817 | 2.90 | 0.999959 |
| 0.28 | 0.30788 | 0.68 | 0.66278 | 1.04 | 0.85865 | 1.44 | 0.95830 | 1.80 | 0.98909 | 3.00 | 0.999978 |
| 0.30 | 0.32863 | 0.70 | 0.67780 | 1.06 | 0.86614 | 1.46 | 0.96105 | 1.82 | 0.98994 | 3.20 | 0.999994 |
| 0.32 | 0.34913 | 0.72 | 0.69143 | 1.08 | 0.87333 | 1.48 | 0.96365 | 1.84 | 0.99074 | 3.40 | 0.999998 |
| 0.34 | 0.36936 | 0.74 | 0.70468 | 1.10 | 0.88020 | 1.50 | 0.96610 | 1.86 | 0.99147 | 3.60 | 1.000000 |
| 0.36 | 0.38933 | | | 1.12 | 0.88079 | | | 1.88 | 0.99216 | | |
| 0.38 | 0.40901 | | | 1.14 | 0.89308 | | | 1.90 | 0.99279 | | |

## APPENDIX E: MATHEMATICAL IDENTITIES

### Table 1

| Some Governing Equations for Incompressible Flow in Differential Form: |
| --- |
| Continuity (C) : $\nabla \cdot \vec{V} = 0$ |
| Momentum (M) : $\rho \frac{D\vec{V}}{Dt} = \rho \vec{g} - \nabla p + \mu \nabla^2 \vec{V}$ |
| Thermal Energy (E) : $\rho c_v \frac{DT}{Dt} = k \nabla^2 T + \Phi$ |

### Table 2

| Vector Identities : scalar $\xi$ , $\vec{\zeta} = \nabla \times \vec{V}$ |
| --- |
| $\nabla \times \nabla \xi = 0$ <br> $\nabla \cdot \left( \nabla \times \vec{V} \right) = 0$ <br> $\nabla^2 \vec{V} = \nabla(\nabla \cdot \vec{V}) - \nabla \times (\nabla \times \vec{V})$ <br> $\left( \vec{V} \cdot \nabla \right) \left( \vec{V} \right) = \frac{1}{2}\nabla \left( \vec{V} \cdot \vec{V} \right) - \vec{V} \times \left( \nabla \times \vec{V} \right)$ <br> $\nabla \times \left( \vec{V} \times \vec{\zeta} \right) = \left( \vec{\zeta} \cdot \nabla \right) \left( \vec{V} \right) + \vec{V} \left( \nabla \cdot \vec{\zeta} \right) - \left( \vec{V} \cdot \nabla \right) \left( \vec{\zeta} \right) - \vec{\zeta} \left( \nabla \cdot \vec{V} \right)$ |

### Table 3

---

## ∇ (del) Operator: Gradient of $\xi$, $\nabla\xi$

Cartesian: $\nabla(\ ) = \frac{\partial(\ )}{\partial x}\hat{i} + \frac{\partial(\ )}{\partial y}\hat{j} + \frac{\partial(\ )}{\partial z}\widehat{k}$, $\quad \nabla\xi = \frac{\partial\xi}{\partial x}\hat{i} + \frac{\partial\xi}{\partial y}\hat{j} + \frac{\partial\xi}{\partial z}\widehat{k}$

Cylindrical: $\nabla(\ ) = \frac{\partial(\ )}{\partial r}\hat{e}_r + \frac{1}{r}\frac{\partial(\ )}{\partial\theta}\hat{e}_\theta + \frac{\partial(\ )}{\partial z}\widehat{k}$, $\quad \nabla\xi = \frac{\partial\xi}{\partial r}\hat{e}_r + \frac{1}{r}\frac{\partial\xi}{\partial\theta}\hat{e}_\theta + \frac{\partial\xi}{\partial z}\widehat{k}$

---

## DIVERGENCE: $\nabla\cdot\vec{V}$, Divergence of $\vec{V}$, div $\vec{V}$

Cartesian: $\vec{V} = u\hat{i} + v\hat{j} + w\widehat{k}$

$$\nabla\cdot\vec{V} = \frac{\partial u}{\partial x} + \frac{\partial v}{\partial y} + \frac{\partial w}{\partial z}$$

Cylindrical: $\vec{V} = v_r\hat{e}_r + v_\theta\hat{e}_\theta + v_z\widehat{k}$

$$\nabla\cdot\vec{V} = \frac{1}{r}\frac{\partial(r\,v_r)}{\partial r} + \frac{1}{r}\frac{\partial v_\theta}{\partial\theta} + \frac{\partial v_z}{\partial z}$$

---

## CURL: $\nabla\times\vec{V}$, Curl of $\vec{V}$, curl $\vec{V}$

Cartesian: $\vec{V} = u\hat{i} + v\hat{j} + w\widehat{k}$,

$$\nabla\times\vec{V} = \left(\frac{\partial w}{\partial y} - \frac{\partial v}{\partial z}\right)\hat{i} + \left(\frac{\partial u}{\partial z} - \frac{\partial w}{\partial x}\right)\hat{j} + \left(\frac{\partial v}{\partial x} - \frac{\partial u}{\partial y}\right)\widehat{k}$$

Cylindrical: $\vec{V} = v_r\hat{e}_r + v_\theta\hat{e}_\theta + v_z\widehat{k}$,

$$\nabla\times\vec{V} = \left(\frac{1}{r}\frac{\partial v_z}{\partial\theta} - \frac{\partial v_\theta}{\partial z}\right)\hat{e}_r + \left(\frac{\partial v_r}{\partial z} - \frac{\partial v_z}{\partial r}\right)\hat{e}_\theta + \left(\frac{1}{r}\frac{\partial}{\partial r}(rv_\theta) - \frac{1}{r}\frac{\partial v_r}{\partial\theta}\right)\widehat{k}$$

---

## LAPLACIAN: $\nabla\cdot\nabla\xi$, Divergence of the Gradient of $\xi$
## $\nabla\cdot\nabla\xi = \nabla^2\xi$ = Laplacian of $\xi$

Cartesian: $\nabla^2\xi = \frac{\partial^2\xi}{\partial x^2} + \frac{\partial^2\xi}{\partial y^2} + \frac{\partial^2\xi}{\partial z^2}$

Cylindrical: $\nabla^2\xi = \frac{1}{r}\frac{\partial}{\partial r}\left(r\frac{\partial\xi}{\partial r}\right) + \frac{1}{r^2}\frac{\partial^2\xi}{\partial\theta^2} + \frac{\partial^2\xi}{\partial z^2}$

---

## VECTOR LAPLACIAN: $\nabla^2\vec{V}$

Cartesian: $\nabla^2\vec{V} = \frac{\partial^2\vec{V}}{\partial x^2} + \frac{\partial^2\vec{V}}{\partial y^2} + \frac{\partial^2\vec{V}}{\partial z^2}$

Cylindrical: $\nabla^2\vec{V} = \left(\nabla^2 v_r - \frac{2}{r^2}\frac{\partial v_\theta}{\partial\theta} - \frac{v_r}{r^2}\right)\hat{e}_r + \left(\nabla^2 v_\theta + \frac{2}{r^2}\frac{\partial v_r}{\partial\theta} - \frac{v_\theta}{r^2}\right)\hat{e}_\theta + \nabla^2 v_z\widehat{k}$

# Table 4

---

## TOTAL DERIVATIVE : (Material derivative)

$$\frac{Db}{Dt} = \frac{\partial b}{\partial t} + (\vec{V} \cdot \nabla)(b) \quad ; \quad b \text{ can be either a scalar or vector}$$

---

Cartesian : $\quad \frac{Db}{Dt} = \frac{\partial b}{\partial t} + u\frac{\partial b}{\partial x} + v\frac{\partial b}{\partial y} + w\frac{\partial b}{\partial z}$

Cylindrical : $\quad \frac{Db}{Dt} = \frac{\partial b}{\partial t} + v_r\frac{\partial b}{\partial r} + \frac{v_\theta}{r}\frac{\partial b}{\partial \theta} + v_z\frac{\partial b}{\partial z}$

---

## Vector $b$ : $\quad \vec{V} = u\hat{i} + v\hat{j} + w\widehat{k}, \quad \vec{a} = a_x\hat{i} + a_y\hat{j} + a_z\widehat{k}$

---

Cartesian : $\quad \frac{D\vec{V}}{Dt} = \vec{a} = \frac{\partial \vec{V}}{\partial t} + u\frac{\partial \vec{V}}{\partial x} + v\frac{\partial \vec{V}}{\partial y} + w\frac{\partial \vec{V}}{\partial z}$

$x$ - comp : $\quad \frac{Du}{Dt} = a_x = \frac{\partial u}{\partial t} + u\frac{\partial u}{\partial x} + v\frac{\partial u}{\partial y} + w\frac{\partial u}{\partial z} = \frac{\partial u}{\partial t} + (\vec{V} \cdot \nabla)(u)$

$y$ - comp : $\quad \frac{Dv}{Dt} = a_y = \frac{\partial v}{\partial t} + u\frac{\partial v}{\partial x} + v\frac{\partial v}{\partial y} + w\frac{\partial v}{\partial z} = \frac{\partial v}{\partial t} + (\vec{V} \cdot \nabla)(v)$

$z$ - comp : $\quad \frac{Dw}{Dt} = a_z = \frac{\partial w}{\partial t} + u\frac{\partial w}{\partial x} + v\frac{\partial w}{\partial y} + w\frac{\partial w}{\partial z} = \frac{\partial w}{\partial t} + (\vec{V} \cdot \nabla)(w)$

---

## Vector $b$ : $\quad \vec{V} = v_r\hat{e}_r + v_\theta\hat{e}_\theta + v_z\widehat{k}, \quad \vec{a} = a_r\hat{e}_r + a_\theta\hat{e}_\theta + a_z\widehat{k}$

---

Cylindrical : $\quad \frac{D\vec{V}}{Dt} = \vec{a} = \frac{\partial \vec{V}}{\partial t} + v_r\frac{\partial \vec{V}}{\partial r} + \frac{v_\theta}{r}\frac{\partial \vec{V}}{\partial \theta} + v_z\frac{\partial \vec{V}}{\partial z}$

$r$ - comp : $\quad \frac{Dv_r}{Dt} - \frac{1}{r}v_\theta^2 = a_r = \frac{\partial v_r}{\partial t} + (\vec{V} \cdot \nabla)(v_r) - \frac{1}{r}v_\theta^2$

$\theta$ - comp : $\quad \frac{Dv_\theta}{Dt} + \frac{1}{r}v_r v_\theta = a_\theta = \frac{\partial v_\theta}{\partial t} + (\vec{V} \cdot \nabla)(v_\theta) + \frac{1}{r}v_r v_\theta$

$z$ - comp : $\quad \frac{Dv_z}{Dt} = a_z = \frac{\partial v_z}{\partial t} + (\vec{V} \cdot \nabla)(v_z)$

$$\text{or,} \quad \vec{a} = a_r\hat{e}_r + a_\theta\hat{e}_\theta + a_z\widehat{k}$$

$$= \left[\frac{Dv_r}{Dt} - \frac{1}{r}v_\theta^2\right]\hat{e}_r + \left[\frac{Dv_\theta}{Dt} + \frac{1}{r}v_r v_\theta\right]\hat{e}_\theta + \frac{Dv_z}{Dt}\widehat{k}$$

---

# REFERENCES

## The cited References and a brief Bibliography of Textbooks for Heat Transfer:

- Alexander, S., Heisler Charts, *Heat Transfer Course Project*, Rice University (2007).

- American Society of Heating, Refrigeration and Air Conditioning, *ASHRAE Handbook of Fundamentals*, New York (1981).

- American Society of Metals, *Metals Handbook*, 8th Edition, ASM, Metals Park, OH (1961).

- Arpaci, V.S., *Conduction Heat Transfer*, Addison-Wesley, Reading, Mass. (1966).

- Arpaci, V.S., and P.S. Larsen, *Convection Heat Transfer*, Prentice-Hall, Englewood Cliffs, N.J. (1984).

- Atkins, H.L. and E. Fried, Interface Thermal Conductance in a Vacuum, *AIAA PAPER 64-253* (1965).

- Barzelay, M.E., K.N. Tong, and G.F. Holloway, Effect of Pressure on Thermal Conductance of Contact Joints, *NACA Tech.* Note 3295 (1955).

- Y. Bayazitoglu, Single-Phase Gaseous Flow, *Encyclopedia of Micro- and Nanofluidics*, Editor: Dongqing Li, Springer, (2008).

- Bayazitoglu, Y. and S. Kakac, Flow Regimes in Microchannel Single Phase Gaseous Fluid Flow, Microscale Heat Transfer- Fundamental and Applications, *Kluwer Academic Publishers*, pp. 75-92, (2005).

- Bayazitoglu, Y. and M.N. Ozisik, *Elements of Heat Transfer*, McGraw Hill (1988).

- Bejan, A., *Convective Heat Transfer*, John Wiley and Sons (1995).

- Bejan, A., *Heat Transfer*, John Wiley and Sons (1993).

- Bergman, T.L., A.S. Lavine, F.P. Incorpera and D.P. Dewitt, *Introduction to Heat Transfer*, John Wiley and Sons, Inc. (2011).

- Bowman, R. A., A. C. Mueller, and W. M. Nagle: "Mean Temperature Difference in Design," *Trans. ASME*, 62, 283-294 (1940).

- Brown, A.I., and S.M. Macro, *Introduction to Heat Transfer*, 3d ed., McGraw-Hill, New York (1958).

- Cebeci, T., and P. Bradshaw, *Physical and Computational Aspects of Convective Heat Transfer*, Springer, New York (1984).

- Chandrupatla, A.R. and V.M.K. Sastri, Laminar Forced Convection Heat Transfer of a Non-Newtonian Fluid in a Square Duct, *Int. J. Heat Mass Transfer*, 20, 1315-1324(1977).

- Chapman, A.J. *Heat Transfer*, Macmillan, New York (1984).

- Darcy, H. Recherches *Experimentales Relatives au Mouvement de L Eau dans les Tuyaux Mallet-Bachelier*, Paris, France (1857)

- Eckert, E.R.G. and R.M. Drake *Analysis of Heat and Mass Transfer*, McGraw-Hill, New York (1972).

- Faghri, A., *Transport Phenomena in Multiphase Systems*, Elsevier Inc. (2006).

- Faghri, A., Y. Zhang and J. Howell *Advanced Heat and Mass Transfer*, Global Digital Press (2010).

- Fanning, J.T., *A Practical Treatise on Hydraulic and Water Supply Engineering*, VanNostrand, New York, (1877) revised ed. (1886).

- Farber, E.A., and R.L. Scorah, Heat Transfer to Water Boiling under Pressure, *Trans. ASME*, 79, 369-384 (1948).

- Fraas, A.P., and M.N. Ozisik, *Heat Exchanger Design*, Wiley, John and Sons (1989).

- Fujii, T., and H. Imura, Natural Convection Heat Transfer from a Plate with Arbitrary Inclination, *Int. J. Heat Mass Transfer*, 15, 755 (1972).

- Gebhart, B., Heat Conduction and Mass Diffusion, *McGraw-Hill*, (1993).

- Giedt, W. H., Investigation of Variation of Point Unit-Heat-Transfer Coefficient around a Cylinder Normal to an Air Stream, *Trans. ASME*, 71, 375-381 (1949).

- Goldstein, R., Measurement of Infrared Absorption of Water Vapor at Temperatures at 1000K, *J. of Quant. Spectrosc. Radiat. Transfer*, 4, 343-352 (1964).

- Goldstein, R. and S. Penner, The Near-Infrared Absorption of Liquid Water at Temperatures between 27-209 C, *J. of Quant. Spectrosc. Radiat. Transfer*, 4, 441-451 (1964).

- Gubareff, G.G., J.E. Janssen, and R.H. Torborg, *Thermal Radiation Properties Survey*, Honeywell Research Center, Honeywell Regulator Company, Minneapolis 1960.

- Gubareff, G.G.J.E. and R.H. Torborg, *Thermal Radiation Properties Survey*, Minneapolis-Honeywell Regulatory Company, Minneapolis MN (1960).

- Grigull, U., and W. Hauf, *Proceedings of 3rd International Heat Transfer Conference*, 2, 182-195 (1966).

- Hampson, H., and M.N. Ozişik, An Investigation into the Condensation of Steam, *Proc. Inst. Mech. Engin.*, London, 1B, 282-284 (1952).

- Hornyak, G. L., J. Dutta, H.F. Tibbals, and A.J. Rao, *Introduction to Nanoscience*, CRC Press, Taylor and Franciss Group, NewYork, NY (2009).

- Hornyak, G. L., J.J Moore, H.F. Tibbals, and J. Dutta, *Fundamentals of Nanothechnology*, CRC Press, Taylor and Franciss Group, NewYork, NY (2009).

- Hornberck, R. W., An All-Numerical Method for Heat Transfer in the Inlet of a Tube, *ASME Paper no. 65-Wa*, HT-36 (1975).

- Hottel, H.C. Radiant Heat Transmission, in W.H. McAdams (ed.), *Heat Transmission*, 3rd ed., McGraw-Hill, New York (1954).

- Howell, J., R. Siegel and P. Menguc, *Thermal Radiation Heat Transfer*, Taylor and Francis (2010).

- Howell, John R., *A Catalog of Radiation Heat Transfer Configuration Factors*, 2nd ed., 2003. (with permission available at http://www.me.utexas.edu/ howell/ )

- *International Critical Tables*, McGraw-Hill, New York, (1926-1930).

- Jakob, M., *Heat Transfer*, vol. 1, Wiley, New York (1949).

- Kandlikar, S. G., D. Schmitt, A.L. Carrano, J.B. Taylor, Characterization of surface roughness effects on pressure drop in single-phase flow in minichannels, *Physics of Fluids*, 17(10), 100606 (2005).

- Kakac, S., L.L. Vasiliev, Y. Bayazitoglu, and Y. Yener, Microscale Heat Transfer- Fundamental and Applications, *Kluwer Academic Publishers,* The Netherlands, 2005.

- Kakac, S., and Y. Yener, *Convective Heat Transfer*, CRC Press (1994).

- Kakac, S., and Y. Yener, *Heat Conduction*, Taylor and Francis Group,LLC, NewYork, NY (2008).

- Kays, W.M., and M.E. Crowford, *Convective Heat and Mass Transfer*, McGraw Hill, New York (1980).

- Kays, W. M., and A. L. London, *Compact Heat Exchangers*, 2d ed., McGraw-Hill, New York 1964.

- Kaviany, M., *Heat Transfer Physics*, Cambridge University Press (2008).

- Kaviany, M., *Essentials of Heat Transfer*, Cambridge University Press (2011).

- Keenan, J. H., F. G. Keyes, Philip G. Hill, and Joan G. Moore, *Steam Tables*, Wiley, New York (1969).

- Kim, J, Y.T. Kang, and C.K. Choi, Analysis of convective instability and heat transfer characteristics of nanofluids, *Phys. Fluids* 16, 2395, (2004)

- Kim, Y, Y.T. Kang, C.K. Choi, Soret and Dufour effects on convective instabilities in binary nanofluids for absorption application, *Inter. J. of Refrigeration*, 30(2), 323-28, (2007).

- Kreith, F. and J.F. Kreider, *Principal of Solar Engineering*, Hemisphere Publishing (1978).

- Kreith, F., R.M. Manglik, and M.S. Bohn, *Principals of Heat Transfer*, Cengage Learning, Stamford, CT (2011)

- Kutateladze, S.S., A Hydrodynamic Theory of Changes in Boiling Process under Free Convection, Iz. Akad. Nauk SSSR, Otd. Tekh, Nauk (4) 524 (1951).

- O. Ley and Y. Bayazitoglu, Temperature distribution during deep hypothermic circulatory arrest in humans, *Journal of Mechanics in Medicine and Biology*, vol.4, pp197-213, (2004).

- Lienhard, J. H., and V. K. Dhir, 'Hydrodynamic Prediction of Peak Pool-Boiling Heat Fluxes from Finite Bodies, *J. Heat Transfer*, 95C, 152-158 (1973).

- Lienhard, J. H. (IV) and Lienhard, J. H. (V), Phlogiston Press, Cambridge, Massachusetts (2008). Updated at web.mit.edu/lienhard/www/ahtt.html (2008).

- *Liquid Metals Handbook*, The Atomic Energy Commission, Department of Navy, Washington, DC (1952).

- Mackey, C.O., L.T. Wright, R.E. Clark, and N.R. Gray, Radiant Heating and Cooling, Part I, *Cornell Univ., Eng. Exp. Sta. Bull.*, 22 (1943).

- McAdams, W.H., *Heat Transmission*, 3rd ed., McGraw-Hill, New York, (1959).

- Mahan, J.R., *Radiation Heat Transfer :A Statistical Approach*, Wiley, NewYork (2002).

- Modest, F. M., *Radiation Heat Transfer*, 2nd ed., Academic Press, NewYork (2003).

- Moody, L.F., Friction Factors for Pipe Flow, *ASME Trans. J. Appl. Mech.* 66, 671(1944).

- Morgan, V. T., The Overall Convective Heat Transfer from Smooth Circular Cylinders, in T. F. Irvine and J. P. Hartnett (eds.), *Advances in Heat Transfer*, 16, Academic, New York, (1975).

- Nikuradse, J. *Laws of Flow in Rough Pipes*, VDI-Forschungsheft 36 (1933).

- Nukiyama, S., The Maximum and Minimum Values of the Heat $Q$ Transmitted from Metal to Boiling Water under Atmospheric Pressure, *J. Jap. Soc. Mech. Eng.*, 37, 367-374 (1934). [Translated in *Int. J. Heat Mass Transfer*, 9, 1419-1433 (1966).

- Ozisik, M.N., *Basic Heat Transfer*, McGraw Hill, NewYork, (1986).

- Ozisik, M.N., Radiation Heat Transfer, *Wiley*, NewYork, (1973).

- Ozisik, M.N., Heat Conduction, *Wiley*, (1993).

  itemOzisik, M.N. and H.R.B. Orlande, Inverse Heat Transfer: Fundamentals and Applications, *Taylor and Francis*, (200).

- Penner, S.S., Quantatitative Molecular Spectroscopy and Gas Emissivities, *Addison-Wesley*, Reading, Mass, (1959).

- Prakash, M, E.P. G., Mechanism of Heat Transport in Nanofluids, *J. of Computer-Aided Materials Design*, 14(1), 109-17 (2007).

- Prasher, R,P. Bhattacharya and P.E. Phelan, Thermal Conductivity of Nanoscale Colloidal Solutions (Nanofluids), *Phys. Rev. Lett.* 94, 25901-04 (2005).

- Reid, R.C., and T.K. Sherwood, *The Properties of Gases and Liquids*, McGraw-Hill, New York, (1966).

- Shah, R. K., and A. L. London, *Laminar Flow: Forced Convection in Ducts*, Academic, New York (1978).

- Shah, R. K., Thermal Entry Length Solutions for a Circular Tube and Parallel Plates, *Proc. Nat. Heat, Mass Transfer Conf.*, 3d, Indiana Inst. Technol., Bombay, vol. 1, Paper no. HMT-11-75 (1975).

- Schneider, P.J., *Conduction Heat Transfer*, Addison-Wesley, (1957).

- Schlichting, H., *Boundary Layer Theory*, 7th ed., McGraw-Hill, New York, (1979).

- Sieber, W., Zusammensetzung Der Von Werk-und Baustoffen Zurückgeworfenen Wärmestrahlung, *Z. Tech. Phys.*, 22, 130-135 (1941).

- Singham, J.R., Table of Emissivity of Surfaces, *Int. J. Heat Mass Transfer*, 5, 67-76 (1962).

- Swet, D.Y., Thermal Radiation, Metal, Semicinductors, Ceramics, Partly Transparent Bodies and Films, Consultant Burau, *Plenum*, NewYork, (1965).

- Tolukian, Y.S. and C.Y. Ho, Eds. *Thermophysical Properties of Matter*, Plenum Press, New York (1972).

- Tolukian,Y.S. and C.Y. Ho, Eds. *Thermophysical Properties of Selected Aerospace Materials*, Properties Information Analysis Center, CINDAS, Purdue University, West Lafayette, IN (1976).

- Tubular Exchanger Manufacturers Association, *Standards*, TEMA, New York (1959).

- Tullius, J.F. and T.K. Tullius and Y. Bayazitoglu, Optimization of short micro pin fins in minichannels, *Int. J. Heat Mass Transfer*, 55, 3921-3932 (2012).

- Tzou, D.Y. R., Macro-to-Microscale Heat Transfer, Taylor and Francis, Washington, DC (1997).

- Vahon, R. I., G. H. Nix, and G. E. Tanger, Evaluation of Constants for the Rohsenow Pool-Boiling Correlation, *J. Heat Transfer Soc*, 239-247 (1968).

- Vargaftik, N.B. *Tables of Thermophysical Properties of Liquids and Gases*, Hemisphere Publishing (1975).

- Wang, X-Q, A. S. Mujumdar, Heat Transfer Characteristics of Nanofluids: A Review, *Inter. J. of Thermal Sciences*, 46, 1-19 (2007).

- Wood, D.H., H. W. Deem, and C.F. Lucks, *Thermal Radiative Properties*, 3, Plenum Press, New York, (1964).

- Xie, H, M. Fujii, X. Zhang, Effect of Interfacial Nanolayer on the Effective Thermal Conductivity of Nanoparticle-fluid Mixture, *Inter. J. of Heat and Mass Transfer*, 48(14), 2926-32, (2005).

- Zhang, Z., *Nano/Microscale Heat Transfer*, McGraw-Hill (2007).

- Zuber, N., On the Stability of Boiling Heat Transfer, *J. of Heat Transfer*, 80C, 711 (1958).

# INDEX

Absolute temperature, 13
Absorption of radiation, 25
Absorptivity:
    definition, 27, 418
    hemispherical, 418
    solar, 518
    spectral hemispherical, 419
Air, properties of, 500
Ammonia, properties of, 501, 503
Atomic oscillations, 3

Baffles, 464
Bernard cells, 357
Biot number, 55
Blackbody, definition of, 26
Blackbody emissive power, 26, 403
Blackbody radiation, 26
Blackbody radiation functions, 417
Boiling:
    film boiling, 392
    free-convection, 386
    nucleate boiling, 387
    pool, 385
Boltzmann constant, 13
Bose-Einstein distribution, 26
Boundary layer:
    drag coefficient, 239
    drag force, 239
    heat transfer coefficient, 241
    thermal, 240
    velocity, 237
Brownian effect of nano fluid, 269
Brownian motion, 19
Buffer layer, 238
Bulk mean fluid temperature, 287

Carbon dioxide, properties of, 501, 503
Carbon monoxide, properties of, 501
Catteneo equation, 17, 71
Characteristic length, 238
Compact heat exchangers, 462, 485, 489

Condensation:
    dropwise, 373
    filmwise, 373
    laminar, 373
    turbulent, 382
    on horizontal tube, 378
    on horizontal tube banks, 379
    on inclined surfaces, 377
    Reynolds number, 380
    on vertical surfaces, 374
Condensers, 384
Conduction:
    equation:
      one-dimensional steady, 65, 69
      one-dimensional unsteady, 187, 193
      Fourier law of, 7
      multilayers, 111
      in semi-infinite solid, 187
      shape factors, 125
      thermal resistance concept, 95
      hollow cylinder, 101
      hollow sphere, 107
      plane wall, 96
Contact conductance, 122
Conduction phenomena, 2
Contact resistance, 122
Configuration factor, 424
Convection:
    boundary conditions, 78
    bulk mean fluid temperature, 287-289
    dimensionless parameters of, 236, 293
    forced (see Forced convection) 235, 285
    free (see Free convection), 335
    heat transfer coefficient
    definition, 18, 23
    friction factor, 285, 290, 311
    hydrodynamic entry region,
    ducts of various cross sections, 297
    boundary-layer thickness, 245
    drag coefficient, 239

heat transfer coefficient, 23
for large Prandtl number, 252
for moderate Prandtl number, 252
for small Prandtl number, 253
friction factor, 290, 293
laminar flow inside ducts, 285
laminar flow over a flat plate, 244
logarithmic mean temperature, 290
liquid metals, 241, 253, 317
mean drag coefficient, 239
noncircular ducts, 314
property variation, 314
surface roughness effects, 314
shape factor, 125
Conversion factors,
Correction for the LMTD, 477
Criteria for lumped systems, 46
Critical Rayleigh number, 356
Crossed-string method, 439

Debye model, 3
Debye temperature, 3
Density of nanofluid, 20
Diffusiophoresis, 269
Dimensionless parameters, 194, 236, 291
Drag coefficient, definition, 239
Drag coefficient for:
cylinder, 262
laminar flow flat plate, 246
turbulent flow flat plate, 257
sphere, 268
Drag force, 239
Dropwise condensation, 384

Effectiveness, 480
Emissivity, 26, 415
total hemispherical, 416
spectral hemispherical, 416
Energy integral equation, 248
Engine oil, properties of, 503
Error function, 189, 519
Ethylene glycol, properties of, 504
Eutectic calcium chloride

solution, properties of, 504
Extended surfaces, 130

Film boiling, 392
Film temperature, 252
Finite differences:
computer solutions, 178
convection boundary condition, 165
heat flux boundary condition, 164
cylinder, 168
hollow cylinder, 172
internal nodes, 162
plane wall, 161
sphere, 176
stability criteria, 215
Fins (see Extended surfaces):
definition, 130
efficiency, 132
equation, 131
of uniform cross section, 131
Forced convection:
over bodies: basic concepts, 235
flat plate, laminar, 244
flat plate, turbulent, 257
heat transfer coefficient, 251, 258
inside ducts, basic concepts, 285
inside ducts, laminar, 293
inside ducts, hydrodynamic length, 300
inside ducts, thermal entry length, 300
inside ducts, turbulent, 310
inside ducts, liquid metals, 317
Fouling resistance, 472
Fourier law, 6
Fourier number, 7
Free convection:
long cylinder, 350
in enclosed spaces, 356
horizontal cylindrical annulus, 363
inclined layer, 356, 360
spherical annulus, 364
over horizontal plate, 343
over inclined plate, 347
over sphere, 352

over vertical plate, 338
Freon-12, properties of, 503
Friction factor, 311

Glycerin, properties of, 504
Graetz number, 303
Grashof number, 336

Heat conduction (see Conduction)
Heat exchangers:
    compact, 461
    counter-flow, 466, 468
    cross-flow, 466, 468
    effectiveness, 480
    fouling resistance, 472
    heat capacity, 481
    multipass flow, 467, 468
    parallel-flow, 466, 468
    types of heat exchangers, 463
    rating, 485
    sizing, 485
Heat flow, 1
Heat flux, definition of,
Heat transfer coefficient:
    radiation, 29
    overall, 120, 469
    external laminar, flat plate, 235
    external turbulent, flat plate, 258
    across cylinder, 262
    across sphere, 268
    inside ducts, 288
    turbulent flow inside ducts, 312
Helium, properties of, 501
Hydraulic diameter, 291
Hydrodynamic entry region, 285
Hydrogen, properties of, 502

Initial condition, 75
Insulating materials, properties of, 511
Integral equation, 244
Integral method, 244
Internal heat generation, 66

Kinematic viscosity, 238
Kirchhoff's law, 419
Knudsen number, 15

LMTD
(logarithmic mean temperature
difference): 474
Lorenz number, 13
Lumped system concept, 41, 46

Macroscopic approach, 19
Mass diffusion equation, 83, 224
Mass diffusivity, 85, 224
Mass flux, 84
Mass diffusion flux, 223
Mass transfer coefficient, 273
Mass transfer in boundary layer flow, 275
Maxwell equation, 25
Mean free path, 15
Mercury, properties of, 504
Methyl chloride, properties of, 504
Microscopic approach, 19
Momentum integral equation, 224
Moody chart, 311, 312

Network Method, 443
Newton's law of cooling, 23
Nitrogen, properties of, 501
Noncircular ducts, 314
Normal emissivity, 418, 516
NTU (Number of Transfer Units)
method, 480
NTU definition, 478
Nucleate boiling, 387
Numerical analysis, 160, 204
Nusselt number, 236, 292

Opaque, 25
Overall heat transfer coefficient, 120
Oxygen, properties of, 502

Particular solution, 51, 278
Peak heat flux, 387, 390

Phonon, 3, 4
Physical properties:
    for gases, 500, 514
    for insulating materials, 509
    for liquid metals,
    for liquids, 506
    for metals, 507, 515
    for nonmetals, 511, 515
    for radiation properties,
    for steam, 501, 513
Planck constant, 3
Planck's law, 402
Pool boiling, 385
Prandtl number, 236
Pumping power, 291

Radiation:
    absorptivity, 418
    emmissivity, 415
    heat transfer coefficient, 29
    Kirchoff law, 419
    network method, 443
    properties of surfaces, 415
    reflectivity, 420
    resistance for, 443
    shape factor,
    thermal, 25
Radiation shields, 451
Radiosity, 442
Rayleigh number, 338
Rayleigh number, critical, 356
Reciprocity relation, 426
Reflectivity: 420
    bi-directional, 421
    diffuse, 420
    hemispherical, 420
    specular, 420
Relaxation time, 18
Retardation time, 18
Reynolds number, 239

Schmidt number, 327
Sherwood number, 326

SI system of units, 34
Specific heat of nano fluid, 20
Stanton number, 258
Statistical fluid, 19
Stefan-Boltzmann constant, 26
Stefan-Boltzmann law, 26
Sulfur dioxide, properties of, 504

Thermal conductivity, 7
Thermal conductivity of nanofluids, 21
Thermal contact resistance, 122
Thermal diffusivity, 72
Thermal entry length, 300
Thermal radiation, 27
Thermal resistance:
    for convection, 96
    for hollow cylinder, 101
    for hollow sphere, 107
    for plane wall, 96
Thermophoresis, 19, 269
Transient-temperature charts:
    for cylinder, 198
    for slab, 193
    for sphere, 203
Transmissivity, 422

Units and dimensions, 34

Velocity boundary layer, 237
View factors:
    algebra, 433
    concept of, 423
    determination, 430
    graphical form, 433
    properties of, 427
    reciprocity relation, 445
    summation relation, 428
Viscous sublayer, 238

Water, properties of, 504
Wiedeman-Franz law, 13
Wien's displacement law, 406